SYMBOL	ATOMIC NUMBER	ATOMIC WEIGHT[a]
MERCURY	Hg	80	200.59
MOLYBDENUM	Mo	42	95.94
NEODYMIUM	Nd	60	144.24
NEON	Ne	10	20.183
NEPTUNIUM	Np	93	(237)
NICKEL	Ni	28	58.71
NIOBIUM	Nb	41	92.906
NITROGEN	N	7	14.0067
NOBELIUM	No	102	(253)
OSMIUM	Os	76	190.2
OXYGEN	O	8	15.9994
PALLADIUM	Pd	46	106.4
PHOSPHORUS	P	15	30.9738
PLATINUM	Pt	78	195.09
PLUTONIUM	Pu	94	(244)
POLONIUM	Po	84	(209)
POTASSIUM	K	19	39.102
PRASEODYMIUM	Pr	59	140.907
PROMETHIUM	Pm	61	(145)
PROTACTINIUM	Pa	91	(231)
RADIUM	Ra	88	(226)
RADON	Rn	86	(222)
RHENIUM	Re	75	186.2
RHODIUM	Rh	45	102.905
RUBIDIUM	Rb	37	85.47
RUTHENIUM	Ru	44	101.07
SAMARIUM	Sm	62	150.35
SCANDIUM	Sc	21	44.956
SELENIUM	Se	34	78.96
SILICON	Si	14	28.086
SILVER	Ag	47	107.870
SODIUM	Na	11	22.9898
STRONTIUM	Sr	38	87.62
SULFUR	S	16	32.064
TANTALUM	Ta	73	180.948
TECHNETIUM	Tc	43	(97)
TELLURIUM	Te	52	127.60
TERBIUM	Tb	65	158.924
THALLIUM	Tl	81	204.37
THORIUM	Th	90	232.038
THULIUM	Tm	69	168.934
TIN	Sn	50	118.69
TITANIUM	Ti	22	47.90
TUNGSTEN	W	74	183.85
URANIUM	U	92	238.03
VANADIUM	V	23	50.942
XENON	Xe	54	131.30
YTTERBIUM	Yb	70	173.04
YTTRIUM	Y	39	88.905
ZINC	Zn	30	65.37
ZIRCONIUM	Zr	40	91.22

[a]Atomic weights based on $^{12}_{6}C$. Mass numbers of isotopes with longest half lives given in parentheses.

Chemistry: A Conceptual Approach

CONSULTING EDITORS' STATEMENT

Some authors are born, others are developed, and some, fortunately, are discovered.

Professor Mortimer belongs to the last group. He was discovered as a brilliant teacher who has a long and richly deserved reputation among his students and his colleagues alike for presenting general chemistry in an authoritative, up-to-the-minute, exciting, compelling, and eminently comprehensible manner. The more we inquired, the more completely we were convinced that Dr. Mortimer is one of those distinguished teachers who have the supreme gift of teaching chemistry as it is meant to be taught.

That is why we encouraged Dr. Mortimer to write a chemistry text just as he teaches chemistry. The happy result is *Chemistry: A Conceptual Approach*— with just enough descriptive chemistry to make the concepts come alive.

To all teachers and students who are seeking a thoroughly teachable text which offers a balanced treatment of modern concepts of chemistry, one which takes into account the superior background of today's high school graduates and is at the same time completely realistic, we are proud to recommend *Chemistry: A Conceptual Approach*.

The proof, we are confident, will come in the using.

CALVIN A. VANDERWERF
HARRY H. SISLER

Chemistry
A Conceptual Approach

Charles E. Mortimer
Muhlenberg College   Allentown, Pennsylvania

Reinhold Publishing Corporation
A Subsidiary of Chapman-Reinhold, Inc.
NEW YORK ■ AMSTERDAM ■ LONDON

To
J. S. M. and C. E. M. *(II)*

Copyright © 1967 by
Reinhold Publishing Corporation
A subsidiary of Chapman-Reinhold, Inc.

First printing . . . . *April 1967*
Second printing . . . . *July 1967*

Designed by Myron Hall III
Illustrated by F. W. Taylor
Chapter headings by Howard Burns

vi

Preface

Nothing today is so far reaching in its importance and yet so widely misunderstood as science. The average person hopelessly confuses science and scientism. The word "scientific" has come to mean not only "systematic and exact" but also "antiseptic, dull, unimaginative, ritualistic, and almost inhuman or superhuman." "Scientific findings" are regarded as final and immutable. But science results from very human endeavor, and its findings are far from immutable. In a recent article, the mathematician, Warren Weaver, says:

> For we now know that science is motivated by curiosity, inspired by imagination, and based on faith. We know that it seeks increasing order, and does not pretend to deal with immutable truth. Magnificent as science is, and superbly useful as are its applications, we know that its apparent objectivity is only superficial, its pronouncements always open to revision. We know that, as is all art, it is culture-bound.

To say that this book attempts to redress the grievance is presumptuous. This book, however, was written in the humble spirit of modern science. The title was chosen to emphasize the fact that the body of scientific knowledge is conceptual, rests on human observation and thought, and is changeable. To those who would point out that the facts and data, with which any chemistry books abounds, are at least secure and not conceptual, I would point out that these too are limited by human powers. Yesterday, a pure metal had an impurity level of $10^{-2}\%$; today, a pure metal may have an impurity level as low as 10^{-6} to $10^{-8}\%$. The properties of yesterday's and today's pure metals are different, and today's most exact measurement is refined by tomorrow. According to Alfred North Whitehead:

> You cannot cling to the idea that we have two sets of experiences of nature, one of primary qualities which belong to the objects perceived, and one of secondary qualities which are the products of our mental excitements. All we know of nature is in the same boat, to sink or swim together. The constructions of science are merely expositions of the character of things perceived.

The strong desire to know "the answers" is characteristic of many students. Such an attitude led to the nineteenth century ideas that physics was virtually a completed field and that inorganic chemistry was approaching the end of its task; it is probably best typified by the patent official of about a hundred years ago who resigned his post because he thought that everything of significance had been invented.

An attempt has been made in this book to show that there are gaps in our chemical knowledge, that some current descriptions and theories are known to be inadequate, that creative imagination plays a role in the development of chemical thought, and that a full understanding of any phenomenon is never obtained—truth is only approached.

The preparation of freshman chemistry students varies greatly, and an effort has been made to meet the needs of the majority. The use of calculus has been avoided since most entering freshmen lack adequate background in this subject.

A degree of flexibility has been attempted in the organization and presentation of material. Some sections may be eliminated, assigned as outside reading, or taken up in a different sequence from that of the book. The chapter on thermodynamics may be omitted without serious consequences to the continuity. The organization of the descriptive chemistry chapters is such as to permit great latitude in the order of presentation.

A comparatively large amount of material on ionic equilibria has been included to support the presentation of qualitative analysis that is a part of the laboratory instruction of many freshman courses. Likewise, theory basic to classical quantitative analysis has been incorporated in several chapters.

No effort has been made to be consistent in the use of chemical nomenclature; in fact, an effort has been made to be inconsistent. Anyone reading in the chemical literature must be familiar with both common and systematic nomenclature. The advantages of systematic nomenclature are obvious, but at times, common names have a brevity or an aptness that recommends their use. It is, of course, both impossible and undesirable to be encyclopedic. However, there is value in using, in proper context, as many current terms as is practical; this is a general practice that has been followed.

I am grateful to Muhlenberg College for granting me a sabbatical leave during which this work was begun. Dr. Calvin A. VanderWerf and Dr. Harry H. Sisler have provided me with encouragement and suggestions that are sincerely appreciated. The staff of the Reinhold Publishing Corporation has been helpful and congenial; I thank especially Mr. Leonard H. Roberts, editor, and Mrs. Cynthia Harris. Mrs. Anna W. Eckensberger expertly typed the manuscript, and I express my gratitude.

Suggestions for the improvement of this book will be welcomed.

CHARLES E. MORTIMER

Contents

Introduction

Chemistry may be defined as the science that is concerned with the characterization, composition, and transformations of matter. This definition, however, is far from adequate. The interplay between the branches of modern science has caused the boundaries between them to be so vague as to make it almost impossible to stake out a field and say "this is chemistry." Not only do the interests of scientific fields overlap, but concepts and methods find universal application. Moreover, this definition fails to convey the spirit of chemistry, for it, like all science, is a vital, growing enterprise, not an accumulation of knowledge. It is self-generating; the very nature of each new chemical concept stimulates fresh observation and experimentation leading to progressive refinement as well as the development of other concepts. In the light of scientific growth, it is not surprising that a given scientific pursuit frequently leads across artificial, human-imposed boundaries.

Nevertheless, there is a common, if somewhat vague, understanding of the province of chemistry, and we must return to our preliminary definition; a fuller understanding should emerge as this book unfolds. Chemistry is concerned with the structure of substances—of what they are composed and how their components are put together. The physical properties of substances provide clues to their structures, serve as a basis for their identification and classification, and indicate uses to which they may be put. Probably the focus of chemistry, however, is the chemical reaction, and chemistry is interested in every conceivable aspect of these transformations, such as: detailed descriptions of how and at what rates reactions proceed, the conditions required to bring about desired changes and to prevent undesired changes, the energy effects accompanying chemical changes, the syntheses of substances that occur in

TABLE 1.1.
PREFIXES USED TO MODIFY UNIT TERMS IN THE METRIC SYSTEM.

Prefix	Abbreviation	Numerical Meaning	
kilo-	k-	$1000 \times$	(10^3)
deci-	d-	$0.1 \times$	(10^{-1})
centi-	c-	$0.01 \times$	(10^{-2})
milli-	m-	$0.001 \times$	(10^{-3})
micro-	μ-	$0.000001 \times$	(10^{-6})

nature and those that have no natural counterparts, the prediction of which reactions are possible and which impossible, and the quantitative mass and energy relationships involved in chemical changes.

1.1   Measurement

The **metric system** of measurement is used in all scientific studies. It is a decimal system which employs several basic units, defined by international agreement; the names of other, related units are derived from those of the basic units by the addition of prefixes (Table 1.1). Thus 1 decimeter is 0.1 meter; 1 centimeter is 0.01 meter; and 1 millimeter is 0.001 meter. Conversion of a measurement from one unit into another in the **English system** (e.g., 1 yard = 3 feet = 36 inches) is unwieldy and time consuming; a decimal system is much to be preferred. Conversion factors between several units of the English system and the metric system are given in Table 1.2.

Almost all units of measurement can be derived from units of length, mass, and time. The metric standard of length is the **meter,** which was originally meant to be one ten-millionth of the distance along a meridian from the north pole to the equator and was defined as the distance between two etched lines, at 0°C, on a platinum-iridium bar kept at the International Bureau of Weights and Measures at Sèvres, France. The

TABLE 1.2.
SOME CONVERSION FACTORS

English System		Metric System	
1	pound (avdp)	453.59	gram
1	inch	2.5400	centimeter
1	quart	0.94633	liter
2.2046	pound (avdp)	1000	gram
0.39370	inch	1	centimeter
1.0567	quart	1	liter

meter has recently been redefined as 1,650,763.73 wavelengths of the orange-red spectroscopic line of $^{86}_{36}$Kr. For the measurement of very small objects, the micron (μ, 10^{-4} cm) and the Ångstrom unit (Å, 10^{-8} cm) are generally employed.

The primary standard of mass is the **kilogram,** which is defined as the mass of a cylinder of a platinum-iridium alloy deposited at the International Bureau of Weights and Measures. The **second** is defined by means of astronomical observations. Two methods are used to derive additional units (Section 1.3) from those of length, mass, and time: the meter-kilogram-second (**mks**) system which is used by most physicists, and the centimeter-gram-second (**cgs**) system which is preferred by most chemists. The two methods, however, are used interchangeably.

Volume may be measured in terms of the volume of a cube 1 cm on a side (1 cubic centimeter, 1 cm^3). However, the unit of capacity employed most frequently in chemistry is the **liter.** The liter is now defined as 1 cubic decimeter (1 dm^3). Hence, 1 liter equals exactly 1000 cm^3, and 1 milliliter (1 ml) equals 1 cm^3. The liter was originally defined as the volume of exactly 1000 g of pure water under normal atmospheric pressure and at 3.98°C (the temperature of maximum density of water). Based on the old definition, 1 liter equaled 1000.028 cm^3. For most purposes, the difference is unimportant.

The selection of a primary standard for a system of measures is arbitrary, and throughout the history of science many different standards have been used. The criteria for the selection of a primary standard are that it be reproducible, unchanging, and capable of being used for precise measurement. A table of the values of important constants in terms of metric units appears in the Appendix.

1.2 Significant Figures

In scientific studies, the number of figures recorded for a measured quantity must reflect the precision with which the measurement has been made and thus the degree of certainty that can be attributed to the reported value. In short, all of the figures must be **significant;** the value must provide as much usable information as is possible but must also avoid giving misinformation.

For example, let us suppose that the mass of an object is determined to be 12.3456 g. The analytical balance commonly employed in chemistry is capable of measuring the mass of an object to a sensitivity of 0.0001 g, and therefore all of the figures reported are significant; the value has six significant figures. There is some uncertainty to the last figure (6), but it is of value, and therefore significant, because it tells us that the true mass lies closer to 12.3456 g than 12.3455 g or 12.3457 g. This is the most precise value we can secure; it is impossible to derive a value containing seven significant figures for the mass of this particular object using a balance with a sensitivity of 0.0001 g.

If we add a zero to the measurement, we indicate a value of *seven* significant figures (12.34560), which is incorrect and misleading. The conclusion to be drawn from the value 12.34560 g is that the true mass lies between 12.34559 g and 12.34561 g, a much closer tolerance than that indicated by the properly reported value, whereas in fact, we have no idea of the magnitude of the integer of fifth decimal place. A zero does not indicate the fact that the fifth decimal place is unknown or undetermined; rather, the zero is interpreted to be as significant as any other figure in the number. A properly determined and recorded mass, such as 42.5630 g, may legitimately include a zero as a significant figure.

Zeros used to locate the decimal place, however, are not significant. The number 0.0005030 has four significant figures; two of the zeros are significant whereas those preceding the numeral 5 are not. Expressing the diameter of a particle as 0.00000001 cm, rather than 1 Å, does not render the measurement any more precise.

Occasionally, difficulty arises in interpreting the number of significant figures in a term such as 6000. Are the zeros significant, or do they merely serve to locate the decimal point? One solution to the problem is to indicate the position of the decimal point as a power of 10 and include only those zeros that are significant in the other portion of the number. Thus, if the value 6000 has, indeed, been determined to four significant figures, it is indicated as 6.000×10^3; otherwise fewer zeros are placed after the decimal point.

Certain values, such as those arising from the definition of terms, are exact. Thus there are *exactly* 1000 ml in 1 liter, and the number 1000 may be considered to possess an infinite number of significant zeros following the decimal point. Other values are not as precise as might normally be expected. For example, if a balance with a sensitivity of 0.0002 g is used to determine 12.3456 g as the mass of an object, the measurement should be recorded as 12.3456 ± 0.0002 g. The uncertainty range (±0.0002 g) gives the reliability of the determination. The last figure of a value recorded without an uncertainty range is understood to be precise plus or minus one digit.

The result of a calculation involving several measured quantities is no more precise than the least reliable quantity used in the calculation. Thus, if necessary, the answer to a calculation is rounded off to give the proper number of significant figures. The result of an **addition** or **subtraction** should be given to the same number of decimal places as that of the term with the least number of decimal places. The answer for the addition

$$
\begin{array}{r}
161.032 \\
5.6 \\
\underline{32.4524} \\
199.0844
\end{array}
$$

should be recorded as 199.1 since the number 5.6 has but one digit following the decimal point.

The answer for calculations involving **multiplication** or **division** is rounded off to the same number of significant figures as is possessed by the least precise term used in the calculation. Thus the result of the multiplication

$$152.06 \times 0.24 = 36.4944$$

should be reported as 36, which conforms to the limitations imposed by the term 0.24. As a matter of fact, this answer is slightly more precise than the least precise term. The value 0.24 indicates a precision of 1 part in 24, whereas the answer indicates the slightly greater precision of 1 part in 36.

1.3 Matter and Energy

Science interprets nature in terms of matter and energy. **Matter** is the material of which the universe is composed; it may be defined as anything that occupies space and has mass. **Mass** is a measure of the quantity of matter in any given body; it is the property of matter that is responsible for its inertia (the tendency of a body to remain at rest when it is at rest, and when it is in motion, to remain in motion in the same direction).

The mass of a body is invariable; the weight of a body is not. **Weight** is the gravitational force of attraction exerted by the earth on a body, and the weight of a given body varies with the distance of that body from the center of the earth. The weight of a body is, of course, directly proportional to its mass as well as the earth's gravitational attraction. Therefore at any given place, two objects of equal mass have equal weights.

The mass of an object may be determined by means of an analytical balance; standard masses are placed on one pan of the instrument to balance the object of unknown mass which is placed on the other pan. When the instrument is "in balance," the gravitational force on one pan equals that on the other, the weights on the two pans are equal, and hence, the masses on the two pans are equal.

The terms mass and weight have long been used interchangeably in chemistry. Such usage is strictly incorrect but is somewhat firmly established through such terms as atomic weight, molecular weight, and weight-percent. Mass determinations are made through weight comparisons, and in writing and speaking, the verb "weigh" is usually less awkward than the phrase "determine the mass." Actually, the pound is a weight unit in the English system, whereas the gram is a mass unit in the metric system. In general, no significant errors arise through this loose usage, and the precise meaning is almost invariably evident from the context in which the terms are used.

Energy is usually defined as the capacity to do work. Work is done when a body is displaced by a force, and the amount of work is equal to the product of the displacement, d and the magnitude of the force in the direction of the displacement, f.

$$w = fd$$

A given force is directly proportional to the acceleration, a, it causes in a body (increase in velocity per unit time); the mass of the body, m, is the proportionality constant.

$$f = ma$$

In the cgs metric system, the unit of force is the dyne when mass is expressed in grams and acceleration in cm/sec^2.

$$1 \text{ dyne} = 1 \text{ g cm/sec}^2$$

One erg is the work done when a force of 1 dyne acts through 1 cm.

$$1 \text{ erg} = 1 \text{ g cm}^2/\text{sec}^2$$

Another unit of work, or energy, is the joule; 1 joule is defined as 10^7 ergs. Since energy may be measured by the amount of work it can do, energy and work are expressed in the same units.

There are many forms of energy (Section 11.1) such as heat energy, electrical energy, kinetic energy (energy of motion), and potential energy (intrinsic energy of an object due to the position of the object). Under appropriate circumstances, one form of energy can be converted into another form; in these transformations, energy is conserved (Sections 11.1 and 11.2).

The chemist frequently expresses quantities of energy in terms of their heat equivalents (calories) rather than their mechanical equivalents (ergs). The **centigrade** temperature scale (which is also called the **Celsius** scale after Anders Celsius, a Swedish astronomer) is employed in scientific studies. This scale is based on the assignment of 0° to the normal freezing point of water and 100° to the normal boiling point of water; it is compared in Figure 1.1 to the **Fahrenheit** temperature scale (named for Daniel Fahrenheit, a German instrument maker).

The specific heat of a substance is the amount of heat required to raise the temperature of 1 g of the substance 1 centigrade degree. The calorie may be defined in terms of the specific heat of water; however, since the density of water changes with temperature, the specific heat changes as well, and it is necessary to specify the temperature interval.

The **calorie** may be defined as the amount of heat required to raise the temperature of 1 g of water from 14.5° to 15.5°C. For many purposes, however, the specific heat of water may be assumed to be constant over the entire temperature range of liquid water. On the other hand, for very

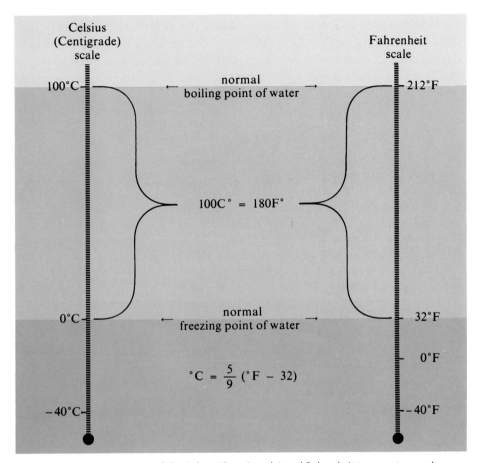

Figure 1.1 *Comparison of the Celsius (Centrigrade) and Fahrenheit temperature scales.*

precise work, the **defined calorie,** equal exactly to 4.1840 joules, is used since very precise determinations of heat energy, in units of joules or ergs, may be made by electrical measurements (Section 11.1).

The unit of heat energy in the English system is the **British thermal unit (Btu).** It is defined as the amount of heat required to raise the temperature of 1 pound of water from 62° to 63°F; 1 Btu equals approximately 252 calories.

According to the Einstein equation

$$E = mc^2$$

where E is energy (in ergs), m is mass (in grams), and c is the speed of light (3.00×10^{10} cm/sec), mass and energy are equivalent and are two manifestations of the same thing. In an ordinary chemical change in which energy is released, the decrease in mass is so small that such phenomena may be interpreted as though mass and energy were each separately conserved. The combustion of 1 kg of carbon to carbon dioxide releases 783 kcal of heat. Since 1 cal is 4.18×10^7 ergs, this quantity of heat equals 3.27×10^{14} ergs. From the Einstein equality, we derive the fact that the mass decrease for this process is 3.63×10^{-7} g; this is such a small quantity that it cannot be detected by measurements employing the most sensitive balances.

SOME SUGGESTED READINGS

Asimov, I., *Intelligent Man's Guide to the Physical Sciences,* New York, Pocket Books, 1950 (paper).

Eddington, Sir A., *New Pathways in Science,* Ann Arbor, The University of Michigan Press, 1959 (paper).

Eddington, Sir A., *The Philosophy of Physical Science,* Ann Arbor, The University of Michigan Press, 1958 (paper).

Farber, E., *The Evolution of Chemistry—A History of Its Ideas, Methods, and Materials,* New York, Ronald, 1952.

Ihde, A. J., and Kieffer, W. F., *Selected Readings in the History of Chemistry,* Easton, Penna., Chemical Education Publishing Co. (paper).

Jeans, Sir J., *The New Background of Science,* Ann Arbor, The University of Michigan Press, 1959 (paper).

Madden, E. H., *The Structure of Scientific Thought,* Boston, Houghton Mifflin, 1960.

Partington, J. R., *A Short History of Chemistry,* New York, Harper, 1960 (paper).

Platt, J. R., *The Excitement of Science,* Boston, Houghton Mifflin, 1962 (paper).

Atomic Structure

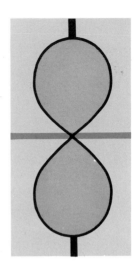

One of the theories that has, in large measure, provided the impetus for the rapid advance of chemistry is the modern atomic theory. Chemical phenomena can effectively be interpreted and correlated on the basis of atoms. In this chapter, concepts of atomic structure and the development of these concepts are discussed.

2.1 The Atom

Through the ages men have been intrigued with the problem of the ultimate constitution of matter. Credit for the first "atomic" theory is usually given to the ancient Greeks; however, this concept may have had its origins in even earlier civilizations. Aristotle (fourth century B.C.) held that matter was continuous and hence, hypothetically, could be divided and subdivided endlessly into smaller and smaller particles. The atomistic school, principally of Leusippus, Democritus, and Epicurus (sixth to fourth centuries B.C.), believed that the subdivision of matter ultimately would yield atoms (from the Greek *atomos* meaning uncut or indivisible) which could not be further reduced. In the first century B.C., the atomic concept was eloquently presented by the Roman poet-philosopher Lucretius in his *De Rerum Natura (The Nature of Things)*.

The ancient's theories were based on abstract thinking alone and not on planned experimentation. Hence, for nearly 2000 years the atomic theory was mere speculation. It formed a part of the thinking of Robert Boyle in his book *The Sceptical Chymist* (1661) and of Isaac Newton in his works *Principia* (1687) and *Opticks* (1704). However, it remained for John Dalton to propose an atomic theory (1803–1807) that was a landmark in the progress of chemistry. Dalton's theory, based on experimentation and chemical laws known at that time, assigned weights and combining capacities to the postulated atoms. Because of its quantita-

9

tive nature, his theory convincingly interpreted many observed facts and stimulated new work and thought. Dalton's theory in its broad outline is still valid; however, some of the particulars must be modified in the light of modern discovery.

Today we know that the division of matter, of any type from any source, into the smallest particles capable of independent prolonged existence would result in the separation of only about 300 completely different kinds of atoms (naturally occurring nuclides). These can be classified according to chemical characteristics into only about 100 groups (elements).

2.2 Subatomic Particles

Although Dalton, like the Greeks, regarded the atom as indivisible, it is now known that the atom consists of even smaller particles into which it may be divided. In fact, certain radioactive atoms spontaneously disintegrate into smaller fragments.

The 100 groups of atoms previously mentioned constitute **elements**, and each group has its own unique set of chemical, as well as physical, characteristics. Atoms of elements can interact to form untold numbers of **compounds** and **mixtures**. They are (except for certain radioactive atoms) capable of prolonged existence and do not subdivide in ordinary chemical reactions. The **atom,** then, is the smallest particle of an element that maintains its chemical identity and characteristics.

However, if atoms are subjected to certain atom-smashing techniques, smaller particles result. These subatomic particles are alike, regardless of the atom from which they arise.

At the present time, approximately 35 different particles have been identified from the subdivision of atoms. Many of these particles are unstable, existing for only a split second, and their status relative to the atom is not completely understood. To add to the confusion, Albert Einstein has shown (Section 2.9) that matter and energy are equivalent; some of the particles identified are probably not particles in any sense of the word but merely bundles of energy. Three types of particles—the **electron, proton,** and **neutron** (see Table 2.1)—are regarded as "fundamental." Whether this term is wisely chosen is questionable since they may arise from some lesser species and one of them, the neutron, is not stable when isolated. However, for purposes of the study of chemistry atomic structure is quite adequately explained on the basis of these three fundamental particles.

2.3 The Electron

The **electron** is the smallest of the fundamental particles; 1836 electrons weigh as much as one proton. The electron and proton have charges of the same magnitude (which is termed the **unit electrical charge**) but of opposite sign; the electron is negative, the proton positive.

TABLE 2.1.
FUNDAMENTAL SUBATOMIC PARTICLES.

Particle	Mass		Charge[b]
	Grams	Unified Atomic Mass Units[a]	
electron	9.1091×10^{-28}	0.000548597	1−
proton	1.67252×10^{-24}	1.00727663	1+
neutron	1.67482×10^{-24}	1.0086654	0

[a] The unified atomic mass unit (u) is 1/12 the mass of a ^{12}C atom (Section 2.9).
[b] The unit charge is 1.60210×10^{-19} coulomb.

The unit electrical charge is 1.602×10^{-19} coulomb. **A coulomb** is the quantity of charge that passes a given point in an electrical circuit in 1 sec when the current is 1 amp. Electrons form a part of all matter; many chemical transformations are the result of electron exchange or electron sharing by atoms. Many of the properties of metals (e.g., electrical conductivity) can be explained on the basis of the mobile electrons characteristic of metals.

1832–1833, Michael Faraday's studies on chemical electrolysis convincingly demonstrated the electrical nature of matter and the equivalence between chemical transformations and the flow of electricity. The term electron (from the Greek meaning *amber*—so called because of the effect of friction on this substance) was first applied by Johnston Stoney in 1874 to the unit of electrical charge that he thought was associated with atoms.

Much of the information about electrons comes from the study of cathode rays which were discovered by Julius Plücker in 1859 (Figure 2.1). When a high voltage is impressed across two electrodes sealed in a

Figure 2.1   Cathode ray tube.

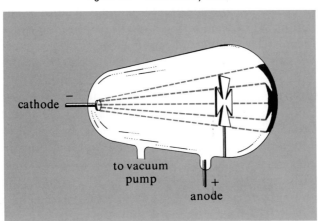

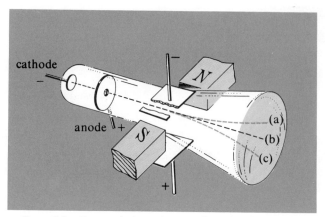

Figure 2.2   Thomson's determination of e/m for the electron.

glass tube from which the air is almost completely withdrawn, rays emanate from the negative electrode (cathode). These rays cause the walls opposite the cathode to glow.

In the 40 years after their discovery, the nature of these cathode rays was extensively investigated, especially by Johann Hittorf (1869), William Crookes (1879), and Joseph J. Thomson (1897). Experiments showed cathode rays to be streams of fast-moving, highly energetic, negatively charged particles. These electrons, which originate from the metal comprising the negative pole, are the same no matter what material is employed for the electrode. An object placed in the path of these cathode rays casts a shadow. Also, the rays cause pinwheels to rotate, and when they are focused on thin metal foils, heat the foils to incandescence.

Since unlike charges attract, these streams of electrons called **cathode rays** are attracted to the positive plate when two charged plates are placed on either side of them, and hence the rays are deflected from their usual straight-line path. The higher the charge on any such particle the greater is the attraction and the greater is the deflection. The magnitude of the deflection also depends *inversely* upon the mass of the particles since a light particle is deflected much more in a given electrical field than a heavy one. Hence, the degree of deflection of these particles under the influence of an electrical field is determined by the ratio of charge to mass, e/m. Cathode rays are deflected in magnetic fields also; in this case, however, deflection is at right angles to the applied field.

J. J. Thomson in 1897 determined the numerical value of e/m by studying the deflection of a beam of cathode rays in a tube around which magnetic and electrical fields, perpendicular to each other, could be simultaneously applied (Figure 2.2). If an electron of charge, e, and mass, m, moving with a velocity, v, enters a magnetic field, as indicated in Figure 2.2, it is deflected at right angles to the field. The electron travels a circular path of radius, r, while in the field and hence strikes the face of the tube at point (a) rather than point (b). The radius, r, can be calculated from measurements of the displacement of this impact spot.

The force of the magnetic field, Hev, equals the centrifugal force operating on the electron which is the mass of the electron, m, times its acceleration (v^2/r for a circular path). Thus

$$Hev = \frac{mv^2}{r} \tag{1}$$

or

$$\frac{e}{m} = \frac{v}{Hr} \tag{2}$$

In an electric field, the electron is deflected toward the positive plate. Under the influence of the electric field alone, the electron would strike the face of the tube in Figure 2.2 at point (c). In the determination of e/m, the intensity of the electric field is adjusted so that there is no net deflection of the electron (impact at (a) on the face of the tube).

In such an instance, the forces of the two fields are equal.

$$Hev = Ee \tag{3}$$

$$v = \frac{E}{H} \tag{4}$$

Substitution of (4) in (2) gives

$$\frac{e}{m} = \frac{E}{H^2 r} \tag{5}$$

If E, H, and r are measured, it becomes possible to determine e/m. The value is

$$e/m = -1.759 \times 10^8 \text{ coulombs/g} \tag{6}$$

Robert A. Millikan in 1909 determined the absolute value of the charge on the electron, e. When X-rays irradiate the atoms of which air is composed, they knock electrons off these atoms. In Millikan's experiment (Figure 2.3), such electrons are picked up by a spray of very fine

Figure 2.3   Millikan's determination of the charge on the electron.

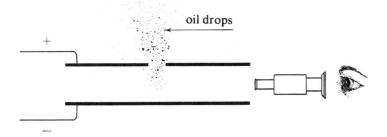

oil drops. These drops are allowed to settle between two horizontal plates. By the use of a telescope, the rate at which a single drop falls under the influence of gravity can be measured and the size of the drop calculated.

When the plates are charged, the rate of fall of the drop is altered by the attraction of the negatively charged drop for the positive plate. Measurement of the rate of fall of the drop in these circumstances enables calculation of the charge on the drop. Since a given drop of oil can pick up one or more electrons, the charges thus calculated are not identical. They are, however, all simple multiples of the same value, 1.602×10^{-19} coulomb, which is assumed to be the charge on a single electron.

Combining this value for e with the value for e/m, one may calculate the mass of the electron. Thus:

$$\frac{e}{m} = -1.759 \times 10^8 \text{ coulombs/g}$$

$$\frac{-1.602 \times 10^{-19} \text{ coulombs}}{m} = -1.759 \times 10^8 \text{ coulombs/g}$$

$$m = 9.11 \times 10^{-28} \text{ g}$$

We have here treated the electron as a discrete particle; this is frequently the most convenient way for the chemist to consider the electron. However, it also possesses wave properties and, at times, is more conveniently treated as a cloud of negative electricity. This concept will be covered in Section 2.12.

2.4   The Proton

If a single electron is removed from an atom, the residue has a charge equal to that of the electron removed but opposite in sign. When the lightest of all atoms, hydrogen, loses its lone electron, a particle which is called a **proton** (Greek, *first*) remains. It is 1836 times the size of the electron, and it bears a unit positive charge, $+1.60 \times 10^{-19}$ coulomb.

Like electrons and cathode rays, protons and positive rays arise in electric discharge tubes. The action of cathode rays rips electrons from atoms of the gas present in the tube, forming **ions** (Greek, *to go*). These ions, being positively charged, move in a direction contrary to that of the cathode rays (which are negatively charged), away from the positive pole toward the cathode. Many of them simply pick up electrons and again become neutral atoms. Some of them, however, reach the cathode and, if a hole has been bored in this electrode, go through it and beyond. These positive rays, or canal rays, were first discovered in 1886 by Eugen Goldstein (Figure 2.4).

In 1898 positive rays were studied by Wilhelm Wien, who determined approximate values of e/m for the positive particles comprising these

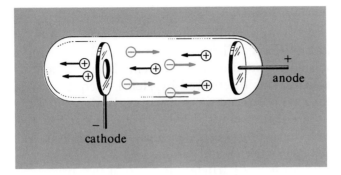

Figure 2.4   Positive rays.

rays by observing their deflection in magnetic and electrostatic fields. By using essentially the same method that he devised for the study of cathode rays, J. J. Thomson in 1906 refined Wien's estimates for e/m for these positive particles.

The positive particles comprising positive rays differ depending upon the gas present in the discharge tube, unlike the electrons of the cathode rays which are identical no matter from what material they arise. When particles have the same size charge, the value of e/m increases with a decrease in the mass of the particle. Hence, for the very small electron, the value of e/m is large; all positive ions have much smaller e/m values than the electron, and the value of e/m obtained depends upon the gas present in the discharge tube.

When hydrogen is used in the tube, the largest of all e/m values for positive ions is observed; it is assumed that positive ions from this source are the fundamental particles—protons. The mass of the proton is 1.67×10^{-24} g. The positive charge on the proton is of exactly the same magnitude as the negative charge on the electron ($1+$ and $1-$ in terms of the unit electrical charge).

2.5   The Neutron

Since atoms are electrically neutral, a given atom must contain as many electrons as protons. To account for the total masses of atoms, the existence of an uncharged particle was predicted by Ernest Rutherford around 1920. Since this particle is uncharged, it was difficult to detect and characterize. However, in 1932 James Chadwick published the results of his work which established the existence of the **neutron** (from Latin, *neutral*). He was able to calculate the mass of the neutron from data on certain nuclear reactions (see Chapter 18) in which neutrons are produced. By taking into account the masses and energies of all particles used and produced in these reactions, Chadwick determined the mass of the neutron. It is very slightly larger in mass than the proton; the neutron has a mass of 1.675×10^{-24} g and the proton, 1.673×10^{-24} g.

2.6   The Nuclear Atom

Certain atoms apparently represent unstable combinations of the fundamental particles. These atoms spontaneously emit rays and are thereby **transmuted** into atoms of different chemical identity. This process, **radioactivity,** was discovered by Henri Becquerel in 1896, and the nature of the rays produced was subsequently elucidated by Rutherford. The three types of rays emitted by naturally occurring radioactive materials (others have now been identified from man-made atoms) were named alpha (α), beta (β), and gamma (γ).

Alpha rays consist of particles made up of two protons and two neutrons. They are ejected from the radioactive atom at speeds around 10,000 miles/sec, carry a 2+ charge (from their two protons), and have an approximate mass of 4 u (Section 2.9). Beta rays are streams of electrons (1– charge) that travel at approximately 80,000 miles/sec. Gamma radiation is essentially a highly energetic form of light; these rays are uncharged and are similar to X-rays.

By the use of alpha particles, Rutherford, in 1911, presented convincing evidence for a nuclear construction of the atom. A radioactive source of alpha rays was placed behind a lead shield. A thin pencil beam of alpha rays emerged through a hole bored in the thick lead shield. This beam was directed against very thin (ca., 0.0004 cm) foils of gold, platinum, silver, or copper. About 99.9% of the alpha particles went right through the foil in use; however, some were deflected from their straight line path, and a few were sent back toward their source. When a alpha particle strikes a screen coated with zinc sulfide, a little flash of light is emitted. By the use of such screens, the scattering of alpha particles could be observed (Figure 2.5).

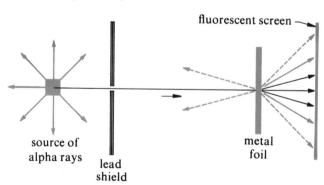

Figure 2.5   *Rutherford's experiment for bombarding a metal foil with alpha rays.*

Rutherford explained the results of these scattering experiments by postulating the existence of a nucleus in the center of the atom. Most of the mass and all of the positive charge of the atom (the protons and neutrons) are concentrated in this nucleus. The electrons, which occupy most of the total volume of the atom, are outside of this nucleus and in rapid motion around it.

It is important that one grasp the scale of this model. If an atom had a diameter of 1 mile, its nucleus would have a diameter on the order of only $\frac{2}{3}$ in. Thus it is easily seen that most of the alpha particles in a scattering experiment would pass undeflected through an atom—most of the volume of an atom is empty space. This is true even though the target foils are about 1000 atoms thick.

If an alpha particle scores a direct hit on a nucleus, it recoils in the direction of its source; such recoils, though few in number, were observed. A near miss with a close approach of a positively charged alpha particle to a positively charged nucleus would result in repulsion of the alpha particle and thus deflection from its straight line path (Figure 2.6). The comparatively light electrons do not cause the deflection of the heavier, fast-moving alpha particles.

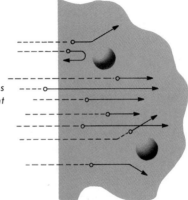

Figure 2.6   Deflections and recoil of alpha particles by nuclei of metal foil in Rutherford's experiment (not to scale).

2.7   Atomic Symbols

An atom may be identified by two numbers: the atomic number, Z, and the mass number, A. The atomic number represents the number of unit positive charges on the nucleus and hence is equal to the number of protons in the nucleus since each proton carries a 1+ charge. An atom, being electrically neutral, must have as many electrons (at 1− each) as it has protons (at 1+ each). Hence, the atomic number also gives the number of electrons in the neutral atom under consideration.

The mass number of an atom is the total number of neutrons and protons (**nucleons**) in the nucleus of the atom. Thus to obtain the number of neutrons in a given nucleus, one must subtract the atomic number (the number of protons) from the mass number (the number of neutrons and protons).

$$\text{number of neutrons} = A - Z$$

It must be emphasized that these are *numbers* of particles and not weights. Hence, the mass *number* represents the total *number* of nucleons in a nucleus and not the mass of the nucleus. However, since the mass of both the proton and the neutron are approximately equal to 1 u (see Section 2.9), the mass number is generally a whole number approximation of the atomic masses. An atom of sodium with an atomic number of 11 and a mass number of 23 would have 11 protons and 12 neutrons in a nucleus in the center of the atom and 11 electrons in motion about that nucleus.

Chemical reactions involve only the extranuclear electrons, and the chemical characteristics of an atom depend upon the number of electrons that it has. All atoms with 11 electrons behave the same chemically, and all such atoms are given the same chemical name—sodium. We shall see later that it is possible to have, within limits, atoms with 11 protons and 11 electrons but a varying number of neutrons. Nevertheless, all atoms with 11 protons in the nucleus and 11 electrons around the nucleus are sodium atoms and comprise what is spoken of as an **element.**

Each element is given a symbol, a practice introduced by the Swedish chemist Jöns Berzelius in the early 1800's. The names of the elements have been decided upon by international agreement, and the symbols are usually the initial letters of the names. Where more than one element begins with the same letter, a second letter (not necessarily the second letter of the name) is added to distinguish them. Most of the symbols for the elements correspond closely to their English names. However, the symbols of some of the elements, known and characterized long ago, have been assigned on the basis of their Latin names (see Table 2.2). The full significance of symbols will be discussed later (Chapter 4).

It is convenient to represent atoms by means of chemical symbols. The atomic number is placed at the lower left corner of the symbol, and the mass number is placed at the upper left corner. (The other two

TABLE 2.2.
SYMBOLS OF ELEMENTS DERIVED FROM LATIN NAMES.

English Name	Latin Name	Symbol
antimony	stibium	Sb
copper	cuprum	Cu
gold	aurum	Au
iron	ferrum	Fe
lead	plumbum	Pb
mercury	hydrargyrum	Hg
potassium	kalium	K
silver	argentum	Ag
sodium	natrium	Na
tin	stannum	Sn

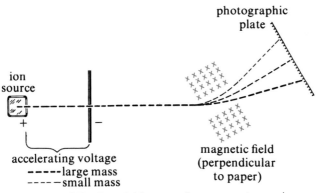

Figure 2.7   *Essential features of a mass spectrograph.*

corners are reserved for other designations: the upper right for the charge if the atom has lost or gained one or more electrons and become an ion; the lower right corner for the number of atoms present in a compound.) Thus the sodium atom previously described would be designated $^{23}_{11}Na$. An atom with the symbol $^{35}_{17}Cl$ has 17 protons and 18 neutrons in the nucleus and 17 extranuclear electrons. An atom of uranium with the designation $^{238}_{92}U$ has 92 protons and 146 neutrons in its nucleus and 92 electrons in motion about this nucleus.

2.8   Isotopes and Isobars

One of the postulates of Dalton's atomic theory is that every atom of a given element is identical in all respects (including mass) to every other atom of that element. Gradually it became clear that this is not true and that atoms of the same element exist that differ from one another in mass. Frederick Soddy proposed the name **isotopes** (Greek, *same place*) for differing atoms of the same element.

The most fruitful method of studying isotopes is by use of a **mass spectrograph.** Instruments of this type were first constructed by Francis W. Aston (1919) and A. J. Dempster (1918) who followed principles developed by J. J. Thomson in 1913. The mass spectrograph (Figure 2.7) separates ions according to their charge to mass ratios; these ions are caused to impinge at different positions on a photographic plate. If an element consists of several types of atoms varying in mass, then ions from that element will have various charge to mass ratios.

When the instrument is operated, atoms of the vaporized material to be studied are converted into positive ions as a result of bombardment by streams of electrons (Section 2.4). These ions are next accelerated by passage through an electric field of several thousand volts. Provided the voltage is held constant, all ions of the same e/m value emerge into a magnetic field with about the same velocity. This velocity, as well as the e/m value and the strength of the magnetic field, determines the radius of the path of the ion in the magnetic field. All other things being equal, lighter ions are deflected more from a straight-line path than heavier ions. Hence, particles of the same e/m will be focused at definite positions on the photographic plate. These positions may be altered by changing the potential used to accelerate the ions. When an electrical device that measures the intensities of the ion beams is substituted for the photographic plate, the instrument is known as a **mass spectrometer.**

Isotopes are atoms with the same atomic number but different mass numbers. They have identical chemical properties. Thus in nature, there are two types of atoms of chlorine: $^{35}_{17}Cl$ and $^{37}_{17}Cl$. Both of these atoms have 17 protons and 17 electrons. The first, however, has 18 neutrons, and the chlorine-37 atom has 20 neutrons. Thus isotopes differ in the number of neutrons in the nucleus. Care should be exercised in the use of the term "isotope." One of these atoms is not chlorine and the other an isotope; *both* are isotopes of the element chlorine.

In nature, some elements exist in only one isotopic form (e.g., sodium, beryllium, and fluorine); however, most elements have more than one isotope—tin has ten. The term **nuclide** is used for atomic species in general.

Isobars are nuclides that have the same mass number but different atomic numbers. Thus $^{36}_{16}S$ and $^{36}_{18}Ar$ are isobars. The total number of nucleons in each of these isobars is the same, but the numbers of protons and neutrons are different. Thus the sulfur isotope has 16 protons and 20 neutrons making a total of 36 nucleons, whereas the argon isotope has 18 protons and 18 neutrons making the same total. Isobars are not alike chemically since chemical characteristics depend upon the number of electrons, which is determined by the atomic number. They are relatively unimportant to the chemist.

2.9 Atomic Weights

The usual standards of mass are not convenient for the measurement of the very small nucleons and nuclides since they give rise to very small numbers. Therefore a standard of mass has been adopted for the measurement of these particles that is on a scale commensurate with them.

The **atomic mass unit** (u) is defined as one-twelfth the mass of the nuclide $^{12}_{6}C$. Note that this gives approximate values of unity to the proton and the neutron. The assignment of the value of 12 u to this isotope of carbon is quite arbitrary; other nuclides could have been used, and, indeed, others have been used at other times (Dalton used hydrogen as his standard). At the present, the masses of all nuclides are expressed as a ratio of their masses to the mass of $^{12}_{6}C$ taken as 12.

On this scale the mass of the proton is 1.007277 u; the neutron is 1.008665 u; the the electron is 0.0005486 u. Given these values one might expect that the mass of any nuclide could be calculated from its atomic number and mass number; such, however, is not the case. For example, the weight of $^{35}_{17}Cl$ would be expected to equal the sum of the weights of 17 protons, 18 neutrons, and 17 electrons. Thus:

$$17(1.007277)\,u + 18(1.008665)\,u + 17(0.0005486)\,u = 35.289005\,u$$

The mass of $^{35}_{17}Cl$ has been accurately determined, however, as 34.96885 u. The difference between the two values is:

$$35.28901\,u - 34.96885\,u = 0.32016\,u$$

This difference in its energy equivalent is spoken of as the **binding energy** of the nuclide in question.

Einstein has shown that energy and mass are equivalent:

$$E = mc^2$$

where E is energy, in ergs; m is mass, in grams; and c is the speed of light, 3.00×10^{10} cm/sec. Thus the energy equivalent of 1 g of matter is

$$E = (1.00\,g)(3.00 \times 10^{10}\,cm/sec)^2$$
$$= 9.00 \times 10^{20}\,g\,cm^2/sec^2$$
$$= 9.00 \times 10^{20}\,ergs$$

Since 1 cal $= 4.184 \times 10^7$ ergs,

$$E = 2.15 \times 10^{13}\,cal$$
$$= 2.15 \times 10^{10}\,kcal$$

Therefore 1 g of matter is equal to over 20 billion kcal of energy.

Binding energy is generally interpreted in terms of the particles of the nucleus. If it were possible to pull the nucleus apart, this would be the energy required to do the job. The reverse process, the condensation of nucleons into a nucleus, would release the binding energy with the attendant decrease in mass.

The removal of electrons from an atom, or the addition of electrons to a nucleus, also involves energy changes which, of course, have mass equivalents. However, these mass equivalents are extremely small; in most cases, it is perfectly valid to assume that the mass of the electron does not change when the electron assumes a position in an atom. The energy effects attributable to the particles of the nucleus are very much larger than those caused by the addition of removal of electrons.

For every atom except ^1_1H (the nucleus of which consists of a single proton), the mass calculated from the masses of the constituent particles exceed the actual mass of the nuclide. Thus every nucleus consisting of two or more nucleons has a binding energy.

The magnitude of the binding energy of a given nucleus indicates the stability of that nucleus toward radioactive decay; the largest binding energies are characteristic of the most stable nuclei. For the purpose of comparison, the values are usually given in terms of binding energy per nucleon. The units commonly employed are millions of electron volts (mev); an electron volt is the energy acquired by an electron when it falls through a potential of 1v. One unified atomic mass unit is equivalent to 931.4 mev. The calorie equivalent of the atomic mass unit is an extremely small number with which to work.

The binding energy of $^{35}_{17}Cl$ (the equivalent of 0.320 u) is:

$$0.320 \text{ u } (931 \text{ mev}/\text{u}) = 298 \text{ mev}$$

This represents only 1.14×10^{-11} cal/atom; the binding energy of 1 g of $^{35}_{17}Cl$, however, would amount to 193 million kcal. The binding energy per nucleon is

$$\frac{298 \text{ mev}}{35 \text{ nucleons}} = 8.5 \text{ mev}/\text{nucleon}$$

Binding energies vary from 1.0 to 8.8 mev/nucleon, most of the values falling between 7.0 and 8.8.

Most naturally occurring elements consist of a mixture of isotopes, and chemical calculations would be hopelessly complicated except for the fact that, with very few exceptions, these mixtures are of constant composition. The element chlorine consists of a mixture of 75.53% $^{35}_{17}Cl$ and 24.47% $^{37}_{17}Cl$. Any sample of chlorine from any source will consist of these two isotopes in this proportion.

It is convenient to use a weighted average for the atomic weight of chlorine. This average may be obtained from the isotopic masses by multiplying each by its fractional abundance and adding the values obtained. Thus

$$0.7553 \text{ (34.97 u)} + 0.2447 \text{ (36.95 u)} = 35.45 \text{ u}$$

The accepted value for chlorine is 35.453 ± 0.001.

There is no atom of chlorine that weighs 35.453 u, but it is convenient to think in terms of one. In even a very small sample of matter there is a huge number of atoms. (There are more atoms in a drop of water than there are people on the face of the earth—a sobering comparison for the behavioral sciences.) Even though a very small sample may be used in an experiment, a very large number of atoms is included, and no mistake is made in assuming that the sample consists of only one type of atom with the average mass. The term **atomic weight** is applied to this average.

Prior to 1961, two different standards were employed for atomic and nuclear weights. Chemists based their scale on the weight of the average oxygen atom taken as exactly 16 (this scale was devised before isotopes were known). The physical atomic weight scale was based on $^{16}_{8}O$, this isotope being assigned a weight of exactly 16. Since naturally occurring oxygen consists of three isotopes (of mass numbers 16, 17, and 18), the value for the average oxygen atom is 16.0044 on the physical scale. The $^{12}_{6}C$ scale, called the **unified scale,** was developed to eliminate this duality.

On this new scale, the average oxygen atom weighs 15.9994. Readers must be careful to note, therefore, what standard an author employs. To aid in the distinction, the National Bureau of Standards suggests the use of the symbol u for the unit of the new unified scale; the symbol amu (atomic mass unit) was previously employed (somewhat ambiguously) for both the physical and chemical atomic weight scales.

Conversion of one scale to another may be accomplished as follows:

1. Multiply the old chemical atomic weight by 1.000275 to obtain the old physical atomic weight.

2. Divide the old chemical atomic weight by 1.000043 to obtain a unified scale reading.

3. Divide the old physical atomic weight scale by 1.000318 to obtain the unified scale equivalent.

2.10 Atomic Spectra

Since the extranuclear electrons of an atom determine its chemical characteristics, the arrangement of these electrons is of primary importance. Rutherford and others early postulated that the electrons were in rapid motion in spherical orbits around the nucleus similar to the way the planets travel around the sun (but with the important distinction that the units of the solar system are not charged). The postulated rapid motion was supposed to overcome, by centrifugal force, the attraction on the negative electron by the positive nucleus.

This simple picture did not stand the close scrutiny of classical physics. According to electromagnetic theory, a charged particle moving under the influence of an attractive force should continuously emit energy, and therefore, the electron should follow a spiral path until it finally falls into the nucleus. The atom should, with the emission of energy, ultimately collapse. The study of atomic spectra led to an answer to this problem.

When a ray of ordinary white light is passed through a prism (Figure 2.8), the beam is spread out into a wide band of colors called a **continuous spectrum.** Light can be considered as consisting of waves of energy (Figure 2.9). For each wave the distance from crest to crest (or trough to trough) is called the **wavelength,** λ. The product of the wavelength and the **frequency,** ν, (or the number of cycles per second) is the speed of light, c.

$$c = \lambda \nu$$

In 1900, Max Planck proposed a quantum theory of light to explain certain properties of radiation. Light is absorbed or emitted only in discrete qualities called **photons.** The energy of the photons is proportional to the frequency of the radiation.

$$E = h\nu$$

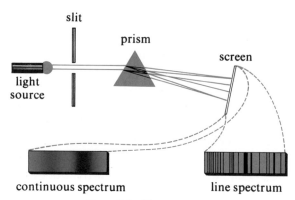

Figure 2.8   The spectroscope.

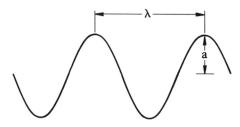

Figure 2.9   Wavelength, λ, and amplitude, a,
of a wave.

The proportionality constant, h, is known as Planck's constant; the value of h is 6.63×10^{-27} erg sec.

Ordinary white light consists of many different wavelengths, and thus when the prism resolves it into a spectrum, every color is observed from violet (short wavelength, highest energy, most refracted by the prism) to red (long wavelength, lowest energy, least refracted by the prism). This continuous spectrum is a rainbow of colors with no discontinuities—violet merger into blue, which merges into green, etc.

When gases or vapors of chemical substances are heated by an electric arc or spark or a Bunsen flame, light is emitted. The resolution of a ray of such light by a prism produces a **line spectrum** (Figure 2.8). This spectrum consists of a number of lines of various colors, each line representing a definite wavelength or energy. Since the spectrum is not continuous, certain wavelengths or energies of light are not emitted. That is, only light of certain definite energy values is given off by the incandescent chemical substance. Each element has its own characteristic line spectrum; there are similarities, but each is unique. The frequencies of the lines emitted by hydrogen in the visible region of the spectrum (the Balmer series) can be expressed by the formula

$$\nu = 3.29 \times 10^{15} \text{ cycles/sec} \left(\frac{1}{2^2} - \frac{1}{n^2} \right)$$

where n is an integer equal to, or greater than, 3.

In 1913, Niels Bohr proposed a theory, based on the spectrum of hydrogen, to explain the configuration of electrons in atoms. Hydrogen has a nucleus consisting of one proton and hence has only one electron. Actually, the Bohr theory is not entirely satisfactory. Even after modification, it still may be applied successfully only to atoms containing a single electron. It does, however, represent the beginnings of the modern quantum theory.

According to Bohr, the electron of hydrogen can exist only in certain spherical orbits (or energy levels, or shells) which are arranged concentrically around the nucleus. These orbits are subject to a quantum restriction: the angular momentum of an electron in an orbit (mvr, where m is the mass of the electron, v is its velocity, and r is the radius of the orbit) must be an integral multiple of the quantity $h/2\pi$.

$$mvr = n\,\frac{h}{2\pi} \qquad n = 1, 2, 3, \ldots$$

Thus an electron moving in any orbit has a definite energy characteristic of that orbit. As long as an electron remains in a given orbit, it neither absorbs nor radiates energy.

Thus the K level ($n = 1$) is the shell closest to the nucleus and is of the smallest radius and lowest energy. The next shell (L, $n = 2$) has a larger radius, and electrons moving in it have higher energies. With increasing distance from the nucleus (K, L, M, N, O; $n = 1, 2, 3, 4, 5$), the radius of the shell increases, and the energy of electrons in that shell increases. No electron in an atom can have an energy that would place it somewhere between the permissible orbits.

If an electron is in an orbit of radius, r, the force of attraction between the nucleus (with a charge of Ze, where Z is the atomic number) and the electron is given by Coulomb's law as Ze^2/r^2. This attraction is exactly balanced by the centrifugal force acting on the electron, mv^2/r (where m is the mass and v the velocity of the electron), which by itself tends to pull the electron away from the nucleus. Therefore,

$$\frac{mv^2}{r} = \frac{Ze^2}{r^2} \tag{7}$$

or

$$v^2 = \frac{Ze^2}{mr} \tag{8}$$

If we solve Bohr's quantum condition for v, we get

$$mvr = \frac{nh}{2\pi} \qquad n = 1, 2, 3, \ldots \tag{9}$$

$$v = \frac{nh}{2\pi mr} \tag{10}$$

Squaring equation (10) and combining the result with equation (8) gives

$$\frac{Ze^2}{mr} = \frac{n^2h^2}{4\pi^2m^2r^2} \tag{11}$$

$$r = \frac{n^2h^2}{4\pi^2mZe^2} \qquad n = 1, 2, 3, \ldots \tag{12}$$

If we solve this expression for the smallest orbit ($n = 1$) of hydrogen ($Z = 1$), we get

$$r = 0.530 \times 10^{-8}\,cm = 0.530\,\text{Å}$$

(The angstrom unit, Å, is equal to 10^{-8} cm.) This quantity is called the **Bohr radius** and is sometimes given the symbol a_0.

The total energy of an electron is equal to the sum of its kinetic energy ($mv^2/2$), which is attributable to its motion, and its potential energy ($-Ze^2/r$), which results from its position in the field of the nucleus.

$$E = \frac{mv^2}{2} - \frac{Ze^2}{r} \tag{13}$$

From equation (8),

$$mv^2 = \frac{Ze^2}{r} \tag{14}$$

and therefore

$$E = \frac{Ze^2}{2r} - \frac{Ze^2}{r} = -\frac{Ze^2}{2r} \tag{15}$$

Substitution of the value of r from equation (12) into equation (15) gives

$$E = -\frac{2\pi^2mZ^2e^4}{n^2h^2} \qquad n = 1, 2, 3, \ldots \tag{16}$$

By means of equation (16) it is possible to calculate the energy of an electron in each of the Bohr orbits.

When the electrons of an atom are arranged as close to the nucleus as possible (in the case of hydrogen, one electron in the K level), they are in the condition of lowest possible energy; such is called the **ground state** or **ground level**. In a spectroscope, the electrons of the material being investigated absorb energy from the electric arc or spark and hence jump to outer, more energetic levels. Such a condition is called an **excited state**.

When an electron falls back to a lower orbit, it emits a definite amount of energy—the difference between the energy required by the outer level, E_2, and the energy required by the inner level, E_1. This energy is emitted as radiation, and since it is a definite amount, it has a characteristic frequency (and wavelength) and produces a characteristic spectral line.

The energy of the photon radiated by the atom is

$$h\nu = E_2 - E_1 \qquad E_2 \rightarrow E_1$$

Substitution of the values of E from equation (10) into this expression gives

$$h\nu = \left(-\frac{2\pi^2 m Z^2 e^4}{h^2}\right)\left(\frac{1}{n_2^2}\right) - \left(-\frac{2\pi^2 m Z^2 e^4}{h^2}\right)\left(\frac{1}{n_1^2}\right)$$

$$= \frac{2\pi^2 m Z^2 e^4}{h^2}\left(\frac{1}{n_1^2} - \frac{1}{n_2^2}\right)$$

and

$$\nu = \frac{2\pi^2 m Z^2 e^4}{h^3}\left(\frac{1}{n_1^2} - \frac{1}{n_2^2}\right)$$

If the constants of this equation are evaluated for hydrogen ($Z = 1$), the frequencies of photons emitted by transitions to the $n = 2$ level from higher levels is given by

$$\nu = 3.29 \times 10^{15} \text{ cycles/sec} \left(\frac{1}{2^2} - \frac{1}{n^2}\right)$$

This agrees with the empirically derived equation describing the spectral lines of the Balmer series.

Hence, each line of a line spectrum compares to a definite drop of an electron from a higher to a lower orbit; the relation between some of the electronic transitions of the hydrogen atom and the spectral lines of the Balmer series is illustrated in Figure 2.10. Certain wavelengths of light are not emitted because there are no corresponding energy drops for an electron in the atom. The removal of an electron to an infinite shell

Figure 2.10 The relation between some electronic transitions of the hydrogen atom and spectral lines of the visible region.

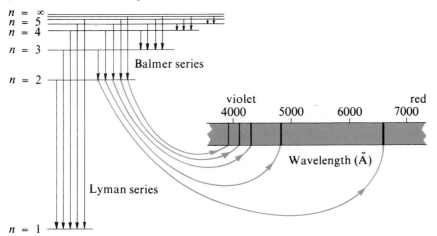

amounts to **ionization** and is accomplished by the application of the **ionization potential** (Section 3.2).

Since atoms differ in size, charge on the nucleus, number of electrons, etc., the spectrum of each element is different. The Bohr theory successfully interprets the spectra of atoms containing only one electron, such as H, He^+, and Li^{2+}.

2.11 The Periodic Law

The periodic classification is of great help in understanding and predicting the electronic configurations of atoms. This system of classification of the elements was first proposed in polished form in 1869 by Julius Lothar Meyer and Dmitri Mendeleev working independently. The modern **periodic law** states that when the elements are arranged in order of increasing atomic number, certain chemical and physical properties recur periodically. The original statement of the periodic law, proposed before atomic numbers were known, was based on atomic weights. Even in this form, this was a promising and useful generalization since atomic numbers and atomic weights increase in a parallel manner with only three exceptions (K, Ni, and I).

Specific properties occur again and again in a list of elements arranged by increasing atomic number. Element 2 is a colorless gas which is extremely unreactive chemically. This same set of properties reappears in elements 10, 18, 36, 54, and 86. Collectively this group of elements is known as the **noble gases.**

The elements intervening between any two noble gases (e.g., between elements 3 to 9, or 11 to 17) comprise a **period.** The use of the term period here can be compared to the use of the same word in the study of the motion of a pendulum. A period is the length of time that it takes for a pendulum to swing out and return to its initial position; here, a period is a number of elements encountered before the reappearance of a given set of properties in a new element.

Every element following a noble gas (elements 3, 11, 19, 37, 55, and 87) is a highly reactive, light, silvery metal—an **alkali metal.** Every element (except number 1, hydrogen) preceding a noble gas (numbers 9, 17, 35, 53, and 85) is an exceedingly reactive nonmetal—a **halogen.** In the period between noble gas number 2 and noble gas number 10, therefore, there is only one alkali metal and only one halogen.

No two elements in any given period are similar; rather, a range of properties is observed in each period. Starting with an alkali metal, the properties change from element to element—the metallic properties fading and being gradually replaced by nonmetallic characteristics; each period ends with a noble gas. All of the periods are alike in that this common pattern of changing properties prevails in each—metal to nonmetal, ending with a noble gas.

Unlike the period of the pendulum which is of constant duration, the period here is of changing amplitude. The first period consists of two elements followed by periods of 8, 8, 18, 18, and 32 (which numbers can be obtained by subtracting the atomic numbers of succeeding noble gases). This poses a problem in arranging the elements into a **periodic chart** or **periodic table**. The most satisfactory solution is the so-called long form of the periodic table found inside the back cover of this book.

The periods consist of those elements that are arranged in horizontal lines in the table; these are organized in such a way that elements of similar properties (called **groups** or **families**) appear in vertical columns. In this table, the set of elements appearing at the bottom and called the lanthanides should actually appear in the body of the chart in proper order by atomic number so that the sixth period has its requisite 32 elements. For convenience in reproduction this is not done; but, properly, the chart should be vertically cut, the sections separated, and the lanthanides inserted in their proper positions. For the actinides which appear below the lanthanides at the bottom of the periodic table, the same considerations pertain; they should be inserted in the seventh period (as yet incomplete).

TABLE 2.3.
MAXIMUM NUMBER
OF ELECTRONS
FOR EACH SHELL.

Shell	n	$2n^2$
K	1	2
L	2	8
M	3	18
N	4	32
O	5	50

Since the periodic table classifies atoms by chemical behavior, and since chemical behavior is determined by electronic configuration, the periodic table may also be said to classify atoms by electronic configuration. The maximum number of electrons that each energy level may hold is given by $2n^2$, where n is the principal quantum number of the shell in question. Hence for the $K(n = 1)$ shell, the maximum number is $2(1)^2$ or 2; for the L ($n = 2$) level, this number is $2(2)^2$ or 8; these maximum electron populations for the first five shells are given in Table 2.3.

In this discussion all elements are considered in their ground states. The first element, hydrogen, has one electron in the K level; the second, helium, has two electrons in this shell. This completes the $n = 1$ shell and the first period. The third element, lithium, has a complete K shell and one electron in the L level. Each succeeding element in the period adds one electron to this level. The second period ends with the noble gas neon ($Z = 10$) which has two electrons in the $n = 1$ level and a complete $n = 2$ level of eight electrons.

A striking fact is encountered in the third period. The initial element of this period, sodium, has completed K and L shells of two and eight electrons, respectively, and an additional electron in the next level, the M level ($n = 3$). One notes that in the first group of elements, lithium and sodium both have one electron in the outer shell. Likewise the second elements of these periods both have two electrons in their outer shells; beryllium has a configuration (by shells) of 2, 2, and magnesium has a configuration of 2, 8, 2.

By comparing the third period elements with the second period elements, we see that the number of electrons in the outer shells (called the **valence shells**) is the same for elements of the same group and that this number is the same as the group number. This similarity in number of valence electrons accounts for the similarities in properties. These facts may be derived from Table 2.4.

TABLE 2.4.
ELECTRONIC CONFIGURATIONS BY SHELLS FOR THE FIRST THREE PERIODS.

Electronic Levels	Group Number							
	IA	IIA	IIIA	IVA	VA	VIA	VIIA	0
K	H 1							He 2
K	Li 2	Be 2	B 2	C 2	N 2	O 2	F 2	Ne 2
L	1	2	3	4	5	6	7	8
K	Na 2	Mg 2	Al 2	Si 2	P 2	S 2	Cl 2	Ar 2
L	8	8	8	8	8	8	8	8
M	1	2	3	4	5	6	7	8

The electronic configurations of the elements of the fourth and subsequent periods are not easily understood in terms of the electronic shells alone; a number of questions arise that may be answered only in terms of later concepts. The fourth period begins with potassium, number 19, which is a member of Group I and has one valence electron in the N ($n = 4$) level, thus giving potassium a configuration of 2, 8, 8, 1. This poses a question. Since the M level can hold a maximum of 18 electrons, why should the final electron of potassium be placed in the N level before the M level has been filled?

Calcium, number 20, has the configuration 2, 8, 8, 2. The next element, scandium ($Z = 21$), has the electronic configuration 2, 8, 9, 2; it differs from the preceding element, calcium, by the addition of an electron not in the outer (or N) level but rather in the second from the outer level—the M level. This element, scandium, is not a member of Group III because it does not have three valence electrons, and it is not placed below aluminum in Group III. Scandium is called a **transition element,** and because the "last" electron was added to the second from the outer shell, it is said to undergo **inner building.** These transition elements (numbers 21 through 30 in the fourth period) are placed in the center of the periodic table, and their groups are given B designations. Inner building cannot be explained on the basis of electronic shells alone.

The electronic configurations of the noble gases pose a question. The first noble gas, helium, has a completed first shell; the second noble gas, neon ($Z = 10$), has a configuration of 2, 8 representing two completed shells (K and L); the third noble gas, argon ($Z = 18$), has the configuration 2, 8, 8. One might suppose that these elements of extremely low chemical reactivity would have all of their electronic shells complete; this must not be a requisite for electronic stability, however, since the third level in argon is not complete but has only an octet of electrons. We shall see later that all of the noble gases have eight electrons in their outer shells with the exception of helium which has the maximum number of electrons that the K level can hold—two.

2.12 Dual Nature of the Electron

In 1900, Max Planck proposed the quantum theory of light, and five years later, Einstein, in his theory explaining the photoelectric effect, reinforced and extended Planck's views on the nature of light. The revolutionary feature of this quantum theory was that light can be assumed to be emitted in small discontinuous bits, called photons. Prior to this time, the properties of light were explained on the basis that light consists of waves of energy, and certain properties (such as diffraction) are still best explained by making such an assumption. The modern physicist treats light as waves of energy when it is convenient to do so and at other times treats light as streams of photons if this is advantageous.

At the present time, the electron is similarly treated—as wave and as particle; however, this dualism evolved in reverse order. Electrons were early considered solely as charged particles (in such experiments as the determination of e/m, e, etc.); later, the wave properties of the electron were investigated.

We have seen that the energy of a photon, E, is related to its frequency, ν, by the expression:

$$E = h\nu$$

Since $\nu = c/\lambda$, where c is the speed of light, and λ the wavelength of the photon,

$$E = \frac{hc}{\lambda}$$

Using Einstein's equation, $E = mc^2$, we derive

$$mc^2 = \frac{hc}{\lambda}$$

or

$$\lambda = \frac{h}{mc}$$

The term mc is equal to the momentum of the photon (mass times velocity).

In 1924, Louis de Broglie postulated that a wavelength can be assigned to an electron:

$$\lambda = \frac{h}{mv}$$

where m is the mass of an electron, and v is its velocity. This postulate has been confirmed by a variety of experimental data.

The application of the postulate to the Bohr theory produces an interesting result. The Bohr restriction

$$mvr = n\frac{h}{2\pi}$$

may be rearranged to

$$2\pi r = n\frac{h}{mv}$$

and therefore

$$2\pi r = n\lambda$$

Thus a standing wave can be accommodated in the Bohr orbit since the circumference of the orbit, $2\pi r$, is an integral multiple of the wavelength of the electron, $n\lambda$.

Consideration of the electron as a wave is very important because the Heisenberg **uncertainty principle** (1926) demonstrates the ultimate futility of any attempt to make the Bohr model more exact and comprehensive. The accurate prediction of the path of a moving body requires that both the position and the velocity (which denotes direction as well as speed) of that body be known at a given gime. Werner Heisenberg showed that it is impossible to measure simultaneously the exact position and exact velocity of a body as small as an electron.

The determination of the position of an object depends upon our ability to observe it, either by noting the interference in the light rays that illuminate the object or, more directly, by noting the variation in some other test signal. Radiation of extremely short wavelength would be needed to detect the electron because of its small size. Such radiation is very energetic (the shorter the wavelength, the more energetic), and hence when it impinges on an electron the impact would cause the direction and speed of the tiny electron to change. Photons of longer wavelength (less energetic) have less effect on the momentum of the electron but, because of their longer wavelength, have less precision in indicating the position of the electron.

The uncertainty in the position, Δx, and the uncertainty in the momentum, Δm, (momentum is mass times velocity) arising from the measuring process are therefore related. An approximate mathematical statement of the Heisenberg uncertainty principle is

$$\Delta x \, \Delta m \approx h$$

The mass of the electron is approximately 9×10^{-28} g, and according to the Bohr model, the velocity of the electron in the $n = 1$ shell of hydrogen is approximately 2×10^8 cm/sec. The momentum of the electron obtained by multiplying these values is

$$(9 \times 10^{-28} \, g)(2 \times 10^8 \, cm/sec) = 2 \times 10^{-19} \, g \, cm/sec$$

If the measured momentum is permitted to be in error by 100%

$$\overset{\circ}{A} = 10^{-8} \, CM$$

$$\Delta x \, \Delta mv \approx h$$

$$\Delta x \, (2 \times 10^{-19} \, g \, cm/sec) \approx 6.6 \times 10^{-27} \, g \, cm^2/sec$$

$$\Delta x \approx \frac{6.6 \times 10^{-27} \, g \, cm^2/sec}{2 \times 10^{-19} \, g \, cm/sec} = 3 \times 10^{-8} \, cm = 3 \, \text{Å}$$

This value is approximately three times the Bohr diameter of the $n = 1$ shell of the hydrogen atom. (If the value $h/2\pi mr$, from the Bohr theory, is used for the velocity of an electron in the $n = 1$ shell and m is used for the mass of the electron, the result is $\Delta x \approx 2\pi r$, or the circumference of the Bohr orbit.)

It appears, then, that an accurate description of the path of an electron in a Bohr orbit is impossible. The wave postulate of de Broglie was used by Erwin Schrödinger to develop a differential equation describing the electron in terms of its wave character.

The **Schrödinger equation** (1926) is the keystone of **wave mechanics**. It reconciles the idea of the quantum restriction on the energy of the electron, originally imposed by Bohr, with the idea of the electron as a standing wave which may be described mathematically in much the same

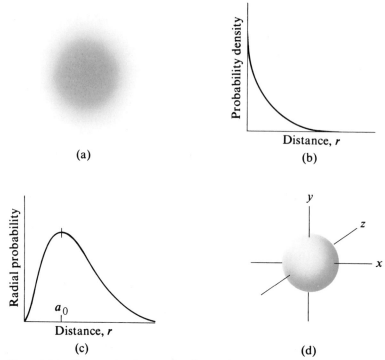

Figure 2.11   *Electron distribution plots for an electron in the n = 1 state of the hydrogen atom. (a) Charge cloud, (b) Probability of finding the electron per unit volume versus distance from nucleus, (c) Probability of finding the electron at a given distance versus distance from the nucleus, (d) Conventional boundary surface for showing the probability distribution in three dimensions (nucleus at origin).*

way as the waves of a vibrating violin string. By means of the Schrödinger equation, a function may be derived that describes an electron as a wave of energy or a cloud of negative charge, thicker in some parts than others.

Max Born proposed an interpretation of the wave equations based on probabilities. If one imagines a corpuscular electron in motion about a nucleus, then the wave equations may be interpreted in terms of the probability (or relative chance) of finding that electron at any given distance from the nucleus. The chance of finding an electron is great in a region where the cloud is thick. This interpretation does not fix electron position nor does it describe electronic paths; it merely predicts where an electron is most likely to be found. Insofar as a corpuscular interpretation of the electron is concerned, it is the best that wave mechanics has to offer.

There are several ways of diagrammatically representing electron charge density or probability density, and some of these for the $n = 1$ state of the electron in the hydrogen atom are shown in Figure 2.11. The electron charge cloud has its greatest density near to the nucleus and becomes thinner as the distance from the nucleus increases (Figure 2.11a); the probability is proportional to the density of the cloud. This means that the probability of finding the electron in the small volume surrounding a point in space is greatest near to the nucleus, but there is a finite probability at all finite distances from the nucleus (Figure 2.11b).

The diagram of Figure 2.11c represents this property in a somewhat different form. Imagine a group of spherical shells of very small thickness arranged concentrically around the nucleus; the total probability of finding the electron in such a shell is plotted against the distance of the shell from the nucleus in Figure 2.11c. The probability per unit volume is greatest close to the nucleus, but the volume of a shell that is close to the nucleus is less than the volume of a shell that is farther out. Hence, the plot shows a maximum at 0.530 Å, or the Bohr radius, a_0. The total probability of finding an electron at all points of distance r from the nucleus is greatest when r is equal to a_0. In terms of the charge cloud concept, a greater amount of the total charge of the electron is found in the spherical shell of radius a_0 than is found in any other shell.

Since there is a probability of finding an electron at all finite distances from the nucleus, the three-dimensional representation of an $n = 1$ electron of the hydrogen atom poses a problem. Such representations, however, are important aids for interpreting chemical phenomena. It is not possible to depict a geometric shape that will encompass a region of 100% probability. However, a surface can be drawn that connects points of equal probability and encloses a volume in which there is a high probability (e.g., 90%) of finding the electron (Figure 2.11d). Alternatively, the figure can be interpreted as representing a contour that encloses a high percentage (90%) of the electronic charge.

The electron, then, may be described as having properties of a particle and a wave. In Chapter 3, we shall see that it is frequently convenient to consider the electron as a particle (in such considerations as ionization, ionization potential, and electron affinity), but it is also advantageous at times to interpret it as a wave (e.g., in some of the later theories of the covalent bond).

The nature of light and of the electron has been the focus of considerable philosophical interest. Heisenberg's enunciation that some of the properties inherent in matter forbid an accurate knowledge of it, Einstein's proof of the equivalence of matter and energy, the use of statistics and chance or probability in the description of nature, and the idea that different concepts can be applied at convenience to a single phenomenon all caused a reappraisal of certain nineteenth century mechanistic and materialistic views.

It is interesting to note that, until recently, Russian scientists were directed to reject the conclusions of much of the scientific work reported here. This is understandable since dialectic materialism—itself a product of nineteenth century materialistic mechanistic concepts—is in direct opposition to the spirit of this work. Soviet philosophers utterly rejected any "convenience theories" and contended that Soviet science should seek to find *the* single objective truth. Since it impeded scientific progress, this prohibition against the use of the work of Heisenberg, Einstein, and others has recently been eased, showing a pragmatism the supposedly pure communist theory rejects.

2.13 Quantum Numbers

Bohr explained spectral lines on the basis of electronic energy shells or levels, assigning each shell a **principal quantum number,** n. Wave mechanics uses this quantum number as well as three additional ones to describe electrons. We can consider that Bohr's shell represents a region where the probability of finding an electron is high. The value of n gives an indication of the position of the shell relative to the nucleus; the larger the value of n, the farther that shell is from the nucleus. Alternatively, if the cloud interpretation of the electron is used, n gives an idea of the size of the cloud—larger values of n indicating larger clouds. These shells must be regarded as discrete and the only permissible electron transitions are between shells, which, according to Bohr, accounts for the spectral lines.

The use of better spectroscopes, however, showed that spectral lines actually consist of groups of fine lines (fine structure). To account for all of these lines, more permissible electron states were necessary; Arnold Sommerfeld in 1916 proposed that Bohr shells consisted of subshells of slightly different energies—that the level of Bohr was actually a group of sublevels. Sommerfeld proposed this in terms of the Bohr quantum theory; however, his idea is incorporated into the modern wave mechanical treatment.

Each principal level has as many subshells as its value of n; there is only one sublevel for the $n = 1$ level, but there are two sublevels for the $n = 2$ level, three for the $n = 3$ level, etc. A **subsidiary quantum number,** l, is introduced, and each subshell is assigned an l value. For each quantum level, n, there are values of l corresponding to every term in the series 0, 1, 2, 3 up to $(n - 1)$. Thus when $n = 1$, the only value of l is 0, and there is only one subshell; when $n = 2$, there are two sublevels having l values of 0 and 1, respectively; and when $n = 3$, the three sublevels have l values of 0, 1, and 2. Notice that the values of l are referred back to the n value of the level in question.

By convention, other letters are used at times to denote sublevels. Thus the $l = 0$ sublevel is designated as an s sublevel; $l = 1$, p; $l = 2$, d; and $l = 3$, f. These spectroscopic notations are the initial letters of adjectives formerly used to describe spectral lines: sharp, principal, diffuse, and fundamental. For l values larger than 3, the letters used proceed alphabetically—*g, h, i,* etc.; however, for the ground states of the known elements, no value of *l* higher than 3 (*f*) need be used. Combining the principal quantum number with these spectroscopic symbols gives a convenient way to denote the subshells as is indicated in Table 2.5 for the first four shells.

The maximum number of electrons in each level is given by the formula $2n^2$. How these electrons of each level are distributed among that level's sublevels is made clear by examining the remaining two quantum numbers.

**TABLE 2.5.
SUBSHELL NOTATIONS**

n	*l*	Spectroscopic Notations
1	0	1*s*
2	0	2*s*
2	1	2*p*
3	0	3*s*
3	1	3*p*
3	2	3*d*
4	0	4*s*
4	1	4*p*
4	2	4*d*
4	3	4*f*

The **spin quantum number,** *s,* characterizes the spin of an electron on its own axis and may have a value of either $-\frac{1}{2}$ or $+\frac{1}{2}$ since only two directions of spin are possible—clockwise and counterclockwise. A spinning charge is a magnet, and electrons of opposed spin have a certain magnetic attraction for one another despite the greater repulsion that they also exhibit because of their like charge. The wave function associated with an electron is termed an **orbital** to distinguish it from the path or orbit of the Bohr theory. Each orbital may hold two electrons, and electrons thus paired in a single orbital have opposed spins. The $n = 1$ level has a maximum electron population of two and but one sublevel (1*s*) to hold them. The 1*s* sublevel must, therefore, consist of a single orbital.

The number of orbitals in the other sublevels may be inferred from the fourth quantum number—the **magnetic quantum number,** *m.* For our purposes, this is the least important quantum number since it describes behavior that is only evident in a magnetic field. A magnetic field has no effect on an *s* electron since an *s* orbital is spherically symmetrical. If such an orbital were turned in a magnetic field, no effect would be observed because a sphere presents the same aspect toward the lines of force no matter what its orientation. This is true for all of the *s* orbitals —1*s*, 2*s*, 3*s*, etc.

Conventional boundary surfaces of *p* orbitals are shown in Figure 2.12. The probability distribution of a *p* orbital is such that more than one different spatial orientation is possible. An infinite number of such orientations might seem possible; however, it is found that each *p* sublevel consists of but three differently oriented *p* orbitals.

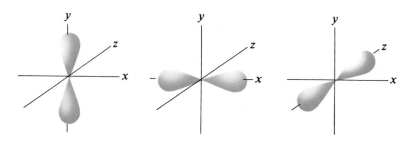

2*p* orbitals

Figure 2.12   *Conventional boundary surfaces of the 2p orbitals.*

These *p* orbitals are identical in terms of energy, and no distinction may be noted between electrons occupying different *p* orbitals in the absence of a magnetic field. However, if spectral studies are run with the source of emission in a magnetic field, certain spectral lines are split into several lines (Zeeman effect)—an effect which disappears when the magnetic field is removed. It is convenient to think in terms of the orientations of the three *p* orbitals of the second level as being along the *x*, *y*, and *z* axes; these orbitals are sometimes given the designations $2p_x$, $2p_y$, $2p_z$.

It is now easy to account for the eight electrons in a complete $n = 2$ level. Two of these electrons, with spins paired, are in the spherical orbital of the 2*s* sublevel; the remaining six are paired in the three orbitals of the 2*p* sublevel.

For any sublevel, the magnetic quantum number, *m*, assumes every value from $-l$ through and including 0 to $+l$. Thus, for $l = 0$, $m = 0$. For $l = 1$, the *m* values are -1, 0 and $+1$—indicating three orbitals. When $l = 2$ (*d* subshell), *m* may have values of -2, -1, 0, $+1$, and $+2$— describing five orbitals each oriented differently in space. Notice that the values of *m* depend upon the value of *l* for the subshell under consideration.

Each electron, therefore, may be described by a set of four quantum numbers—*n* giving the relative distance of the electron from the nucleus, *l* giving the subshell and the shape of the orbital for the electron (each orbital of a given subshell is equivalent in energy), *m* designating the orientation of the orbital in space, and *s* stating the spin of the electron.

The **exclusion principle** of Wolfgang Pauli (1924) states that no two electrons in the same atom may have identical sets of all four quantum numbers. Even if two electrons have the same values for *n*, *l*, and *m*, they will differ in their *s* values. The quantum numbers are summarized in Table 2.6 by use of the 32 electrons of the *n* = 4 level as an example.

TABLE 2.6.
QUANTUM NUMBERS FOR THE ELECTRONS OF THE n = 4 LEVEL.

n	*l*	*m*	*s*	Number of Electrons by Subshells
4	0 (*s*)	0	$\pm\frac{1}{2}$	2
	1 (*p*)	−1	$\pm\frac{1}{2}$	
		0	$\pm\frac{1}{2}$	6
		+1	$\pm\frac{1}{2}$	
	2 (*d*)	−2	$\pm\frac{1}{2}$	
		−1	$\pm\frac{1}{2}$	
		0	$\pm\frac{1}{2}$	10
		+1	$\pm\frac{1}{2}$	
		+2	$\pm\frac{1}{2}$	
	3 (*f*)	−3	$\pm\frac{1}{2}$	
		−2	$\pm\frac{1}{2}$	
		−1	$\pm\frac{1}{2}$	
		0	$\pm\frac{1}{2}$	14
		+1	$\pm\frac{1}{2}$	
		+2	$\pm\frac{1}{2}$	
		+3	$\pm\frac{1}{2}$	

2.14   Magnetic Moment

Three types of magnetic behavior are known: **diamagnetism, paramagnetism,** and **ferromagnetism.** Diamagnetic substances are weakly repelled by a magnetic field, while paramagnetic materials are drawn into a magnetic field. Ferromagnetism, exhibited by iron, is a comparatively rare phenomenon and is an extreme form of paramagnetism.

A single spinning electron behaves like a small magnet (Section 2.13). Despite the large repulsion between two electrons caused by their negative charges, electrons of opposed spin have a slight magnetic attraction for each other. Two electrons that are paired in an orbital have opposed spins, and their magnetic moments oppose each other and cancel. However, the magnetic properties of **unpaired electrons** (electrons occupying orbitals singly) cause atoms containing such electrons to be paramagnetic, and the larger the number of unpaired electrons, the greater the magnetic moment.

There are actually two effects that contribute to the paramagnetism of an atom: the spin of the unpaired electrons and the orbital motion of the electrons. The magnetic moment associated with the orbital motion of electrons is related to the orientation of the orbitals in regard to the magnetic field and hence is related to the magnetic quantum number, m. In the same way that a pair of electrons has no net spin magnetic moment (and the sum of the s values equals zero), a filled or half-filled subshell has no resultant orbital magnetic moment, and the sum of the values of m for all of the electrons of the subshell is zero.

The magnetic properties of some atoms are due to both effects; this is true for the lanthanides in which the unpaired f electrons lie deep within the atom and are well shielded from the surface. For many atoms, however, the effect of the orbital motion is quenched by the environment of the atom, and this contribution is negligible. In such cases, the number of unpaired electrons (n in the following equation) and the spin magnetic moment (in Bohr magnetons) are approximately related by the expression:

$$\text{spin magnetic moment} = \sqrt{n(n + 2)}$$

A material is diamagnetic if all of its electrons are paired. Diamagnetism is a universal property of matter, but it is obscured by the stronger paramagnetic effect when unpaired electrons are present. Diamagnetism arises from the interaction of the magnetic field with filled orbitals and is a function of the electronic charge density.

Magnetic measurements have helped to determine the electronic configurations of many elements and thereby to establish the hypothetical order in which the orbitals may be assumed to fill. The electronic configurations, by orbitals, of the first five elements are given in Table 2.7.

Table 2.7.
ELECTRONIC CONFIGURATIONS
OF THE FIRST FIVE ELEMENTS

	1s	2s	2p
$_1$H	1		
$_2$He	2		
$_3$Li	2	1	
$_4$Be	2	2	
$_5$B	2	2	1

A question arises concerning the electronic distribution of the sixth element, carbon. Since there are three $2p$ orbitals, does the next electron belong in the $2p$ orbital already holding one electron, or does it belong in another $2p$ orbital?

Hund's rule of maximum multiplicity, which has been confirmed by magnetic measurements, provides an answer for this and similar questions. Hund's rule states that electrons are distributed among the orbitals of a subshell in such a way as to give the maximum number of unpaired electrons. Hence, each of the two $2p$ electrons of carbon must assume its own orbital instead of pairing with the other in a single orbital.

If we adopt the convention of using minus numbers first (for values of both m and s), the six electrons of carbon have the sets of quantum numbers indicated in Table 2.8.

TABLE 2.8.

QUANTUM NUMBERS FOR THE ELECTRONS OF CARBON

n	l	m	s
1	0	0	$-\frac{1}{2}$
1	0	0	$+\frac{1}{2}$
2	0	0	$-\frac{1}{2}$
2	0	0	$+\frac{1}{2}$
2	1	-1	$-\frac{1}{2}$
2	1	0	$-\frac{1}{2}$

The next electron added, for nitrogen, would have the quantum numbers 2, 1, $+1$, $-\frac{1}{2}$.

If we represent the orbitals by circles, the order of filling for the first ten electrons may be shown by the numbers entered in these circles:

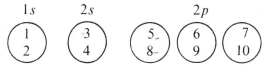

Electrons are negatively charged and repel each other. Hence, they spread out and occupy the $2p$ orbitals singly before they begin to pair. After each of the $2p$ orbitals holds one electrons, pairing occurs because less energy is required to overcome the interelectronic repulsion and add an electron to an orbital already holding an electron than is required to place an electron in the next-higher empty orbital—a $3s$ orbital. This general order of orbital filling is observed for all subshells.

The spectroscopic notations for electronic configurations convey this information in a different form. The spectroscopic terms for the sub-shells are used with superscripts indicating the number of electrons in each subshell. Thus the electronic configuration of carbon may be indicated as $1s^2\, 2s^2\, 2p^2$. This clearly presents the first two quantum numbers—the number stands for n and the letter may be related to l—but the second two quantum numbers must be inferred indirectly.

Someone unfamiliar with this system must guard against interpreting all even-numbered superscripts as indicating a situation where all electrons are paired. This is not the case. In carbon, for example, we know that there are two unpaired electrons despite the fact that all of the superscripts are even numbers.

A way of circumventing this difficulty is to repeat the designation for each orbital of an incomplete subshell. Thus the electronic configuration of carbon would be indicated as $1s^2\quad 2s^2\quad 2p^1\quad 2p^1$; that of the following element, nitrogen, would be $1s^2\quad 2s^2\quad 2p^1\quad 2p^1\quad 2p^1$; and that of the next element oxygen, would be $1s^2\quad 2s^2\quad 2p^2\quad 2p^1\quad 2p^1$. After some experience with this spectroscopic system of notation, such a device is unnecessary.

2.15   Electronic Structures of the Elements

We are now in a position to show how the periodic table relates to electronic structure and thus to answer the questions raised in Section 2.11. To do this we shall use the **aufbau prinzip (building principle)** of Pauli. In this *hypothetical process*, the electronic structure of an element is correctly deduced by successive addition of electrons into orbitals arranged in order of increasing energy until the proper number of electrons for that element has been accommodated.

It is assumed that each electron enters the lowest energy level available to it, and since all of the orbitals of a given sublevel have equivalent energies, this amounts to an arrangement by sublevels. It is possible for a simple orbital of one level (e.g., a $4s$) to have a *lower* energy than a more complicated orbital of an *inner* level (e.g., a $3d$), and hence the $4s$ sublevel fills before the $3d$. The order of filling, then, is not by increasing value of n, but may be derived from the energy level diagram for atomic orbitals given in Figure 2.13. In the use of this diagram, one may consider the orbitals as being filled starting at the bottom of the chart and proceeding upward. Remember that there are three orbitals in a p sublevel, five orbitals in a d sublevel, and seven orbitals in an f sublevel.

The spectroscopic notations for the electronic structures of the elements of the first three periods are easily written since the symbols occur in order of principal quantum number. Thus a few typical notations for elements of this period are:

$$\text{He } (Z = 2) \qquad 1s^2$$

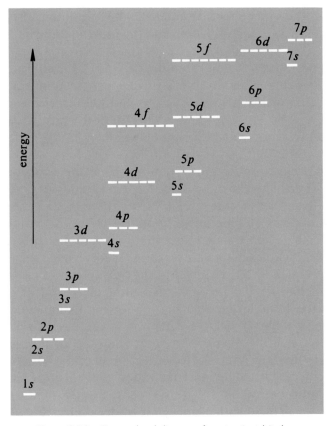

Figure 2.13   Energy level diagram for atomic orbitals.

Li $(Z = 3)$ $1s^2\ 2s^1$

N $(Z = 7)$ $1s^2\ 2s^2\ 2p^3$

Ne $(Z = 10)$ $1s^2\ 2s^2\ 2p^6$

Na $(Z = 11)$ $1s^2\ 2s^2\ 2p^6\ 3s^1$

P $(Z = 15)$ $1s^2\ 2s^2\ 2p^6\ 3s^2\ 3p^3$

Ar $(Z = 18)$ $1s^2\ 2s^2\ 2p^6\ 3s^2\ 3p^6$

In discussing the configurations of the remaining elements, we shall indicate only the outer orbitals. The first overlap of orbital energies is observed with potassium $(Z = 19)$, and the configuration is ... $3s^2\ 3p^6$ $4s^1$ despite the fact that $3d$ orbitals are vacant. Likewise, calcium $(Z = 20)$ has the configuration: ... $3s^2\ 3p^6\ 4s^2$. With scandium $(Z = 21)$ the $3d$ sublevel comes into use: ... $3s^2\ 3p^6\ 3d^1\ 4s^2$, and with the series from scandium to zinc this sublevel is gradually filled. The configuration of zinc $(Z = 30)$ is ... $3s^2\ 3p^6\ 3d^{10}\ 4s^2$. The elements 21 to 30 are the first transition series (B families) and are spoken of as exhibiting inner building since the last electron was added to the second from the outer shell. With element 31, gallium, the $4p$ sublevel begins: ... $3s^2$ $3p_6$ $3d^{10}$ $4s^2$ $4p^1$, and the fourth period ends with krypton: ... $3s^2$ $3p^6$ $3d^{10}$ $4s^2$ $4p^6$.

The fifth period starts with rubidium ($Z = 37$), the additional electron over krypton being added to the $5s$ subshell. A second transition series follows, starting with yttrium ($Z = 39$) and adding electrons to the $4d$ sublevel: ... $4s^2$ $4p^6$ $4d^1$ $5s^2$. This period ends with the series from indium to xenon with electrons being added to the $5p$ level. Xenon has the configuration: ... $4s^2$ $4p^6$ $4d^{10}$ $5s^2$ $5p^6$.

The sixth period is much more complicated as far as orbital overlap is concerned. The first element, cesium ($Z = 55$), adds one electron in the $6s$ sublevel to the xenon core: ... $4d^{10}$ $5s^2$ $5p^6$ $6s^1$, and the second element, barium ($Z = 56$), has an additional electron that completes the $6s$ sublevel. We here come upon one complication of the aufbau procedure. The $4f$ and $5d$ sublevels are so close in energy that the next electron (for lanthanum, $Z = 57$) is added to the $5d$ sublevel (thus lanthanum is a transition element) but the next succeeding electron (for cerium, $Z = 58$) adds to the $4f$ sublevel rather than following its immediate predecessor into the $5d$ sublevel. Thus for La we have: ... $4d^{10}$ $5s^2$ $5p^6$ $5d^1$ $6s^2$, and for Ce: ... $4d^{10}$ $4f^1$ $5s^2$ $5p^6$ $5d^1$ $6s^2$. For the elements 58 to 71 (cerium to lutetium), the electrons are added to the $4f$ sublevel.

These elements are called **inner-transition** elements; for such elements, electron addition occurs in the third from the outer shell. After the $4f$ sublevel has been filled with element 71, the next electron adds to the $5d$ sublevel. Thus for hafnium ($Z = 72$), we have ... $4d^{10}$ $4f^{14}$ $5s^2$ $5p^6$ $5d^2 6s^2$. This third transition series is completed and the $5d$ shell filled with element 80, mercury: ... $4d^{10}$ $4f^{14} 5s^2 5p^6 5d^{10} 6s^2$. The period ends with electrons being added to the $6p$ sublevel in elements 81 to 86.

The seventh period is incomplete and includes many artificial man-made elements. This period follows the pattern established by the sixth period with 87 and 88 adding electrons to the $7s$ sublevel, 89 adding an electron to the $6d$ sublevel, and the remaining known elements (from 90 on) constituting a second inner transition series and exhibiting an electron buildup of the $5f$ sublevel.

Many mnemonic devices have been proposed to help remember the order of filling of subshells. One such system suggests that electrons add to that subshell with the lowest value of $(n + l)$. Thus the decision to place the final electron of potassium in the $4s$ sublevel rather than in the $3d$ rests on the fact that the sum of the n and l values for the $4s$ sublevel is $(4 + 0)$ or 4, while that of the $3d$ sublevel is $(3 + 2)$ or 5. When two orbitals that have the same numerical value of $(n + l)$ are candidates for filling, the one with the lower n value is used. Thus the final electron in scandium goes into the $3d$ sublevel ($n + l = 5$) rather than the $4p$ sublevel ($n + l = 5$).

Another device employed is illustrated as follows. The spectroscopic notations for the subshells are written in indented fashion; when these are joined by downward vertical lines, the proper sequence emerges.

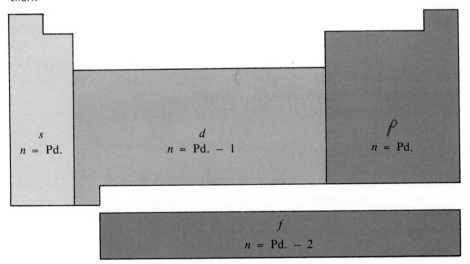

The use of both of these mnemonics requires that one remember that an exception must be made in the case of the inner-transition elements— one electron is placed in the $5d$ level before the $4f$ level is filled.

Probably the best memory aid is the periodic table itself. In the schematic periodic table of Figure 2.14 certain areas of the chart are marked with subshell notations. The electron added to make an element different from its preceding neighbor (the so-called differentiating electron) in any region of the chart is of the type indicated for that region. The principal quantum number of this final electron is given by the period number for the A family elements, the period number minus one for the

Figure 2.14   Type of differentiating electron related to position of the element in the periodic chart.

transition elements, and the period number minus two for the inner-transition elements.

To determine the electronic configuration of any element, one starts with hydrogen and on the basis of the periodic table accounts for every electron added until the desired element is reached. Thus for gadolinium ($Z = 64$): the first period gives $1s^2$; the second period, $2s^2\,2p^6$; the third, $3s^2\,3p^6$; the fourth, $4s^2\,3d^{10}\,4p^6$; and the fifth, $5s^2\,4d^{10}\,5p^6$. The sixth period—in which gadolinium is found—starts with $6s^2$ for cesium and barium, and then adds $5d^1$ for lanthanum. The electron added for element 57 (cerium) begins on the $4f$ subshell, and since gadolinium is the seventh element in this $4f$ series, the final term is $4f^7$. Rearranging these terms in proper sequence gives: $1s^2\,2s^2\,2p^6\,3s^2\,3p^6\,3d^{10}\,4s^2\,4p^{10}$ $4f^7\,5s^2\,5p^6\,5d^1\,6s^2$.

The aufbau method is convenient and gives fairly accurate results (Section 2.16); however, it has an inherent danger. As one thinks in terms of the addition of electrons to build up atoms, it is all too easy to ignore the attendant addition of protons and neutrons to the nucleus and the fact that an electron added in any step of the procedure is not isolated but is entering a field dominated by increasingly larger and larger number of electrons. Thus the order of sublevels based on energy, changes from element to element in the periodic table. There is no one standard order of sublevels that accurately describes the conditions existing in all atoms. The aufbau order reflects the order of filling and the relative energy positions of the orbitals as one encounters them in this hypothetical filling procedure.

In processes involving the loss of an electron (ionization), frequently the electron lost is not the last one added. Thus the configuration of iron ($Z = 26$) is $1s^2\,2s^2\,2p^6\,3s^2\,3p^6\,3d^6\,4s^2$, and upon ionization, the first electron removed is a $4s$ electron even though the last electron added by the aufbau procedure is a $3d$ electron. One must conclude that for iron the $3d$ subshell has a lower energy than the $4s$ subshell—a conclusion contrary to the aufbau order. In potassium ($Z = 19$), which precedes iron, the $4s$ sublevel has a lower energy than the $3d$, and hence the electron removed in the ionization of potassium is the same as the last one added by the aufbau method—a $4s$ electron.

Iron occurs in nature as iron and potassium as potassium; they are not prepared by additions to atoms of lower atomic number. Hence the aufbau order should be regarded as what it is—an artificial device to permit us to correlate electronic configurations.

In general this need not bother us. The aufbau principle may be used to arrive at a satisfactory electronic configuration for an element. In ionization procedures, electrons are usually lost in reverse order of the principal quantum number—that is, highest value of n first. For this reason, spectroscopic notations are properly written by increasing value of n and not by any hypothetical order of filling.

2.16   Half-filled and Filled Subshells

The electronic configurations predicted by the aufbau procedure are confirmed by spectral and magnetic studies for most elements. There are a few, however, that exhibit slight variations from the standard pattern. In certain instances, it is possible to explain these variations on the basis of the enhanced stability of a filled or half-filled subshell.

The predicted configuration for the $3d$ and $4s$ subshells in the chromium atom is $3d^4 4s^2$, whereas the experimentally derived configuration is $3d^5 4s^1$. Presumably the stability gained by having one unpaired electron in each of the five $3d$ orbitals (half-filled subshell) accounts for the fact that the $3d^5 4s^1$ configuration is the one observed. The existence of a half-filled subshell also accounts for the fact that the configuration for the $4d$ and $5s$ subshells of molybdenum is $4d^5 5s^1$ rather than the predicted $4d^4 5s^2$.

For copper the predicted configuration for the last two subshells is $3d^9 4s^2$, whereas the accepted structure is $3d^{10} 4s^1$. The explanation for this deviation lies in the superior stability of the $3d^{10} 4s^1$ configuration resulting from the completed $3d$ subshell. Silver and gold also have configurations with completely filled d subshells instead of the $(n - 1)d^9$ ns^2 configurations predicted. In the case of palladium, two electrons are involved—the only case with a difference of more than one electron. The predicted configuration for the last two subshells of palladium is $4d^8 5s^2$; the observed configuration is $5d^{10} 5s^0$.

That half-filled and filled subshells contribute to the stability of atoms is also borne out in cases where the aufbau order is followed. Thus nitrogen, phosphorus, and arsenic show unusual properties (e.g., unexpectedly high ionization potentials) because of the fact that they all have half-filled p subshells. Zinc, cadmium, and mercury have properties that can be traced to the fact that all of their subshells are filled. The noble gases have unusually stable configurations with all of their subshells complete.

Some deviations from predicted configurations are observed other than those that can be accounted for on the basis of filled or half-filled subshells, particularly among elements of higher Z. The inner transition elements frequently depart from predicted configurations but never by more than one electron. The competing sublevels of these atoms ($4f$ and $5d$) lie close together in energy, and hence such deviations are not surprising. For our purposes such exceptions are not important. The chemistry of the elements is, in the main, satisfactorily explained on the basis of the predicted configurations.

2.17   Types of Elements

We may classify the elements according to their electronic configurations into four types.

1. *The noble gases.* In the periodic tables, the noble gases are found at the end of each period in group 0. They are colorless gases, chemically, unreactive, and diamagnetic. An examination of Figure 2.13 shows that the arrangement $ns^2 np^6$ is exceptionally stable. Discontinuities in the energy level diagram occur after these configurations are attained. The next electron added is added with a much higher energy to a quantum level of the next higher n. With the exception of helium ($Z - 2$), all of the noble gases have outer configurations of $ns^2 np^6$. No atom has a complete outer shell with the exception of helium and neon.

2. *The representative elements.* These elements comprise the A families of the periodic table and include metals and nonmetals. They exhibit a wide range of chemical behavior and physical characteristics. Some of the elements are diamagnetic and some are paramagnetic; the compounds of these elements, however, are generally diamagnetic and colorless. They are characterized as having all of their electronic shells either complete or stable (e.g., $ns^2 np^6$) except their outer shells to which the last electron may be considered as having been added. This outer shell is termed the valence shell; electrons in it are valence electrons. The number of valence electrons for each atom is the same as the group number. The chemistry of these elements depends upon these valence electrons.

3. *The transition elements.* These elements are found in the B families of the periodic table. They are characterized by inner building—the "last" electron being an inner d electron. Electrons from the two outermost shells are used in chemical reactions. All of these elements are metals; most of them are paramagnetic and form highly colored paramagnetic compounds.

4. *The inner-transition elements.* The elements are found at the bottom of the periodic table and properly should follow group IIIB. The sixth-period series that follows lanthanum (14 elements) is called the lanthanide series; the seventh-period series is known as the actinide series. The last electron added to each element is an f electron added to the third from the outer shell. Hence, the outer three shells may be involved in the chemistry of these elements. All of the inner-transition elements are metals. The elements are, in general, paramagnetic, and the compounds derived from them are paramagnetic and highly colored.

SOME SUGGESTED READINGS

Booth, V. H., *The Structure of the Atom,* New York, Macmillan, 1964 (paper).

Cooper, D. G., *The Periodic Table,* Washington, Butterworth, 1964 (paper).

Day, M. C., Jr., and Selbin, J., *Theoretical Inorganic Chemistry,* New York, Reinhold, 1962.

Gamow, G., *The Atom and Its Nucleus,* Englewood Cliffs, N.J., Prentice-Hall, 1961 (paper).

Gamow, G., *Thirty Years That Shook Physics,* Garden City, N.Y., Doubleday 1966.

Hochstrasser, R. M., *Behavior of Electrons in Atoms,* New York, Benjamin, 1964 (paper).

Kompaneyets, A., *Basic Concepts in Quantum Mechanics,* New York, Reinhold, 1966 (paper).

Lagowski, J. J., *The Structure of Atoms,* Boston, Houghton Mifflin, 1964 (paper).

Sisler, H. H., *Electronic Structure, Properties, and the Periodic Law,* New York, Reinhold, 1963 (paper).

Thomson, G., *The Atom,* New York, Oxford, 1962 (paper).

PROBLEMS

2.1 The element boron consists of two naturally occurring isotopes: $^{10}_5B$ which has a mass of 10.01294 u and $^{11}_5B$ which has a mass of 11.00931 u. If the atomic weight of boron is 10.811, what percent of each of the two isotopes is naturally occurring boron?

2.2 Use the masses given in Problem 2.1 and values found in this chapter to calculate the binding energy of (a) $^{10}_5B$ and (b) $^{11}_5B$. 1 u equals 931 mev.

2.3 If element X consists of 92.0% of atoms with a mass of 28.0 u each, 5.0% of atoms with a mass of 29.0 u each, and 3.0% of atoms with a mass of 30.0 u each, what is the atomic weight of X?

2.4 Give the values for all four quantum numbers for each electron in fluorine $(Z = 9)$. Write them to indicate Hund's rule (negative values first).

2.5 What is scientific determinism? Does Heinsenberg's uncertainty principle contradict this doctrine?

2.6 Write spectroscopic notations for the electronic configurations of: (a) Xe $(Z = 54)$, (b) Cd $(Z = 48)$, (c) V $(Z = 23)$, (d) Ra $(Z = 88)$, (e) Tb $(Z = 65)$, (f) Ir $(Z = 77)$.

2.7 Each of the following sets of quantum numbers represent an electron that has been the last electron added to complete the electronic configuration of an element according to the aufbau procedure. What element does each set indicate?

Element	n	l	m	s
A	3	1	0	$-\frac{1}{2}$
B	4	3	-3	$+\frac{1}{2}$
C	5	0	0	$+\frac{1}{2}$
D	5	1	$+1$	$+\frac{1}{2}$
E	6	2	-1	$-\frac{1}{2}$

2.8 Give the values of l, m, and s for the last electron added according to the aufbau principle to the electronic configuration of every element in the following groups of the periodic table: (a) I A, (b) VII A, (c) IV B, (d) II B, (e) IV A.

2.9 Ions are formed from atoms by the removal of one or more electrons (positive ions) or by the addition of one or more electrons (negative ions). or by the addition of one or more electrons (negative ions). Write the spectroscopic notation for the electronic configuration of each of the following ions: (a) S^{2-}, (b) Cu^+, (c) Cu^{2+}, (d) Fe^{3+}, (e) I^-, (f) Hg^{2+}, (g) Pb^{2+}, (h) Cr^{3+}, (i) Nd^{3+}.

2.10 (a) State the number of unpaired electrons in each of the ions listed in Problem 2.9. (b) Which of these ions would you predict to be diamagnetic and which paramagnetic?

2.11 (a) What would be the magnetic moment, in Bohr magnetons, of ions with 1, 2, 3, 4, or 5 unpaired electrons? (b) What is the magnetic moment of the ion V^{3+}?

2.12 (a) How can magnetic data help to determine the true structure of chromium? (b) of copper? (See Section 2.16.)

2.13 Complete the following table:

Symbol	Atomic Number	Mass Number	Protons	Neutrons	Electrons
Sn	50	120			
Ag		109			
	53	127			53
Ar				22	18
Cs^+				78	

2.14 What number would you predict for the atomic number of the noble gas of the seventh period (as yet unknown)?

2.15 Define the following terms: (a) binding energy, (b) atomic weight, (c) radioactivity, (d) Hund's rule of maximum multiplicity, (e) Pauli's exclusion principle, (f) half-filled subshell, (g) element.

2.16 Compare and contrast: (a) nucleon–nuclide, (b) isotope–isobar, (c) ground state–excited state, (d) inner-transition element–transition element, (e) cathode rays–canal rays, (f) line spectrum–continuous spectrum, (g) period–group.

2.17 (a) Calculate the de Broglie wavelength for an electron in the $n = 1$ Bohr level of the hydrogen atom. (b) If the electron has a mass of 9.11×10^{-28} g, what is the velocity of this electron?

2.18 (a) The Bohr radius for the $n = 1$ orbit, a_0, is 0.530 Å. Calculate the radii of the $n = 2$ and $n = 3$ orbits. (b) By means of equation (9), calculate the energy of an electron in each of the $n = 1$, $n = 2$, and $n = 3$ orbits. The value of e, the charge on the electron, is 4.80×10^{-10} esu; 1 esu = $1 \ g^{1/2} \ cm^{3/2}/sec$. (c) Use your answers from part (b) to calculate the frequencies and wavelengths corresponding to electron transitions from the $n = 3$ level to the $n = 1$ level, from the $n = 2$ level to the $n = 1$ level, and from the $n = 3$ level to the $n = 2$ level.

2.19 (a) Use the approximate expression for Heisenberg's uncertainty principle given in Section 2.12 to calculate the uncertainty in the velocity of a particle with a mass of 1.0 g when the uncertainty in the particle's position is 1.0 Å. (b) Perform the same calculation for the proton (mass, 1.7×10^{-24} g).

3

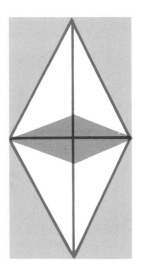

Chemical Bonding

It is the electrons of atoms that are responsible for chemical bonding, and there are two principal ways in which this bonding occurs. **Ionic,** or **electrovalent, bonding** is characterized by electron transfer; one of the reacting atoms loses one or more electrons, and the other atom gains one or more electrons. In **covalent bonding,** electrons are not transferred but are shared; a bond so formed consists of a pair of electrons shared by two atoms.

It is obvious, then, that an understanding of electronic configuration, a principal topic of the last chapter, is fundamental to an understanding of chemical bonding. Other properties of the elements, such as atomic size, are also important to a discussion of chemical bonding and will be considered in the opening sections of this chapter. These properties are effectively correlated by the periodic table in the same way that the periodic table systematizes electronic configuration.

3.1 Atomic Sizes

The determination of atomic sizes poses a problem. If the atom is viewed as a sphere, the radius of the atom should be the distance from the center of the nucleus to the outer reaches of the last electron. But the electron cloud of an atom has a varying intensity, and the probability of finding an electron extends over a wide area. It is impossible to isolate and measure a single atom.

The most useful approach to the problem of atomic size is that which determines so-called **atomic** (or **covalent**) **radii**. It is possible to measure the distance between the nuclei of two covalently bonded atoms by diffraction or spectroscopic methods. This bond distance is then apportioned between the bonded atoms to arrive at values for atomic radii.

For example, a radius of 0.99 Å is derived for the chlorine atom by dividing the distance from chlorine nucleus to chlorine nucleus in the Cl—Cl bond (1.98 Å) by two. In like manner, dividing the Br—Br bond distance (2.28 Å) by two gives a value of 1.14 Å for the atomic radius of bromine.

Atomic radii thus calculated may be added to give bond distances that agree fairly well with those that have been directly determined. Thus the atomic radius of chlorine, 0.99 Å, may be added to the atomic radius of bromine, 1.14 Å, to arrive at a value of 2.13 Å for the Cl—Br bond distance. This procedure may also be reversed; the atomic radius of chlorine, 0.99 Å, may be subtracted from the C—Cl bond distance, 1.76 Å, to derive the atomic radius of carbon, 0.77 Å.

Changing the environment of an atom may cause its effective size to vary; hence, discrepancies sometimes arise when this method of assigning atomic radii is used. Nevertheless, the data of Table 3.1 are useful in establishing trends and making generalizations. Within a group of the periodic table, an increase in atomic radius is generally observed from top to bottom (Figures 3.1 and 3.2). Such a trend is expected since the larger atoms of a group employ more electron levels than the smaller atoms.

In general, a decrease in atomic radius is observed from left to right across any period (Figure 3.3). The outermost electrons of the elements of a given period all have the same principal quantum number. As the atomic number increases from element to element across a period, the

Figure 3.1   Atomic and ionic radii of the group I A elements.

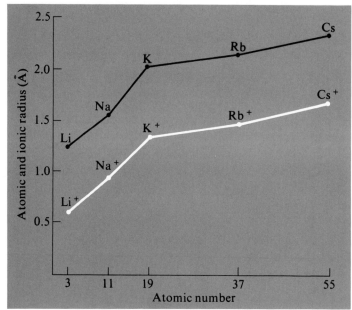

TABLE 3.1.
ATOMIC RADII[a].

1	2	3	4	5	6	7	8	9	10	11	12	13	14	15	16	17	18
1 H 0.37																	2 He —
3 Li 1.23	4 Be 0.89											5 B 0.80	6 C 0.77	7 N 0.74	8 O 0.74	9 F 0.72	10 Ne —
11 Na 1.57	12 Mg 1.36											13 Al 1.25	14 Si 1.17	15 P 1.10	16 S 1.04	17 Cl 0.99	18 Ar —
19 K 2.03	20 Ca 1.74	21 Sc 1.44	22 Ti 1.32	23 V 1.22	24 Cr 1.17	25 Mn 1.17	26 Fe 1.17	27 Co 1.16	28 Ni 1.15	29 Cu 1.17	30 Zn 1.25	31 Ga 1.25	32 Ge 1.22	33 As 1.21	34 Se 1.17	35 Br 1.14	36 Kr —
37 Rb 2.16	38 Sr 1.91	39 Y 1.62	40 Zr 1.45	41 Nb 1.34	42 Mo 1.29	43 Tc —	44 Ru 1.24	45 Rh 1.25	46 Pd 1.28	47 Ag 1.34	48 Cd 1.41	49 In 1.50	50 Sn 1.41	51 Sb 1.41	52 Te 1.37	53 I 1.33	54 Xe —
55 Cs 2.35	56 Ba 1.98	57* La 1.69	72 Hf 1.44	73 Ta 1.34	74 W 1.30	75 Re 1.28	76 Os 1.26	77 Ir 1.26	78 Pt 1.29	79 Au 1.34	80 Hg 1.44	81 Tl 1.55	82 Pb 1.54	83 Bi 1.52	84 Po 1.53	85 At —	86 Rn —
87 Fr —	88 Ra —																

*	58 Ce 1.65	59 Pr 1.65	60 Nd 1.64	61 Pm —	62 Sm 1.66	63 Eu 1.85	64 Gd 1.61	65 Tb 1.59	66 Dy 1.59	67 Ho 1.58	68 Er 1.57	69 Tm 1.56	70 Yb 1.70	71 Lu 1.56

[a] Radii given in angstrom units.

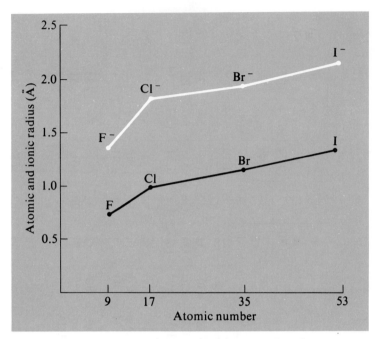

Figure 3.2   Atomic and ionic radii of the group VII A elements.

Figure 3.3   Atomic radii of the elements of the fourth period.

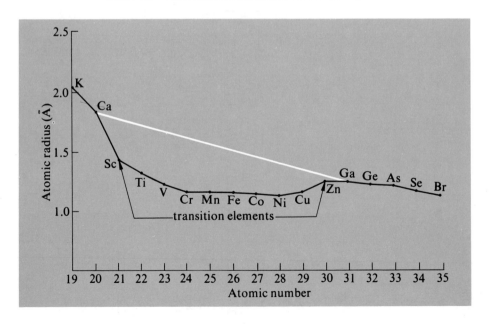

additional electron is added to the same level or to an inner level, and it is important to remember that the number of protons in the nucleus is also increased. This increase of positive charge on the nucleus tends to draw in the electron shells, and the result is that the atoms decrease in size.

The transition elements and inner-transition elements show some minor variations. Across a period the observed decrease in atomic radius for the transition elements is not so pronounced as that for the representative elements; also, there is a slight increase in size at the end of each transition series. These variations are due to the fact that the electrons of the transition elements are filling inner d orbitals; after these orbitals are filled, the next electrons must enter the p orbitals of the next higher principal quantum number.

The elements of the inner-transition series exhibit small, almost constant, radii. The differentiating electrons of these elements are lodged in the third from the outer level. This inner electron cloud effectively screens the increasing nuclear charge from the outer, size-determining, electrons. This **screening effect,** or **shielding effect,** caused by the completed buildup of the inner f orbitals, also accounts for the fact that the elements after the lanthanides are unusually small (the **lanthanide contraction**); thus hafnium ($Z = 72$) is smaller than zirconium ($Z = 40$).

3.2 Ionization Potentials

The amount of energy required to remove the most loosely held electron from an isolated gaseous atom in its ground state is the **ionization energy** of the element.

$$A \rightarrow A^+ + e^-$$

Ionization energies are usually determined by spectroscopic methods. The light emitted as a result of electronic transitions within an atom gives rise to a line spectrum since the energies of such electrons are quantized. However, when an electron is removed from an atom, its energy is no longer quantized, and the light emitted as a result of its transitions produces a continuous spectrum rather than a line spectrum. Thus the evaluation of an ionization energy proceeds by determining the limit to which an electron can be excited without producing ionization.

The **ionization potential** is the minimum potential required to produce ionization. The ionization potential of an atom is measured in volts (Section 9.1); however, it is numerically equal to an ionization energy expressed in electron volts, which are energy units. One electron volt is the energy acquired by an electron when it falls through a potential difference of 1 v; 1 ev equals 3.83×10^{-20} cal. The value of an ionization energy expressed in electron volts is customarily called an ionization potential; even though this terminology is not strictly correct, it is widely employed and is used in this book.

Certain atoms produce negative ions by the addition of one or more electrons. The terms ionization energy and ionization potential pertain *only* to the production of positive ions by the *removal* of an electron. Some of the positive ions thus described (such as ions derived from the noble gases or from elements that commonly form only negative ions) are never produced in ordinary chemical reactions.

The magnitude of the ionization potential of an element (Table 3.2) depends upon several factors. The larger the atomic radius, the easier it is to remove an electron and the smaller the ionization potential. This arises from the fact that in larger atoms the electron to be removed is at a greater distance from the positively charged nucleus. Thus ionization potential is inversely proportional to atomic radius; the smallest potential of a period is on the left, and the smallest potential of a group is on the bottom.

The magnitude of the positive charge on the nucleus is another factor of importance. An enhanced nuclear charge would be expected to make it more difficult to remove an electron. Such an effect is observed across a period where increasing nuclear charge parallels decreasing size, and hence ionization potential increases from left to right in any period. However, the nuclear charge may, at times, be partially screened by inner electrons. The ionization potentials of the transition elements do not increase across a period at the same rate as those of the representative elements; the ionization potentials of the inner-transition elements remain almost constant. For these types of elements, the shielding effect of the inner electrons partially counterbalances the increasing nuclear charge.

As a rule, and particularly for A family elements, the ionization potential decreases from top to bottom in a group of the periodic table. Increasing nuclear charge, which would call for increasing ionization potential, must be more than compensated for by increasing atomic size, the screening effect of inner electrons, and the fact that the electron is being removed from a higher and higher level.

Electronic configuration is the last factor to be considered. We noted in Section 2.16 that certain configurations are unusually stable. Thus the noble gases have high ionization potentials owing, in part, to their very stable electronic arrangements. We shall return to this important fact in Section 3.4. Other elements have relatively stable electronic arrangements. Elements with filled subshells (e.g., Be, Mg, Zn, Cd, and Hg) have high ionization potentials which are out of line with those of the other elements of their period. Nitrogen, phosphorus, and arsenic have unexpectedly high ionization potentials because in each case it is necessary to break up a half-filled p subshell to remove an electron.

TABLE 3.2.
FIRST IONIZATION POTENTIALS OF THE ELEMENTS[a].

(handwritten note: lower number gives up electron easier)

1	2	3	4	5	6	7	8	9	10	11	12	13	14	15	16	17	18
1 H 13.6																	2 He 24.6
3 Li 5.4	4 Be 9.3											5 B 8.3	6 C 11.3	7 N 14.5	8 O 13.6	9 F 17.4	10 Ne 21.6
11 Na 5.1	12 Mg 7.6											13 Al 6.0	14 Si 8.1	15 P 11.0	16 S 10.4	17 Cl 13.0	18 Ar 15.8
19 K 4.3	20 Ca 6.1	21 Sc 6.6	22 Ti 6.8	23 V 6.7	24 Cr 6.8	25 Mn 7.4	26 Fe 7.9	27 Co 7.9	28 Ni 7.6	29 Cu 7.7	30 Zn 9.4	31 Ga 6.0	32 Ge 8.1	33 As 10	34 Se 9.8	35 Br 11.8	36 Kr 14.0
37 Rb 4.2	38 Sr 5.7	39 Y 6.6	40 Zr 7.0	41 Nb 6.8	42 Mo 7.2	43 Tc —	44 Ru 7.5	45 Rh 7.7	46 Pd 8.3	47 Ag 7.6	48 Cd 9.0	49 In 5.8	50 Sn 7.3	51 Sb 8.6	52 Te 9.0	53 I 10.4	54 Xe 12.1
55 Cs 3.9	56 Ba 5.2	57* La 5.6	72 Hf 5.5	73 Ta 6	74 W 8.0	75 Re 7.9	76 Os 8.7	77 Ir 9.2	78 Pt 9.0	79 Au 9.2	80 Hg 10.4	81 Tl 6.1	82 Pb 7.4	83 Bi 8	84 Po —	85 At —	86 Rn 10.7
87 Fr —	88 Ra 5.3																

*	58 Ce 6.9	59 Pr 5.8	60 Nd 6.3	61 Pm —	62 Sm 5.6	63 Eu 5.7	64 Gd 6.2	65 Tb 6.7	66 Dy 6.8	67 Ho —	68 Er —	69 Tm —	70 Yb 6.2	71 Lu 5.0

[a] Potentials given in electron volts.

(Whereas chromium has a half-filled $3d$ subshell, the electron removed is not from this sublevel.)

In general, then, the ionization potential increases from left to right in any period and from bottom to top in any group. It must be remembered that ionization potential is related to the energy *required* to remove an electron. Thus the elements most active in losing electrons (metallic behavior) are those with the *lowest* ionization potentials and are found in the lower left of the periodic table. This reactivity in terms of electron loss decreases as one moves upward or to the right from this corner of the chart.

In Figure 3.4 the ionization potentials of the elements are plotted against atomic number. Particularly striking are the maxima of the curve that occur at the atomic numbers of the noble gases and the minima that represent the ionization potentials of the group I A elements. Also evident are the general upward trends for each period. Minor variations may be ascribed to effects which have been mentioned previously.

What we have described here are **first** ionization potentials. The **second** ionization potential of an element relates to the energy required to remove *one* electron from a $1+$ ion of that element.

$$A^+ \longrightarrow A^{2+} + e^-$$

The *third* ionization potential pertains to a process in which *one* electron is removed from a $2+$ ion.

$$A^{2+} \longrightarrow A^{3+} + e^-$$

Figure 3.4   *First ionization potentials of the elements versus atomic number.*

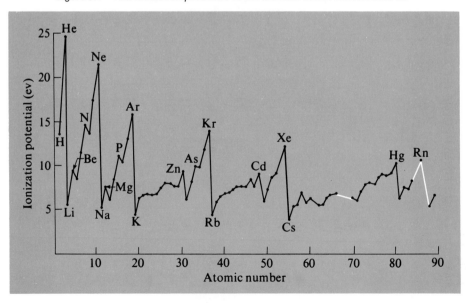

Even higher ionization potentials may be determined. When the term ionization potential is not further qualified, it is understood that the first ionization potential is meant.

Predictably, for any given element, the third ionization potential is higher than the second, and the second is higher than the first. It is more difficult to remove an electron (1− charge) from a 2+ ion than from a 1+ ion; likewise, it is more difficult to remove an electron from a 1+ ion than from a neutral atom. The high values observed for third and fourth ionization potentials indicate that few highly charged positive ions exist under ordinary conditions.

3.3 Electron Affinities

Electron affinity is the energy *released* when an electron is added to an isolated atom in its ground state. It should be noted that in this process a negative ion is produced from a neutral atom; as such, this is not the reverse of the process that determines ionization potential. In the determination of the ionization potential of chlorine, energy is *required* to bring about the transformation:

$$Cl \rightarrow Cl^+ + e^-$$

The electron affinity of chlorine is the energy *released* by the process:

$$e^- + Cl \rightarrow Cl^-$$

The numerical value of the electron affinity of chlorine, however, is the same as the ionization potential of the negative chloride ion.

The electron affinity of an element is usually determined indirectly by calculation from thermodynamic data (Section 6.12); uncertainties in the values employed in the calculation lead to electron affinities of questionable accuracy. Values are available for only a few elements.

On the basis of the electron affinity data that are available, predictions based on reasoning analagous to that used in discussing ionization potentials appear generally to be borne out. With some exceptions, smaller atoms have higher electron affinities than larger atoms (Table 3.3) since the added electron is lodged closer to the positively charged nucleus in a small atom than in a large atom. However, this effect may be partially negated by the repulsion of electrons already present in the atom. The concentration of negative charge in a small shell is greater than the concentration of negative charge obtained when the same number of electrons are placed in a large shell. This may, in part, explain the low value of the electron affinity of fluorine.

Electron affinity also depends upon the electronic configurations of the elements. Elements with relatively stable electronic configurations do not accept additional electrons readily; therefore the noble gases are assigned electron affinities of 0. Also, since the electronic configuration

TABLE 3.3.

ELECTRON AFFINITIES OF THE
GROUP VII A ELEMENTS (ev).

Element	Electron Affinity
fluorine	3.6
chlorine	3.8
bromine	3.5
iodine	3.2

of each of the group VII A elements is one electron short of a noble gas configuration, the elements of group VII A have, on the average, the highest electron affinities of any group of the periodic table.

Thus electron affinity roughly increases from left to right in any period and from bottom to top in any group. If the noble gases are ignored, the most active electron acceptors should be in the upper right corner of the periodic table, and this activity in terms of electron gain should decrease as one moves to the left or down in the periodic table.

Some second (and higher) electron affinities have been determined. These values relate to processes in which an electron is added to a negative ion; under these circumstances energy is required, not released.

3.4 The Ionic Bond

When an element that has a comparatively low ionization potential and an element that has a relatively high electron affinity combine, electrons are transferred, and an **ionic** (or **electrovalent**) **compound** is produced. For example, in the reaction of a sodium atom with a chlorine atom, an electron is transferred from sodium to chlorine, and charged particles, or ions, result. The sodium ion has a charge of 1+ since it has a nuclear charge of 11+ and only 10 electrons; the chloride ion has a 1− charge since its nucleus contains 17 protons and it has 18 electrons. Positive ions are called **cations,** and negative ions are called **anions.** These names are derived from the terminology of electrochemistry (Chapter 9).

The reactions and compounds of the A family elements are at times conveniently indicated by using the symbols of the elements under consideration together with dots for their valence electrons. For A family elements, the valence electrons are the only ones involved in chemical reactions. The positions of the dots around the symbol have no significance; electrons are distributed in three dimensions and in the manner previously discussed. Using such a notation, the equation for the reaction of sodium and chlorine is

$$Na\cdot + \cdot \overset{\cdot\cdot}{\underset{\cdot\cdot}{Cl}}: \longrightarrow Na^+ : \overset{\cdot\cdot}{\underset{\cdot\cdot}{Cl}}:^-$$

Care must be exercized in interpreting such equations since not all of the electrons present in the atom or ion are shown. The electronic configuration of sodium is $1s^2\,2s^2\,2p^6\,3s^1$, and that of chlorine is $1s^2\,2s^2\,2p^6\,3s^2\,3p^5$. After the reaction, the sodium ion attains a configuration identical with that of neon ($1s^2\,2s^2\,2p^6$), and the configuration of the chloride ion is the same as that of argon ($1s^2\,2s^2\,2p^6\,3s^2\,3p^6$). The sodium and chloride ions may be said to be **isoelectronic** (of the same electronic configuration) with neon and argon, respectively.

In ionic reactions, most of the representative elements attain an electronic configuration isoelectronic with a noble gas (the post-transition metals such as gallium and indium cannot attain them). Much has been made of this fact. Undoubtedly, the $ns^2\,np^6$ (octet) arrangement of electrons in the outer shell of a noble gas is very stable; this, in part, accounts for the values of the ionization potentials and electron affinities observed for the A family elements and the stabilities of their ionic compounds. Important as this generalization is, however, we shall see later that the attainment of a noble gas configuration is not the most fundamental driving force for the ionic reaction. Nevertheless, an A family element generally reacts through the loss or gain of electrons in such a way as to secure an octet of electrons in its outer shell; for those ions where the $n = 1$ shell is the only one present, two electrons form a stable structure (compare the first noble gas, helium).

In the reaction of sodium and chlorine, the total number of electrons lost by sodium, must equal the total number of electrons gained by chlorine. Thus the number of sodium ions produced is the same as the number of chloride ions produced. These ions attract each other to form a **crystal** (Figure 3.5) with the evolution of energy (the lattice energy).

Figure 3.5   Sodium chloride crystal lattice.

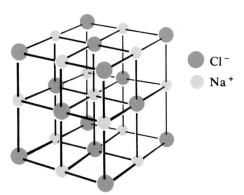

Cl⁻

Na⁺

The lattice energy is a measure of the amount of energy *required* to separate the positive and negative ions of a crystal, or it may be considered to be a measure of the energy *evolved* when the positive and negative ions form a crystal.

Even though there are the same number of sodium ions as chloride ions in a sodium chloride crystal, no pair of ions may be considered as belonging to each other. Rather, each sodium ion is surrounded by six chloride ions and each chloride ion is surrounded by six sodium ions, the geometry of the crystal is such that the repulsion of like-charged ions is more than compensated for by the attraction of oppositely charged ions. This mutual attraction of positive and negative ions is what holds the crystal together; indeed, the ionic bond may be considered to be just this.

The formula for this ionic compound, sodium chloride, is NaCl. From our examination of the sodium chloride crystal, we can see that this formula does not describe a unit of one sodium ion and one chloride ion, for such does not exist under ordinary conditions. Rather, the formula of an ionic compound gives the simplest ratio of ions present in a crystal; the actual number of ions present in any crystal (which would be very large) depends upon the size of the crystal under study.

When oxygen undergoes an ionic reaction, each oxygen atom (electron configuration $1s^2\ 2s^2\ 2p^4$) accepts two electrons and attains the neon configuration ($1s^2\ 2s^2\ 2p^6$); the oxide ion has a charge of $2-$. In the reaction of sodium with oxygen, two atoms of sodium are required for every one atom of oxygen since it is necessary that there be a balance between electrons lost and electrons gained. Thus the equation for this reaction is

$$2\mathrm{Na}\cdot + \overset{\cdot\cdot}{\mathrm{O}}: \longrightarrow 2\mathrm{Na}^+ + :\overset{\cdot\cdot}{\mathrm{O}}:^{2-}$$

The formula of the product, sodium oxide, is Na_2O. In the formula the subscript 2 for sodium and the subscript 1 (understood) for oxygen indicate the simplest ratio of ions present in any crystal of this substance. The geometry of the sodium oxide crystal is different from that of the sodium chloride crystal and is such that these ions are accommodated in the ratio of two sodium ions to one oxide ion.

The **electrovalence number** of an element is the charge (including sign) of the ion derived from that element after an electrovalent reaction. If we follow the octet principle, the electrovalence number of any of the group I A elements should be $1+$; group VII A, $1-$; group II A, $2+$; group VI A, $2-$. These charges are derived from the number of valence electrons characteristic of any element of a given group and the number of electrons that need to be lost (positive electrovalence) or gained (negative electrovalence) in order for the element to attain a noble gas configuration.

From these ionic charges, formulas may be derived on the basis of the fact that the *total* positive ionic charge of any compound must equal the *total* negative ionic charge of that compound. Calcium is a group II A metal, has two valence electrons, and has an electrovalence number of 2+. We have already determined that the electrovalence number of chlorine is 1− and that the electrovalence of oxygen is 2−. Thus the formula of calcium chloride is $CaCl_2$, and that of calcium oxide is CaO. In a similar manner one can derive the formulas of aluminum oxide (Al_2O_3), sodium sulfide (Na_2S), and potassium nitride (K_3N) from the predicted electrovalence numbers of aluminum (3+), oxygen (2−), sodium (1+), sulfur (2−), potassium (1+), and nitrogen (3−). We shall see later that not all of the compounds predicted by this method exist, and not all of those that do exist are truly ionic in character.

Metals are elements that tend to lose electrons in an ionic reaction, whereas nonmetals, if they enter into an ionic reaction at all, gain electrons. Whether two atoms will react to form an ionic compound depends upon several energy considerations. The three most important to the present discussion are the ionization energy of the metal, the electron affinity of the nonmetal, and the lattice energy of the resulting crystal.

The ionization of a sodium atom absorbs energy (ionization energy).

$$1.96 \times 10^{-19} \text{ cal/atom} + Na(g) \longrightarrow Na^+(g) + e^-(g)$$

The symbol (g) indicates a gaseous species. Energy is evolved when a chlorine atom gains an electron (electron affinity).

$$e^-(g) + Cl(g) \longrightarrow Cl^-(g) + 1.46 \times 10^{-19} \text{ cal/atom}$$

But the amount is insufficient to supply that required for the ionization of a sodium atom. The deficit is supplied by the condensation of the two ions into a crystal lattice (lattice energy).

$$Na^+(g) + Cl^-(g) \longrightarrow NaCl(crystal) + 3.04 \times 10^{-19} \text{ cal}$$

Thus energy is evolved by the overall process.

$$Na(g) + Cl(g) \longrightarrow NaCl(crystal) + 2.54 \times 10^{-19} \text{ cal}$$

This is a simplification. Other factors are involved (Section 6.12) such as the energy required to separate the sodium atoms from the form in which they customarily occur.

Two additional considerations should be borne in mind. First, the ionization potentials listed in Table 3.2 are **first** ionization potentials. For a bivalent ion such as Ca^{2+}, the second ionization potential must also be considered; second and higher order ionization potentials are always larger than first ionization potentials. Second, when more than one electron is added to an atom in the preparation of a negative ion, energy is *required* not released. Thus for the formation of the oxide ion, the addition of the first electron releases energy, but the addition of the second electron requires energy (Section 3.3); for the overall process, energy is required, not evolved. In the reaction of sodium with oxygen, therefore, the lattice energy of sodium oxide would have to supply the energy required for the preparation of the oxide ion as well as that needed for the ionization of sodium.

Certain metals fulfill the requirements for reaction but still cannot possibly produce ions that are isoelectronic with noble gases. The electronic configuration of the last two shells of zinc is $\cdots 3s^2 3p^6 3d^{10} 4s^2$. In order for zinc to attain the configuration of argon ($\cdots 3s^2 3p^6$), it would have to lose 12 electrons. An electron loss of this magnitude is never observed; the energy required is unobtainable in any known process. Nevertheless, zinc does react with nonmetals, but an ion with a 2+ charge is produced in these reactions.

The electronic configuration of the Zn^{2+} ion is one of some stability (although not as stable as a noble gas configuration); all of the subshells present are filled ($1s^2 2s^2 2p^6 3s^2 3p^6 3d^{10}$). Ions that are not isoelectronic with noble gases but have configurations in which all of the subshells present are complete are sometimes spoken of as **pseudonoble gas ions.** Other examples are Cd^{2+}, Hg^{2+}, Cu^+, Ag^+, Ga^{3+}, In^{3+}, and Tl^{3+}.

It is impossible for most of the transition elements to produce ions with any type of regular electronic configuration. Sc^{3+}, Y^{3+}, and La^{3+} have noble gas configurations, and some of the ions of elements of the copper family (group I B) and the zinc family (group II B) have pseudonoble gas structures. For the rest, however, the attainment of a noble gas or a pseudonoble gas structure is impossible since the existence of any ion with a charge higher than 3+ is doubtful under ordinary conditions.

These elements form ions with irregular electronic configurations, and most of them (although not all of them) have more than one electrovalence number. Thus depending upon reaction conditions, iron forms either the Fe^{2+} ion or the Fe^{3+} ion. The configuration of Fe^{2+} is $1s^2 2s^2 2p^6 3s^2 3p^6 3d^6$ and that of Fe^{3+} is $1s^2 2s^2 2p^6 3s^2 3p^6 3d^5$; Fe^{3+} is more stable than Fe^{2+} since Fe^{3+} has a half-filled $3d$ subshell. Notice that for these elements, more than the outer shell of electrons may be used for chemical bonding; such is common for transition elements. Some other common transition element ions are Cr^{2+}, Cr^{3+}, Mn^{2+}, Co^{2+}, Co^{3+}, Ni^{2+}. Copper forms the Cu^{2+} ion in addition to the pseudonoble gas ion Cu^+.

Most of the inner-transition element ions are quite irregular. The most common electrovalence number of these elements is 3+ which entails for each of the lanthanides, the loss of their $6s^2$ and $5d^1$ electrons.

Some of the compounds we have discussed are not purely ionic in character; this will be a topic for Section 3.8. Nevertheless, the ionic concept here applied is a convenient and important generalization.

3.5 Ionic Radius

The radii of ions have been determined by X-ray diffraction of ionic crystals. Such studies give the distances between the centers of adjacent ions, and it is a problem to apportion these distances. When bond distances of covalent molecules are apportioned to secure covalent radii (Section 3.1), one starts with a bond between two like atoms which can be divided equally. In ionic crystals the positive and negative ions are, of necessity, different sizes.

One solution to this problem is to study a crystal of a compound with a very small cation and a very large anion such as lithium iodide (Figure 3.6a). The assumption is then made that the iodide ions touch each other, and the iodide–iodide distance (d in the illustration) is divided in half to give the radius of the iodide ion. Such an apportionment of the anion–anion distance (d) is impossible for a crystal of the more common

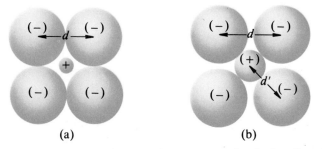

(a)   (b)

Figure 3.6 Determination of ionic radii. (See text for further discussion.)

type illustrated in Figure 3.6 (b) since there is no anion–anion contact. Once the radius of the iodide ion has been fixed as a standard, other ionic radii can be calculated by subtracting the radius of the standard ion from the cation–anion distance (d' in Figure 3.6b) of another crystal. For example, the radius of the potassium ion could be calculated by subtracting the radius of the iodide ion from the K^+ to I^- distance in the potassium iodide crystal. Table 3.4 lists some ionic radii.

A positive ion is always smaller than the neutral atom from which it is derived (Figure 3.1). Thus the radius of Na is 1.57 Å; the radius of Na^+ is 0.95 Å. In the formation of the sodium ion, the loss of an electron represents the loss of the entire $n = 3$ shell of the sodium atom. Furthermore, the loss of an electron creates an imbalance in the proton–electron ratio; since the protons outnumber the electrons in the positive ion, the electrons of the ion are drawn in closer to the nucleus.

For similar reasons, a 2+ ion is larger than a 3+ ion. Thus

$$Fe = 1.17 \text{ Å} \qquad Fe^{2+} = 0.75 \text{Å} \qquad Fe^{3+} = 0.60 \text{Å}$$

TABLE 3.4. IONIC RADII.[a]				
IA	IIA	IIIA	VIA	VIIA
Li^+ 0.60	Be^{2+} 0.31		O^{2-} 1.40	F^- 1.36
Na^+ 0.95	Mg^{2+} 0.65	Al^{3+} 0.50	S^{2-} 1.84	Cl^- 1.81
K^+ 1.33	Ca^{2+} 0.99	Ga^{3+} 0.62	Se^{2-} 1.98	Br^- 1.95
Rb^+ 1.48	Sr^{2+} 1.13	In^{3+} 0.81	Te^{2-} 2.21	I^- 2.16
Cs^+ 1.69	Ba^{2+} 1.35	Tl^{3+} 0.95		

[a] Radii given in angstrom units.

A negative ion is always larger than its parent atom. Thus the radius of the fluorine atom is 0.72 Å, and that of the fluoride ion is 1.36 Å (Figure 3.2). In the formation of the fluoride ion, the addition of an electron to the $2p$ subshell causes an enhanced repulsion between electrons, and the $n = 2$ shell expands. The fluoride ion has nine protons and ten electrons.

Within a period, isoelectronic positive ions show a decrease in ionic radius from left to right. This is because of the increasing nuclear charge. The same trend is observed for the isoelectronic negative ions of a period.

Within a group of the periodic table, the ions increase in size from top to bottom. Electrons are being added with higher and higher values of n, and the screening effect of the inner electrons is increasing (see Figures 3.1 and 3.2).

3.6 The Covalent Bond

When two nonmetals react, a covalent compound is produced. The characteristic of this bond is that electrons are shared by the bonded atoms; electron transfer does not occur. Since nonmetals have high ionization potentials, they do not lose electrons in chemical reactions. Rather, a successful reaction between two nonmetals requires that both of the reacting elements have at least a slight attraction for additional electrons (Section 3.3). Thus two atoms of helium (which does not exhibit this attraction) do not bond to each other; rather, helium exists as a monatomic gas.

On the other hand, two atoms of hydrogen combine to form a **molecule,** H_2, for which the symbol H:H is frequently used. Each of the bonded atoms supplies one electron to the covalent bond. One covalent bond consists of a pair of electrons that is shared by both of the bonded atoms. While the electrons must be considered as belonging to the molecule as a whole, each hydrogen atom can now be thought of as having the noble gas configuration of helium; this consideration is based on the premise that both shared electrons contribute to the stable configuration of each hydrogen atom. Remember that for both hydrogen and helium, only the $n = 1$ shell is involved; this shell is complete when occupied by two electrons. Another designation used to show the bonding in the hydrogen molecule is H—H, where the dash depicts one covalent bond (two electrons).

In a hydrogen atom, the electron is symmetrically distributed around the nucleus; in a hydrogen molecule this distribution is altered so that most of the electronic charge is concentrated between the two nuclei (Figure 3.7). The strength of this bond comes from the attraction of the positively charged nuclei for the negative electron cloud of the bond; electron–electron and nucleus–nucleus repulsions are more than compensated for by this attraction.

Figure 3.7 Representation of the electron distribution in a hydrogen molecule.

The formula, H_2, describes a discrete unit—a molecule—and hydrogen gas consists of a collection of such molecules. There are no molecules in strictly ionic materials. The formula Na_2Cl_2 is incorrect because sodium chloride is an ionic compound, and the simplest ratio of ions in a crystal of sodium chloride is 1 to 1; a molecule of formula Na_2Cl_2 does not exist. However, for covalent materials a formula such as H_2O_2 can be correct; here, the formula describes a molecule containing two hydrogen atoms and two oxygen atoms.

The hydrogen molecule can be described as being **diatomic** (containing two atoms). Other elements exist as diatomic molecules. An atom of any group VII A element has seven valence electrons. By the formation of a covalent bond between two such atoms, each atom attains an octet configuration characteristic of the noble gases. Thus fluorine gas consists of F_2 molecules:$\ddot{\underset{..}{F}}:\ddot{\underset{..}{F}}:$; only the electrons between the two atoms are shared and form a part of the covalent bond (although the molecular orbital theory considers that all of the electrons affect the bonding— Section 3.14).

More than one covalent bond may form between two atoms. A nitrogen atom (group V A) has five valence electrons. The diatomic molecule

N_2 is assigned the structure

$$:N:::N:$$

Here six electrons are shared in three covalent bonds (usually called a triple bond). Notice that as a result of this formulation, each of the nitrogen atoms can be considered as having an octet of electrons.

The nonmetallic elements that exist as diatomic molecules are H_2, F_2, Cl_2, Br_2, I_2, N_2, and O_2. (Oxygen is a special case and will be discussed in Section 3.14.) These elements are always indicated in this way in chemical equations.

Binary compounds are those formed from two different elements. Diatomic molecules may or may not result from the reaction of two non-metals. (Notice the difference in the meaning of the terms **binary** and **diatomic**.) Thus the reaction of hydrogen with chlorine produces diatomic molecules, while the reaction of hydrogen and oxygen produces molecules with a total of three atoms each. The formation of these molecules may be indicated as follows (although these are not proper chemical equations—see Chapter 4):

$$H\cdot + \cdot\ddot{C}\ddot{l}: \rightarrow H:\ddot{C}\ddot{l}:$$

$$2H\cdot + \cdot\ddot{O}: \rightarrow H:\ddot{O}:$$
$$\qquad\qquad\qquad \underset{}{H}$$

Notice that for these molecules, the hydrogen atoms can be considered as having a stable $n = 1$ shell; the other atoms have characteristic noble gas octets.

The electron-dot formulas we have been using are called **valence bond structures** or **Lewis structures,** named after Gilbert N. Lewis who proposed this theory of covalent bonding in 1916. The Lewis theory emphasized the attainment of noble gas configurations on the part of atoms in covalent molecules. On this basis, one would predict that the group VII A nonmetals would form one covalent bond to attain a stable octet; group VI A, two covalent bonds; group V A, three covalent bonds; and group IV A, four covalent bonds. Such predictions are borne out in many compounds such as:

$$\begin{array}{ccc}
H & :\ddot{C}\ddot{l}: & \\
H:\overset{\cdot\cdot}{\underset{H}{C}}:H & :\ddot{C}\ddot{l}:\overset{}{\underset{:\ddot{C}\ddot{l}:}{C}}:\ddot{C}\ddot{l}: & H:\overset{\cdot\cdot}{\underset{H}{N}}:H \\
\text{methane, } CH_4 & \text{carbon tetrachloride, } CCl_4 & \text{ammonia, } NH_3
\end{array}$$

$$\begin{array}{cc}
:\ddot{C}\ddot{l}:\overset{\cdot\cdot}{\underset{:\ddot{C}\ddot{l}:}{P}}:\ddot{C}\ddot{l}: & \qquad :\ddot{C}\ddot{l}:\ddot{O}:\ddot{C}\ddot{l}: \\
\text{phosphorus trichloride, } PCl_3 & \text{dichlorine oxide, } Cl_2O
\end{array}$$

Some molecules contain double and triple bonds:

$$:\overset{..}{O}::C::\overset{..}{O}: \qquad \overset{\displaystyle H \qquad H}{\underset{\displaystyle H \qquad H}{:\overset{.}{C}::\overset{.}{C}:}} \qquad H:C:::C:H$$

carbon dioxide, CO_2 ethylene, C_2H_4 acetylene, C_2H_2

3.7 The Coordinate Covalent Bond

The Lewis theory incorporates another type of covalent bond in which *both* of the shared electrons come from but *one* of the bonded atoms; such a bond is called a **coordinate covalent,** or **dative, bond.** Thus the $POCl_3$ molecule may be diagrammed by adding an oxygen atom to the PCl_3 molecule:

$$:\overset{..}{\underset{..}{C}l}:\overset{..}{P}:\overset{..}{\underset{..}{C}l}: + :\overset{..}{O}: \longrightarrow :\overset{\displaystyle :\overset{..}{O}:}{\underset{\displaystyle :\overset{..}{C}l:}{\overset{..}{\underset{..}{C}l}:P:\overset{..}{\underset{..}{C}l}:}}$$

For a phosphorus to chlorine bond, in either PCl_3 or $POCl_3$, one of the electrons is supplied by the phosphorus atom, and the other electron is supplied by a chlorine atom. For the coordinate covalent phosphorus to oxygen bond, both of the bonding electrons are supplied by the phosphorus atom.

A prediction of the number of covalent bonds that an atom forms in a molecule may be incorrect if the molecule contains a coordinate covalent bond. Since phosphorus has five valence electrons, phosphorus would be expected to satisfy the octet principle through the formation of three covalent bonds. This prediction is correct for PCl_3; however, it is not correct for $POCl_3$ if the coordinate covalent bond is included in the count. Likewise, oxygen (six valence electrons) would be expected to attain an octet configuration through the formation of two covalent bonds; in $POCl_3$ the stability of the oxygen atom is provided for by the formation of but one coordinate covalent bond.

An arrow is sometimes used to designate a coordinate covalent bond. The arrow is positioned pointing away from the atom that supplies the electron pair for the bond (the **donor**) and toward the atom that shares the bonding electrons but does not contribute electrons for bond formation (the **acceptor**). This type of designation is employed in formulas in which simple covalent bonds are indicated by dashes. $POCl_3$ may be diagrammed

$$\begin{array}{c} O \\ \uparrow \\ Cl-P-Cl \\ | \\ Cl \end{array}$$

Another frequently cited example of the coordinate covalent bond is that found in the ammonium ion, NH_4^+. This ion may be considered as having been produced by the formation of a coordinate covalent bond between a proton (a hydrogen atom stripped of its electron) and the nitrogen of an ammonia molecule.

$$H:\overset{..}{\underset{H}{N}}:H + H^+ \rightarrow \left[H:\overset{\overset{\displaystyle H}{}}{\underset{\underset{\displaystyle H}{..}}{N}}:H \right]^+$$

The concept of the coordinate covalent bond is useful in writing Lewis structures; however, undue importance should not be attached to this distinction. All electrons are alike no matter what their source. All of the bonds in the ammonium ion are identical; thus it is impossible to distinguish between them. Likewise, it is impossible to locate the 1+ charge of the ion on any one atom of the ion.

In addition, not too much importance should be attached to the electron-dot formulas. These do not accurately depict the geometry of covalent molecules nor the electron concentrations in molecules. Further, processes used to derive Lewis structures are not necessarily descriptive of the chemical reactions used to produce the compounds under consideration.

3.8   Transition Between Ionic and Covalent Bonding

Chemical reactions and physical measurements support the belief that most chemical compounds are intermediate in character between the purely ionic and the purely covalent. The best examples of ionic bonds are found in compounds between the metals of low ionization potential of the lower left of the periodic table and the nonmetals of high electron affinity found in the upper right of the periodic table. In such compounds electron transfer is definite and complete; these compounds exist as a collection of ions in ionic crystals with characteristically high melting points (Section 3.10).

A pure covalent bond is found in molecules formed from two *identical* atoms such as Cl_2. The electron-attracting ability of one chlorine atom is exactly the same as the electron-attracting ability of any other, and the electron cloud of the bond is distributed equally between the two chlorine atoms. Or, one could say that the bonding electrons are shared equally by the chlorine atoms. The melting points of solids consisting of covalent molecules are low because the molecules, unlike ions, do not have charges of any magnitude to keep them in a solid modification (Section 3.10).

Most compounds fit somewhere between these two extremes. The diagrams of Figure 3.8 show that the deformation of the electron clouds of ions (particularly anions) leads ultimately to the formation of molecules

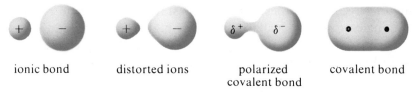

ionic bond   distorted ions   polarized   covalent bond
                                   covalent bond

Figure 3.8   Transition between ionic and covalent bonding.

and predominantly covalent compounds. Kasimir Fajans, in 1923, proposed a set of criteria to predict the degree of ion deformation in compounds.

We shall use melting points as a rough guide to covalent character. This is not an entirely reliable criterion, however, since certain highly covalent substances occur in giant-molecule solid modifications in which all the atoms of the solid are joined through a network of covalent bonds (Section 3.10), and such solids have as high, or higher, melting points as ionic substances. Nevertheless, meaningful comparisons may be made between compounds of comparable crystal structure.

Fajans identified several factors which he said lead to ion deformation and enhanced covalence. **Fajans' rules,** with an example for each, are given in the following list; they are best understood if one thinks in terms of the distortion of the electron cloud of the anion by the cation. Ion deformation occurs, and is favored, in compounds containing:

1. *A large anion* (large, easily deformable electron cloud).
    MgF_2; melting point = 1396°C; ionic radius F^- = 1.36 Å
    MgI_2; melting point = 632°C; ionic radius I^- = 2.16 Å

2. *A small cation* (high concentration of positive charge).
    $BeCl_2$; melting point = 440°C; ionic radius Be^{2+} = 0.31 Å
    $BaCl_2$; melting point = 962°C; ionic radius Ba^{2+} = 1.35 Å

3. *High charge on anion* (electrons held by much smaller number of protons).
    KCl; melting point = 776°C; ionic radius Cl^- = 1.81 Å
    K_2S; melting point = 471°C; ionic radius S^{2-} = 1.84 Å

4. *High charge on cation* (high concentration of positive charge).
    $NaCl$; melting point = 801°C; ionic radius Na^+ = 0.95 Å
    YCl_3; melting point = 680°C; ionic radius Y^{3+} = 0.92 Å

5. *Ions that are not isoelectronic with noble gases.*
    $NaCl$; melting point = 801 °C; ionic radius Na^+ = 0.95 Å
    $CuCl$; melting point = 422°C; ionic radius Cu^+ = 0.96 Å

Boron (group III A—three valence electrons) has a small atomic radius, is a nonmetal, and forms covalent compounds. If a B^{3+} ion were to form, its small size and high positive charge would cause such distortion in an anion that a predominantly covalent compound would result. Likewise, aluminum chloride is a predominantly covalent material (consisting of Al_2Cl_6 molecules in the vapor state). Truly ionic compounds containing cations with a charge of 3+ or higher are rare, and such exist only when the cation is a very large one. Certain highly charged cations exist, in hydrated form, in water solution, however (Sections 8.2 and 8.3).

Tin and lead are group IV A elements and are metallic in character. These elements are frequently said to form 2+ and 4+ ions in such compounds as $SnCl_2$, $SnCl_4$, $PbCl_2$, and $PbCl_4$. The compounds with "4+ cations" are undoubtedly not ionic at all but covalent; this is not unexpected since Sn and Pb both have four valence electrons, and the formation of four covalent bonds gives them noble gas structures.

The compounds of Sn^{2+} and Pb^{2+} have more ionic character (lower charge on the cation). It is surprising that lead (or tin) forms a 2+ ion (without a noble gas configuration) at all, even though the resulting compounds are not strongly ionic. The atom of lead is large, and its valence electrons are far away from the nucleus and screened by inner electrons, so that lead has low enough ionization potentials to function as an electron donor in ionic reactions. The valence shell of lead contains two $6s$ electrons and two $6p$ electrons; it is the loss of the $6p$ electrons that forms the Pb^{2+} ion. If one reasons that a Pb^{4+} ion (a pseudo-noble gas ion) should form in analagous manner, Fajans' rules predict ion distortion that would result in the formation of covalent molecules.

Likewise, the metals antimony and bismuth, of group V A, are reported to form 3+ and 5+ "ions." Such compounds are probably even more covalent than those of tin and lead, particularly those in which antimony and bismuth have 5+ charges. Ion distortion and enhanced covalence is also observed in transition metal compounds.

Another approach to the problem of bonds of intermediate character is that which considers the polarization of covalent bonds (Figure 3.8); in this view, the ionic bond is an extreme case of the polarization of a covalent bond by the dislocation of electron charge density.

Two *like* atoms form a pure covalent bond in which the bonding electrons are shared exactly equally. However, when two *different* atoms are joined by a covalent bond, the electrons of the bond are not shared equally. No matter how similar such atoms may be, there will be some difference in their electron attracting abilities. As predicted by electron affinities (Section 3.3), chlorine has a larger attraction for electrons than does bromine. Thus in the molecule $:\overset{..}{Br}:\overset{..}{Cl}:$ the electrons of the covalent bond are more strongly attracted by the chlorine atom than the bromine atom, and the electron cloud of the bond is distorted toward the chlorine atom. Therefore the chlorine end of the molecule is negative with respect to the bromine end of the molecule. The molecule as a whole is electrically neutral since it contains as many protons as electrons; however, polarity arises from an unequal distribution of the bonding electrons in the molecule. The Br—Cl bond is spoken of as a polar covalent bond. Since the charges of this polar bond are not as large as the $1+$ or $1-$ charges found on ions, they are usually indicated by the symbols δ^+ and δ^-

Obviously, the greater the difference in electron attracting ability between two atoms joined by a covalent bond the more polar the bond will be. Figure 3.8 shows that if this unequal sharing is carried to an extreme, a situation arises where one of the bonded atoms has all of the bonding electrons, and separate ions result.

Many of the physical properties of certain covalent compounds reflect the polar nature of their molecules—for example, melting point, surface tension, heat of vaporization, bond energy, and dipole moment. These properties will be studied in later chapters. A molecule with positive and negative charge centers is spoken of as a dipole, and the dipole moment of the molecule may be defined as the product of the charge times the distance between the positive and negative centers. The dipole moment of a compound may be calculated from the measurement of the compound's dielectric constant. In an electric field, polar molecules orient themselves with their positive ends toward the negative plate and their negative ends toward the positive plate (Figure 3.9). This orientation influences the amount of charge that a pair of electrically charged plates can hold. The dielectric constant of a compound can be determined by comparing the charge on a pair of plates with the compound between them to the charge on the plates when they are separated by a vacuum, voltage constant.

The dipole moments of nonpolar molecules, such as H_2, Cl_2, and Br_2, are zero. The more polar the bond of a diatomic molecule, the larger is

Figure 3.9　Effect of an electrostatic field on the orientation of polar molecules.

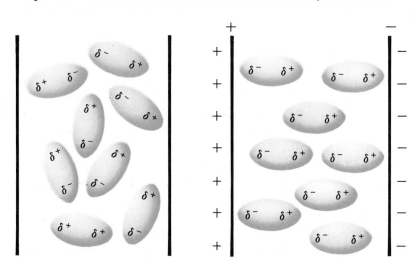

the dipole moment of the molecule. Linus Pauling has used the dipole moment of a compound to calculate the **partial ionic character** of its covalent bond. Dipole moment, μ, is defined as the product of the distance separating equal charges of opposite sign and the magnitude of the charge. If hydrogen chloride were completely ionic, the H^+ and Cl^- ions would each bear a unit charge (1.60×10^{-19} coulomb). Since the bond distance between the H and Cl atoms of hydrogen chloride is 1.27 Å, the dipole moment of the hypothetical, completely ionic, HCl would be:

$$\mu = (1.60 \times 10^{-19} \text{ coulomb})(1.27 \times 10^{-8} \text{ cm})$$
$$= 2.03 \times 10^{-27} \text{ coulomb cm}$$
$$= 6.10 \text{ D}$$

Dipole moments are customarily expressed in debye units; $1 \text{ D} = 3.33 \times 10^{-28}$ coulomb cm. The experimentally derived dipole moment of HCl is 1.03 D. Thus the observed dipole moment is 0.17 times the value calculated for the hypothetical, ionic, compound.

$$\frac{1.03 \text{ D}}{6.10 \text{ D}} = 0.17$$

Based upon dipole moment measurements, the HCl bond appears to be 17% ionic. Bonds with a partial ionic character of over 50% should be classed as ionic.

3.9 Electronegativity

The ability of an atom in a molecule to attract electrons to itself is called the relative **electronegativity** of the atom. Thus the polarity of the HCl molecule may be said to arise from the difference between the electronegativity of hydrogen and that of chlorine; since chlorine is more electronegative than hydrogen, the chlorine end of the molecule is the negative end of the dipole. In general, electronegativities of the elements are related to the same atomic parameters as are ionization potentials, and trends in electronegativities approximately parallel those in ionization potentials.

Unlike ionization potentials, however, electronegativities cannot be determined by a definite, direct, measurement. There is no agreement as to how they should be calculated, and many systems of measurement have been proposed. Several electronegativity scales have been derived from atomic radii and electronic configurations. Electronegativity determinations have been based on measurements of dipole moments; this scheme employs the same type of data as that used for the determination of the partial ionic character of the HCl bond.

A system has been devised using the average of the ionization potential and the electron affinity of each element as the electronegativity of that element. It is logical that a measure of the electron-attracting ability of an atom of a covalent bond can be based on these measurements. Thus, a large electronegativity value is observed when the atom has a high ionization potential (small tendency to lose an electron completely) and a high electron affinity (great tendency to gain an electron completely). Unfortunately, electron affinities have been calculated for only a few elements, and some of these values are of questionable accuracy.

The electronegativity scale devised by Pauling is the one most used (Table 3.5) and is based on experimentally derived values of **bond energies.** The bond energy of the Cl—Cl bond, for example, is the energy required to separate the Cl_2 molecule into two atoms of chlorine (*not* ions).

$$9.63 \times 10^{-20} \, cal/bond + \; :\ddot{C}l:\ddot{C}l: \; \rightarrow 2:\ddot{C}l\cdot$$

This bond energy relates to a pure covalent bond in which the electrons are shared equally, and there is no polarity. In like manner, the bond energy of the H—H bond, another nonpolar bond, can be experimentally determined.

$$1.73 \times 10^{-19} \, cal/bond + H:H \rightarrow 2H\cdot$$

An expected value of the bond energy of the H—Cl bond can be calculated by taking the arithmetic mean of the bond energies of the H—H and Cl—Cl bonds.

$$\frac{0.96 \times 10^{-19} \, cal/bond + 1.73 \times 10^{-19} \, cal/bond}{2} = 1.35 \times 10^{-19} \, cal/bond$$

The experimentally determined value of the bond energy of the H—Cl bond, however, is larger than this calculated value.

$$1.71 \times 10^{-19} \, cal/bond + H:\ddot{C}l: \; \rightarrow H\cdot + \; :\ddot{C}l\cdot$$

The difference between the two values is given the symbol Δ.

$$\Delta = 1.71 \times 10^{-19} \, cal/bond - 1.35 \times 10^{-19} \, cal/bond$$
$$= 3.6 \times 10^{-20} \, cal/bond$$

The calculated value is based on equal electron sharing; the actual bond is polar. The energy that must be expended to separate the electrons of a covalent bond when they are closely associated with one of the bonded atoms is larger than that required when the bonding electrons are equally shared. One can think in terms of the need to overcome the attraction of the δ^+ and δ^- produced in the case of unequal sharing.

Thus, for a polar bond, the experimental bond energy is always larger than the calculated bond energy, and the magnitude of the difference, Δ, depends upon the degree of polarity of the bond. For highly polar bonds, which result when atoms of widely different electron attracting

TABLE 3.5.
ELECTRONEGATIVITIES OF THE ELEMENTS[a].

1 H 2.1																	2 He —
3 Li 1.0	4 Be 1.5											5 B 2.0	6 C 2.5	7 N 3.0	8 O 3.5	9 F 4.0	10 Ne —
11 Na 0.9	12 Mg 1.2											13 Al 1.5	14 Si 1.8	15 P 2.1	16 S 2.5	17 Cl 3.0	18 Ar —
19 K 0.8	20 Ca 1.0	21 Sc 1.3	22 Ti 1.5	23 V 1.6	24 Cr 1.6	25 Mn 1.5	26 Fe 1.8	27 Co 1.8	28 Ni 1.8	29 Cu 1.9	30 Zn 1.6	31 Ga 1.6	32 Ge 1.8	33 As 2.0	34 Se 2.4	35 Br 2.8	36 Kr —
37 Rb 0.8	38 Sr 1.0	39 Y 1.2	40 Zr 1.4	41 Nb 1.6	42 Mo 1.8	43 Tc 1.9	44 Ru 2.2	45 Rh 2.2	46 Pd 2.2	47 Ag 1.9	48 Cd 1.7	49 In 1.7	50 Sn 1.8	51 Sb 1.9	52 Te 2.1	53 I 2.5	54 Xe —
55 Cs 0.7	56 Ba 0.9	57–71 La–Lu 1.1–1.2	72 Hf 1.3	73 Ta 1.5	74 W 1.7	75 Re 1.9	76 Os 2.2	77 Ir 2.2	78 Pt 2.2	79 Au 2.4	80 Hg 1.9	81 Tl 1.8	82 Pb 1.8	83 Bi 1.9	84 Po 2.0	85 At 2.2	86 Rn —
87 Fr 0.7	88 Ra 0.9	89– Ac– 1.1–1.7															

[a] Based on Linus Pauling, *The Nature of the Chemical Bond, Third Edition.* © 1960 by Cornell University Press. Used with the permission of Cornell University Press.

abilities are joined, Δ is large. Hence, calculated values of Δ have been empirically related to electronegativities of Table 3.5. The electronegativity difference between two bonded atoms is not directly proportional to the Δ for the bond; rather, Pauling has shown that the difference in electronegativities is directly related to the square roots of the Δ values.

The electronegativity values obtained by any of the methods described are quite similar indicating that the concept of electronegativity is a valid, if inexact, one. In general, electronegativity increases from left to right across any period (with increasing number of valence electrons) and from bottom to top in any group (with decreasing size). Thus the most highly electronegative elements are found in the upper right corner of the periodic table (ignoring the noble gases) and the least electronegative elements are found in the lower left corner of the chart. These trends parallel those noted for ionization potentials and electron affinities. The electronegativities of the elements are plotted against atomic number in Figure 3.10.

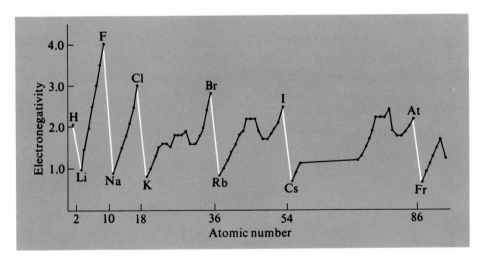

Figure 3.10 Electronegativity versus atomic number.

Metals are elements that have small attractions for valence electrons (low electronegativities); except for the noble gases, nonmetals have large attractions (high electronegativities). Thus electronegativities (as well as ionization potentials and electron affinities) can be used to rate metallic reactivities and nonmetallic reactivities, and the positions of the elements in the periodic table are helpful in making predictions concerning chemical reactivity (Figure 3.11).

Electronegativities can be used to predict the type of bonding to be found in a compound. When two elements of widely different electronegativity combine, an ionic compound is produced; thus, the electro-

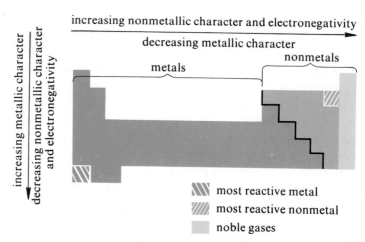

Figure 3.11   The relation between position in the periodic classification and metallic or nonmetallic reactivity.

negativity difference between sodium and chlorine is 2.1, and NaCl is an ionic compound.

Covalent bonding occurs between nonmetals where the electronegativity differences are not so large. In such cases, the electronegativity differences give an indication of the degree of polarity of the covalent bonds. If the electronegativity difference is zero or very small, an essentially nonpolar bond with equal, or almost equal, sharing of electrons can be assumed. The larger the electronegativity difference, the more polar is the covalent bond, the bond being polarized in the direction of the atom with the larger electronegativity. Thus, from electronegativities, we can predict that HF is the most polar, and has the largest bond energy, of any of the hydrogen halides (see Table 3.6).

The type of bonding that occurs between two metals (the metallic bond), where electronegativity differences are also relatively small, will be considered in Section 3.15.

TABLE 3.6.
SOME PROPERTIES OF THE HYDROGEN HALIDES.

Hydrogen halide	Dipole moment (D)	Bond Energy (cal/bond)	Electronegativity of halogen	Electronegativity difference between hydrogen and halogen
HF	1.91	2.24×10^{-19}	F = 4.0	1.9
HCl	1.03	1.71×10^{-19}	Cl = 3.0	0.9
HBr	0.78	1.45×10^{-19}	Br = 2.8	0.7
HI	0.38	1.18×10^{-19}	I = 2.5	0.4

3.10 Properties of Ionic and Covalent Compounds

The properties of ionic compounds are best understood on the basis of the structure of the ionic crystal (Section 3.4, Figure 3.5). The electrostatic forces between the ions in such a crystal are moderately strong forces. Thus ionic crystals are hard. In the process of melting, thermal energy must be supplied to overcome these forces sufficiently for the crystal to liquefy, and therefore ionic substances have relatively high melting points. The boiling points of ionic materials are high since the vaporization of ionic liquids is opposed by the strong electrostatic attractions between ions.

The ions in a crystal are held in a definite geometric pattern. The structure is such that the electrostatic attractions between positive and negative ions more than compensate for the repulsions that exist between ions of like charge. Thus ionic crystals are brittle because the stability of the crystals depend upon the preservation of their geometric patterns (Figure 3.12). Ionic compounds are good conductors of electricity when molten or in solution (but not in the crystalline state where the ions are not free to move); also, ionic materials are very soluble in polar solvents (Chapter 8).

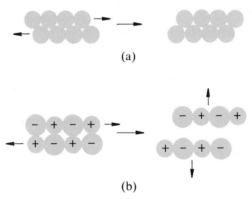

Figure 3.12   *Effect of deformation on (a) a metallic crystal, and (b) an ionic crystal.*

Molecules occupy the lattice points in a crystal of a covalent compound. Polar molecules are held in the crystal lattice by the orientation of their dipoles—the negative end of one molecule attracting the positive end of another (Figure 3.13). Such forces of attraction are not nearly so strong as those encountered in ionic crystals. Nonpolar molecules are held in a crystal lattice by van der Waals forces. These forces are extremely weak (and are common to all matter); they are thought to be caused by the motion of electrons and are sometimes called fluctuating dipoles. Hence, at a given instant one portion of an otherwise neutral

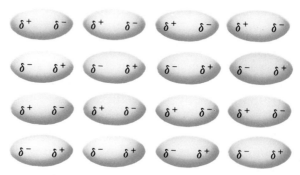

Figure 3.13   Orientation of polar molecules in a crystal.

molecule may have a very small negative charge associated with it because it has a slightly higher than average concentration of electrons. At the next instant, however, that same portion may be relatively positive because of a slight deficiency of electronic charge.

Because of the very weak nature of the forces holding nonpolar molecular crystals together, such crystals are soft and have low melting points. Liquids of nonpolar materials are quite volatile and have low boiling points; compounds of this type are usually gases under normal conditions. Nonpolar compounds do not conduct electricity in the liquid state or in solution because of the absence of charged particles to respond to the electric field. Nonpolar liquids are poor solvents for ionic compounds.

Polar covalent compounds have properties intermediate between those of ionic compounds and nonpolar covalent compounds. Because of the dipole attractions, polar compounds have higher melting points and boiling points and are less volatile than nonpolar materials. Polar molecular crystals are harder than nonpolar molecular crystals. These properties are not so extreme as those of ionic substances. Polar covalent compounds are not conductors of electricity, however, because the negative and positive charges of the dipole are contained in the same particle, and this particle is consequently attracted toward both poles of an electric field equally. The best solvents for ionic materials are in this classification of substances.

It is relatively simple to predict the degree of polarity of a given diatomic molecule by means of electronegativities. For molecules containing more than two atoms, it is essential that the geometry of the molecule also be known before a prediction as to the overall polarity of the compound can be made. Thus, for a molecule of the type A_2B, two geometric arrangements are possible: angular (I) or linear (II).

$$A—B$$
$$|$$
$$A \qquad A—B—A$$

structure I   structure II

Let us assume that atom A is more electronegative than atom B. Hence, in either structure, the A—B bonds are polar, but there are two such bonds to consider in each structure. In structure I, the center of gravity of positive charge coincides with the center of the B atom, while the center of gravity of negative charge lies at some point equidistant between the two A atoms. Since the molecule exhibits charge separation, it is polar. In structure II, however, the center of gravity of negative charge lies at the same point as that of the positive charge—the center of the B atom. Hence, the dipoles of the two bonds effectively neutralize one another, and the molecule is nonpolar. CO_2 is a nonpolar molecule corresponding to structure II; H_2O and SO_2 are polar molecules corresponding to an angular arrangement of atoms such as that of structure I.

More complicated molecules lend themselves to similar analysis. Thus BF_3 is a nonpolar molecule even though the individual B—F bonds are strongly polar. The reason for this is that BF_3 is a planar molecule:

All of the bond angles are equivalent, and all of the bond distances are equal; the dipoles of the three bonds cancel one another. The centers of positive and negative charge coincide in the center of the B atom. The compound NF_3, on the other hand, is polar. The difference in electronegativity between boron and fluorine is much larger than that between nitrogen and fluorine, but in NF_3 the dipoles of the bonds do not cancel one another because the molecule is arranged in a three-dimensional trigonal pyramid:

Here the center of positive charge of the molecule coincides with the center of the nitrogen atom, while the center of negative charge is approximately in the center of the triangular base of the pyramid.

Network, or **atomic, crystals** are crystals in which the lattice points are occupied by atoms that are joined by a network of covalent bonds. It is impossible to distinguish molecules or ions; in fact, the whole crystal may be visualized as one giant molecule. An example of such a crystal is the diamond in which carbon atoms are joined by covalent bonds in a three-dimensional structure (Figure 3.14). Such materials have high melting points, high boiling points, low volatilities, and are extremely hard because of the large number of covalent bonds that would have to

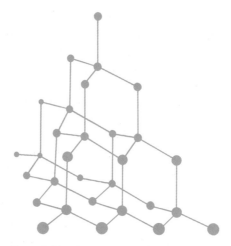

Figure 3.14   Arrangement of atoms in a diamond crystal.

be ruptured to destroy the crystal structure. They are also nonconductors of electricity.

The last type of crystal, the metallic crystal, will be discussed in Section 3.15.

3.11   Resonance

In many instances, the observed properties of a molecule are not satisfactorily represented by the Lewis structure assigned to the molecule
according to the principles outlined so far in this chapter.   Thus the
diagram

$$\ddot{S}.$$
$$:\ddot{O}. \quad :\ddot{O}\cdot$$

which satisfies the octet principle by means of a double covalent bond
and a coordinate covalent bond, does not relate the true character of the
bonds in the SO_2 molecule.   It is known that this molecule is angular and
that both *sulfur to oxygen linkages are perfectly equivalent in all respects
including bond distance.*   The diagram we have drawn indicates two different bond distances (characteristically, single bonds are longer than
double bonds).

In such cases, two or more valence bond structures can usually be
used, in combination, to depict the molecule.   The molecule is said to be
a resonance hybrid of the electronic structures.   For SO_2,

$$\ddot{S}.$$
$$:\ddot{O}. \quad :\ddot{O}\cdot \qquad \longleftrightarrow \qquad \cdot\ddot{S}.$$
$$\qquad\qquad\qquad\qquad\qquad :\ddot{O}. \quad :\ddot{O}\cdot$$

structure I   structure II

There is only one form of SO_2; the above notation does not mean that this compound is a mixture of two types of molecules, one indicated by resonance structure I and the other by II. Nor does this symbolism denote a situation where the electrons oscillate in such a way as to make the molecule appear in form I at one moment and in form II at the next. The symbol ($\leftrightarrow$) does not denote motion. Neither resonance structure alone adequately represents the molecule, but the one *single* structure of the SO_2 molecule can be imagined by taking into account both resonance structures. Thus both of the bonds of SO_2 are intermediate in character between a single bond and a double bond.

The problem is one of representation within the framework of the classical valence bond approach, and the problem arises because the approach is limited, not because of any freakishness on the part of resonating molecules. How can one draw bonds of fractional magnitude? The Lewis notation, even with its inadequacies, is retained because of its convenience.

Resonance can also be used to explain the charge distribution in molecules and ions. For example, the carbonate ion (CO_3^{2-}) is an anion with a 2− charge (two electrons gained from the cation) and with covalent bonds holding the carbon and oxygen atoms together. The ion is planar, all bonds are equivalent, and all oxygen atoms are equally negative. The resonance forms are

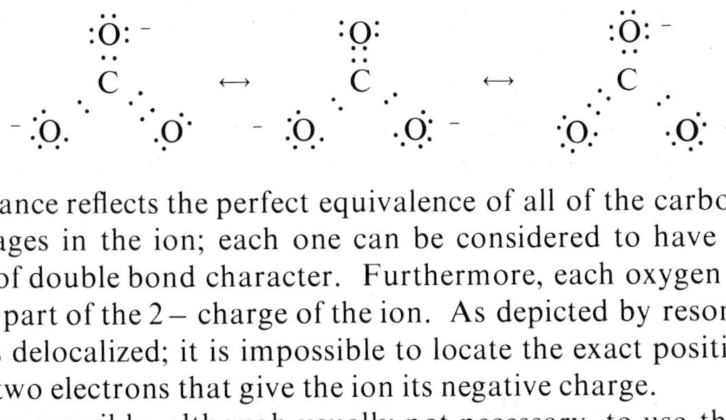

Resonance reflects the perfect equivalence of all of the carbon to oxygen linkages in the ion; each one can be considered to have the same amount of double bond character. Furthermore, each oxygen atom has an equal part of the 2− charge of the ion. As depicted by resonance, the charge is delocalized; it is impossible to locate the exact position of the "extra" two electrons that give the ion its negative charge.

It is also possible, although usually not necessary, to use the concept of resonance to indicate the charge distribution of a polar molecule. The structure of hydrogen chloride can be illustrated in the following way:

Calculations from dipole moment measurements show HCl to have a 17% partial ionic character (Section 3.8). We conclude that structures I and II contribute to the resonance hybrid in a ratio of 83 to 17%. The resonance structures of SO_2 contribute equally to the hybrid since they are equivalent structures. This is also true of the resonance forms of the carbonate ion, but it is not always the case.

Resonance hybrids are always more stable than a single valence bond representation of a molecule would indicate. Thus the energy required to break the H—Cl bond is more than that calculated for a structure in which the bonding electrons are equally shared (Section 3.9). This difference is called the **resonance energy**.

3.12   Directional Characteristics of the Covalent Bond

Resonance can, properly applied, serve to adjust the valence bond theory into closer accord with reality, but certain other extensions need to be applied to the valence bond view. We have seen that certain ions exist that do not have noble gas configurations and that some of these ions are quite stable. Some molecules exist in which atoms have configurations other than those the octet principle would lead us to expect.

There are a few molecules, of relatively minor importance, that have an odd number of valence electrons to be distributed among the constituent atoms (Section 3.14). It is manifestly impossible to divide up an odd number of electrons in such a way as to give each atom of the molecule a configuration of eight electrons (an even number). There is a resonance treatment for this type of molecule in which the embarrassing odd electron is delocalized, but the molecular orbital description of these species is probably the most satisfactory (Section 3.14). There are not many stable odd electron molecules; usually odd electron species are very reactive and, consequently, short-lived.

More important are the molecules that have an even number of valence electrons but contain atoms with valence shells of less than, or more than, eight electrons. Examples of this are BF_3, where the central boron atom has six valence electrons*

and PCl_5 and SF_6 where the phosphorus and sulfur atoms have ten and twelve valence electrons, respectively.

For the elements of the second period, only four bonding orbitals are available ($2s$ and $2p$), and thus the maximum covalence of these ele-

---

*There is some evidence that BF_3 is a resonance hybrid of the structure illustrated above and such structures as:

There is a question as to whether or not the very electronegative fluorine forms a double bond with boron, however, and these double bond structures are probably only minor contributors.

ments is limited to four. But, the elements of the third and subsequent periods have many more orbitals available in their outer electron shells; compounds are known in which these elements form four, five, six, or (infrequently) an even higher number of covalent bonds. It appears, then, that the criteria for covalent bond formation should be centered on the electron pair rather than the attainment of an octet.

A hydrogen atom has one electron in a $1s$ orbital; this orbital can accommodate two electrons of opposed spin. When two such atoms approach each other closely, the $1s$ orbitals interpenetrate or overlap. A covalent bond is formed when this occurs, the electron clouds of the atoms reinforcing each other in the bonding region between the nuclei. The resulting electron cloud of the covalent bond is not the sum of the electron clouds of the atoms; because of the pull of two nuclei, most of the electronic charge is concentrated in the area between the two nuclei (Figure 3.7). The strength of the bond comes partly from the spin neutralization of the electron pair, but more from the attraction of the positively charged nuclei for the electron cloud of the bond.

The sum of the potential energies of two hydrogen atoms are plotted against internuclear distance, R, in Figure 3.15. The potential energy of the atoms when separated by an infinite distance is zero. The attraction between the atoms (formation of a covalent bond) causes the potential energy of the system to decrease as the atoms are brought together.

Figure 3.15 *Potential energy versus internuclear distance for the formation of H_2 from two hydrogen atoms. The dissociation energy, d, and the equilibrium internuclear distance, R_0, are indicated.*

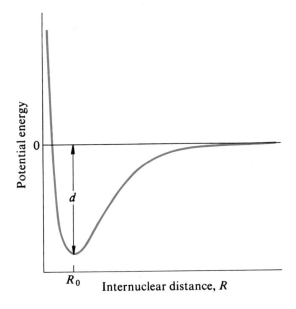

However, at very small internuclear distances, the repulsive force between the two positive nuclei causes the energy of the system to increase rapidly. The minimum in the curve occurs at an equilibrium internuclear distance, R_0, which is the bond distance of the molecule (0.74 Å for the H_2 molecule). The atoms of the molecule vibrate about this position. The dissociation energy, d, is approximately the bond energy of the molecule (1.73×10^{-19} cal/bond for H_2). Actually, slightly less energy than d is required to separate the bonded atoms because the atoms are not at rest; they possess kinetic energy and vibrate about the distance R_0.

The formation of a covalent bond requires that the constituent orbitals overlap, and the most stable bonding occurs when the orbital overlap is at a maximum within the limits imposed by the internuclear forces of repulsion. This means not only that the atoms must approach each other as closely as possible but also that the orbitals, in certain cases, must be aligned properly. The p orbitals of an atom can be considered to be directed in space along the Cartesian coordinates x, y, and z (Figure 2.9). The production of a stable covalent bond in a p orbital of a given atom requires that the orbital of its bonding partner be aligned with the axis of the p orbital under consideration. Furthermore, the atoms will be directed along such an axis in the final molecule. The covalent bond, then, is directed in space.

The ionic bond consists of the mutual attraction of positive and negative ions. The forces of attraction radiate from the ions in all directions; consequently, the ionic bond has no directional character, operates at comparatively large distances, and involves no set pair of ions.

For the formation of a covalent bond, an orbital must be available to accommodate a pair of electrons of opposed spin. No distinction need be made as to the source of the electrons for the bond; hence, there is no real difference between simple and coordinate covalent bonding. Orbitals are positions where the probability of finding a pair of electrons is high; if such a position is available in an atom, a covalent bond may be formed through its use regardless of whether it is partially occupied in the atom or not. The orbitals most commonly used in bonding are the s, p, and d orbitals of the outer shell and, in some cases, the d orbitals of the second from the outer shell. With the exception of these inner d orbitals, electrons of inner orbitals are usually bound too tightly to be involved in covalent bond formation.

The electronic configuration of oxygen is $1s^2\, 2s^2\, 2p_x^2\, 2p_y^1\, 2p_z^1$, which indicates an electron pair in the $2p_x$ orbitals and an unpaired electron in each of the other $2p$ orbitals. In the formation of the molecule H_2O, a $1s$ electron from one hydrogen atom pairs with the $2p_y$ electron of the oxygen atom, and a $1s$ electron from another hydrogen atom pairs with the $2p_z$ electron. Since the bonding p orbitals of the oxygen atom are

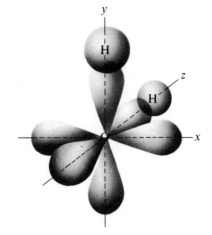

Figure 3.16 Expected directional character of the bonds in the H_2O molecule.

directed at right angles to one another, the covalent bonds formed might be expected to be directed in this manner (Figure 3.16). The actual H—O—H bond angle in the water molecule is 104.5°. A molecule of this type is given the notation p^2 which refers back to the bond-forming orbitals of the central atom of the molecule (Figure 3.17); p^2 molecules are always angular.

Figure 3.17 Directional characteristics of some covalent bonds. (* Indicates hybridized orbitals.)

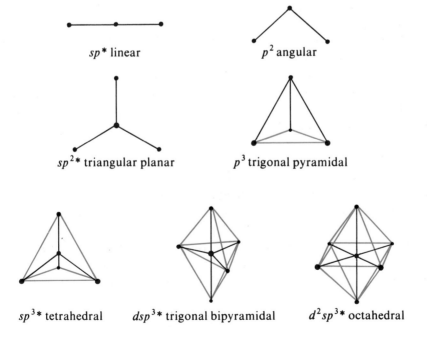

sp* linear p^2 angular

sp^2* triangular planar p^3 trigonal pyramidal

sp^3* tetrahedral dsp^3* trigonal bipyramidal d^2sp^3* octahedral

Nitrogen has the configuration $1s^2\,2s^2\,2p^1\,2p^1\,2p^1$. The compound NH_3 utilizes the three $2p$ orbitals of nitrogen which are directed in the characteristic right angles. The molecule (a p^3 type) would be expected to have its three N—H bonds directed to the corners of a trigonal pyramid (Figure 3.17). This is the shape of the NH_3 molecule, but the H—N—H angles are about 107.3° instead of the expected 90°.

The element carbon has the electronic configuration $1s^2\,2s^2\,2p^1\,2p^1$. One might expect that the simple hydride of carbon would have the formula CH_2—a p^2 angular type. Instead, the formula of the simplest hydride of carbon is CH_4. The Lewis structure H:C:H (with H above and H below) gives no indication of the types of electrons used or the geometry of the molecule. We can consider that the electrons of the $2s$ orbital of carbon are unpaired with one promoted to the empty $2p$ orbital—an excited state. Bonding then occurs between the electrons of the carbon atom in the excited state and the $1s$ electrons of four hydrogen atoms. This can be illustrated:

	$1s$	$2s$	$2p$.
C (ground state)	⇅	⇅	↑ ↑
C (excited state)	⇅	↑	↑ ↑ ↑
CH_4	⇅	⇅	⇅ ⇅ ⇅
		H	H H H

The energy required to unpair and promote one of the two $2s$ electrons is provided by the formation of the four covalent bonds.

The question now arises: how are such bonds directed in space? One might logically expect that three bonds would be directed at right angles to each other (p^3) and, since s orbitals are spherically symmetrical, the fourth essentially undirected. This is not the case; chemical and physical evidence shows that all of the C—H bonds are spatially equivalent in CH_4. One may consider that the total electron cloud of the excited carbon atom consisting of one electron in the $2s$ orbital and one electron in each of the three $2p$ orbitals is divided into four equal portions and that new **hybrid** orbitals are produced, each equivalent to the other. This phenomenon is termed the **hybridization of orbitals.** The hybrid sp^3 orbitals are directed from the carbon atom to the corners of a regular tetrahedron (Figure 3.17), and the H—C—H angles are 109° 28′. Quantum mechanical calculations show that greater bond strength results with this arrangement of bonding orbitals than if the simple atomic orbitals are used; a greater overlap of bonding orbitals in the molecule is possible.

In H_2O and NH_3, the observed deviation in bond angles from the expected 90° may be ascribed to the partial hybridization of the bonds. If one imagines the unshared electron pairs of the oxygen atom as occupying two of the four corners of a tetrahedron and the two hydrogen atoms occupying the other two corners, it is easy to see why the bond angle of 104.5° observed for water is not far from the 109.5° tetrahedral bond angle. The NH_3 molecule can be considered in the same manner except that nitrogen has only one pair of unshared electrons and hydrogen atoms occupy three of the four corners of the tetrahedron. Here the observed bond angle of 107.3° is even closer to the tetrahedral bond angle. Another, very similar, interpretation of the geometries of the ammonia and water molecules is given in the next section.

The molecular geometries of some other hybrid bond types are illustrated in Figure 3.17; d orbitals, as well as s and p, may be involved in hybridization. Examples of molecules containing hybrid bonds follow.

Berrylium chloride has a significant amount of covalent character; $BeCl_2$ molecules have been identified in the vapor state. These molecules exhibit sp hybridization.

Boron trichloride is a triangular planar molecule with sp^2 hybridization.

Sulfur hexafluoride molecules have d^2sp^3 (or sp^3d^2) hybridization and are octahedral.

The molecule PF_5 is a dsp^3 (or sp^3d) type and is trigonal bipyramidal.

The addition of a fluoride *ion* to PF_5 produces the ion PF_6^-. The fluoride ion has an octet of electrons and may be considered to add two electrons to a d orbital of phosphorus in the formation of the PF_6^- ion. (Formation of a coordinate covalent bond?)

		3s	3p	3d

$$PF_6^-\quad 1s^2\ 2s^2\ 2p^6\quad \begin{array}{c}\boxed{\uparrow\downarrow}\\ F\end{array}\quad \begin{array}{c}\boxed{\uparrow\downarrow\ \uparrow\downarrow\ \uparrow\downarrow}\\ F\ F\ F\end{array}\quad \begin{array}{c}\boxed{\uparrow\downarrow\ \uparrow\downarrow\ \ \ \ \ }\\ F\ F\end{array}$$

Thus, the PF_6^- ion is octahedral (sp^3d^2).

3.13   Electron Pair Repulsions and Molecular Geometry

The orientation that a set of atoms assumes in the formation of a given molecule may be explained qualitatively on the basis of electrostatic repulsions between electron pairs. In the application of this concept, attention is directed to the valence level of the central atom of the molecule, and the diagrams for the example that follow show only the electrons of this level of the central atom.

Mercury has two electrons in its valence level ($6s^2$); these are used to form two covalent bonds with two chlorine atoms in the mercuric chloride molecule, $HgCl_2$. The molecule is linear:

$$Cl:Hg:Cl$$

The geometry of the $HgCl_2$ molecule is such that the two electron-pair bonds are as widely separated as possible, and thus the electrostatic repulsion between them is minimized. Molecules of the type $B:A:B$ are invariably linear; berylium, zinc, cadmium, and mercury form such molecules which may be said to exhibit sp hybridization.

The boron trifluoride molecule is triangular and planar.

$$\begin{array}{c} F \\ \overset{\cdot\cdot}{B} \\ F\ \overset{\cdot\ \ \cdot}{}\ F \end{array}$$

Each of the bond angles of the molecule is 120°, and this arrangement provides the greatest possible separation between the three electron pairs.

In the methane molecule, CH_4, the central carbon atom has four pairs of electrons in bonds. The Lewis structure, which does not depict the molecular geometry, is

$$\begin{array}{c} H \\ H:\overset{\cdot\cdot}{C}:H \\ H \end{array}$$

The electrostatic repulsions between the bond pairs are at a minimum when the bonds are directed toward the corners of a regular tetrahedron (Figure 3.18); in this configuration, all of the bonds are equidistant from one another. Each of the H—C—H bond angles is 109° 28', the so-called **tetrahedral angle.** This molecular geometry is a common one.

Figure 3.18   Geometries of methane (CH_4), ammonia (NH_3), and water (H_2O) molecules.

The structure of ammonia

$$H:\ddot{N}:H$$
$$\overset{\cdot\cdot}{H}$$

can also be related to the tetrahedron (Figure 3.18). The nitrogen has three electron pairs engaged in bonding and a fourth pair, which is called a **lone pair of electrons.** The four pairs assume a slightly distorted tetrahedral configuration which causes the atoms of the molecule to have a trigonal pyramidal arrangement. The bond pairs, which are under the influence of two positive charge centers, are more localized and take up less volume than the lone pair, which is under the influence of but one positive charge center. In addition, the charge concentration of the lone pair is closer toward the central atom than that of a bond pair. Hence, the lone pair exerts a greater repulsion on a bond pair than a given bond pair exerts on another bond pair. As a result, the three bonds of the NH_3 molecule are forced slightly closer together than is normal for the tetrahedral arrangement. Thus each of the H—N—H bond angles is 107.3° rather than the tetrahedral angle of 109.5°.

The NF_3 molecule has a structure similar to that of NH_3.

$$F\overset{\ddot{N}}{\underset{F}{\diagup\mid\diagdown}}F$$

In this molecule, the very electronegative fluorine atoms attract the bonding electrons strongly, and the regions of high charge concentration of the bonds are farther from the nitrogen atom in NF_3 than they are in NH_3. As a result, a N—F bond is contracted compared to a N—H bond, and because of the repulsion due to the lone pair, the N—F bonds are closer together than the N—H bonds. The F—N—F bond angles in NF_3, therefore, are only 102.1° rather than 107.3° as are the H—N—H bond angles in NH_3.

The lone pair also influences the polarity of the NF_3 molecule (Section 3.10). Nitrogen trifluoride has a dipole moment of only 0.24 D, a surprisingly low value in view of the highly polar nature of the N—F bonds. Each of the N—F bonds is polarized in the direction of the fluorine atom, giving the molecule a dipole with a negative end in the direction of the base of the NF_3 pyramid. The contribution of the lone pair to the dipole moment, however, works in the opposite direction and reduces the total polarity of the molecule.

The water molecule has two bond pairs and two lone pairs.

$$:\ddot{O}:H$$
$$\ddot{H}$$

The four electron pairs are arranged in an approximately tetrahedral manner (Figure 3.18) so that the atoms of the molecule have a V-shaped configuration. The bond angle of the water molecule (104.5°) is less than the H—N—H bond angle of NH_3. For the reasons discussed previously, the strengths of the repulsion forces decrease in the general order: lone pair–lone pair (L-L) > lone pair–bond pair (L-B) > bond pair–bond pair (B-B). Hence, the two lone pairs of the H_2O molecule force the O—H bond together more closely than the N—H bonds of the NH_3 molecule, which are influenced by only one lone pair.

When the central atom of a molecule has six electron-pair bonds (e.g., in SF_6), the geometry that is adopted is that of the regular octahedron (Figure 3.19a) in which the bonds are equidistant and all positions are equivalent. In this configuration, the electrostatic repulsions are as small as possible for this type of molecule, and all bond angles are 90°.

The electron pairs of species such as IF_5 and BrF_5, which have five bond pairs and one lone pair, are also directed to the corners of an octahedron. Since all of the positions of an octahedron are equivalent, the atoms of the molecule are arranged in a square pyramid (Figure 3.19b), which may be slightly distorted.

In species such as IF_4^- and BrF_4^-, which have two lone pairs and four bond pairs the lone pairs assume positions 180° from one another (Figure 3.19c), which minimizes the L-L repulsion. The molecules, therefore, have square planar geometries.

Figure 3.19 Geometries of molecules in which the central atom has six electron pairs.

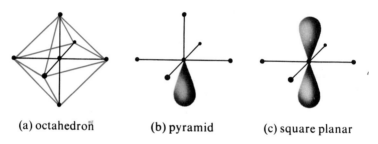

(a) octahedron   (b) pyramid   (c) square planar

The analysis of species with five electron pairs on the central atom is less straightforward. The configuration that minimizes electron-pair repulsions is the trigonal bipyramid (Figure 3.20a); this is the arrangement assumed by the PCl_5 molecule. In this configuration, however, the polar positions (numbers 1 and 3 of the diagram) are different from the equatorial positions (numbers 2, 4, and 5). Equatorial atoms are coplanar, and any bond angle formed by two equatorial atoms and the central atom is 120°. The polar atoms are at right angles to the equatorial plane; any bond angle defined by a polar atom, the central atom, and an equatorial atom is 90°.

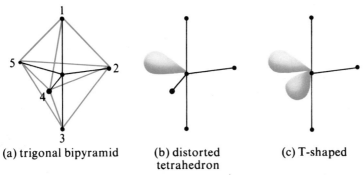

| (a) trigonal bipyramid | (b) distorted tetrahedron | (c) T-shaped |

Figure 3.20   Geometries of molecules in which the central atom has five electron pairs.

The tellurium atom of $TeCl_4$ has four bond pairs and a lone pair. The structure of the molecule may be related to that of a trigonal bipyramid in which the lone pair occupies an equatorial position (Figure 3.20b). The L-B repulsions are far more significant than B-B repulsions. In an octahedral configuration, all the bond angles are 90°, whereas in a trigonal bipyramidal configuration, there are bond angles of 90° and 120°. If the lone pair were directed toward a polar position, it would form angles of approximately 90° each with three equatorial bond pairs. In an equatorial position, the lone pair forms angles of approximately 90° each with only two bond pairs (those directed toward the polar atoms).

Molecules with three bond pairs and two lone pairs, such as ClF_3 and BrF_3, have both of their lone pairs in the equatorial plane, giving the atoms of the molecule a T-shape (Figure 3.20c). Why the two lone pairs are not directed toward polar positions, at a 180° angle from one another, is not immediately obvious. Only the interactions between electron pairs that are directed at an angle of 90° need be considered; interactions at 120°, or wider angles, are negligible in comparison. With the lone pairs directed toward polar positions, six 90° L-B repulsions occur.

With the lone pairs directed toward equatorial positions, however, there are only four 90° L-B repulsions and two B-B repulsions (which are much smaller than L-B repulsions). If one lone pair were to be directed toward a polar position and the second toward an equatorial position, the molecule would have one 90° L-L repulsion (the strongest type of repulsion), three 90° L-B repulsions, and two 90° B-B repulsions. Therefore, the configuration that minimizes electrostatic repulsions is that with both lone pairs in the equatorial plane.

3.14   Molecular Orbitals

Molecular structure has so far been depicted by forms that relate back to the electronic configurations of the constituent atoms. The **method of molecular orbitals** is an alternative approach. In this method, orbitals are associated with the molecule as a whole, and the configuration of the molecule is obtained by entering electrons into these molecular orbitals in an aufbau order analagous to that employed in the filling of atomic orbitals. Corresponding to the practice of indicating atomic orbitals by the letters s, p, and d, molecular orbitals are assigned the similar Greek letter designations σ (sigma), π (pi), and δ (delta).

In the case of very simple diatomic molecules, a united atom concept can be used to derive molecular orbitals. Thus if two hydrogen atoms are brought together, the resulting united atom would have two protons and two electrons. These electrons can be placed in the $1s$ orbital. Separation of the two nuclei to form the H_2 molecule then provides a σ bond (Figures 3.7 and 3.21).

If this united atom concept were used for a hypothetical He_2 molecule, the four electrons of the combined helium atoms could not be accommodated in the σ $1s$ orbital—two of the four electrons would have to be promoted to a higher orbital. The promoted electrons would be in an excited state and would act as a disruptive influence in the molecule— they are called **antibonding electrons;** the electrons paired in the orbital of the σ-bond are called **bonding electrons.** The electron density of an antibonding orbital is low in the internuclear region. One-half the difference between the number of bonding electrons and the number of antibonding electrons gives the number of covalent bonds in the molecule. Thus for He_2: $(\frac{1}{2})(2-2) = 0$, and the net effect is no bond.

The notations for these two examples are:

$$2H(1s^1) \longrightarrow H_2[(\sigma 1s)^2]$$
$$2He(1s^2) \longrightarrow He_2[(\sigma 1s)^2(\sigma^* 1s)^2]$$

In these notations, the superscript stands for the number of electrons in each orbital; the star indicates an antibonding orbital.

The electron clouds of the molecular orbitals and the atomic orbitals from which they are derived are diagrammed in Figure 3.21. If the diagram of the bonding orbital $\sigma 1s$ is superimposed on the diagram of the

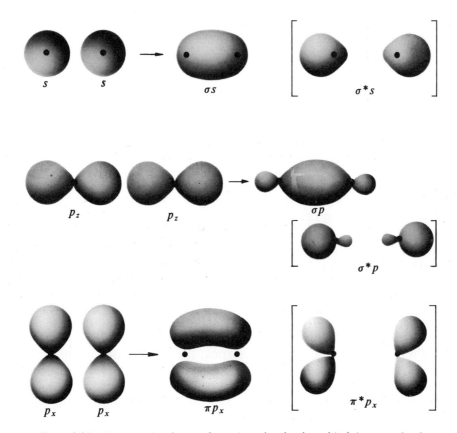

Figure 3.21   Approximate shapes of atomic and molecular orbitals (cross sections).

antibonding orbital σ^*1s, no large accumulation of electronic charge is indicated in the bonding area between the nuclei. Hence, for the hypothetical He_2 molecule, the electron distribution is roughly the same as that of two helium atoms.

A qualitative energy level diagram for the formation of $\sigma 1s$ and σ^*1s molecular orbitals from the $1s$ atomic orbitals of two atoms is shown in Figure 3.22. The energy of the σ-bonding orbital is lower than that of either atomic orbital from which it may be considered to have been derived (see also Figure 3.15), whereas the energy of the σ^* antibonding orbital is higher. This is always true. When two atomic orbitals are combined, the resulting bonding molecular orbital represents a decrease in energy, and the antibonding molecular orbital represents an increase in energy; s atomic orbitals from any quantum level give rise to σ and σ^* molecular orbitals.

Exact mathematical treatment of electrons in molecular orbitals, under the influence of more than one nucleus, is not usually possible. An

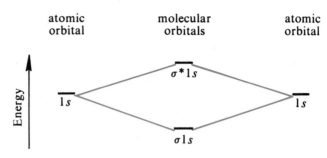

Figure 3.22   *Energy level diagram for the formation of σ and σ^* molecular orbitals from the 1s orbitals of two atoms.*

approximation of the electron probability densities in molecular orbitals can be obtained from the wave descriptions of the atomic orbitals of the constituent atoms. The diagrams of molecular orbitals in Figure 3.21 are thus derived. In this illustration, the bonds formed by p electrons should be interpreted as having been formed along the x axis. Thus the p_x electrons combine to form a σp bond (the subscript x is usually omitted since these are the only type of p electrons that can form a σ bond). The p_y electrons unite in a different manner to form a π bond, which may be specifically designated πp_y. The axis of the p_z electrons is at right angles to that of the p_y electrons; the p_z electrons form a π bond similar to the πp_y but at right angles to it (see Figure 3.24). Antibonding π^* orbitals are also shown in Figure 3.21.

If the x axis is taken as a reference for bond formation, the aufbau order for simple diatomic molecules is

$$\sigma 1s \;\; \sigma^*1s \;\; \sigma 2s \;\; \sigma^*2s \;\; \sigma 2p \; \begin{Bmatrix} \pi 2p_y \\ \pi 2p_z \end{Bmatrix} \begin{Bmatrix} \pi^*2p_y \\ \pi^*2p_z \end{Bmatrix} \sigma^*2p$$

Each orbital can hold two electrons. This order can be derived from an examination of Figure 3.23. The three $2p$ orbitals of the isolated atoms are **degenerate** (of equal energy). This degeneracy is split in the formation of molecular orbitals; the σ-bonding orbital (derived from p_x atomic orbitals) has a lower energy than either of the two degenerate π-bonding orbitals (derived from p_y and p_z atomic orbitals). In diatomic molecules formed from atoms with more than one electronic shell, the inner shells do not appreciably affect the bonding; such electrons are called **nonbonding electrons.**

The notation for the F_2 molecule is

$$2F(1s^2 \; 2s^2 \; 2p^5) \longrightarrow F_2[K\,K(\sigma 2s)^2 \; (\sigma^*2s)^2 \; (\sigma 2p)^2 \; (\pi 2p)^4 \; (\pi^*2p)^4]$$

The symbols $K\,K$ indicate nonbonding electrons, and the subscripts x, y, and z have been omitted. The number of bonds here represented is $(\frac{1}{2})$ $(8 - 6)$ or 1.

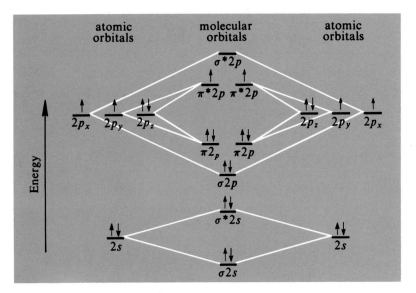

Figure 3.23 Energy level diagram of O_2.

The notation for O_2 is

$$2O(1s^2\ 2s^2\ 2p^4) \rightarrow O_2[KK(\sigma2s)^2\ (\sigma*2s)^2\ (\sigma2p)^2\ (\pi2p)^4\ (\pi*2p)^2]$$

The number of bonds is $(\frac{1}{2})(8 - 4) = 2$. The Lewis structure for O_2, :Ö::Ö:, illustrates the double bond but does not show that oxygen is paramagnetic (two unpaired electrons). The last term of the molecular orbital designation, $(\pi*2p)^2$, accounts for the two unpaired electrons of the oxygen molecule. There are two antibonding π orbitals available $(\pi*2p_x$ and $\pi*2p_y)$; the two electrons do not pair but occupy these orbitals singly according to Hund's rule (Figure 3.23).

The notation for N_2 (Figure 3.24), which indicates a triple bond, is

$$2N(1s^2\ 2s^2\ 2p^3) \rightarrow N_2[KK(\sigma2s)^2\ (\sigma*2s)^2\ (\sigma2p)^2\ (\pi2p)^4]$$

We have said that it is impossible to diagram a valence bond structure utilizing the octet rule for a molecule with an odd number of valence electrons. Nitrogen oxide, NO, is such a molecule (an **odd electron mole-**

Figure 3.24 Pi-bonding system of N_2.

cule); since five valence electrons are contributed by the nitrogen atom and six valence electrons by the oxygen atom, the total number of valence electrons for the molecule is eleven. The method of molecular orbitals gives the following description of the bonding of the NO molecule.

$$N(1s^2 \ 2s^2 \ 2p^3) + O(1s^2 \ 2s^2 \ 2p^4) \longrightarrow$$
$$NO[K K (\sigma 2s)^2 \ (\sigma^*2s)^2 \ (\sigma 2p)^2 \ (\pi 2p)^4 \ (\pi^*2p)^1]$$

Thus $(\frac{1}{2})(8 - 3)$, or $2\frac{1}{2}$, bonds are indicated.

In some molecules and ions, **multicenter,** or **delocalized,** bonding exists in which some bonding electrons serve to bond more than two atoms together. The description of these species by the valence bond approach requires the use of resonance structures. An example of multicenter bonding is the carbonate ion (Figure 3.25). This ion is triangular and

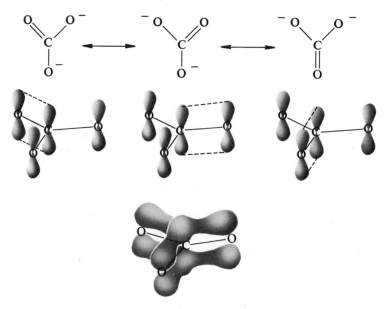

Figure 3.25   Multicenter π-bonding system of the carbonate ion and the relationship to resonance structures.

planar; each O—C—O bond angle is 120°. The carbon atom is joined to each oxygen atom by a σ bond, and in addition, each atom contributes a p orbital toward the formation of a multicenter π-bonding system that encompasses all of the atoms of the ion. A similar bonding system is found in the nitrate ion, NO_3^-, and the SO_3 molecule (Section 3.11); other examples of multicenter bonding will be encountered in later chapters.

In reality, such descriptions as the preceding one for the carbonate ion incorporate facets of both the valence bond and molecular orbital approaches. The method of molecular orbitals shows that all of the electrons of the valence shells of the atoms of a molecule play a part in the bonding of the molecule or ion. This is probably a better depiction of the actual state of a molecule than the valence bond concept in which some of the valence electrons are indicated as unshared and uninvolved in the formation of the molecule. The method of molecular orbitals is complicated, especially for molecules containing more than two atoms, and the aufbau order is not rigidly fixed for such species. Decisions as to which electrons are nonbonding, bonding, and antibonding are sometimes difficult to make. The valence bond theory offers a simplicity and convenience that make it, despite its shortcomings, an important generalization.

3.15 The Metallic Bond

The **metallic bond** is the attraction that holds the atoms of two or more metals together in an alloy or that bonds the atoms of a pure metal together in a crystal. The metallic bond is distinctly different from either the ionic bond or the covalent bond, but there are also similarities between it and both of the other bond types.

The most characteristic chemical properties of the metals are derived from their low ionization potentials and low electronegativities. The metallic crystal may be thought of as being made up of positive metal ions and mobile electrons in such a proportion as to make the whole electrically neutral. As a first approximation, we can imagine a lattice of these positive ions held together by a "sea of electrons" which permeates the crystal lattice. Only the most loosely held electrons of the metal atoms are involved in the mobile electron sea. In the case of many metals this includes only the electrons of the outer shell, but for the transition and inner transition metals, some of the electrons of the inner orbitals may be involved as well.

An examination of ionization potentials shows that the electrons of inner orbitals are held tightly and therefore are associated with the individual positive metal ions and not the crystal as a whole. The first to fourth ionization potentials of some A family metals are listed in Table 3.7. Notice that after the valence electrons have been removed, there is a decided jump in the level of the energy required to remove the next electron (this place is marked with a vertical line).

Metallic crystals are close-packed structures; each of the positive ions has a comparatively large number of close neighbors. It is impossible for an atom to form simultaneously as many covalent bonds as would be needed to bind such an arrangement of atoms together, particularly metal atoms which have few valence electrons. The mobile electron sea acts as the binding force to hold the positive ions together. This attraction is strong as evidenced by the close-packed arrangement of the posi-

TABLE 3.7.
IONIZATION POTENTIALS OF THE THIRD-PERIOD METALS.

Metal	Group	Ionization Potentials (ev)			
		First	Second	Third	Fourth
Na	IA	5.1	47.3	71.7	98.9
Mg	IIA	7.6	15.0	80.1	109.3
Al	IIIA	6.0	18.8	28.4	120.0

tive ions and the high densities and high melting points of most metals (but not all metals—there are other factors to be considered such as atomic radius and number of vacant electron orbitals).

Like the ionic bond, the metallic bond is essentially nondirectional; the covalent bond is always a directional bond in molecules and in atomic crystals. Unlike ionic crystals, however, the positions of the positive ions can be altered without destroying the crystal because of the uniform charge distribution provided by the mobile electrons. Thus metallic crystals are usually deformed easily, and most metals are malleable (capable of being pounded into shapes) and ductile (capable of being drawn into wire).

The bonding in metals may be regarded as an extreme type of non-localized bonding encorporating all of the atoms of the metallic crystal, and a resonance treatment has been postulated. In a lithium crystal, each atom has eight close neighbors and one valence electron. The crystal may be approximately represented as a resonance hybrid of such structures as the following. Whereas only four atoms are shown in these structures, the actual bonding includes all of the atoms of the crystal and is three-dimensional.

$$
\begin{array}{cccc}
\mathrm{Li\!-\!Li} & \mathrm{Li\ \ Li} & \mathrm{Li^+\ Li} & \mathrm{Li\ \!-\!Li^-} \\
\mathrm{Li\!-\!Li} & \mathrm{Li\ \ Li} & \mathrm{Li\ \!-\!Li^-} & \mathrm{Li^+\ \ Li} \\
\mathrm{I} & \mathrm{II} & \mathrm{III} & \mathrm{IV}
\end{array}
$$

$$
\begin{array}{cc}
\mathrm{Li\ \ Li^+} & \mathrm{Li^-\!-\!Li} \\
\mathrm{Li^-\!-\!Li} & \mathrm{Li\ \ Li^+} \\
\mathrm{V} & \mathrm{VI}
\end{array}
$$

In structures III, IV, V, and VI, ionic forms are indicated, and one lithium atom (the one holding a negative charge) in each of these structures is shown as bonded to two other atoms. Hence, it appears that more than one valence orbital of each lithium atom must be involved in the metallic bonding. Lithium has the electronic configuration $1s^2\ 2s^1$, and it is assumed that a vacant $2p$ orbital (which is not far removed energetically from the $2s$) is used; this orbital is called the metallic orbital.

The quantum mechanical treatment of the metallic crystal proceeds by combining the wave functions of the atomic orbitals into sets of orbitals (or **bands**) for the entire crystal, much like the method of molecular orbitals. The process is more complicated, however, because the orbitals of a large number of atoms must be considered (all of the atoms in the crystal) unlike the situation in a covalent molecule where the orbitals of a comparatively few atoms need to be taken into account.

The $2s$ orbitals of two lithium atoms are degenerate when the atoms are very far apart. However, when the two atoms are brought together, this degeneracy is split into two levels by the interaction of the atoms (Figure 3.26), and the magnitude of the splitting increases as the distance between the atoms decreases. The Li_2 molecule exists in the vapor state; the curve of Figure 3.26 showing the higher energy level may be regarded as that for a σ^*-antibonding molecular orbital, whereas the curve for the lower energy level may represent a σ-bonding orbital. In Li_2, only the bonding orbital is occupied.

If seven lithium atoms are brought together, the degeneracy of the orbitals of the isolated atoms is split into seven levels (Figure 3.27). Each atom contributes one level to the aggregate, which is called a band. In a large number (N) of isolated lithium atoms, the $2s$ orbitals are of equal energy, but this degeneracy is removed as the atoms are brought

Figure 3.26   Energy of the 2s orbitals of two lithium atoms as a function of interatomic distance.

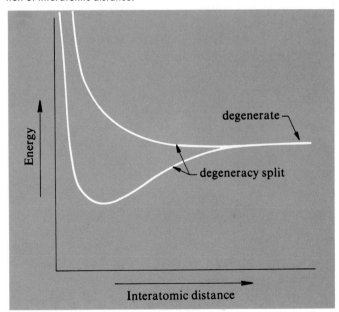

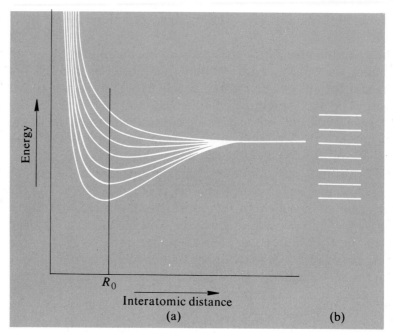

Figure 3.27 *(a) Energy of 2s orbitals versus interatomic distance for a collection of seven atoms. (b) Energy level diagram corresponding to the interatomic distance R_0.*

together, giving rise to N levels of slightly different energies. Each level of this band may accommodate two electrons of opposed spin.

As long as a fairly large number of atoms is considered, the spread between the levels is not significantly widened by an increased number of atoms. With uniform interatomic spacing, the orbital overlap is not significantly altered when the number of atoms is increased, and it is this orbital interaction that produces the effect on the energy levels. The gradual addition of atoms causes the increasing number of levels of the band to be more and more crowded together rather than affecting the spread of the band. As a result, the separation in energy between the levels of a band is very small even for samples of extremely small size. Even at very low temperatures, the electrons have enough energy to move from level to level within a band, and for all practical purposes the band represents a continuum of energy.

Each level of a band may accommodate two electrons of opposed spin. If N atoms contribute N levels to a band, the band is capable of holding $2N$ electrons. Since N lithium atoms have a total of N valence electrons, it would appear that half of the levels of the lithium valence band should be unoccupied. However, the band derived from the $2p$ orbitals of lithium must also be considered.

In an isolated lithium atom, the three $2p$ orbitals are only slightly higher in energy than the $2s$ orbitals. The band derived from the $2p$

orbitals fans out and overlaps the band from the 2s orbitals (Figure 3.28). At the normal equilibrium interatomic distance, R_0, the two bands may be considered to form one. Since each atom contributes three 2p orbitals and one 2s orbital, the band resulting from the combination of N atoms would consist of $4N$ levels capable of holding $8N$ electrons. Hence the lithium band is only one-eighth filled.

If this band overlap did not occur, the valence band of beryllium (electronic configuration, $1s^2 2s^2$) would be full, and beryllium would not conduct electricity. Beryllium is a metallic conductor because the band resulting from the overlap of the 2s and 2p orbitals is only one-quarter filled.

Metallic bonding generally arises from the interaction of the orbitals of the valence shell only. The interatomic spacing of a metallic crystal is determined by the overlap of the valence orbitals, and the orbitals of the inner shells do not interact appreciably at this distance. Consequently, the bands derived from inner orbitals, which are completely occupied, are narrow (Figure 3.28). In a crystal, no electron can have

Figure 3.28   (a) Overlap of 2s and 2p bands. (b) Energy level diagram for the interatomic distance R_0.

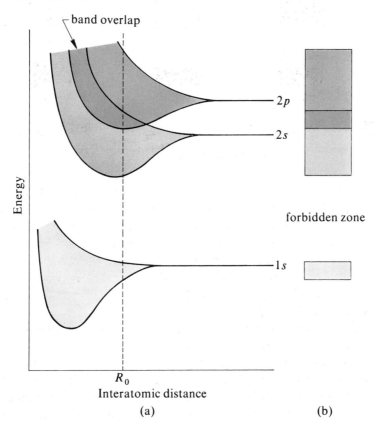

an energy that does not fall within the limits of a band; hence the region of an energy level diagram between the bands is called a **forbidden energy zone**.

In a metallic crystal, then, the electrons are held by all of the atoms of the crystal, and transference between the levels of a band requires the addition of very little energy. Thus metals can, through their electrons, absorb light of a wide range of wavelengths and immediately radiate it. This causes the lustrous appearance of metals. The high electrical conductivity is because of the mobility of the valence electrons, and in conductors, the valence band is either partially filled or overlapped by an unfilled conduction band. The rapid motion possible for the valence electrons explains the excellent heat conductivity of metals since the electrons can take up heat as kinetic energy and transfer it rapidly to all parts of the metal. Heat conductivity of other species takes place through the motion of ions or molecules—a much slower process.

Energy level diagrams for **insulators, conductors,** and **semiconductors** are shown in Figure 3.29. The conduction band of an insulator is widely

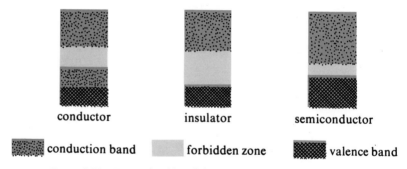

Figure 3.29   *Energy level band diagrams for three types of solids.*

separated from a filled valence band by a forbidden zone. The diamond, which is an insulator, has been described as a network crystal with localized bonding between atoms (Figure 3.14). In the construction of a band model for the diamond crystal, the symmetry of the atomic spacings imposes limitations on the orbital overlap so that a large forbidden zone is generated between a filled valence band and a conduction band. Band overlap, particularly for heavier atoms, is at times much more complicated than presented here.

A semiconductor is a material that has a low conductivity, intermediate between that of a conductor and an insulator; this conductivity increases markedly with increasing temperature. For a semiconductor, the forbidden energy zone between the filled valence band and the conduction band is sufficiently narrow that electrons can be raised from the valence band to the conduction band by thermal excitation. The vacancies left by the removal of the electrons from the valence band permit electrons in the valence band, as well as those in the conduction band, to move under the influence of an electric field. The presence of impurities can narrow the forbidden energy zones of certain substances; these materials are called impurity semiconductors.

The most active metals are those on the left of the periodic table. These metals have the lowest ionization potentials, and their valence electrons are the freest. Toward the right in the periodic table, the metallic properties fade. Thus there is a point where the atoms have an increasing tendency to hold onto their valence electrons and form covalent bonds with them. The bonding in some metals has a large amount of covalent character, and the properties of some metals, germanium, for example, suggest a crystal structure bordering on that of the network crystals.

TABLE 3.8.
TYPES OF CRYSTALLINE SOLIDS.

Crystal	Particles	Attractive Forces	Properties	Examples
ionic	positive and negative ions	electrostatic attractions	high m.p. hard, brittle good electrical conductor, fused	NaCl, BaO, KNO_3
polar molecular	polar molecules	dipole–dipole	low m.p. soft poor electrical conductor	H_2O, BrCl, SO_2
nonpolar molecular	nonpolar molecules	van der Waals forces	very low m.p. soft poor electrical conductor	H_2, Cl_2, CO_2, CCl_4
network	atoms	covalent bonds	very high m.p. very hard nonconductor of electricity	C (diamond) SiC, AlN
metallic	positive ions mobile electrons	metallic bonds	fairly high m.p. hard or soft malleable and ductile good electrical conductor	Ag, Cu, Na, Fe, K

Most of the phenomena of chemistry do not show abrupt changes, and chemical bonding is a continuum. We have discussed the transition between ionic and covalent bonding; compounds exist in which the bonding is intermediate in character between ionic and metallic bonding and between covalent and metallic bonding. The properties of the types of crystalline solids are summarized in Table 3.8.

3.16 Nomenclature of Binary Compounds

Common, or **trivial, names** of compounds are those that have been assigned by popular usage; they usually give no clue as to the exact chemical composition of the compound. If all chemical compounds were named in such a way, it would be an almost impossible task to learn the names of the materials with which the chemist works. Instead, **systematic** nomenclature is used; systematic names follow rules designed to relate the name of a compound to its composition. Certain common names such as water, H_2O, and ammonia NH_3, are so firmly entrenched that they continue to be employed.

Ionic binary compounds are named with the metal first and the nonmetal second; covalent binaries are usually named with the less electronegative element first. For all binary compounds, the ending-*ide* is substituted for the usual ending of the element appearing last in the name. (All compounds ending in -*ide,* however, are not binaries; there are a few exceptions, such as the cyanides and the hydroxides.)

For compounds where only one formula is possible, the procedure outlined in the preceding paragraph will produce a definitive name. There is no ambiguity in the names sodium oxide (Na_2O), calcium chloride ($CaCl_2$), silver bromide (AgBr), zinc sulfide (ZnS), or hydrogen fluoride (HF); for each of these combinations of elements, only one compound is known.

However, some metals (particularly the transition metals) have more than one electrovalence. Thus there are two chlorides of iron: $FeCl_2$ and $FeCl_3$. One way of dealing with this problem is to change the suffix of the name of the metal (Latin names are employed when the symbol derives from the Latin); the ending -*ous* is used to indicate the lower valence of the metal, and -*ic* is used for the higher valence state. Thus $FeCl_2$ is ferrous chloride, and $FeCl_3$ is ferric chloride. Difficulties arise in the use of this method since some element pairs form more than two compounds. Furthermore, the system requires that the possible electrovalences of all of the metals be known in order to assign the proper suffix. The 2+ state of iron is its lower (ferrous); the 2+ state of copper is its higher (cupric).

A more systematic method than the preceding is to indicate the electrovalence of the metal in Roman numerals after the English name of the metal; suffixes for the metals are not employed. Thus: $FeCl_2$ is iron(II) chloride; $FeCl_3$ is iron(III) chloride; Cu_2O is copper(I) oxide; and HgS is mercury(II) sulfide. The number applies to the electrovalence of the metal (or more properly the oxidation number—see Chapter 7) and not to any numbers appearing as subscripts in the formulas.

A system of nomenclature that is particularly useful for series of compounds formed between two nonmetals employs Greek prefixes. One of the prefixes: *mono-* (1), *di-* (2), *tri-* (3), *tetra-* (4), *penta-* (5), *hexa-* (6), *hepta-* (7), *octa-* (8), etc., is added to the name of each element to indicate the number of atoms of that element in the molecule being named. The prefix *mono-* is frequently omitted. Hence, the names of the oxides of nitrogen are:

N_2O	dinitrogen oxide
NO	nitrogen oxide
N_2O_3	dinitrogen trioxide
NO_2	nitrogen dioxide
N_2O_4	dinitrogen tetroxide
N_2O_5	dinitrogen pentoxide

3.17 Ternary Compounds

Many compounds are known in which both electrovalent and covalent bonding occur. Usually these are ternary compounds (containing three elements) with oxygen as one of the constituent elements. Sodium sulfate, Na_2SO_4, is such a compound.

A crystal of sodium sulfate consists of sodium ions, Na^+, and sulfate ions, SO_4^{2-}, arranged in a crystal lattice in the proper stoichiometric ratio of 2 to 1. When sodium sulfate is dissolved in water, these ions separate from the crystal and move about independently of one another in solution. The sulfate ion is held together, as an entity, by covalent bonding; it does not break apart in water solution.

Such polyatomic, covalently bonded anions are common, and some are listed in Table 3.9. On the other hand, only a few polyatomic cations are of importance, for example, the ammonium ion, NH_4^+ and the bismuthyl ion, BiO^+. (This excludes complex ions, which are discussed in Chapter 16.)

In aqueous solution, each ion is closely associated with a few water molecules; in fact, the formation of these hydrated ions is primarily responsible for the process of solution of ionic compounds in water. These aqueous, or hydrated, ions are usually indicated by the symbol (aq), placed after the formula; the number of water molecules closely associated with a given ion is not indicated thereby and in many cases is not known. In addition to a primary sheath of water molecules, other water molecules are loosely associated. The solution process is described in Section 8.2, and the nature of hydrated ions is the topic of Section 8.3.

TABLE 3.9.
COMMON POLYATOMIC ANIONS.

Formula	Name	Formula	Name
$C_2H_3O_2^-$	acetate	ClO^-	hypochlorite
AsO_4^{3-}	arsenate	OH^-	hydroxide
AsO_3^{3-}	arsenite	NO_3^-	nitrate
BO_3^{3-}	borate	NO_2^-	nitrite
CO_3^{2-}	carbonate	ClO_4^-	perchlorate
ClO_3^-	chlorate	MnO_4^-	permanganate
ClO_2^-	chlorite	PO_4^{3-}	phosphate
CrO_4^{2-}	chromate	SO_4^{2-}	sulfate
CN^-	cyanide	SO_3^{2-}	sulfite
$Cr_2O_7^{2-}$	dichromate		

Certain compounds of hydrogen, which are covalent when pure, dissolve in water to produce solutions containing ions. In these cases, a reaction occurs which may be indicated:

$$HNO_3 + H_2O \rightarrow H_3O^+ + NO_3^-$$

or

$$HNO_3 \rightarrow H^+(aq) + NO_3^-(aq)$$

Compounds that dissociate in water solution to produce H_3O^+, or H^+ (aq), ions are called **acids.**

Because of its small size, the unassociated proton (H^+) does not exist in ordinary chemical systems; in pure acids, the hydrogen atom is covalently bonded to the rest of the molecule, and in aqueous solutions the proton is hydrated. There is evidence that the proton bonds to a water molecule by means of a pair of electrons of the oxygen atom to form an ion, H_3O^+, called the **hydronium ion.** The three hydrogen atoms of the H_3O^+ ion are equivalent, and the ion is in the form of a trigonal pyramid with the oxygen atom at the apex.

Thus the hydronium ion is assumed to resemble the ammonium ion, NH_4^+, which has four equivalent hydrogen atoms arranged tetrahedrally around the nitrogen atom (Section 3.7).

$$H^+ + H_2O \rightarrow H_3O^+$$

$$H^+ + NH_3 \rightarrow NH_4^+$$

The hydronium ion is known to occur in a few crystalline hydrates of acids such as H_3O^+, ClO_4^-; H_3O^+, Cl^-; and H_3O^+, NO_3^-.

Thermal and electrical conductivity experiments indicate that the H_3O^+ ion is associated with three additional water molecules (by means of hydrogen bonds, Section 7.11) in water solution, and a pyramidal $H_9O_4^+$ ion has been postulated (Figure 3.30). Other types of experimental evidence tend to support the idea that several types of hydrated species exist simultaneously in solution. We shall represent the hydrated proton as $H^+(aq)$ unless it is especially convenient to employ the formula H_3O^+, as it is in the discussion of the Brønsted theory (Section 13.3).

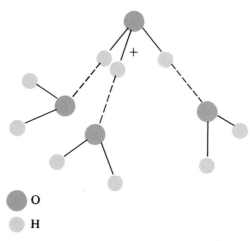

○ O

● H

Figure 3.30   Proposed structure of $H_9O_4^+$ ion.

Alkalies are compounds containing a metal cation and the hydroxide ion, OH^-. An alkali and an acid react in water by a **neutralization** reaction.

$$H^+(aq) + OH^-(aq) \rightarrow H_2O$$

A salt composed of the cation of the alkali and the anion of the acid may be obtained by evaporating a solution derived from a neutralization reaction.

The usual ternary acids derived from oxygenated anions are named according to the name of the central element (the element other than oxygen) to which the ending -ic is added. Thus H_3BO_3 is boric acid. Often there are two ternary acids containing the same elements. In such instances, the endings -ic and -ous are used to distinguish between them, the -ous ending denoting the one with the lower number of oxygen atoms. Thus HNO_3 is nitric acid, and HNO_2 is nitrous acid.

There are a few series of acids for which two names are not enough. The prefix *per-* can be used to denote one additional oxygen; the prefix *hypo-* can be used to denote one less oxygen. Thus perchloric acid, $HClO_4$, has one *more* oxygen than chloric acid, $HClO_3$; hypochlorous acid, $HClO$, has one *less* oxygen than chlorous acid, $HClO_2$. A system of nomenclature for more complicated polyatomic ions is discussed in Section 16.2.

The names of the polyatomic anions (Table 3.9) themselves are derived from the acid names by changing the *-ic* ending to *-ate* and the *-ous* ending to *-ite*. Hence, NO_3^-, the nitrate ion, is derived from HNO_3, nitric acid; ClO^-, the hypochlorite ion, is derived from $HClO$, hypochlorous acid. Salts are named by combining the cation name with the anion name; $NaNO_2$ is sodium nitrite.

Some binary compounds function as acids in water solution. The combination of the prefix *hydro-* and the suffix *-ic* is used to indicate a water solution of a binary acid. For example, a water solution of hydrogen chloride, HCl, is called hydrochloric acid. The names of salts of binary acids have the customary *-ide* ending.

SOME SUGGESTED READINGS

Ballhausen, C. J., and Gray, H., *Molecular Orbital Theory,* New York, Benjamin, 1965 (paper).

Barrow, G. M., *The Structure of Molecules,* New York, Benjamin, 1963 (paper).

Brey, W., *Physical Methods for Determining Molecular Geometry,* New York, Reinhold, 1965 (paper).

Charette, J. J., *Introduction to the Theory of Molecular Structure,* New York, Reinhold, 1966.

Day, M. C., Jr., and Selbin, J., *Theoretical Inorganic Chemistry,* New York, Reinhold, 1962.

Drago, R. S., *Physical Methods in Inorganic Chemistry,* New York, Reinhold, 1965.

Gould, Edwin, S., *Inorganic Reactions and Structure,* New York, Holt, Rinehart, and Winston 1962.

Gray, H. B., *Electrons and Chemical Bonding,* New York, Benjamin, 1964 (paper).

Klixbull-Jorgensen, C., *Orbitals in Atoms and Molecules,* New York, Academic, 1962 (paper).

Lagowski, J. J., *The Chemical Bond,* Boston, Houghton Mifflin, 1966 (paper).

Liberles, A., *An Introduction to Molecular-Orbital Theory,* New York, Holt, Rinehart, and Winston, 1966 (paper).

Linnett, J. W., *The Electronic Structure of Molecules,* New York, Wiley, 1964.

Pauling, L., and Hayward, R., *The Architecture of Molecules,* San Francisco, Freeman, 1964.

Pauling, L., *The Nature of the Chemical Bond,* Ithaca, N. Y., Cornell University Press, 1960.

Ryschkewitsch, G. E., *Chemical Bonding and the Geometry of Molecules,* New York, Reinhold, 1963 (paper).

Sebera, D. K., *Electronic Structure and Chemical Bonding,* Waltham, Mass., Blaisdell, 1964 (paper).

Sisler, H. H., *Electronic Structure, Properties and the Periodic Law,* New York, Reinhold, 1963 (paper).

Sonnessa, A. J., *Introduction to Molecular Spectroscopy*, New York, Reinhold, 1966 (paper).

Spice, J. E., *Chemical Binding and Structure*, New York, Pergamon, 1964 (paper).

PROBLEMS

3.1 Which is larger? (a) Al or Cl, (b) Cu^+ or Cu^{2+}, (c) O or O^{2-}, (d) P or O, (e) Na or Mg, (f) Cr^{2+} or Cr^{3+}, (g) Ca or Mg, (h) Cu or Zn.

3.2 Which has the higher first ionization potential? (a) Ca or Ba, (b) Ga or In, (c) K or Ca, (d) F or Ne, (e) Br or Cl, (f) C or O.

3.3 Give examples of (a) noble gas ions, (b) pseudonoble gas ions, (c) inert-pair ions, (d) irregular ions.

3.4 What explanation can you offer for the minima that occur at Ga, In, and Tl in the curve showing first ionization potential versus atomic number (Figure 3.4)?

3.5 Use dots for valence electrons and chemical symbols to diagram the octet structures of the following. State the type of bonding that is found in each and indicate all ionic charges. (a) $MgCl_2$, (b) Cl_2O, (c) $POCl_3$, (d) S_2Cl_2, (e) Cs_2O, (f) H_2CO, (g) $SOCl_2$, (h) H_2CCl_2, (i) N_2, (j) Rb_2S, (k) NCCN, (l) NOCl (nitrogen is the central atom).

3.6 Diagram the Lewis structures of the following; use dashes to represent covalent bonds. (a) HCN, (b) SiO_2, (c) H_2NOH, (d) C_2H_2, (e) $COCl_2$.

3.7 Which compound of each of the following pairs is the more covalent according to Fajans' rules? (a) $GaCl_3$ or $InCl_3$, (b) $BeCl_2$ or BeI_2, (c) FeO or Fe_2O_3, (d) CuO or CuS, (e) $SnCl_2$ or $SnCl_4$, (f) $SnCl_2$ or $PbCl_2$.

3.8 The bond distance between the H and F atoms of hydrogen fluoride is 0.917 Å, and the dipole moment of HF is 1.91 D. Calculate the partial ionic character of HF.

3.9 Which is more polar: a Cl—O bond or a F—O bond? Explain.

3.10 What type or crystal is formed by each of the following? (a) HF, (b) Kr, (c) Ti, (d) Si, (e) P_4, (f) RbBr.

3.11 Diagram the resonance forms of ozone, O_3.

3.12 (a) Diagram a Lewis structure for SO_3. (b) All of the bonds of SO_3 are of equal length. Show how resonance explains this fact. (c) Sulfur trioxide vapor consists of molecules of zero dipole moment. What conclusion as to the geometry of the SO_3 molecule can be made from this fact?

3.13 The nitrite ion, NO_2^-, is angular with the nitrogen atom as the central atom. The two N—O bond distances are equal and the oxygen atoms are equally negative. Diagram the resonance forms of NO_2^-.

3.14 Indicate the bond type (*sp*, p^2, etc.) and the molecular geometry of the following covalent compounds. (a) $CdCl_2$, (b) Cl_2O, (c) $GaCl_3$, (d) AsH_3, (e) AsF_5, (f) CCl_4, (g) $SnCl_4$, (h) $SnCl_2$.

3.15 (a) Explain the answers to Problem 3.14 on the basis of electron pair repulsions. (b) Which of the molecules would have a dipole?

3.16 Use the concept of electron pair repulsions to predict the molecular geometry of the following. (a) SiF_4, (b) SF_4, (c) XeF_4, (d) XeF_2, (e) AsF_6^-, (f) $TeCl_5^-$.

3.17 (a) Write the molecular orbital designation for carbon monoxide. (b) How many bonds are indicated by (a)? (c) With what other diatomic molecule is CO isoelectronic? (d) Write the molecular orbital designation for the cyanide ion, CN^-, which may be considered to be formed from a carbon atom, a nitrogen atom, and an electron.

3.18 When sodium is reacted with oxygen, sodium peroxide (Na_2O_2) is obtained, whereas potassium and oxygen yield potassium superoxide (KO_2). (a) Give the molecular orbital designations for the peroxide ion, O_2^{2-}, and the superoxide ion, O_2^-. (b) State the number of bonds in each structure. (c) Predict whether the ions would be diamagnetic or paramagnetic.

3.19 (a) Draw an energy level diagram for the NO molecule similar to Figure 3.23 for the O_2 molecule. How many bonds are represented for the molecule? (b) How many bonds would NO^+ have? (c) How many bonds would NO^- have? (d) Which of these species are paramagnetic?

3.20 Name the following. (a) FeO, (b) CuO, (c) K_2O, (d) Cr_2O_3, (e) Mg_3N_2, (f) S_5N_2, (g) PCl_5, (h) $Fe_3(PO_4)_2$, (i) $K_2Cr_2O_7$, (j) $Mg(NO_2)_2$.

3.21 State formulas for: (a) copper(II) chromate, (b) ferric perchlorate, (c) dichlorine heptoxide, (d) gold(III) oxide, (e) barium oxide, (f) chromous chloride, (g) zinc sulfide, (h) tetraphosphorus trisulfide, (i) calcium arsenate, (j) chlorous acid.

4

Chemical Equations and Quantitative Relationships

We have discussed the assignment of symbols to represent elements and formulas to represent compounds. This convenient shorthand can be extended into representations of chemical reactions, which are known as chemical equations. Symbols and their derivatives—formulas and equations—are not merely abbreviations; rather, the chemist greatly extends their utility through a method of interpretation which will be one of the principal topics of this chapter. **Stoichiometry** is that branch of chemistry that deals with the weight relations between elements and compounds as represented by formulas and equations.

4.1   The Gram Atom, Avogadro's Number

Ignoring the isotopic composition of the elements for the moment, let us consider that we have one atom of fluorine that weighs 19.0 u and one atom of hydrogen that weighs 1.0 u*. The fluorine atom is 19 times heavier than the hydrogen atom. If we take 10 atoms of each, the collection of fluorine atoms weighs 190.0 u, and the collection of hydrogen atoms weighs 10.0 u; the ratio of the sample weights is 19 to 1. If we take N atoms of fluorine and N atoms of hydrogen, the two samples will weigh $19.0 \times N$ u and $1.0 \times N$ u, respectively, and the total weights will still be in the ratio of 19 to 1. Provided that we take an equal number of atoms of each element, the ratio of the total weights of the two samples will be constant and the same as the ratio of the weights of the individual atoms.

We can turn this around to get a more valuable statement. If we have samples of fluorine and hydrogen in a weight ratio of 19.0 to 1.0 (the ratio of their atomic weights), there is an equal number of atoms in each

---

*For most problem work, atomic weights will be rounded off to the first figure following the decimal point.

sample. This is true regardless of what units of weight are used. Thus a sample of fluorine weighing 19.0 lb will contain the same number of atoms as a sample of hydrogen weighing 1.0 lb. A 19.0 g sample of fluorine will contain the same number of atoms as a 1.0 g sample of hydrogen.

The quantity of an element having a weight in grams numerically equal to that element's atomic weight is the **gram atomic weight** of that element; or more briefly, such a sample of an element is called a **gram atom.** A gram atom of any element, then, contains the same number of atoms as a gram atom of any other element. The number of atoms in a gram atom is called **Avogadro's number** (N), named for Amedeo Avogadro who first interpreted the behavior of gases in terms of the number of reacting atoms (Section 5.7). The value of Avogadro's number has been determined by electrochemical and crystallographic techniques as 6.023×10^{23}.

Avogadro's number is also the number of unified atomic mass units in 1 g. Suppose we take 2000 bags of sugar weighing 5 lb each; the collection will weigh 10,000 lb or 5 tons (since there are 2000 lb in 1 ton). If we take 2000 bags of sugar weighing 10 lb each, the total would weigh 20,000 lb or 10 tons. Notice in both cases, that we take the same number of bags as there are pounds in a ton. Notice also, that the weight of each collection in tons is numerically the same as the weight, in pounds, of a single bag of sugar from that collection. By analogy, suppose we take N atoms weighing x u each; the total collection will weigh $x \cdot N$ u. Since there are N unified atomic mass units in 1 g, this collection also weighs $x \cdot N/N$ g.

The magnitude of Avogadro's number is difficult to imagine. If all of the atoms in a gram atom were converted into 1 in.^{3} ice cubes, there would be enough ice cubes to cover the 50 states of the United States to a depth of about 650 miles! In the preceding discussion, we used the atomic weight of an element as the weight of a single atom of that element. The atomic weight of an element, however, usually is not the weight of any individual atom; rather, the atomic weight of an element is an average and takes into account the existence of isotopes (Section 2.9). It is easily seen that there is virtually a 100% chance of getting a collection of atoms of an element with an average weight equal to the atomic weight of that element since there is such a large number of atoms in even a very small sample. We do not work with solitary atoms; therefore, we may continue to think in terms of atoms with weights equal to atomic weights. The relationships thus derived are perfectly valid for samples of a realistic size.

4.2   The Mole

The molecular weight of a compound can be obtained by adding the atomic weights of the constituent atoms. A **gram molecular weight** is that quantity of a compound that has a weight, in grams, numerically equal to the compound's molecular weight; it is usually referred to as a **mole.**

The formula HF indicates a molecule formed from one atom of hydrogen and one atom of fluorine. Thus, a 1.0 u hydrogen atom combines with a 19.0 u fluorine atom to produce a molecule that weighs 20.0 u. If we take N atoms of hydrogen (1.0 g—a gram atom), this sample will require N atoms of fluorine (19.0 g—a gram atom) to produce N molecules of hydrogen fluoride (20.0 g—a mole). A mole, therefore, contains Avogadro's number of molecules.

A molecule of ammonia, NH_3, consists of one atom of nitrogen and three atoms of hydrogen; therefore, N molecules of ammonia will contain N atoms of nitrogen and $3N$ atoms of hydrogen. One gram atom of nitrogen (14.0 g) and 3 gram atoms of hydrogen (3.0 g) are required to make 1 mole of ammonia (17.0 g).

For the elements that occur as diatomic molecules, a mole consists of 2 gram atoms. A gram *atom* of oxygen would weigh 16.0 g and contain 6.023×10^{23} *atoms.* But, oxygen occurs as O_2 molecules. When one speaks of a *mole* of oxygen, reference is made to 6.023×10^{23} *molecules,* which would weigh 32.0 g since each molecule consists of two atoms.

Ionic compounds require a different interpretation. Since there are no molecules in truly ionic species, the term **gram formula weight** is sometimes used in place of gram molecular weight (or mole) for such compounds. We shall not follow such a procedure. It is difficult to classify many compounds as ionic or covalent (Section 3.8). Much is to be gained by a uniform treatment of all compounds, and the mole concept is easily extended and applied to compounds known to be ionic.

Thus for the ionic compound sodium chloride, NaCl, 1 mole would weigh 58.5 g (23.0 g of sodium plus 35.5 g of chlorine). This weight would contain N of the units represented by the formula NaCl (not molecules) or N sodium ions and N chloride ions. One mole of sodium chloride, then, consists of a total of $2N$ ions.

One mole of calcium chloride, $CaCl_2$, contains a total of $3N$ ions—N calcium ions (40.1 g) and $2N$ chloride ions (2×35.5 g)—and weighs 111.1 g.

A mole, then, always contains 6.023×10^{23} of the units described by the formula under consideration. If these units are molecules, a mole consists of 6.023×10^{23} molecules. If these units are collections of ions, 1 mole consists of 6.023×10^{23} such units; in these cases, the total number of ions in 1 mole is Avogadro's number times the number of ions in each unit.

It is frequently necessary to speak of quantities of ions without reference to the compound from which they are derived. In such cases, 1 mole consists of 6.023×10^{23} ions. Thus 1 mole of Cl^- ions weighs 35.5 g and contains 6.023×10^{23} Cl^- ions.

4.3   Chemical Calculations

The units of measure must be included as an integral part of any meaningful measurement. It makes very little sense to say that an object weighs 9.0, for this could mean 9.0 lb, 9.0 g, 9.0 oz, or any of a host of other weights. Furthermore, any terms employed in a calculation should include proper labels, and these should undergo the same mathematical operations as the numbers. In any calculation, if the units appearing in both numerator and denominator are canceled, those remaining will appear as a part of the answer and will give the answer its true dimension. If the answer does not have the units sought, then a mistake has been made in the calculation setup.

The use of dimensions in solving problems is illustrated in the following examples:

Example 4.1   Given the conversion: 454 g = 1.00 lb, how many pounds are there in 1.00 kg (1000 g)?

Solution   One would probably reason as follows:

$$454 \text{ g} = 1.00 \text{ lb}$$

Therefore

$$1.00 \text{ g} = \left(\frac{1}{454}\right) \text{lb}$$

and

$$1000 \text{ g} = 1000 \left(\frac{1}{454}\right) \text{lb} = 2.20 \text{ lb}$$

The same line of reasoning can be followed using a properly labeled conversion factor. From

$$454 \text{ g} = 1.00 \text{ lb}$$

the factor

$$\left(\frac{1.00 \text{ lb}}{454 \text{ g}}\right)$$

can be derived. Since the numerator and denominator are equivalent, this factor is equal to unity. Our problem can be stated:

$$? \text{ lb} = 1000 \text{ g}$$

By the use of the factor, we can solve the problem:

$$? \text{ lb} = 1000 \text{ g} \left(\frac{1.00 \text{ lb}}{454 \text{ g}}\right) = 2.20 \text{ lb}$$

Notice that the gram labels have canceled leaving the answer in the desired units, pounds.*

We have noted that the factor is equal to unity. A second, perfectly valid factor (454 g/1.00 lb)—the reciprocal of that used in the preceding

*Cancellation will not be indicated in future problems.

solution—can also be derived. The use of this factor leads to a rather peculiar result:

$$? \text{ lb} = 1000 \text{ g} \left(\frac{454 \text{ g}}{1.00 \text{ lb}} \right) = 454,000 \text{ g}^2/\text{lb}$$

The answer, while mathematically correct, is not particularly useful nor does it answer the question. Since this answer does not have the desired label, a calculation error is indicated.

Several factors may be used, in series, in the setup for the solution of a problem.

Example 4.2   How many grams are there in 0.0150 ton?

Solution   We can state the problem:

$$? \text{ g} = 0.0150 \text{ ton}$$

To convert tons to pounds, we use 1.00 ton = 2000 lb and derive the factor (2000 lb/1.00 ton). The problem now reads:

$$? \text{ g} = 0.0150 \text{ ton} \left(\frac{2000 \text{ lb}}{1.00 \text{ ton}} \right)$$

The factor to convert pounds to grams is (454 g/1.00 lb), and thus

$$? \text{ g} = 0.0150 \text{ ton} \left(\frac{2000 \text{ lb}}{1.00 \text{ ton}} \right) \left(\frac{454 \text{ g}}{1.00 \text{ lb}} \right)$$

$$= 13,600 \text{ g}$$

$$= 1.36 \times 10^4 \text{ g}$$

4.4   The Law of Constant Composition

The law of constant composition (or the law of definite proportions) was first put forward by Joseph Proust in 1799 and states that a pure compound always consists of the same elements combined in the same proportions by weight. In the preceding sections the assumption is tacitly made that compounds are of definite composition, and, indeed, such is a logical consequence of modern atomic and molecular theory.

The composition of a given compound can be determined by chemical analysis, and the formula of the compound is usually derived from these analytical data (Section 4.5). However, the calculation of the percent composition from a formula is sometimes necessary and is readily accomplished.

Example 4.3   What is the percent composition by weight of Fe_2O_3?

Solution   One mole of Fe_2O_3 contains

$$2 \text{ gram atoms of Fe} = (2 \times 55.8) \text{ g} = 111.6 \text{ g}$$

$$3 \text{ gram atoms of O} = (3 \times 16.0) \text{ g} = \underline{ 48.0 \text{ g}}$$

$$159.6 \text{ g}$$

The percent Fe is

$$\frac{111.6 \text{ g Fe}}{159.6 \text{ g Fe}_2\text{O}_3} \times 100\% = 69.9\% \text{ Fe in Fe}_2\text{O}_3$$

The percent O is

$$\frac{48.0 \text{ g O}}{159.6 \text{ g Fe}_2\text{O}_3} \times 100\% = 30.1\% \text{ O in Fe}_2\text{O}_3$$

(The same result, of course, could have been obtained by subtracting 69.9% from 100.0%.)

Other simple stoichiometric problems can be solved by use of the proportions represented by formulas.

Example 4.4 What weight of oxygen must be combined with 100 g of iron to produce Fe_2O_3?

Solution

$$1 \text{ gram atom Fe} = 55.8 \text{ g Fe}$$

Therefore, 100 g Fe is

$$100 \text{ g Fe} \left(\frac{1 \text{ gram atom Fe}}{55.8 \text{ g Fe}} \right) = 1.79 \text{ gram atom Fe}$$

from the formula Fe_2O_3,

$$2 \text{ gram atom Fe} = 3 \text{ gram atom O}$$

Hence,

$$1.79 \text{ gram atom Fe} \left(\frac{3 \text{ gram atom O}}{2 \text{ gram atom Fe}} \right) = 2.69 \text{ gram atom O}$$

Since 1 gram atom O = 16.0 g O,

$$2.69 \text{ gram atom O} \left(\frac{16.0 \text{ g O}}{1 \text{ gram atom O}} \right) = 43.0 \text{ g O}$$

The entire calculation can be performed in one step:

$$? \text{ g O} = 100 \text{ g Fe} \left(\frac{1 \text{ gram atom Fe}}{55.8 \text{ g Fe}} \right) \left(\frac{3 \text{ gram atom O}}{2 \text{ gram atom Fe}} \right) \left(\frac{16.0 \text{ g O}}{1 \text{ gram atom O}} \right)$$

$$= 43.0 \text{ g O}$$

A similar, but shorter, way to solve this problem is to note the ratio of weights of oxygen to iron in Fe_2O_3 as in the calculation of Example 4.3.

$$? \text{ g O} = 100 \text{ g Fe} \left(\frac{48.0 \text{ g O}}{111.6 \text{ g Fe}} \right) = 43.0 \text{ g O}$$

Example 4.5 An iron ore contains 70.0% Fe_2O_3. What weight of iron, in pounds, can theoretically be obtained from 1.00 ton of the ore?

Solution A factor can be derived from the fact that the ore is 70.0% Fe_2O_3. Thus

$$70.0 \text{ lb } Fe_2O_3 = 100 \text{ lb ore}$$

From the formula Fe_2O_3,

$$2 \text{ lb atom Fe} = 1 \text{ lb mole } Fe_2O_3$$

or

$$111.6 \text{ lb Fe} = 159.6 \text{ lb } Fe_2O_3$$

The solution of the problem then is

$$? \text{ lb Fe} = 2000 \text{ lb ore} \left(\frac{70.0 \text{ lb } Fe_2O_3}{100 \text{ lb ore}} \right) \left(\frac{111.6 \text{ lb Fe}}{159.6 \text{ lb } Fe_2O_3} \right)$$

$$= 979 \text{ lb Fe}$$

4.5 Determination of Formulas

The **simplest,** or **empirical,** formula is that derived from the simplest ratio of atoms in a compound. The **molecular formula** of a particular compound is based on the actual numbers of atoms that comprise a molecule of that compound. For some compounds, the molecular and the simplest formulas are identical, for example, H_2O, CO_2, NH_3, and SO_2. For many compounds, however, the molecular and simplest formulas are different. The simplest formulas NH_2, BNH_2, CH, and CH_2O correspond to the molecular formulas N_2H_4, $B_3N_3H_6$, C_6H_6, and $C_6H_{12}O_6$. Notice that for the atomic radio of the simplest formula, the actual ratio of a molecule is reduced to the lowest possible set of whole numbers.

Obviously, there is no molecular formula for an ionic compound since there are no molecules. Formulas of ionic compounds are, in reality, simplest formulas and state the simplest ratio of ions in an ionic crystal.

To determine the simplest formula of a compound, an experimentally determined analysis of the compound is needed.

Example 4.6 A sample of a compound contains 6.30 g of carbon and 5.60 g of oxygen. What is the simplest formula of the compound?

Solution The analysis states a weight ratio; formulas are based on atomic ratios. Since a gram atom of any element contains 6.023×10^{23} atoms, conversion of the weight ratio to a gram atom ratio gives the atomic ratio desired.

$$? \text{ gram atom C} = 6.30 \text{ g C} \left(\frac{1 \text{ gram atom C}}{12.0 \text{ g C}} \right) = 0.525 \text{ gram atom C}$$

$$? \text{ gram atom O} = 5.60 \text{ g O} \left(\frac{1 \text{ gram atom O}}{16.0 \text{ g O}} \right) = 0.350 \text{ gram atom O}$$

Dividing both numbers by the smaller number gives the ratio (C to O) 1.5 to 1, or, in whole numbers, 3 to 2. Therefore the simplest formula is C_3O_2.

Example 4.7   What is the simplest formula of an oxide of phosphorus containing 43.6% phosphorus and 56.4% oxygen?

Solution   In 100 g of compound there would be 43.6 g P and 56.4 g O.

$$? \text{ gram atom P} = 43.6 \text{ g P} \left(\frac{1 \text{ gram atom P}}{31.0 \text{ g P}} \right) = 1.41 \text{ gram atom P}$$

$$? \text{ gram atom O} = 56.4 \text{ g O} \left(\frac{1 \text{ gram atom O}}{16.0 \text{ g O}} \right) = 3.53 \text{ gram atom O}$$

Dividing by the smaller number gives the atomic ratio 1.0 to 2.5. The simplest whole number ratio, therefore, is 2 to 5, and the formula is P_2O_5.

Additional information is necessary to assign a molecular formula to a compound. The number of atoms that constitute a molecule can be ascertained by diffraction techniques, or the molecular weight of the compound can be experimentally determined.

Example 4.8   What is the molecular formula of the compound described in Example 4.7 if the compound has a molecular weight of 284?

Solution   The weight obtained by adding the atomic weights indicated by the simplest formula, P_2O_5, is 142. Since the actual molecular weight is 284, there must be twice as many atoms present in a molecule as is indicated by the simplest formula. Therefore the molecular formula is P_4O_{10}.

4.6   Chemical Equations

Chemical equations are representations of reactions in terms of the symbols and formulas of the elements and compounds involved. The reactants are indicated on the left and the products on the right. An arrow is used instead of the customary equal sign of the algebraic equation; it may be considered as an abbreviation for the word "yields."

The **law of conservation of mass** states that there is no detectable change in mass during the course of an ordinary chemical reaction.* This law was first stated formally by Antoine Lavoisier in his work *Traite Elementaire de Chemie* (1789) although the quantitative methods of prior workers assumed such a principle. Insofar as chemical equations are concerned, the law of conservation of mass means that there must be as many atoms of each element, combined or uncombined, indicated on the left of an equation as there are on the right.

*This is demonstrably untrue for nuclear transformations. In these cases, Einstein's postulate of the equivalence of mass and energy (Section 2.9) satisfactorily accounts for the conversion of a small amount of mass into energy. Rigorously, a law of conservation of mass–energy should be stated. The energy changes observed in ordinary chemical reactions are probably the result of concomitant mass changes, but such changes in mass are too small to be experimentally detected. Therefore, the law of conservation of mass, as stated, is valid for all reactions except those involving nuclear change (Chapter 18).

Chemical equations report the results of experimentation. One of the goals of chemistry is the discovery and development of principles that make it possible to predict the products of chemical reactions; careful attention will be given to any such generalizations. However, all too often the products of a particular set of reactants must be memorized, and any prediction is subject to modification if experiment dictates. What may appear reasonable on paper is not necessarily what occurs in the laboratory.

The first step, then, in writing a chemical equation is to ascertain the products of the reaction in question. Carbon disulfide, CS_2, reacts with chlorine, Cl_2, to produce carbon tetrachloride, CCl_4, and disulfur dichloride, S_2Cl_2. To represent this, we write

$$CS_2 + Cl_2 \rightarrow CCl_4 + S_2Cl_2$$

This equation is not correct quantitatively and violates the law of conservation of mass. Although one carbon atom and two sulfur atoms are indicated on both the left side and the right side of the equation, only two chlorine atoms (one Cl_2 molecule) appear on the left to balance the six chlorine atoms shown on the right. The equation can be balanced* by indicating that three molecules of chlorine should be used for the reaction. Thus

$$CS_2 + 3Cl_2 \rightarrow CCl_4 + S_2Cl_2$$

The simple types of chemical equations are balanced by trial and error as the following examples will illustrate. When steam is passed over hot iron, hydrogen gas and an oxide of iron having the formula Fe_3O_4 are produced. Thus

$$Fe + H_2O \rightarrow Fe_3O_4 + H_2$$

It is tempting to substitute another oxide of iron, FeO, for the Fe_3O_4 since that would immediately produce a balanced equation. Such an equation, however, would be without value; experiment indicates that Fe_3O_4, not FeO, is a product of the reaction. Balancing an equation is never accomplished by altering the formulas of the products of the reaction. In the equation for the reaction of iron and steam, three atoms of Fe and four molecules of H_2O must be taken to give the iron and oxygen atoms required for the formation of Fe_3O_4.

$$3Fe + 4H_2O \rightarrow Fe_3O_4 + H_2$$

The equation is now balanced except for hydrogen, and the hydrogen may be brought into balance as follows:

$$3Fe + 4H_2O \rightarrow Fe_3O_4 + 4H_2$$

---

*Strictly speaking, the expression is not an "equation" until it is balanced.

In much the same manner we can balance an equation for the complete combustion of ethane (C_2H_6) in oxygen. The products of this reaction are carbon dioxide and water.

$$C_2H_6 + O_2 \rightarrow CO_2 + H_2O$$

To balance the two carbon atoms of C_2H_6, the production of two molecules of CO_2 must be indicated, and the six hydrogen atoms of C_2H_6 require that three molecules of H_2O be produced.

$$C_2H_6 + O_2 \rightarrow 2CO_2 + 3H_2O$$

Only the oxygen remains to be balanced; there are seven atoms of oxygen on the right and only two on the left. In order to get seven atoms of oxygen on the left, we would have to take $3\frac{1}{2}$ (or $\frac{7}{2}$) molecules of O_2.

$$C_2H_6 + \tfrac{7}{2}O_2 \rightarrow 2CO_2 + 3H_2O$$

Customarily, equations are written with whole number coefficients. By multiplying through by two, we get

$$2C_2H_6 + 7O_2 \rightarrow 4CO_2 + 6H_2O$$

4.7   Problems Based on Chemical Equations

An equation can be interpreted in several different ways. Consider, for example,

$$2H_2 + O_2 \rightarrow 2H_2O$$

On the simplest level, this equation shows that hydrogen reacts with oxygen to produce water. On the atomic–molecular level, it states that two molecules of hydrogen react with one molecule of oxygen to produce two molecules of water. In more practical, quantitative, terms, it can be read as a statement that 2 moles of hydrogen react with 1 mole of oxygen to produce 2 moles of water, or, in terms of actual weights, 4.0 g of hydrogen reacts with 32.0 g of oxygen to produce 36.0 g of water. Pound moles, ton moles, or any other type of moles can be used as long as the use of units is consistent. The weights derived from chemical equations can be interpreted as simple weight ratios; they can be used with any units of weight. Thus, the equation states that 4.0 lb of hydrogen reacts with 32.0 lb of oxygen to yield 36.0 lb of water.

Stoichiometric problems, then, are readily solved by reference to the equation describing the chemical change in question.

Example 4.9   How many grams of HCl are required to produce 15.0 g of Cl_2, according to the following reaction?

$$MnO_2 + 4HCl \rightarrow MnCl_2 + Cl_2 + 2H_2O$$

Solution   The equation states that 4 moles of HCl (molecular weight,

36.5) produce 1 mole of Cl_2 (molecular weight, 71.0). Thus

$$? g \; HCl = 15.0 \; g \; Cl_2 \left(\frac{4(36.5) \; g \; HCl}{71.0 \; g \; Cl_2} \right) = 30.8 \; g \; HCl$$

Example 4.10 One of the reactions occurring in a blast furnace used to reduce iron ore is

$$Fe_2O_3 + 3CO \rightarrow 2Fe + 3CO_2$$

What weight of CO, in pounds, is needed to reduce 100 lb of Fe_2O_3?

Solution From the equation, 1 mole of Fe_2O_3 (molecular weight, 159.6) reacts with 3 moles of CO (molecular weight, 28.0). Thus

$$? \; lb \; CO = 100 \; lb \; Fe_2O_3 \left(\frac{3(28.0) \; lb \; CO}{159.6 \; lb \; Fe_2O_3} \right) = 52.6 \; lb \; CO$$

4.8   Heat of Reaction

The heat that is liberated or absorbed in the course of a chemical re-action is an important and integral part of the reaction. Reactions that evolve heat are called **exothermic** reactions; those that absorb heat are called **endothermic** reactions. A **heat of reaction** can be regarded as a manifestation of the difference in **heat content,** or **enthalpy,** H, between the products of a reaction and the reactants. For an exothermic re-action, the products have a lower enthalpy than the reactants so that the heat of the reaction, ΔH, is negative; the system evolves heat. The prod-ucts of endothermic reactions have a higher enthalpy than the reactants; ΔH is positive, and heat is absorbed.

The heat contents of chemical substances depend upon the tempera-ture and pressure. By convention, ΔH values are generally reported at $25°C$ ($298°K$) and standard atmospheric pressure (Section 5.2). In other words, for exothermic reactions, all the heat above that necessary to maintain the temperature of the chemical substances at $25°C$ goes into what is called the heat of reaction. For endothermic reactions, the heat of reaction is the heat required to secure products at $25°C$ from reactants at the same temperature. The practice of indicating the temperature as a subscript (ΔH_{298}) will not be followed.

Thermochemical equations may be written in which the heat of re-action is included as a reactant or product. The value of ΔH used is that required when the equation is read in gram molar quantities. It is neces-sary to specify the state of every material indicated by the equation. This is done by placing a designation after each symbol and formula of the equation: (g) for gas, (l) for liquid, (s) for solid, and (aq) for in water solution. In the following thermochemical equations, the heats shown are different because water is in different states, and 21.0 kcal of heat is required to convert 2 moles of $H_2O(l)$ to 2 moles of $H_2O(g)$ at $25°C$.

$$2H_2(g) + O_2(g) \rightarrow 2H_2O(l) + 136.6\,kcal$$
$$2H_2(g) + O_2(g) \rightarrow 2H_2O(g) + 115.6\,kcal$$

An endothermic reaction is shown in either of two ways:

$$12.40\,kcal + H_2(g) + I_2(s) \rightarrow 2HI(g)$$

or, with the heat transposed to the right-hand side of the equation:

$$H_2(g) + I_2(s) \rightarrow 2HI(g) - 12.40\,kcal$$

Notice that when the heat value is written on the right-hand side of the equation, its sign is the opposite of that for the ΔH for the reaction. By means of thermochemical equations, it is possible to solve problems involving heat effects in much the same manner that simple stoichiometric problems are solved.

> **Example 4.11** The heat of combustion of *n*-pentane (C_5H_{12}) is -845 kcal/mole. How much heat can be obtained from the complete combustion of 100 g of C_5H_{12}?
>
> **Solution** The balanced thermochemical equation for the combustion is
>
> $$C_5H_{12}(g) + 8O_2(g) \rightarrow 5CO_2(g) + 6H_2O(l) + 845\,kcal$$
>
> This equation shows that 845 kcal of heat is liberated by the combustion of 72.0 g of C_5H_{12}.
>
> $$?\,kcal = 100\,g\,C_5H_{12}\left(\frac{845\,kcal}{72.0\,g\,C_5H_{12}}\right) = 1170\,kcal$$

A device called a **calorimeter** is used to measure heats of reaction. In the typical calorimeter, a reaction vessel is placed in the center of a larger, well-insulated vessel containing a weighed quantity of water. The reaction is run between known quantities of reactants, and the heat evolved increases the temperature of the water and the calorimeter. The rise in temperature is determined by a sensitive thermometer. The number of calories liberated by the reaction is the product of the rise in temperature and the total heat capacity of the calorimeter and its contents. The **heat capacity** of a substance is the amount of heat required to increase the temperature of the substance by 1°C. The heat capacity of a calorimeter must be determined by experiment. Since the specific heat of water is known (ca., 1 cal/g°), the "water equivalent" of the calorimeter is often determined. Thus the heat capacity needed to calculate a heat effect by the use of a calibrated calorimeter can be obtained from the amount of water used in the experiment and the water equivalent of the calorimeter.

> **Example 4.12** A bomb-type calorimeter is used to determine the heat of combustion of sulfur; 0.1000 gram atom of sulfur (rhombic) is put in the bomb which is then filled with oxygen under pressure. The bomb is placed

in the calorimeter vessel which is filled with 900.0 g of water. The calorimeter has a water equivalent of 214.0 g. The reaction mixture is ignited electrically, and the reaction causes the temperature to increase from 22.105° to 28.474°C. From these data, calculate the heat of combustion of rhombic sulfur. Assume that the specific heat of water is 1.000 cal/g° over the temperature range of the experiment.

Solution   The rise in temperature is

$$28.474°C - 22.105°C = 6.369°C$$

The number of calories evolved by the reaction is

$$? \text{cal} = (900.0 + 214.0) \text{ g H}_2\text{O} \ (6.369°\text{C}) \left(\frac{1 \text{ cal}}{1 \text{ g H}_2\text{O } 1°\text{C}} \right) = 7095 \text{ cal}$$

This is the amount of heat liberated by the combustion of 0.1 gram atom of sulfur; for 1 gram atom;

$$? \text{kcal} = 1.000 \text{ gram atom S} \left(\frac{7095 \text{ cal}}{0.1000 \text{ gram atom S}} \right) \left(\frac{1 \text{ kcal}}{1000 \text{ cal}} \right) = 70.95 \text{ kcal}$$

$$\Delta H = -70.95 \text{ kcal/mole}$$

The thermochemical equation for the reaction is

$$\text{S(s, rhombic)} + \text{O}_2(\text{g}) \rightarrow \text{SO}_2(\text{g}) + 70.95 \text{ kcal}$$

There is no significant increase, or decrease, in pressure accompanying this reaction. For reactions in which there is an attendant pressure change (e.g., those in which there are more moles of gaseous products than there are moles of gaseous reactants), the determination of the enthalpy of reaction requires that a correction be made to the value obtained by the method outlined above. Enthalpy is defined as the heat effect under constant pressure; the calorimeter bomb determines the heat effect under constant volume.

4.9   Law of Hess

The **heat of formation** (ΔH_f°) of a compound is the change in enthalpy for the reaction in which 1 mole of the compound in its standard state is formed from its constituent elements in their standard states. The **standard state** of a substance is the state that is stable at 25°C and atmospheric pressure.

In the preceding section, the heat of combustion of *2* moles of $H_2(\text{g})$ to *2* moles of $H_2\text{O(l)}$ appears as -136.6 kcal; from this value, the heat of formation of $H_2\text{O(l)}$ can be derived: -68.3 kcal/mole. Likewise in Section 4.8, the preparation of *2* moles of HI(g) is shown to be endothermic with ΔH equal to $+12.40$ kcal; from this, the heat of formation of HI(g) can be derived: $+6.20$ kcal/mole. As we shall see, enthalpies of formation are important since they can be used to calculate heats of reaction that are not conveniently measured directly.

The basis of many thermochemical calculations is the **law of constant heat summation** established experimentally by G. H. Hess in 1840. This **law of Hess** states that the change in enthalpy for any chemical reaction is constant, whether the reaction occurs in one step or in several steps. Thus thermochemical equations can be treated as algebraic equations; for example, they may be added, subtracted, multiplied by a factor, or divided by a factor. As an illustration, let us calculate the heat of formation of $CH_4(g)$; it is impossible to measure directly this change in enthalpy.

The heats of combustion of $CH_4(g)$, $H_2(g)$, and C(graphite) are directly measurable.

$$CH_4(g) + 2O_2(g) \rightarrow CO_2(g) + 2H_2O(l) + 212.8 \text{ kcal} \qquad (1)$$

$$2H_2(g) + O_2(g) \rightarrow 2H_2O(l) + 136.6 \text{ kcal} \qquad (2)$$

$$C(\text{graphite}) + O_2(g) \rightarrow CO_2(g) + 94.1 \text{ kcal} \qquad (3)$$

Reversing equation (1) gives

$$2H_2O(l) + CO_2(g) \rightarrow CH_4(g) + 2O_2(g) - 212.8 \text{ kcal} \qquad (4)$$

The thermochemical equation for the formation of $CH_4(g)$ from the constituent elements is obtained by adding equations (2), (3), and (4) and canceling the terms common to both sides of the equation.

$$C(\text{graphite}) + 2H_2(g) \rightarrow CH_4 (g) + 17.9 \text{ kcal}$$

Heats of formation are convenient to use for thermochemical calculations. Thus the heat of hydrogenation of ethene, $C_2H_4(g)$,

$$C_2H_4(g) + H_2(g) \rightarrow C_2H_6(g)$$

can be calculated from the heat of formation of ethane, $C_2H_6(g)$ and the heat of formation of ethene. The thermochemical equation for the formation of ethene, which is endothermic, is written in reverse form and the sign of the heat effect adjusted accordingly.

$$2C(\text{graphite}) + 3H_2(g) \rightarrow C_2H_6(g) + 20.2 \text{ kcal}$$
$$C_2H_4(g) \rightarrow 2C(\text{graphite}) + 2H_2(g) + 12.5 \text{ kcal}$$

Addition of these equations gives

$$C_2H_4(g) + H_2(g) \rightarrow C_2H_6(g) + 32.7 \text{ kcal}$$

Examination of the preceding problem, as well as similar problems, reveals that a heat of reaction can be calculated by subtracting the sum of the heats of formation of the reactants from the sum of the heats of formation of the products. Notice that compounds alone are assigned ΔH_f values. To calculate the heat of reaction for

$$Fe_2O_3(s) + 3CO(g) \rightarrow 2Fe(s) + 3CO_2(g)$$

the heats of formation of the compounds represented in the equation are treated in the following manner.

$$\Delta H = 3 \Delta H_f(CO_2) - [\Delta H_f(Fe_2O_3) + 3 \Delta H_f(CO)]$$
$$\Delta H = 3(-94.1) - [(-196.5) + 3(-26.4)]$$
$$\Delta H = -282.3 + 275.7 = -6.6 \text{ kcal}$$

The reaction can be written:

$$Fe_2O_3(s) + 3CO(g) \longrightarrow 2Fe(s) + 3CO_2(g) + 6.6 \text{ kcal}$$

4.10 Law of Dulong and Petit

In 1819, Pierre Dulong and Alexis Petit discovered that at room temperature the atomic heat capacity of most solid elements is equal to 6.1 cal/° gram atom. The **atomic heat capacity** is defined as the product of the specific heat (the amount of heat needed to increase the temperature of 1 g of the substance by 1°C) and the atomic weight of the element.

$$(\text{atomic weight})(\text{specific heat}) = 6.1 \text{ cal/° gram atom}$$

The law of Dulong and Petit is only approximate, and values from 6.0 to 6.4 have been reported for the atomic heat capacity; it is most closely followed by the heavier metals.

Example 4.13 At 20°C, chromium has a specific heat of 0.110 cal/° g. What is the approximate atomic weight of chromium?

Solution

$$\text{atomic weight} = \left(\frac{6.1 \text{ cal/° gram atom}}{0.110 \text{ cal/° g}}\right) = 55 \text{ g/gram atom}$$

The correct atomic weight of chromium is 52.0, and the answer is in error by approximately 6%.

4.11 Equivalent Weights of Elements

The equivalent weight of an element may be defined in several ways, all of which amount to much the same thing. One convenient method is to use 1.008 g of hydrogen (the atomic weight of hydrogen to four significant figures) as a standard. On this basis, one **gram equivalent weight** of an element is that weight of the element that combines with, or is otherwise chemically equivalent to, 1.008 g of hydrogen.

In a gram mole of the compound H_2O, 16.000 g of oxygen is combined with 2(1.008) g of hydrogen; the equivalent weight of oxygen, thus, is $\frac{1}{2}(16.000)$ or 8.000. The formula HCl shows that 1.008 g of hydrogen is equivalent to 35.45 g of chlorine (the atomic weight of chlorine to four figures); thus 35.45 g of chlorine constitutes a gram equivalent weight of this element. The equivalent weight of calcium can be derived from the formula $CaCl_2$. Since 40.08 g of calcium reacts with 2(35.45) g of chlorine and the equivalent weight of chlorine has been established as 35.45, the equivalent weight of calcium must be $\frac{1}{2}$(40.08) or 20.04.

Equivalent weights were called combining weights in the early chemical literature. Theoretically, one combining weight of an element will react with exactly one combining weight of another element. Thus 20.04 g of calcium will react with 8.00 g of oxygen. Allowance must be made, however, for the fact that some elements have more than one equivalent weight. For example, iron in $FeCl_2$ has an equivalent weight of $\frac{1}{2}$(55.85) since one iron atom is combined with two chlorine atoms; in $FeCl_3$, iron has an equivalent weight of $\frac{1}{3}$(55.85). For most A family elements, however, each element exhibits only one equivalent weight in its *ionic* binary compounds.

Another definition of equivalent weight is based on the **valence,** or **combining capacity,** of the elements. The term valence was coined before the electronic nature of chemical bonding was realized. Valence is a pure number and can be defined as the number of bonds an atom of the element forms in the compound under consideration. The valence of hydrogen is 1 in all of its compounds. In H_2O, oxygen has a valence of 2 since a single oxygen atom forms a bond with each of two hydrogen atoms. The valence of an element in an ionic compound corresponds to the absolute value of the electrovalence number of that element (the number without regard to sign). Thus the valence of sodium in Na_2O is 1, of calcium in CaO is 2, and of aluminum in Al_2O_3 is 3.

The equivalent weight of an element in a given compound is the atomic weight of the element divided by the valence of the element in that compound. Thus, if an atom of an element forms three bonds in the compound under consideration, the equivalent weight of the element is $\frac{1}{3}$ of its atomic weight. Since the valence of hydrogen is 1, the relationship between this definition of equivalent weight and the preceding one based on 1.008 g of hydrogen is evident.

Equivalent weights can be determined with great accuracy and have been used to establish atomic weights. The atomic weight of an element is equal to the product of the equivalent weight of the element and the valence of the element. The following example illustrates how atomic weights have been ascertained from equivalent weights in conjunction with approximate atomic weights determined by means of the law of Dulong and Petit.

> *Example 4.14* An oxide of chromium is 68.42% chromium. What is the equivalent weight of chromium in this compound? In Example 4.13, the approximate atomic weight of chromium was determined as 55 by the law of Dulong and Petit. What is the exact atomic weight of chromium?
>
> *Solution* The equivalent weight of chromium in the compound is the weight that will react with an equivalent weight of oxygen (8.000).

$$? \text{ g Cr} = 8.000 \text{ g O} \left(\frac{68.42 \text{ g Cr}}{31.58 \text{ g O}} \right) = 17.333 \text{ g Cr}$$

(One additional figure is carried so that the final answer will have four significant figures.)

The valence of chromium in the oxide can be determined from the approximate atomic weight and the equivalent weight. Thus

$$\text{valence} = \frac{55}{17.333} = 3.2$$

The valence of chromium in the oxide must be 3 since it is impossible to have fractional valences. The exact atomic weight of chromium, therefore, is:

$$3(17.333) = 52.00$$

SOME SUGGESTED READINGS

Kieffer, W. F., *The Mole Concept in Chemistry*, New York, Reinhold, 1962 (paper).

Nash, L., *Stoichiometry*, Reading, Mass., Addison-Wesley, 1966 (paper).

PROBLEMS

4.1 How many carbon atoms are there in a 1.00 carat diamond? One carat is 0.200 g.

4.2 (a) Which of the following compounds contains the highest percentage of iron: Fe_2O_3, Fe_3O_4, $FeCl_2$, $Fe(C_2H_3O_2)_2$? (b) Which contains the lowest percentage of iron?

4.3 (a) What weight percentage of CaC_2 is carbon? (b) What weight percentage of $MgSiF_6$ is fluorine?

4.4 What weight of silicon is combined with 3.50 g of chromium in the compound chromium silicide, Cr_2Si_3?

4.5 A sample of a compound contains 9.30 g P, 4.90 g N, and 15.98 g Cl. What is the simplest formula of the compound?

4.6 A compound is 54.88% Cr and 45.12% S. What is the simplest formula of the compound?

4.7 What weight of antimony is theoretically obtainable from 1.00 ton of stibnite that is 85.0% pure Sb_2S_3?

4.8 What weight of chromium is theoretically obtainable from 1.00 ton of chromite that is 70.0% pure $FeCr_2O_4$?

4.9 What weight of beryllium fluoride, BeF_2, can be prepared from 10.0 g of beryllium and 10.0 g of fluorine?

4.10 Diphosphorus tetraiodide may be prepared by the reaction

$$5P_4O_6 + 8I_2 \rightarrow 4P_2I_4 + 3P_4O_{10}$$

What weight of P_2I_4 can be prepared from 5.00 g P_4O_6 and 8.00 g I_2?

4.11 Boron carbide, B_4C, is prepared by the reaction of B_2O_3 and carbon in an electric furnace. Write a chemical equation for the reaction assuming that carbon monoxide, CO, is produced together with boron carbide. What minimum amount of carbon is needed to prepare 150 g of B_4C?

4.12 A 5.00 g sample of a mixture of $CaCO_3$ and $CaSO_4$ is heated to decompose the carbonate

$$CaCO_3(s) \rightarrow CaO(s) + CO_2(g)$$

The final weight of the sample is 4.50 g. What percentage of the original mixture is $CaCO_3$?

4.13 A 3.50 g sample of a mixture of $NaHCO_3$ and $CaCO_3$ is heated. The compounds decompose as follows:

$$CaCO_3(s) \rightarrow CaO(s) + CO_2(g)$$

$$2NaHCO_3(s) \rightarrow Na_2CO_3(s) + CO_2(g) + H_2O(g)$$

What percentage of the original mixture was $CaCO_3$ if the sample weighs 2.00 g after ignition?

4.14 The molecular weight of borazole is 80.4 and the simplest formula of this compound is BNH_2. What is the molecular formula of borazole?

4.15 A sample of a metal oxide weighs 9.66 g and contains 6.30 g of the metal. The specific heat of the metal is 0.136 cal/g°. What is the best value for the atomic weight of the metal that can be derived from these data?

4.16 The heat of combustion of pentane, $C_5H_{12}(g)$, to $CO_2(g)$ and $H_2O(l)$ is -845.2 kcal/mole. What is the heat of formation of pentane if the heat of formation of $CO_2(g)$ is -94.1 kcal/mole and the heat of formation of $H_2O(l)$ is -68.3 kcal/mole?

4.17 What is the enthalpy change at 25°C for the reaction

$$SO_3(g) + H_2O(l) \rightarrow H_2SO_4(l)$$

The heat of formation of $SO_3(g)$ is -94.5 kcal/mole, of $H_2O(l)$ is -68.3 kcal/mole, and of $H_2SO_4(l)$ is -193.9 kcal/mole.

4.18 What is the heat of the reaction

$$3NO_2(g) + H_2O(l) \rightarrow 2HNO_3(l) + NO(g)$$

The heats of formation of the pertinent compounds are: $NO_2(g)$, $+8.09$ kcal/mole; $H_2O(l)$, -68.32 kcal/mole; $HNO_3(l)$, -41.40 kcal/mole; and $NO(g)$, $+21.60$ kcal/mole.

4.19 For the reaction of the monatomic elements

$$H(g) + Cl(g) \rightarrow HCl(g)$$

ΔH is -103.16 kcal. The heat of formation of $HCl(g)$ is -22.06 kcal/mole and the heat of dissociation of $H_2(g)$

$$H_2(g) \rightarrow 2H(g)$$

is $+104.18$ kcal/mole of H_2. What is the heat of dissociation of $Cl_2(g)$?

4.20 A 12.45 g sample of $P_4O_{10}(s)$ is reacted with a stoichiometrically equivalent quantity of water in a vessel placed in a calorimeter containing 950.0 g of water. The temperature of the calorimeter and contents increased from 22.815°C to 26.885°C. If the water equivalent of the calorimeter was 165.0 g, what is the enthalpy change for the following reaction?

$$P_4O_{10}(s) + 6H_2O(l) \rightarrow 4H_3PO_4(s)$$

4.21 Compare the heating value of hydrogen gas and carbon monoxide gas per gram of fuel assuming combustion to $H_2O(l)$ and $CO_2(g)$. The heats of formation are: $H_2O(l)$, -68.32 kcal/mole; $CO(g)$, -26.24 kcal/mole; $CO_2(g)$, -94.05 kcal/mole.

4.22 Calculate the enthalpy change of the reaction

$$C_6H_6(l) + 3H_2(g) \rightarrow C_6H_{12}(l)$$

from the following heats of combustion: $C_6H_6(l)$, -781.0 kcal/mole; $H_2(g)$, -68.3 kcal/mole; $C_6H_{12}(l)$, -936.9 kcal/mole.

4.23 Phosphorus is prepared industrially by heating a mixture of phosphate rock, sand, and coke in an electric furnace. The overall reaction is

$$2Ca_3(PO_4)_2(s) + 6SiO_2(s) + 10C(s) \rightarrow P_4(g) + 10CO(g) + 6CaSiO_3 \quad (1)$$

What weight of calcium silicate, $\overline{CaSiO_3}$, is produced from a run in which 150 lb of phosphorus is prepared?

4.24 A mixture of sodium oxide, Na_2O, and barium oxide, BaO is treated with dilute sulfuric acid. Barium sulfate, $BaSO_4$, precipitates but sodium sulfate, Na_2SO_4, is soluble. If 1.43 g of $BaSO_4$ is obtained from 4.70 g of the mixed oxides, what percentage of the original mixture is BaO?

4.25 The iodate ion (IO_3^-) from a 2.0000 g sample of ceric iodate was reduced to iodide (I^-) and precipitated as 2.2366 g of silver iodide, AgI. The specific heat of cerium is 0.0423 cal/g°. From these data, calculate: (a) the equivalent weight of cerium in ceric iodate, (b) the formula of ceric iodate, and (c) the atomic weight of cerium.

5

Gases

There are three physical states of matter—solid, liquid, and gas. Under suitable conditions, most substances can be made to exist in any of the three states. However, under ordinary conditions of pressure and temperature, only certain covalent compounds and some nonmetallic elements are gases.

5.1 The Gaseous State

A study of the properties of gases leads to the conclusion that gases consist of widely separated molecules in rapid motion. The most familiar gas, air, is actually a mixture of gases. Experiments show that any two (or more) gases can be used in any proportion to prepare a perfectly homogeneous mixture; no such generalization can be made for liquids. This fact can be explained by the assumption that the molecules of any gas are separated by comparatively large distances making it possible for one gas to accommodate molecules of other gases. This molecular model can also be used to explain the compressibility of gases; compression is the forcing of gas molecules closer together.

Gases expand to fill any container. For example, bromine gas, which is red-brown in color, can be observed to diffuse uniformly throughout any container into which it is being introduced. Odorous gases released in a room can soon be detected in all parts of the room. The premise that gas molecules are in constant, rapid motion accounts for the diffusion of gases. Furthermore, gas molecules in their random motion strike the walls of the container, and these myriad impacts explain the fact that gases exert pressure.

5.2 Pressure

It is common to think of force as the application of physical strength or power—as pushing. In terms that permit measurement, we can define force as that which causes a change in the state of rest or motion of an object. One dyne is the force that causes 1 g of matter to change its speed by 1 cm/sec in 1 sec; thus 1 dyne is 1 g cm/sec^2. Increase in speed per unit time is termed **acceleration,** and force, is therefore, mass times acceleration. The weight of an object is a result of gravity acting on the object's mass; a body falling under the influence of gravity has an acceleration of 980.7 cm/sec^2. Hence, weight is a measure of force; in the English system, pounds is frequently used for such a measure.

Pressure is defined as force per unit area. Thus the pressure of a gas is the force the gas exerts on the walls of the container divided by the surface area of the container. Pressure is frequently expressed in dynes per square centimeter or pounds per square inch.

The atmosphere exerts a pressure on the surface of the earth. The instrument used to measure atmospheric pressure is called a **barometer** and was first devised by Evangelista Torricelli, a pupil of Galileo. A tube, sealed at one end, is filled with mercury and inverted in an open container of mercury (Figure 5.1). The mercury falls in the tube but does not completely run out; the pressure of the atmosphere on the surface of the mercury in the dish supports the column. Practically no pressure is exerted on the upper surface of the mercury in the column. Since mercury is not very volatile at room temperature, the amount of mercury vapor in the space above the liquid mercury in the tube is small; air has been excluded. A vacuum obtained in this manner is called a Torricellian vacuum. The pressure inside the tube and above the reference level indicated in Figure 5.1 is due only to the weight of the mercury column; this is equal to the atmospheric pressure outside the tube and above this level.

The height of mercury in the tube serves as a measure of the atmospheric pressure, and pressure is frequently recorded in centimeters, or millimeters, of mercury. Remember that pressure is force *per unit area.*

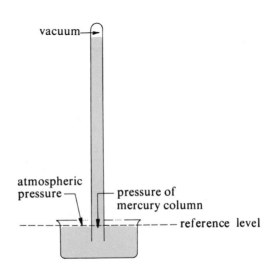

Figure 5.1   Barometer.

Whether the tube has a relatively large or small cross sectional area, a given atmospheric pressure will support the mercury in a tube to the same height.

The pressure of the atmosphere changes from day to day at a given altitude and also changes with altitude itself. A **standard atmosphere** (atm) is defined as the pressure that will support a column of mercury to a height of 76.0 cm at 0°C and sea level. It is necessary to specify the temperature and altitude since the density of mercury varies with temperature and the force of gravity varies with altitude; both of these factors affect the height of the mercury in the column.

Centimeters, or millimeters, of mercury can readily be converted into other pressure units. For example, a column of mercury 76.00 cm high and 1.000 cm^2 in cross section has a volume of 76.00 cm^3. This volume of mercury weighs 1034 g since mercury has a density of 13.60 g/cm^3 (at 0°C). At sea level the acceleration of gravity is 980.7 cm/sec^2, and, therefore, the force at the base of the mercury column is

$$1034 \text{ g} \times 980.7 \text{ cm/sec}^2 = 1.013 \times 10^6 \text{ g cm/sec}^2$$
$$= 1.013 \times 10^6 \text{ dynes}$$

Since this force is acting on 1 cm^2, the pressure indicated is 1.013×10^6 dynes/cm^2. In the English system, 1 atm is 14.7 lb/in.^{2}

A **manometer,** a device used to measure the pressure of a sample of gas (Figure 5.2), is patterned after the barometer. In Figure 5.2, the right arm of the manometer is open to the atmosphere; thus atmospheric pressure is exerted on the mercury in this arm. The left arm is connected to a container of gas, allowing the gas sample to exert pressure on the mercury. Since the mercury level is lower in the left arm than that in the right, the illustration indicates a situation where the gas pressure is

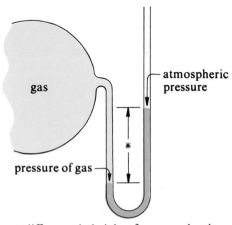

* difference in height of mercury levels

Figure 5.2   A type of manometer.

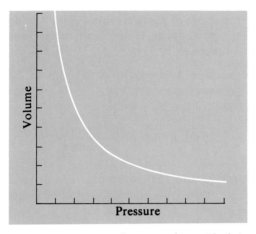

Figure 5.3 Pressure–volume curve for an ideal gas (Boyle's law).

greater than atmospheric pressure. If the gas sample were under a pressure equal to atmospheric pressure, the mercury would stand at the same level in both sides of the U tube. In the experiment illustrated in Figure 5.2, the difference in height between the two mercury levels (in cm or mm) must be added to the atmospheric pressure (in cm or mm) to obtain the pressure of the gas. If the pressure of the gas were less than atmospheric, the mercury in the left arm would stand higher than that in the right arm, and the difference in height would have to be subtracted from atmospheric pressure.

5.3 Boyle's Law

The quantitative relationship between the volume and pressure of a sample of gas was first summarized by Robert Boyle in 1662. **Boyle's law** states: at constant temperature, the volume of a sample of gas varies inversely with the pressure under which it is measured. If the pressure is doubled, the volume is reduced to half of its former value; if the pressure is cut in half, the volume is doubled. Mathematically,

$$V \propto \frac{1}{P}$$

$$V = \frac{k}{P} \qquad \text{or} \qquad PV = k$$

The value of the constant depends upon the size of the sample and the temperature. The pressure–volume curve for this equation (Figure 5.3) is the first quadrant branch of a hyperbola (negative values for volumes and pressures do not exist). A plot of V versus $1/P$ is a straight line through the origin with a slope equal to the constant.

Example 5.1   A sample of a gas occupies 360 ml under a pressure of 625 mm of mercury. At constant temperature, what volume will the sample occupy under a pressure of 750 mm?

Solution   The pressure *increases* from 625 mm to 750 mm. Hence, the volume must *decrease* a proportional amount, so that the pressures must be set up in a factor of less than unity.

$$? \text{ ml} = 360 \text{ ml} \left(\frac{625 \text{ mm}}{750 \text{ mm}} \right) = 300 \text{ ml}$$

Example 5.2   At 0°C and 5.00 atm pressure, a given sample of a gas occupies 100 liters. If the gas is compressed to 30.0 liters at 0°C, what will be the final pressure?

Solution   The volume decreases from 100 to 30.0 liters. Therefore the pressure increases, and the factor must be greater than unity.

$$? \text{ atm} = 5.00 \text{ atm} \left(\frac{100 \text{ liters}}{30.0 \text{ liters}} \right) = 16.7 \text{ atm}$$

5.4   Charles' Law

Boyle's law describes the behavior of gases under conditions of constant temperature. Studies to determine the effect of temperature change on the volume and pressure of a gas sample were first undertaken by Jacques Charles (1787), and this work was considerably extended by Joseph Gay-Lussac (1802).

For each centigrade degree rise in temperature, the volume of a gas expands $\frac{1}{273}$ of its value at 0°C and constant pressure. If a 273 ml sample of gas at 0°C is heated to 1°C, the volume of the sample increases by $\frac{1}{273}$ of 273 ml, or 1 ml. At 10°C, the volume of the sample would be 283 ml; at −1°, the sample would occupy 272 ml.

Let V equal the volume of a gas sample at temperature t (in °C) and V_0 equal the volume of the sample at 0°C. Then

$$V = V_0 + \frac{1}{273} t V_0$$

or

$$V = V_0 \left(1 + \frac{t}{273} \right) = V_0 \left(\frac{273 + t}{273} \right)$$

It is convenient to use the absolute temperature scale, on which temperatures are measured in degrees Kelvin (°K). A reading on this scale is obtained by adding 273 to the centigrade value; temperatures on the absolute scale may be denoted by T. Thus:

$$T = t + 273$$

Substituting this in the equation for the dependence of volume on temperature, we get

$$V = V_0\left(\frac{T}{273}\right) = \left(\frac{V_0}{273}\right)T$$

Since the volume of a given gas sample at 0°C is a constant under constant pressure, this can be expressed as

$$V = kT$$

The numerical value of k depends upon the size of the gas sample and the pressure.

Charles' law states, therefore, that the volume of a sample of gas varies *directly* with the *absolute* temperature. Volume is not directly proportional to the centigrade temperature. Thus doubling the absolute temperature doubles the volume of the gas; doubling the centigrade temperature does not.

The absolute temperature scale was first proposed by William Thomson, Lord Kelvin (1848), and the unit is named in his honor. Any absolute measurement scale must be based on a zero point that represents the complete absence of the property being measured; on such scales, negative values are impossible. Thus, 0 cm represents the complete absence of length, and one can say that 10 cm is twice 5 cm in length because these are absolute measurements. The centigrade temperature scale is not an absolute one; 0°C is the freezing point of water, not the lowest possible temperature. Because of this, negative centigrade temperatures are possible. On the other hand, the Kelvin scale is absolute; 0°K is the lowest possible temperature, and negative Kelvin temperatures are as impossible as negative volumes or negative lengths.

If volume versus temperature is plotted for a sample of gas, a straight line results such as is illustrated in Figure 5.4. Since volume is directly proportional to absolute temperature, the volume of the gas theoretically should be zero at absolute zero. Upon cooling, gases liquefy and then solidify before temperatures this low are reached; no substance exists in the gaseous state at absolute zero. However, the straight line curve can be extrapolated to zero volume. The temperature that corresponds to zero volume is −273.15°C; many lines of experimental evidence have confirmed this as absolute zero. The Kelvin degree is the same size as the centigrade degree; however, for the Kelvin scale, the zero point is moved to −273.15°C. Conversion to the Kelvin temperature scale can be accomplished, therefore, by adding 273.15 algebraically to the centigrade reading. For most problem work, this value can be rounded off to 273 without entailing significant error. The centigrade, Fahrenheit, and Kelvin temperature scales are compared in Figure 5.5. It is important to

Volume
-273
-200
-100
0
100
200
Temperature (°C)

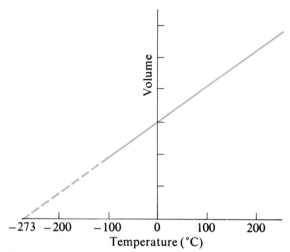

Figure 5.4 Temperature–volume curve for an ideal gas (Charles' law).

remember that temperatures must be expressed on the absolute scale for most calculations involving gases.

In like manner, the relationship between pressure and temperature can be derived; a temperature–pressure curve is similar to the temperature–volume curve illustrated in Figure 5.4. The pressure of a gas varies directly with absolute temperature, volume constant:

$$P = kT$$

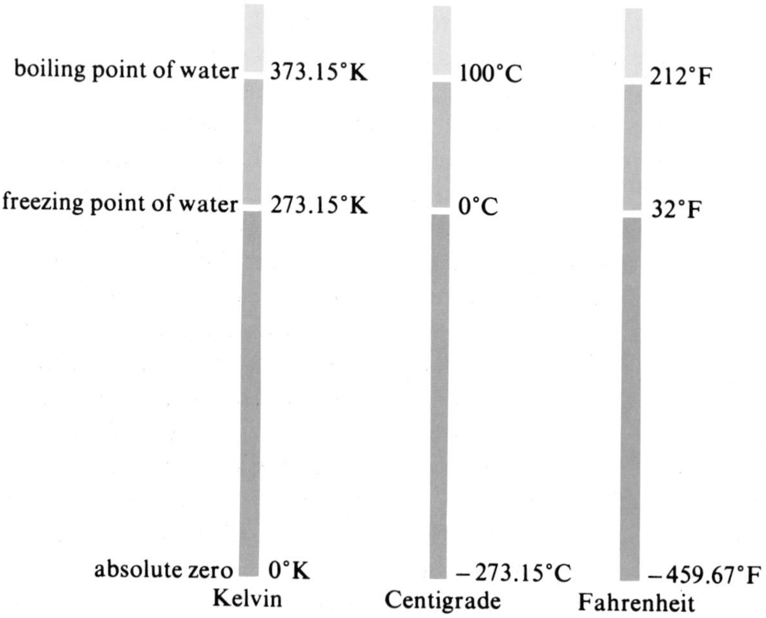

boiling point of water
373.15°K
100°C
212°F
freezing point of water
273.15°K
0°C
32°F
absolute zero
0°K
-273.15°C
-459.67°F
Kelvin
Centigrade
Fahrenheit

Figure 5.5 Comparison of temperature scales.

It is convenient to define standard reference conditions for work with gases. By convention, **standard temperature and pressure (STP)** are 0°C (273°K) and 760 mm Hg (1 atm) pressure; values for properties of gases are recorded at STP unless otherwise specified.

Example 5.3 A sample of gas has a volume of 79.5 ml at 45°C. What volume will the sample occupy at 0°C, pressure constant?

Solution Since the temperature decreases from 318° to 273°K, the volume must decrease. A factor of less than unity must be employed.

$$? \text{ ml} = 79.5 \text{ ml} \left(\frac{273°\text{K}}{318°\text{K}} \right) = 68.3 \text{ ml}$$

Example 5.4 A 10.0 liter container is filled with a gas to a pressure of 2.00 atm at 0°C. At what temperature will the pressure inside the container be 2.50 atm?

Solution Since the pressure increases, the temperature must increase. Thus

$$? \, °\text{K} = 273°\text{K} \left(\frac{2.50 \text{ atm}}{2.00 \text{ atm}} \right) = 341°\text{K (or } 68°\text{C)}$$

5.5 Ideal Gas Law

By combining Boyle's law and Charles' law, it is possible to solve problems in which all three variables—volume, temperature, and pressure—change.

Example 5.5 A gas measures 462 ml at 35°C and 800 m pressure. Calculate the volume of the gas at STP.

Solution A combined gas law problem is best solved by considering each of the changes in conditions independently. First, the temperature decrease from 308° to 273°K would call for the volume to decrease by a factor of 273/308. Second, the pressure decreases from 800 to 760 mm. Since volume is inversely proportional to pressure, such a change in pressure would increase the volume by a factor of 800/760.

$$? \text{ ml} = 462 \text{ ml} \left(\frac{273°\text{K}}{308°\text{K}} \right) \left(\frac{800 \text{ mm}}{760 \text{ mm}} \right) = 431 \text{ ml}$$

We can derive a mathematical statement for the combined gas law. Since $V \propto 1/P$ and $V \propto T$,

$$V \propto \frac{T}{P}$$

This proportionality can be changed to an equality by the use of a constant:

$$V = k \frac{T}{P}$$

or

$$PV = kT$$

The value of k in this equation depends upon the size of the gas sample. When 1 mole of gas is used, the constant is given the designation R and has the numerical value 0.08206 liter atm/°K mole provided the volume is expressed in liters, the pressure in atmospheres, and the temperature in degrees Kelvin. Other values for R are used when other dimensions for these variables are employed. The general form of the equation is

$$PV = nRT$$

where n is the number of moles of the gas under investigation. A gas that follows this equation exactly is called an **ideal gas;** the equation is known as the **equation of state** for an ideal gas.

> *Example 5.6*   What volume will 10.0 g of carbon monoxide occupy at STP? Assume that CO is an ideal gas.
>
> *Solution*   The molecular weight of CO is 28.0, and 10.0 g constitutes 10.0/28.0 or 0.357 mole. The problem is solved by substituting in the equation of state.
>
> $$(1 \text{ atm}) \ V = (0.357 \text{ mole}) (0.0821 \text{ liter atm}/°K \text{ mole}) (273°K)$$
>
> $$V = 8.00 \text{ liters}$$

5.6   Kinetic Theory

So far we have examined the laws that correlate observed facts concerning the behavior of gases. The theory that offers a model to explain these laws and observations is known as the **kinetic theory** of gases. This theory was first proposed in substantially the following form by August Krönig (1856) and Rudolf Clausius (1857). However, the theory had its roots in the previous work of many others, notably Daniel Bernoulli (1738) and James Joule (1845–1851); also, later workers, in particular James Clerk-Maxwell (1860) and Ludwig Boltzmann (1871), did much to extend the concept.

The kinetic theory postulates the following for an ideal gas:

1. Gases consist of molecules widely separated in space. The total volume of the molecules is negligible in comparison with the volume of the gas as a whole.

2. Gas molecules are in constant, rapid, straight-line motion colliding with each other and their container. These collisions are perfectly elastic; energy may be transferred from molecule to molecule, but there is no net decrease in kinetic energy.

3. Gas molecules translate heat energy into kinetic energy. At a given instant, different molecules have different kinetic energies; however, the average kinetic energy of the molecules depends upon the temperature and increases as temperature increases. The molecules of any gas have the same average kinetic energy at a given temperature.

4. No attractive forces exist between the molecules of an ideal gas.

According to the kinetic theory, the gas pressure is caused by molecular collisions with the walls of the container. Therefore, the larger the number of molecules per unit volume—the molecular concentration— the larger is the number of collisions and the higher is the pressure. Reducing the volume of a gas crowds more molecules into a given space resulting in a larger molecular concentration and a porportionally higher pressure. Hence, the kinetic theory accounts for Boyle's law.

The average kinetic energy of the molecules of a gas is proportional to the absolute temperature. At absolute zero, the molecules are at rest, and since the molecular volume of an ideal gas is negligible, the volume of an ideal gas at absolute zero is theoretically zero. As the absolute temperature is increased, the molecules move at increasing speeds. Hence, as the temperature increases, collisions of gas molecules with the walls of the container are more vigorous and more frequent which accounts for the increased pressures observed when gases are heated. If the pressure is not permitted to change when a gas is heated, then its volume must increase so that the number of collisions will be reduced to compensate for the increased intensity of the collisions.

The equation of state for an ideal gas may be derived as follows. Consider a sample of gas containing N molecules having a mass of m each. If this sample is enclosed in a cube l cm on a side, the total volume of the gas is l^3 cm^3. Although the molecules are moving in every possible direction, the derivation is simplified if we assume that one-third of the molecules ($\frac{1}{3} N$) are moving in the direction of the x axis, one-third in the y direction, and one-third in the z direction. For a very large number of molecules, this is a valid simplification since the velocity of each molecule may be divided into an x component, a y component, and a z component.

The pressure of the gas on any wall (surface area l^2 cm^2) is due to the impacts of the molecules on that wall. The force of each impact can be calculated from the change in momentum per unit time. Consider the shaded wall in Figure 5.6 taking only those molecules moving in the

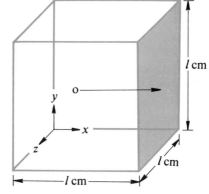

Figure 5.6   Derivation of the ideal gas laws.

direction of the x axis into account. A molecule moving in this direction will strike this wall every $2l$ cm of its path since after an impact it must go to the opposite wall (a distance of l cm) and return (a distance of l cm) before the next impact. If the molecule is moving with a velocity of u cm/sec, in 1 sec it will have gone u cm and have made $u/2l$ collisions with the wall under consideration.

Momentum is mass times velocity. Before an impact, the momentum of the molecule is mu; after an impact, the momentum is $-mu$ (the sign is changed because the direction is changed—velocity takes into account speed *and* direction). Therefore the *change* in momentum equals $2mu$.

In 1 sec, a molecule makes $u/2l$ collisions, and the change in momentum per collision is $2mu$. Therefore, in 1 sec, the total change in momentum per molecule is

$$\left(\frac{u}{2l}\right)2mu = \frac{mu^2}{l}$$

The total change in momentum (force) for all of the molecules striking the wall in 1 sec is

$$\frac{N}{3} \times \frac{mu^2}{l}$$

In this expression, u^2 is the average of the squares of all of the molecular velocities.

Pressure is force per unit area, and the area of the wall is l^2 cm^2. Therefore the pressure on the wall under consideration is

$$P = \frac{Nmu^2}{3l} \times \frac{1}{l_2} = \frac{Nmu^2}{3l^3}$$

Since the volume of the cube is l^3 cm^3, $V = l^3$, and

$$P = \frac{Nmu^2}{3V} \qquad \text{or} \qquad PV = \frac{1}{3} Nmu^2$$

This can be written: $PV = (\frac{2}{3}N)(\frac{1}{2}mu^2)$.

The kinetic energy of any body is one-half the product of its mass times the square of its speed. The average molecular kinetic energy, therefore, is $\frac{1}{2} mu^2$. By substitution,

$$PV = \frac{2}{3}N(KE)$$

The average molecular kinetic energy, KE, is directly proportional to the absolute temperature, T, and the number of molecules, N, is proportional to the number of moles, n. Substitution of these terms requires the inclusion of a constant since these are proportionalities and not equalities. The required constant can be combined with the $\frac{2}{3}$ (also a constant), and thus

$$PV = nRT$$

5.7 Avogadro's Principle

According to the kinetic theory, the molecules of two different gases at the same temperature have the same average kinetic energy. If we allow the subscript to relate the measured property to gas 1 and gas 2,

$$KE_1 = KE_2$$

and

$$\tfrac{1}{2}m_1u_1^2 = \tfrac{1}{2}m_2u_2^2$$

or

$$m_1u_1^2 = m_2u_2^2$$

If we take equal volumes of these two gases, and if these are collected at the same pressure as well as the same temperature,

$$P_1V_1 = P_2V_2$$

From the relationship $PV = \tfrac{1}{3}Nmu^2$,

$$\tfrac{1}{3}N_1m_1u_1^2 = \tfrac{1}{3}N_2M_2U_2^2$$

or

$$N_1m_1u_1^2 = N_2m_2u_2^2$$

But, $m_1u_1^2 = m_2u_2^2$, and therefore

$$N_1 = N_2$$

We conclude, therefore, that equal volumes of any two gases at the same temperature and pressure contain the same number of molecules. This is a statement of **Avogadro's Principle,** which Avogadro derived in a much more empirical manner than described here.

Conversely, equal numbers of molecules of any two gases under the same conditions of temperature and pressure will occupy equal volumes. A mole of any substance contains 6.023×10^{23} molecules (Avogadro's number—Sections 4.1 and 4.2). If we take 6.023×10^{23} molecules of a gas, they will occupy 22.414 liters at STP; the same is true of 6.023×10^{23} molecules of any other gas. Hence, a gram molecular weight of any gas occupies 22.414 liters at STP; this volume is called the **STP molar volume.** For most calculations, this value is rounded off to 22.4 liters.

Avogadro's principle was almost entirely ignored after its presentation in 1811. Stanislao Cannizzaro was the first to see the full significance of this principle, and he was largely responsible for its universal acceptance (1858–1864) after the death of Avogadro. This principle enables the introduction of the weight of a gas sample as one of the variables in a calculation. Furthermore, the molecular weight of a gas can be calculated from the density of the gas.

Example 5.7   What is the density of fluorine gas at STP?

Solution   The molecular weight of F_2 is 38.0. At STP, 38.0 g of F_2 occupies 22.4 liters. Therefore the density is: 38.0 g/22.4 liters = 1.70 g/liter.

Example 5.8   What volume will 10.0 g of carbon dioxide occupy at 27°C and 2.00 atm?

Solution   The molecular weight of CO_2 is 44.0.   Therefore at STP, 22.4 liters of CO_2 will weigh 44.0 g.   To find the volume of 10.0 g of CO_2 at STP:

$$? \text{ liters } = 10.0 \text{ g} \left(\frac{22.4 \text{ liters}}{44.0 \text{ g}}\right) = 5.09 \text{ liters}$$

To convert this volume from STP to the conditions specified in the problem:

$$? \text{ liters } = 5.09 \text{ liters} \left(\frac{300°\text{K}}{273°\text{K}}\right)\left(\frac{1.00 \text{ atm}}{2.00 \text{ atm}}\right) = 2.80 \text{ liters}$$

This problem can also be solved by use of the equation of state, $PV = nRT$.   The number of moles, n, is 10.0/44.0, or 0.227.

$$(2.00 \text{ atm}) \; V = (0.227 \text{ mole}) (0.0821 \text{ liter atm}/°\text{K mole}) (300°\text{K})$$
$$V = 2.80 \text{ liters}$$

Example 5.9   A gas has a density of 0.991 g/liter at 91°C and 750 mm pressure.   What is the molecular weight of the gas?

Solution   If we take 0.991 g of the gas, the sample will occupy 1.00 liter under the conditions specified.   Converting this volume to STP, we get

$$? \text{ liter } = 1.00 \text{ liter} \left(\frac{273°\text{K}}{364°\text{K}}\right)\left(\frac{750 \text{ mm}}{760 \text{ mm}}\right) = 0.740 \text{ liter}$$

Therefore at STP, 0.740 liter of the gas weights 0.991 g.   The weight of 22.4 liters of the gas at STP is the gram molecular weight.

$$? \text{ g } = 22.4 \text{ liters} \left(\frac{0.991 \text{ g}}{0.740 \text{ liter}}\right) = 30.0 \text{ g}$$

Alternatively, we can solve this problem by means of the equation of state. The pressure is 750 mm/760 mm = 0.987 atm; the volume is 1.00 liter; and the temperature is 364°K.   If we let the number of moles, n, equal 0.991/M, where M is the molecular weight, we get

$$PV = nRT$$
$$(0.987 \text{ atm})(1.00 \text{ liter}) = \left(\frac{0.991}{M} \text{ mole}\right)(0.0821 \text{ liter atm}/°\text{K mole})(364°\text{K})$$
$$M = 30.0$$

Cannizzaro was the first to use data on gas densities to assign atomic weights.   He based his atomic weight scale on hydrogen and assigned the hydrogen atom a weight of 1, a value which is close to that currently used for hydrogen.   Thus since carbon dioxide gas has a density 22 times larger than that of hydrogen gas, CO_2 was assigned a molecular weight of 44, comparable to H_2 = 2.   Carbon dioxide contains 27.3% carbon, so one molecular weight of carbon dioxide must contain 12 units of carbon. Similar data for other gaseous compounds containing carbon are summarized in Table 5.1. Notice that the smallest weight of carbon in a molecular weight of any compound is 12, and that the other weights are multiples of 12. One concludes, therefore, that carbon has an atomic weight of 12, and that the compounds of Table 5.1 contain 1, 2, 2, 1, 1, and 3 atoms of carbon per molecule, respectively.

TABLE 5.1.
COMPOSITION OF SOME CARBON COMPOUNDS.

	Molecular Weight	% Carbon	Weight of Carbon per Mole (g)
carbon dioxide	44	27.3	12
cyanogen	52	46.2	24
ethane	30	80.0	24
hydrogen cyanide	27	44.4	12
methane	16	80.0	12
propane	44	81.8	36

5.8 Gay-Lussac's Law of Combining Volumes

In 1808, Gay-Lussac reported the results of his experiments with reacting gases. When measured at constant temperature and pressure, the volumes of gases used or produced in a chemical reaction can be expressed in ratios of small whole numbers. This is a statement of **Gay-Lussac's law of combining volumes.**

For the reaction

$$H_2(g) + Cl_2(g) \rightarrow 2HCl(g)$$

Gay-Lussac found that a given volume of hydrogen reacts with an equivalent volume of chlorine to produce twice this volume of hydrogen chloride. For example, at fixed temperature and pressure, 10 liters of hydrogen will react with 10 liters of chlorine to produce 20 liters of hydrogen chloride. The law is applicable only to gases; the volumes of liquids or solids cannot be treated in a comparable fashion.

The equation shows that equal numbers of hydrogen and chlorine molecules are required for the reaction. According to Avogadro's principle, equal numbers of hydrogen and chlorine molecules are contained in equal volumes of these gases. Also, the number of hydrogen chloride molecules produced by the reaction is twice the number of hydrogen molecules used, and therefore, the volume of hydrogen chloride produced is twice the volume of the hydrogen used.

The total volume of the reacting gases need not equal the volume of the gases produced. This is illustrated by another of Gay-Lussac's examples:

$$2CO(g) + O_2(g) \rightarrow 2CO_2(g)$$

For this reaction, two volumes of carbon monoxide and one volume of oxygen are required to produce two volumes of carbon dioxide. The equation for the reaction shows a molecular ratio of carbon monoxide to oxygen to carbon dioxide of 2 to 1 to 2, which is the same as the observed volume ratio. These observations, as the previous ones, are consistent with Avogadro's principle. Thus if 2 liters of carbon monoxide contain $2x$ molecules, such a sample would require 1 liter of oxygen (x molecules) to produce 2 liters of carbon dioxide ($2x$ molecules).

Historically, Gay-Lussac's law of combining volumes preceded Avogadro's principle, and Avogadro derived his statement to explain Gay-Lussac's law.

Simple problems involving volumes of gases can be solved by the use of Gay-Lussac's law of combining volumes.

Example 5.10   What volume of ammonia can be prepared, theoretically, from the reaction of 15 liters of hydrogen and 15 liters of nitrogen?   All gases are measured at STP.

Solution   The equation for the reaction shows that one volume of nitrogen reacts with three volumes of hydrogen to produce two volumes of ammonia.

$$N_2 + 3H_2 \rightarrow 2NH_3$$

The complete reaction of the nitrogen supplied is impossible since 15 liters of nitrogen would require 45 liters of hydrogen, and we have only 15 liters of hydrogen. The hydrogen, therefore, is the limiting factor, and the nitrogen is present in excess.

$$? \text{ liters NH}_3 = 15 \text{ liters H}_2 \left(\frac{2 \text{ liters NH}_3}{3 \text{ liters H}_2} \right) = 10 \text{ liters NH}_3$$

The amount of nitrogen required for this reaction is

$$? \text{ liters N}_2 = 15 \text{ liters H}_2 \left(\frac{1 \text{ liter N}_2}{3 \text{ liters H}_2} \right) = 5 \text{ liters N}_2$$

which means that there are 10 liters of unreacted nitrogen left over from the original 15 liters supplied.

5.9   Weight–Volume Relationships in Reactions

Gay-Lussac's law of combining volumes does not contradict the law of conservation of mass. Listed beneath each formula of the following equation are three equivalent terms derived from the equation. Volumes given are measured at STP.

$$2CO(g) \ + \ O_2(g) \ \longrightarrow \ 2CO_2(g)$$

2 moles	1 mole	2 moles
2(22.4) liters	22.4 liters	2(22.4) liters
2(28) g = 56 g	32 g	2(44)g = 88 g

The total weight of the reactants (56 g + 32 g = 88 g) equals the weight of the product (88 g), but the total volume of the reactants (67.2 liters) does not equal the volume of the product (44.8 liters). Each of the three gases involved in the reaction has a different density. In a reaction such as this one, where the volume decreases, the average density increases.

The fact that a gram molecular weight of a gas occupies 22.4 liters at STP can be utilized in stoichiometric calculations.

Example 5.11   How many grams of iron are needed to produce 100 liters of hydrogen gas (at STP)?

Solution   The equation for the reaction is

$$3Fe(s) + 4H_2O(g) \longrightarrow Fe_3O_4(s) + 4H_2(g)$$

According to this equation, 3 gram atoms of iron (167.5 g) produce 4 moles of hydrogen (89.6 liters). Therefore

$$? \text{ g Fe} \ = \ 100 \text{ liters H}_2 \left(\frac{167.5 \text{ g Fe}}{89.6 \text{ liters H}_2} \right) = \ 187 \text{ g Fe}$$

English units of measure can be employed in calculations of this type. A pound molecular weight, or pound mole, contains 2.732×10^{26} molecules and occupies 359 ft^3 at STP.

Example 5.12   How many cubic feet of carbon monoxide (measured at STP) are needed to reduce 1.00 ton of Fe_2O_3?

Solution   The equation

$$Fe_2O_3(s) + 3CO(g) \longrightarrow 2Fe(s) + 3CO_2(g)$$

shows that 1 pound mole of Fe_2O_3 (159.6 lb) requires 3 pound moles of CO (3 × 359 ft^3). Thus

$$? \text{ ft}^3 \text{ CO} \ = \ 2000 \text{ lb Fe}_2O_3 \left(\frac{1077 \text{ ft}^3 \text{ CO}}{159.6 \text{ lb Fe}_2O_3} \right) = \ 13,500 \text{ ft}^3 \text{ CO}$$

5.10   Dalton's Law of Partial Pressures

The behavior of a mixture of gases that do not react with one another is frequently of interest. The partial pressure of a component of such a gaseous mixture is the pressure that the component would exert if it were the only gas present in the volume under consideration. **Dalton's law of partial pressures** (1801) states that the total pressure of a mixture of gases is equal to the sum of the partial pressures of the component gases. If the total pressure is P_{total}, and the partial pressures are $p_1, \ p_2, \ p_3, \ldots,$ then,

$$P_{total} \ = \ p_1 + p_2 + p_3 + \cdots$$

   Suppose we have 1 liter of gas A at 0.2 atm pressure and 1 liter of gas B at 0.4 atm pressure. If these two gases are mixed in a 1 *liter container,* temperature constant, the pressure of the mixture is 0.6 atm.

   According to the kinetic theory, at constant temperature molecules of gas A have the same average kinetic energy as molecules of gas B. Furthermore, the kinetic theory states that there are no attractive forces between gas molecules that do not react chemically. Hence, the act of mixing two or more gases does not change the average kinetic energy of any of the component gases, and each gas exerts the pressure that it would exert if it were the only gas present in the container.

   For a mixture of gas A and gas B, let the pressure of gas A equal p_A and the number of moles of gas A equal n_A. Then,

$$p_A V = n_A RT$$

or

$$p_A = n_A \left(\frac{RT}{V} \right)$$

Likewise, for gas B,

$$p_B = n_B \left(\frac{RT}{V} \right)$$

But, $P_{total} = p_A + p_B$, and therefore

$$P_{total} = (n_A + n_B) \left(\frac{RT}{V} \right)$$

But

$$p_A = n_A \left(\frac{RT}{V} \right)$$

or

$$\left(\frac{RT}{V} \right) = \left(\frac{p_A}{n_A} \right)$$

Substituting this in the equation above, we get

$$P_{total} = (n_A + n_B) \left(\frac{p_A}{n_A} \right)$$

Solving for p_A gives

$$p_A = \left(\frac{n_A}{n_A + n_B} \right) P_{total}$$

In like manner,

$$p_B = \left(\frac{n_B}{n_A + n_B} \right) P_{total}$$

   The quantity $n_A/(n_A + n_B)$ is called the **mole fraction** of A; it is the ratio of the number of moles of gas A to the total number of moles of gas present. The partial pressure of a component of a gaseous mixture is equal to the mole fraction times the total pressure.

The preparation of gas mixtures at constant pressure is a less common situation. When gases are mixed at constant pressure, the total volume of the mixture is equal to the sum of the volumes of the component gases at that pressure. Thus if 200 ml of oxygen at 1 atm pressure is mixed with 800 ml of nitrogen at 1 atm pressure, the resulting mixture occupies 1000 ml at a pressure of 1 atm. The composition of this mixture approximates that of air. In this final mixture, the oxygen exerts a partial pressure of 0.2 atm, and the nitrogen exerts a partial pressure of 0.8 atm.

In the laboratory, it is often convenient to collect a gas over water. In such experiments, water vapor is mixed with the collected gas, and the total pressure of the gas sample must be corrected by subtracting the pressure due to the water vapor. In Figure 5.7, the total pressure of the gas sample is equal to the barometric pressure, since the water stands at

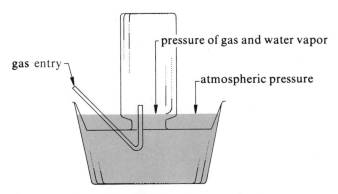

Figure 5.7   Collection of a gas over water.

the same level inside the bottle as outside of it. To obtain the pressure of the gas being investigated, it is necessary to subtract the vapor pressure of water at the temperature of the experiment (Table 5.2) from the barometric pressure.

Example 5.13   A 370 ml sample of oxygen is collected over water at 23°C and 753 mm pressure. What volume would this sample of oxygen occupy dry and at STP?

Solution   At 23°C, the vapor pressure of water is 21.1 mm. The initial pressure of the oxygen, therefore, is 753 mm minus 21 mm, or 732 mm; the initial temperature is 296°K. A pressure change to 760 mm would decrease the volume by 732 mm/760 mm; changing the temperature to 273° K would cause the volume to decrease by a factor of 273°K/296°K. Thus

$$? \text{ ml} = 370 \text{ ml} \left(\frac{732 \text{ mm}}{760 \text{ mm}}\right) \left(\frac{273°\text{K}}{296°\text{K}}\right) = 329 \text{ ml}$$

TABLE 5.2.
VAPOR PRESSURE OF WATER.

Temperature (°C)	Pressure (mm)	Temperature (°C)	Pressure (mm)
0	4.6	25	23.8
1	4.9	26	25.2
2	5.3	27	26.7
3	5.7	28	28.3
4	6.1	29	30.0
5	6.5	30	31.8
6	7.0	31	33.7
7	7.5	32	35.7
8	8.0	33	37.7
9	8.6	34	39.9
10	9.2	35	42.2
11	9.8	40	55.3
12	10.5	45	71.9
13	11.2	50	92.5
14	12.0	55	118.0
15	12.8	60	149.4
16	13.6	65	187.5
17	14.5	70	233.7
18	15.5	75	289.1
19	16.5	80	355.1
20	17.5	85	433.6
21	18.7	90	525.8
22	19.8	95	633.9
23	21.1	100	760.0
24	22.4	105	906.1

Example 5.14 A mixture of 40.0 g of oxygen and 40.0 g of helium has a total pressure of 900 mm. What are the partial pressures of oxygen and helium in the mixture?

Solution The molecular weight of O_2 is 32.0; 40.0 g of O_2 is 40.0/32.0, or 1.25, mole. Helium is a monatomic gas; atomic weight = 4.00. Therefore 40.0/4.0, or 10.0, moles are present in the mixture. The total number of moles of gases is 11.25. The partial pressure of O_2 is

$$? \text{ mm} = \left(\frac{1.25 \text{ moles}}{11.25 \text{ moles}}\right) 900 \text{ mm} = 100 \text{ mm}$$

The partial pressure of He is

$$? \text{ mm} = \left(\frac{10.00 \text{ moles}}{11.25 \text{ moles}}\right) 900 \text{ mm} = 800 \text{ mm}$$

5.11 Graham's Law of Effusion

Suppose that a mixture of two gases is confined under fixed conditions temperature and pressure, and we wish to investigate the rates at which these gases effuse through a small orifice in the wall of the container. The molecules of two different gases at the same temperature have the same average kinetic energy, and thus

$$\tfrac{1}{2}m_1 u_1^2 = \tfrac{1}{2}m_2 u_2^2$$

or
$$m_1 u_1^2 = m_2 u_2^2$$

rearranging, we obtain

$$\frac{u_1^2}{u_2^2} = \frac{m_2}{m_1}$$

Extracting square roots gives

$$\frac{u_1}{u_2} = \sqrt{\frac{m_2}{m_1}}$$

It is logical to assume that the rate, R, at which a gas will stream through an orifice is proportional to the average velocity of the gas molecules. Also, the ratio of the molecular masses, m_2/m_1, is the same as the ratio of the molecular weights, M_2/M_1.

$$\frac{R_1}{R_2} = \sqrt{\frac{M_2}{M_1}}$$

Thus the ratio of the rates of effusion of two gases, under identical conditions of temperature and pressure, equals the inverse ratio of the square roots of the molecular weights of the two gases. Thomas Graham experimentally derived this **law of effusion** in his studies of 1828–1833.

It is not surprising that of two molecules with the same kinetic energy, the lighter one will move more rapidly than the heavier one. Graham's law confirms this and gives the quantitative relationship. The molecular weights of oxygen and hydrogen are 32 and 2, respectively; hence, hydrogen molecules will effuse $\sqrt{32/2}$ or 4 times faster than oxygen molecules under the same conditions.

This principle has been used for the separation of isotopes. Naturally occurring uranium consists of 0.7% ^{235}U and 99.3% ^{238}U, and therefore, the gaseous uranium hexafluoride produced by the reaction of uranium and fluorine consists of a mixture of $^{235}UF_6$ and $^{238}UF_6$. This mixture is passed, at low pressure, through a porous barrier. The lighter $^{235}UF_6$ effuses 1.004 times faster than $^{238}UF_6$ ($\sqrt{352/348}$); hence, the emerging gas has a higher $^{235}UF_6$ content than the original mixture. This procedure must be repeated thousands of times to effect a significant separation.

5.12   Molecular Velocities

In Section 5.6, we derived the expression

$$PV = \tfrac{1}{3} N m u^2$$

For 1 mole of a gas, the number of molecules, N, is Avogadro's number, and the product of this times the mass of a single molecule, m, is the molecular weight, M.

$$PV = \tfrac{1}{3} M u^2$$

Also for 1 mole, $PV = RT$, and thus

$$RT = \tfrac{1}{3} M u^2$$

Rearranging and solving for the molecular velocity, we obtain

$$\mathit{VELOCITY} =\quad u = \sqrt{\frac{3RT}{M}}$$

The velocity, u, in this equation, as in previous equations, is the root-mean-square velocity. This is the value obtained by taking the square root of the average of the squares of all of the molecular velocities, and it represents the velocity of a molecule possessing average kinetic energy at the temperature under consideration.

In order to solve the equation for the root-mean-square velocity, R must be expressed in appropriate units. R equals 8.3143×10^7 g cm^2/ sec^2 °K mole, a fact that may be derived from the ideal gas law by substituting P in dynes/cm^2 (which is g/cm^2 sec^2) and V in cm^3. The root-mean-square velocity of hydrogen at 0°C is 1.84×10^5 cm/sec or 1.84 km/sec. This represents a speed of about 4100 miles per hour!

The diffusion of one gas through another gas does not occur at speeds commensurate with this. Although a given molecule travels at a high speed, its direction is continually being changed through collisions with other molecules. At 1 atm pressure and 0°C, a hydrogen molecule, on the average, undergoes about 1.4×10^{10} collisions in 1 sec. The average distance traveled between collisions is only 1.3×10^{-5} cm; this value is called the **mean free path** of hydrogen.

Not all of the molecules of a gas possess the same kinetic energy, and the velocities of molecules are distributed over a wide range. The nature of this distribution is described by the **Maxwell-Boltzman distribution law.** Figure 5.8 shows the distribution of molecular velocities of a gas at two temperatures. Because of the collisions of molecules and consequent exchange of energy, the velocity of a given molecule is continually changing. However, since a large number of molecules is involved, the distribution of molecular velocities of the total collection is constant.

At the higher temperature, the curve is broadened and shifted to higher velocities. Three measures of central tendency are indicated on

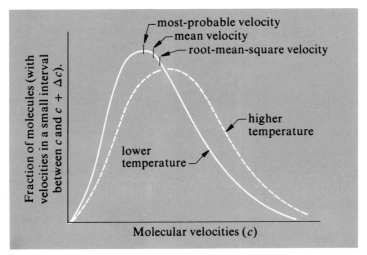

Figure 5.8 *Distribution of molecular velocities.*

the curve; in addition to the root-mean-square velocity, the mean velocity and the most-probable velocity are noted. The mean velocity is simply the average of all of the molecular velocities. The most-probable velocity is the maximum of the curve; more molecules possess this velocity than any other. A simple example may help to clarify this. Suppose that we have the following collection of unspecified measurements: 1, 2, 2, 2, 3, and 8. The most-probable value is 2. The mean (or average) is the sum of all of the values divided by the number of measurements (18/6), or 3. The root-mean-square value is obtained by dividing the sum of the squares $(1 + 4 + 4 + 4 + 9 + 64 = 86)$ by the number of measurements $(86/6 = 14.33)$ and extracting the square root of this average $(\sqrt{14.33} = 3.78)$.

5.13 Deviations from the Ideal Gas Laws

The gas laws describe the behavior of an ideal or perfect gas—a gas defined by the kinetic theory. Under ordinary conditions of temperature and pressure, real gases follow the behavior expressed by these laws rather closely. This is not true, however, at high pressures and low temperatures.

The kinetic theory assumes that gas molecules are points in space and that their volume is negligible; hence, at $0°K$, at which temperature molecular motion ceases, the volume of an ideal gas is zero. Real gases, of course, do not have zero molecular volumes, and while the space between the molecules can be reduced by increasing the pressure, the molecular volume cannot be compressed. At pressures up to a few atmospheres, the gas molecules are widely separated, and the free space between the molecules is large in comparison to the molecular volume. Under such conditions, neglecting the volume of the molecules does not introduce a large error. However, at high pressures, the molecules of a gas are relatively close together, and the molecular volume constitutes a significant fraction of the total volume. Under these conditions, the volume of a real gas is materially larger than that predicted for an ideal gas.

The kinetic theory also assumes that there are no attractive forces between gas molecules. This assumption is belied by the fact that all gases can be liquefied. At high temperatures, gas molecules move so rapidly that the attractive forces between molecules are effectively overcome. On the other hand, at low temperatures, the forces of attraction pull the molecules together so that the volume observed is less than that predicted by the ideal gas law.

It is interesting to note that these two effects work in opposite directions—one to increase the volume and the other to decrease the volume. Thus, under moderate conditions, the ideal gas law is followed fairly closely by real gases. However, under more extreme conditions, the net deviation depends upon which of the effects is dominant.

The equation of state for an ideal gas was modified to take into account these two sources of error by Johannes van der Waals in 1873. The **van der Waals equation** for 1 mole of a gas is

$$\left(P + \frac{a}{V^2}\right)(V - b) = RT$$

The numerical values of the constants a and b are determined by experiment; these values are specific to the gas under consideration (see Table 5.3).

TABLE 5.3.
VAN DER WAALS CONSTANTS.

	a liter^2 atm/mole^2	b liter/mole
H_2	0.244	0.0266
He	0.0341	0.0237
N_2	1.39	0.0391
O_2	1.36	0.0318
Cl_2	6.49	0.0562
NH_3	4.17	0.0371
CO	1.49	0.0399
CO_2	3.59	0.0427

The constant b is subtracted from the total volume of the gas to correct for that portion of the volume that is not compressible because of the intrinsic volume of the gas molecules.

The pressure term of the equation is corrected by a factor a/V^2 to take into account the intermolecular attractions, which are called van der Waals attractions (Section 3.10). These attractive forces draw the gas molecules together. Hence, this effect augments pressure in reducing the volume of the gas, and the correction term is added to P.

When the volume of a mole of gas is large (and pressure is low), the effect of subtracting b from the volume is negligible, as is the magnitude of the correction term a/V^2. Under such conditions, gases follow the ideal gas law.

5.14   Liquefaction of Gases

Liquefaction of a gas occurs under conditions that permit the intermolecular attractive forces to bind the gas molecules together in the liquid form. If the pressure is high, the molecules are close together, and the effect of the attractive forces is appreciable. The attractive forces are opposed by the motion of the gas molecules; thus liquefaction is favored by low temperatures where the average kinetic energy of the molecules is low. The behavior of a gas deviates more and more from ideality as the temperature is lowered and the pressure is raised. At extremes of these conditions, gases liquefy.

The higher the temperature of a gas, the more difficult it is to liquefy and the higher the pressure that must be employed. For each gas, there is a temperature above which it is impossible to liquefy the gas no matter how high the applied pressure. This temperature is called the **critical temperature** of the gas under consideration. The **critical pressure** is the minimum pressure needed to liquefy a gas at its critical temperature. The critical constants of some common gases are listed in Table 5.4.

The critical temperature of a gas gives an indication of the strength of the intermolecular attractive forces of that gas. A substance with weak attractive forces would have a low critical temperature; above this temperature, the molecular motion is too violent to permit the relatively weak forces to hold the molecules in the liquid state. The substances of Table 5.4 are listed in order of increasing critical temperature; the magnitude of the intermolecular attractive forces (related to the a of Table 5.3) increases in this same order. Helium, which has weak attractive forces, can exist as a liquid below 5.3°K only; the strong attractive forces of water permit it to be liquefied up to a temperature of 647.2°K. The critical constants have been used to evaluate the constants of the van der Wall equation.

The data of Table 5.4 show that it is necessary to cool many gases below room temperature (ca., 295°K) before these substances can be liquefied. Commercial liquefaction procedures make use of the **Joule-Thomson effect** to cool gases. When a compressed gas is allowed to expand to a lower pressure, as, for example, through a small orifice, the

TABLE 5.4.
CRITICAL POINT DATA.

Gas	Critical Temperature (°K)	Critical Pressure (atm)
He	5.3	2.26
H_2	33.3	12.8
N_2	126.1	33.5
CO	134.0	35.0
O_2	153.4	49.7
CH_4	190.2	45.6
CO_2	304.2	73.0
NH_3	405.6	111.5
H_2O	647.2	217.7

gas cools. In the expansion, work is done against the intermolecular attractive forces. The energy used in performing this work must be taken from the kinetic energy of the gas molecules themselves; hence, the temperature of the gas decreases. This effect was studied by James Joule and William Thomson (Lord Kelvin) in the years 1852–1862. The liquefaction of air is accomplished by first allowing cooled compressed air to expand. The temperature of the air falls to a lower level. This cooled air is used to precool entering compressed air, so that expansion of this compressed air results in the attainment of even lower temperatures. The cooled expanded air is recycled through the compression chamber. Eventually, the cooling and compression produces liquid air.

SOME SUGGESTED READINGS

Hildebrand, J. H., *An Introduction to Molecular Kinetic Theory*, New York, Reinhold, 1964 (paper).

Kauzmann, W., *Thermal Properties of Matter: Kinetic Theory of Gases*, New York, Benjamin, 1966 (paper).

Loeb, L. B., *The Kinetic Theory of Gases*, New York, Dover, 1961 (paper).

Parsonage, N. G., *The Gaseous State*, New York, Pergamon, 1966 (paper).

Present, R. D., *Kinetic Theory of Gases*, New York, McGraw-Hill, 1958.

PROBLEMS

5.1   The space above the liquid mercury in a column of a barometer is occupied only by mercury vapor (Figure 5.1). The vapor pressure of mercury at 20°C is 0.00120 mm. Assuming mercury vapor to be an ideal monatomic gas, calculate the number of atoms of mercury per milliliter at this temperature and pressure.

5.2   If a barometer were constructed using water instead of mercury, to what height would the water rise at 0°C under a barometric pressure of 1.00

atm? The vapor pressure of water is 4.6 mm at 0°C. Assume that the density of water at 0°C is 1.00 g/cm^3.

5.3 What is the total pressure of a mixture of 10.0 g of $O_2(g)$ and 10.0 g of $CO_2(g)$ confined to a volume of 20.0 liters at 0°C?

5.4 A 50.0 ml bulb is filled with a gas to a pressure of 1.00 atm at 0°C. What pressure will develop inside the sealed bulb at 100°C?

5.5 The volume of a gas sample is 150 ml at 100°C and 0.92 atm. What is the temperature when the volume of the sample is 200 ml and the pressure is 1.62 atm?

5.6 A sample of an ideal gas is passed through water and 500 ml collected at 22°C. The wet gas exerts a pressure of 755 mm. The sample of gas, when dried and confined in the same volume, exerts the same pressure, 755 mm, at 30°C. From these data, calculate the vapor pressure of water at 22°C.

5.7 A 1.00 liter sample of neon is collected over water at 27°C and 747 mm pressure. If the gas is dried and placed in a 1.50 liter container at 72°C, what pressure will it exert?

5.8 What is the density of helium gas at 100°C and 790 mm pressure? Assume He to be an ideal gas.

5.9 Calculate the molecular weight of a gas that has a density of 1.59 g/liter at 50°C and a pressure of 730 mm.

5.10 A 390 ml sample of a gas collected at 92°C and 730 mm pressure weighs 1.00 g. What is the molecular weight of the gas?

5.11 A 0.200 g sample of a compound that contains only carbon, hydrogen, and oxygen was burned to $CO_2(g)$ and H_2O. The CO_2 gas from the combustion occupied 161 ml at 20°C and 755 mm, and 0.120 g of H_2O was collected. What is the empirical formula of the original compound?

5.12 Calculate the pressure exerted by 1.00 mole of NH_3 gas confined to a volume of 1.00 liter at 27°C by (a) the ideal gas law and (b) van der Waals equation.

5.13 If gas molecules are assumed to be rigid spheres, the value of b (in cm^3/mole) in the van der Waals equation is

$$b = \tfrac{2}{3}\pi d^3 N$$

where d is the assumed diameter of a molecule (in cm) and N is Avogadro's number. For helium, $b = 0.0237$ liter/mole. (a) What fraction of the total volume of helium gas, at STP, is molecular volume? (b) What is the diameter of a helium atom?

5.14 Calculate the root-mean-square velocity of an oxygen molecule at (a) 0°C and (b) 100°C.

5.15 What effect would doubling the absolute temperature have on the root-mean-square velocity of a gas?

5.16 A mixture is prepared from 15.0 liters of ammonia and 15.0 liters of chlorine. These substances react according to the equation

$$2NH_3(g) + 3Cl_2(g) \rightarrow N_2(g) + 6HCl(g)$$

If the volumes of all of the gases are measured at the same temperature and pressure, list the volumes of all of the substances present at the conclusion of the reaction.

5.17 A mixture of ethane and oxygen is placed in a 1.00 liter container at a total pressure of 760 mm. The mixture is ignited and reacts according to the equation

$$2C_2H_6(g) + 7O_2(g) \rightarrow 4CO_2(g) + 6H_2O(g)$$

It is known that the original mixture contained excess oxygen over that required for complete reaction of the ethane. Assume that all of the gases follow the ideal gas law and that the temperature of the experiment, which remains constant throughout, is high enough for the water to be gaseous. (a) If the final pressure is 800 mm, what mole fraction of the original mixture was ethane? (b) What weight percentage?

5.18 A mixture of $NO(g)$ and $NO_2(g)$ is confined in a 500 ml bulb at room temperature and 760 mm pressure. Another 500 ml bulb is filled, at the same temperature, with oxygen gas to a pressure of 760 mm. The two bulbs are joined and the nitrogen oxide reacts with oxygen according to the equation

$$2NO(g) + O_2(g) \rightarrow 2NO_2(g)$$

The final volume is 1000 ml. The pressure measured at the original temperature and at the conclusion of the reaction is 703 mm. What was the mole fraction of NO gas in the original $NO-NO_2$ mixture?

5.19 The separation of $_1^2D$ from $_1^1H$ may be accomplished by effusion of a mixture of gases containing these two isotopes through a porous barrier. (a) Which pair of gases would be more readily separated by this method: H_2 and D_2, HCl and DCl, or NH_3 and ND_3? (b) The enrichment ratio per pass is the same as the ratio of the rates of effusion. Calculate the enrichment ratio for each of the three pairs of gases.

5.20 Calculate the density of a gas at STP if a given volume of the gas effuses through an apparatus in 5.00 min and the same volume of oxygen, at the same temperature and pressure, effuses through this apparatus in 6.30 min.

5.21 Aluminum reacts with aqueous acid to produce hydrogen gas

$$2Al(s) + 6H^+(aq) \rightarrow 2Al^{3+}(aq) + 3H_2(g)$$

What weight of aluminum is needed to produce 1.00 liter of hydrogen at 20°C and 750 mm pressure?

5.22 What volume of ammonia (measured at STP) would be formed by the reaction of 100 g of calcium cyanamide with water?

$$CaNCN(s) + 3H_2O(g) \rightarrow CaCO_3(s) + 2NH_3(g)$$

5.23 What volume of hydrogen (measured at STP) would result from the complete reaction of 25.0 g of iron with excess steam according to the equation

$$3Fe(s) + 4H_2O(g) \rightarrow Fe_3O_4(s) + 4H_2(g)$$

5.24 Dinitrogen tetroxide gas, N_2O_4, dissociates into nitrogen dioxide gas, NO_2; the extent of dissociation depends upon the temperature and pressure.

$$N_2O_4(g) \rightleftharpoons 2NO_2(g)$$

Upon dissociation, 1.00 mole of N_2O_4 occupies 38.2 liters at 50°C and 1.00 atm. (a) What is the total number of moles of gas that result from the partial dissociation of 1.00 mole of N_2O_4 under these conditions?   (b) What molar percentage of the original quantity of N_2O_4 is dissociated? (c) What mole fraction of the final gas mixture is NO_2? (d) What are the partial pressures of N_2O_4 and NO_2 in the final gas mixture?

5.25 At 75°C and 1.00 atm pressure the density of a mixture of N_2O_4 and NO_2 prepared by allowing N_2O_4 to dissociate is 1.85 g/liter (see Problem 5.24). What fraction of the original number of moles of N_2O_4 is dissociated into NO_2?

5.26 When lead(II) nitrate is heated, it decomposes:

$$2Pb(NO_3)_2(s) \rightarrow 2PbO(s) + 4NO_2(g) + O_2(g)$$

If 500 ml of gas, measured at 15°C and 765 mm, is collected from the decomposition of a sample of $Pb(NO_3)_2$, what is the weight of the sample?

6

Liquids and Solids

As a gas is cooled, the molecules come together, under the influence of the intermolecular attractive forces, and form a liquid. Molecular motion is more restricted in the liquid state than in the gaseous state. The molecules are closer together in liquid than in gas, and hence, the attractive forces exert a stronger influence. Further cooling produces a solid. In crystalline solids, the molecules assume positions in crystal lattices, and the motion of the molecules is restricted to vibration about these fixed points.

6.1 The Liquid State

The liquid state is intermediate in character between the complete molecular randomness that characterizes gases and the orderly arrangement of molecules typical of crystalline solids. In liquids, the molecules are moving slowly enough for the intermolecular forces of attraction to hold them together in a definite volume; however, the molecular motion is too rapid for the attractive forces to fix the molecules into the definite positions of a crystal lattice. Hence, a liquid retains its volume but not its shape; liquids flow.

The space between the molecules of liquids is reduced almost to a minimum by the intermolecular attractions; a change in pressure has almost no effect on the volume of a liquid. An increase in temperature, however, increases the volume of most liquids slightly and consequently decreases the liquid density. As the temperature of a liquid is increased, the kinetic energy of the molecules increases, and this increased molecular motion works against the attractive forces. This expansion is, however, of a much lower order than that observed for gases in which the effect of the attractive forces is negligible.

160

Two miscible liquids will diffuse into each other when placed together. If a liquid is carefully overlaid with a second, less dense liquid, a sharp boundary line will be observed between the two. This boundary will gradually become less distinct, and, in time, will disappear completely as the molecules of the two liquids mix. The diffusion of liquids, however, is a much slower process than the diffusion of gases. Since the molecules of liquids are relatively close together, the mean-free path of liquid molecules is relatively short; liquid molecules suffer many more collisions per unit time than do gas molecules.

Any liquid exhibits resistance to flow, a property known as **viscosity.** One way of determining the viscosity of a liquid is to measure the time that it takes for a definite amount of the liquid to pass through a tube of small diameter under a given pressure. Resistance to flow is largely due to the attractions between molecules, and the measurement of the viscosity of a liquid gives a simple estimate of the strength of these attractions. Allowance should be made, however, for other factors such as molecular weight and the structure of the molecules. Liquids with large, irregularly shaped molecules are generally more viscous than liquids with small, spherical molecules. In general, as the temperature of a liquid is increased, the cohesive forces are less able to cope with the increasing molecular motion, and the viscosity decreases. On the other hand, increasing the pressure generally increases the viscosity of a given liquid.

Another property of liquids related to the intermolecular forces of attraction is surface tension. A molecule in the center of a liquid is attracted equally in all directions by surrounding molecules. However, molecules on the surface of a liquid are attracted only toward the interior of the liquid (Figure 6.1). Therefore, the surface molecules are pulled inward, and the surface area of a liquid tends to be minimized. This accounts for the spherical shape of liquid drops. **Surface tension** is a measure of this inward force on the surface of a liquid, the force which must be overcome to expand the surface area. The surface tension of a liquid decreases with increasing temperature since the increased molecu-

Figure 6.1 Schematic diagram indicating the unbalanced intermolecular forces on the surface molecules of a liquid.

lar agitation tends to decrease the effect of the intermolecular cohesive forces.

6.2 Evaporation

The kinetic energy of the molecules of a liquid follows a Maxwell-Boltzman distribution similar to the distribution of kinetic energy among gas molecules (Figure 5.8). The kinetic energy of a given molecule of a liquid is continually changing as the molecule collides with other molecules, but at any given instant, some of the molecules of the total collection have relatively high energies and some have relatively low energies. The molecules with kinetic energies high enough to overcome the attractive forces of surrounding molecules can escape from the liquid and enter the gas phase if these high-energy molecules are close to the surface and moving in the right direction; they use part of their energy in working against the attractive forces when they escape.

In time, the loss of a number of high-energy molecules causes the average kinetic energy of the molecules remaining in the liquid to fall, and the temperature of the liquid falls proportionately. When liquids evaporate from an open container at room temperature, heat flows into the liquid from the surroundings to maintain the temperature of the liquid. Thus the supply of high-energy molecules is replenished, and the process continues until all of the liquid has evaporated. The total quantity of heat required to vaporize a mole of liquid at a given temperature is called the **molar heat of vaporization** of that liquid.

The transfer of heat from the surroundings explains why a swimmer emerging from the water becomes chilled as the water evaporates from his skin. Likewise, the regulation of body temperature is, in part, accomplished by the evaporation of perspiration from the skin. Various cooling devices have made use of this principle; a water cooler of the Middle East consists of a jar of unglazed pottery filled with water. The water saturates the clay of the pottery and evaporates from the outer surface of the jar, thus cooling the water remaining in the jar.

The rate of evaporation increases as the temperature of a liquid is raised. When the temperature is increased, the average kinetic energy of the molecules increases, and the number of molecules with energies high enough for them to escape into the vapor phase constitutes an increased fraction of the total number of molecules.

6.3 Vapor Pressure

When an evaporating liquid is confined in a closed container, the vapor molecules cannot escape from the vicinity of the liquid, and in the course of their random motion, some of the vapor molecules return to the liquid. The rate of return depends upon the concentration of molecules in the vapor: the more vapor molecules per unit volume, the greater the chance that some of them will strike the liquid and be re-captured. Thus a situation develops in which the vaporization of the liquid is opposed by the condensation of the vapor. Eventually, the system reaches a point where the rate of condensation equals the rate of vaporization.

Such a condition, in which the rates of two exactly opposite tendencies are equal, it called a state of **equilibrium.** At equilibrium, the concentration of molecules in the vapor state is constant because molecules are leaving the vapor through condensation at the same rate that molecules are being added to the vapor through vaporization. Similarly, the quantity of liquid is a constant. It is important to note that equilibrium does not imply a static situation; in any system, the numbers of molecules present in both phases are constant because the two opposing changes are taking place at equal rates and not because vaporization and condensation have ceased. In a closed container, equilibrium is the only situation that can prevail for any length of time. If the rate of vaporization were greater than the rate of condensation for an extended period, all of the substance would eventually become vapor. The reverse situation is equally improbable; all of the material would end as liquid.

The pressure of vapor in equilibrium with a liquid at a given temperature is called the **vapor pressure.** If the temperature of a liquid–vapor system is constant, the vapor pressure will be constant. The pressure of the vapor depends upon the average kinetic energy of the vapor molecules (which is constant since the temperature is constant) and the concentration of vapor molecules. The concentration of vapor molecules, as well as their average kinetic energy, is fixed by temperature since the vapor concentration must be such that the rate of condensation is equal to the rate of vaporization, and the rate of vaporization is dictated by the temperature. For any sample of a liquid at a given temperature, then, the equilibrium concentration of vapor is constant, regardless of the size of the sample or the dimensions of the container. The absolute quantity of vapor may not be the same from system to system, but the vapor concentration is. If the volume of vapor is changed, the consequent alteration of the vapor concentration causes the rate of condensation to increase or decrease until the concentration is reestablished at its former, equilibrium, value. Hence, vapor pressure is fixed by temperature alone; volume changes do not alter it. A list of the vapor pressures of water at various temperatures appears in Table 5.2.

As the temperature is increased, the vapor pressure of a liquid increases. We have noted that an increase in temperature causes the rate of vaporization to increase; equilibrium is possible only if the rate of condensation increases proportionately, and this will occur only when the concentration of vapor molecules becomes adjusted to a higher level. This factor and the augmented kinetic energy of the vapor molecules accompanying a rise in temperature account for the observed increase in vapor pressure.

Figure 6.2 shows the temperature–vapor pressure curves for ethyl ether, ethyl alcohol, and water. The curve for each substance could be extended to the critical temperature of that substance; at this point, the vapor pressure would equal the critical pressure. Above the critical temperature, only one phase—the gas phase—can exist.

Liquids with weak intermolecular attractive forces have relatively high vapor pressures. Thus at 20°C, ethyl ether has a vapor pressure of 442 mm, and water has a vapor pressure of 17.5 mm; these data indicate that the forces of attraction are stronger in water than in ethyl ether.

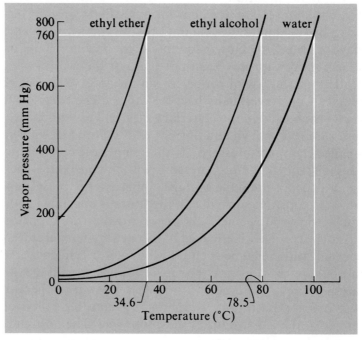

Figure 6.2   Vapor pressure curves for water, ethyl alcohol, and ethyl ether.

6.4   Boiling Point

The temperature at which the vapor pressure of a liquid equals the atmospheric pressure is called the **boiling point** of the liquid. At this temperature, vapor produced in the interior of a liquid results in the bubble formation and turbulence characteristic of boiling. Bubble formation is impossible at temperatures below the boiling point; the atmospheric pressure on the surface of the liquid prevents the formation of bubbles with internal pressures that are less than atmospheric.

The temperature of a boiling liquid remains constant until all of the liquid has been vaporized. In an open container, the maximum vapor pressure that can be attained by any liquid is the atmospheric pressure. We have noted in the preceding section that the vapor pressure of a liquid is determined by temperature alone; hence, if the vapor pressure is fixed, the temperature is fixed. Heat must be added to a boiling liquid to maintain the temperature since in the boiling process the high-energy molecules are lost by the liquid. If the rate of heat addition is increased above the minimum needed to maintain the temperature of the boiling liquid, the rate of boiling increases, but the temperature of the liquid does not rise.

The boiling point of a liquid changes with changes in external pressure. For example, water will boil at 97.7°C at a pressure of 700 mm and at 101.4°C at 800 mm; only at a pressure of 760 mm will water boil at 100°C. The **normal boiling point** of a liquid is defined as the temperature at which the vapor pressure of the liquid equals 760 mm. Boiling points given in reference books are understood to be normal boiling points.

The normal boiling points of ethyl ether (34.6°C), ethyl alcohol (78.5° C), and water are indicated on the vapor pressure curves of Figure 6.2. The boiling point of a liquid can be read from its vapor pressure curve by finding the temperature at which the vapor pressure of the liquid equals the prevailing pressure. The fluctuations in atmospheric pressure at any one place cause a maximum variation of about 2°C in the boiling point of water. However, from place to place, the variations can be greater than this. The average barometric pressure at sea level is 760 mm; at higher elevations, average barometric pressures are less. Thus at an elevation of 5000 feet above sea level, the average barometric pressure is 635 mm; at this pressure, water boils at 95.1°C. Water boils at 90.1°C at 528 mm, which is the average atmospheric pressure at 10,000 feet above sea level.

If a liquid has a high normal boiling point or decomposes when heated, it can be made to boil at low temperatures by reducing the pressure. Such a procedure is followed in vacuum distillation; water can be made to boil at 10°C, which is considerably below room temperature, by adjusting the pressure to 9.2 mm (see Table 5.2 and Figure 6.2). Many food products are concentrated by removing unwanted water under reduced pressure; in these procedures, the product is not subjected to temperatures that bring about decomposition or discoloration.

A pressure cooker is frequently used to increase the temperature at which food is cooked in water and thus shorten cooking time. As heat is supplied, the steam produced increases the pressure above the surface of the water (which started out at atmospheric pressure when the pressure cooker was sealed). An escape valve is set so that steam is released when the desired pressure inside the cooker is reached. Thus the water inside the cooker boils at a temperature higher than 100°C—the exact temperature depending on the setting of the pressure valve.

The normal boiling point gives a general indication of the strength of the intermolecular cohesive forces of a liquid (Section 3.10). The boiling point of nonpolar materials, which are held together by van der Waals forces, generally increases with increasing molecular weight. High molecular weight materials have a large number of electrons to participate in the formation of the fluctuating dipoles that characterize van der Waals forces. However, predictions of the boiling point of a substance based on molecular weight must be made with caution. On the basis of molecular weight alone, one would predict a boiling point for water (molecular weight, 18) about 200 to 300 degrees less than the observed 100°C; water is a polar material with exceptionally strong forces of attraction (Section 7.11).

6.5   Heat of Vaporization

The **molar heat of vaporization, ΔH_v,** is that quantity of energy that must be supplied to vaporize a mole of a liquid at a specified temperature. Heats of vaporization are usually recorded at the normal boiling point; Table 6.1 lists such molar heats of vaporization in kilocalories per mole for some liquids.

TABLE 6.1.
HEATS OF VAPORIZATION OF SOME LIQUIDS AT THEIR NORMAL BOILING POINTS.

Liquid	t_b Normal Boiling Point (°C)	ΔH_v Heat of Vaporization (kcal/mole)	$\Delta H_v / T_b$ (cal/°K mole)
water	100.0	9.72	26.0
benzene	80.1	7.35	20.5
ethyl alcohol	78.5	9.22	26.2
carbon tetrachloride	76.7	7.17	20.5
chloroform	61.3	7.02	21.0
carbon disulfide	46.3	6.40	20.0
ethyl ether	34.6	6.21	20.2

In Section 6.2, a kinetic picture of the vaporization process was presented, and the heat of vaporization was interpreted from this viewpoint. A slightly different interpretation follows, based on a consideration of the heat content (or enthalpy, H) of the vapor and of the liquid. The temperature of a vapor is the same as the temperature of the liquid with which it is in equilibrium; hence, the molecules of each phase have the same average kinetic energy. However, the phases differ in total internal energy, which includes potential energy as well as kinetic energy. The molecules of the liquid are held together by cohesive forces; the molecules of the vapor are essentially free. When the liquid is converted into a gas, energy must be supplied to separate the molecules. Thus the energy of the gas phase is higher than that of the liquid phase by the amount of this difference.

The difference in heat content of the phases (ΔH) takes into account another factor. The volume of a gas is considerably larger than the volume of the liquid from which it is derived (e.g., about 1700 ml of steam is produced by the vaporization of 1 ml of water at 100°C); energy must be supplied to do the work of pushing back the atmosphere to make room for the vapor. The heat of vaporization includes both the energy required to overcome the intermolecular cohesive forces and the energy needed to expand the vapor.

When a mole of vapor is condensed to a liquid, the difference in heat content of the phases is released rather than absorbed. In this instance, the heat effect is called the molar heat of condensation and is numerically equal to the molar heat of vaporization at the same temperature.

The heat of vaporization of a given liquid decreases as the temperature increases and equals zero at the critical temperature of the substance. This parallels an increase in the fraction of high-energy molecules; at the critical temperature, all of the molecules have sufficient energy to vaporize.

In general, the higher the heat of vaporization of a substance, the stronger are the intermolecular forces of attraction; this relationship is similar to that between the normal boiling point and these forces. Frederick Trouton, in 1884, discovered that for many liquids the heat of vaporization is directly proportional to the normal boiling point. **Trouton's rule** states that the heat of vaporization, in calories per mole, divided by the normal boiling point, in °K, is a constant: 21 cal/°K mole. Thus

$$\frac{\Delta H_v}{T_b} = 21 \text{ cal/°K mole}$$

The rule is only approximate, as the values listed in Table 6.1 attest. The marked deviations of water and ethyl alcohol are due to the unusually strong intermolecular attractions of these liquids (Section 7.11).

6.6 The Freezing Point

As a liquid is cooled, the molecules move more and more slowly. Eventually, a temperature is reached where some of the molecules have low enough kinetic energies to allow the intermolecular attractions to hold them in a crystal lattice; the substance then starts to freeze. Gradually, the low-energy molecules assume positions in the crystal lattice; the molecules remaining in the liquid have a higher temperature because of the loss of these low-energy molecules. Heat must be removed from the liquid to maintain the temperature. The **freezing point** of a liquid is the temperature at which solid and liquid are in equilibrium at 1 atm pressure. At the freezing point, the temperature of the solid–liquid system remains constant until all of the liquid is frozen. The quantity of heat that must be removed to freeze a mole of a substance at the freezing point is called the **molar heat of crystallization.** It represents the difference in the heat content (ΔH) between the liquid and the solid.

At times, the molecules of a liquid, as they are cooled, continue the random motion characteristic of the liquid state at temperatures below the freezing point; such liquids are referred to as **undercooled** or **supercooled.** These systems can usually be caused to revert to the freezing temperature and the stable solid–liquid equilibrium by scratching the interior walls of the container with a stirring rod or by adding a seed crystal around which crystallization can occur. The crystallization process supplies heat, and the temperature is brought back to the freezing point until normal crystallization is complete.

Some undercooled liquids can exist for long periods, or permanently, in this state. When they are cooled, molecules solidify in a random arrangement typical of the liquid state rather than in an orderly geometric pattern of a crystal. Such substances have relatively high viscosities and are generally of a complex molecular form for which crystallization would be difficult. They are frequently called amorphous solids, vitreous materials, or glasses; examples include glass, tar, and certain plastics. Some materials (e.g., glass) can be obtained in the crystalline form by careful cooling and can revert very slowly to this form from the undercooled state. Amorphous solids have no definite freezing or melting point; rather, these transitions take place over a temperature range. They exhibit conchoidal fracture rather than the cleavage along definite planes at definite angles shown by crystalline materials.

When a crystalline substance is heated, the temperature at which solid–liquid equilibrium is attained under air at 1 atm pressure is called the **melting point;** it is, of course, the same temperature as the freezing point of the substance. The quantity of heat that must be *added* to melt a mole of the material at the melting point is called the **molar heat of fusion** and is numerically equal to the heat of crystallization. The heat of fusion of water at 0°C is 1.44 kcal/mole.

6.7   Vapor Pressure of a Solid

Molecules in a crystal vibrate about their lattice positions. There is a distribution of kinetic energy among these molecules similar to that for liquids and gases but on a lower level. Energy is transmitted from molecule to molecule so that the energy of any molecule is not indefinitely constant. The high-energy molecules on the surface of the crystal can overcome the attractive forces of the crystal and escape into the vapor phase. If the crystal is in a closed container, equilibrium is eventually reached in which the rate of the molecules leaving the solid equals the rate of the vapor molecules returning to the crystal. The vapor pressure of a solid at a given temperature is a measure of the number of molecules in the vapor at equilibrium.

Every solid has a vapor pressure, although some pressures are of very low order. The magnitude of the vapor pressure is inversely proportional to the strength of the attractive forces; thus ionic crystals have very low vapor pressures.

Since the ability of molecules to escape the intermolecular forces of attraction depends upon their kinetic energies, the vapor pressure of a solid increases as the temperature increases. The temperature–vapor pressure curve for ice is illustrated in Figure 6.3. This curve intersects the vapor pressure curve for water at the freezing point, which is $0°C$ $(273.15°K)$. The vapor pressures plotted are the partial pressures of the compound H_2O under air at a total pressure of 1 atm. At the freezing point, the vapor pressure of solid and liquid are equal. If this were not true, one form would gradually be converted into the other. For example, if the vapor pressure of the liquid were higher than that of the solid, the vapor concentration would be higher than the equilibrium value for the solid–vapor system. In this circumstance, the rate of crys-

Figure 6.3   Vapor pressure curves for ice and water near the freezing point.

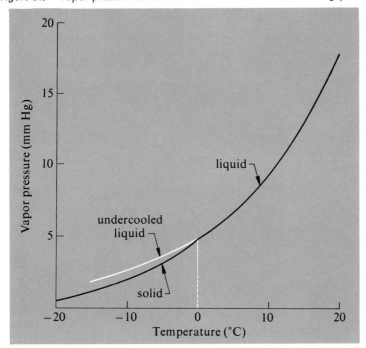

tallization would increase, the amount of solid would increase, and the concentration of vapor would decrease. This would cause more of the liquid to vaporize in order to reestablish the equilibrium vapor pressure of the liquid. The process would continue until all of the liquid was converted into solid. At a given temperature, the stable form is that which has the lower vapor pressure.

6.8 Phase Diagrams

The temperature–pressure phase diagram for water conveniently illustrates the conditions under which water can exist as solid, liquid, or vapor, as well as the conditions that bring about changes in the state of water. Figure 6.4 is a schematic representation of the water system; it is not drawn to scale, and some of its features are exaggerated to give prominence to important details. Every substance has a unique phase diagram which must be derived from experimental observations.

In Figure 6.4, temperature is plotted against total pressure. Curve *OC*, the vapor pressure curve for liquid, terminates at the critical point, *C*. Any point on this line describes a set of temperature and pressure conditions under which liquid and vapor can exist in equilibrium. The extension *DO* is the curve for undercooled liquid; systems between liquid and vapor described by points on this line are **metastable.** (The term metastable is applied to systems that are not in the most stable state pos-

Figure 6.4   Pressure–temperature diagram for water (not drawn to scale).

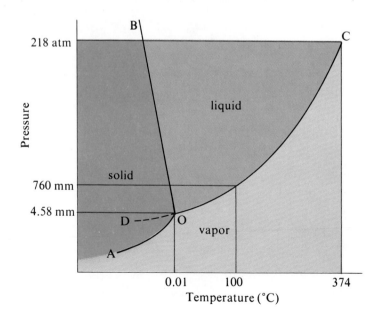

sible at the temperature in question.) Curve AO is the vapor pressure curve for solid and represents a set of points that describe the possible conditions for solid–vapor equilibria. The line BO, the melting point curve, represents conditions for equilibria between solid and liquid.

These curves intersect at point O, the triple point. Solid, liquid, and vapor can exist together, in equilibrium, under the conditions represented by this point—0.01°C (273.16°K) and a pressure of 4.58 mm due to the vapor. When a point described by the temperature–pressure coordinates falls in one of the regions labeled solid, liquid, or vapor, a situation is indicated where only one phase can exist under the conditions described.

It is important to recognize the limitations of this diagram. The diagram does not indicate the quantities of the phases in equilibrium, nor does it describe any system that is not in equilibrium. Furthermore, this phase diagram pertains to the behavior of water in the absence of any other substance—a one-component system. Ordinary laboratory work is performed in open beakers in air under atmospheric pressure; at times, the presence of air accounts for small differences in behavior from that predicted by the diagram. Thus water containing dissolved air freezes at a lower temperature than pure water (Section 8.9). This restriction also means that the total pressures of any system described by the diagram cannot be due in any part to the pressure of a gas other than water vapor. The easiest way to interpret this phase diagram for water is to visualize the total pressure acting on a system in mechanical terms, for example, as a piston acting on a cylinder containing the material comprising the system.

Thus the diagram indicates that only liquid will exist under a total pressure of 760 mm and at a temperature of 50°C. This is the case if the liquid is confined in a cylinder at 50°C with 760 mm pressure, exerted by a piston, on the liquid; the vapor pressure of water at 50°C (92.5 mm) is not high enough to force back the piston and make room for a vapor phase. However, if water at 50°C is confined under air in a closed container at a total pressure of 760 mm, an equilibrium will exist between water and vapor in which the partial pressure of the water vapor is 92.5 mm; this situation, and others like it, can be interpreted only indirectly from the phase diagram.

The triple point indicated on the diagram is the temperature (0.01°C) at which solid, liquid, and vapor exist together in equilibrium in the *absence of air* and at a total pressure, due entirely to water vapor, of 4.58 mm. In the presence of air and under a total pressure of 1 atm, the three phases are in equilibrium at 0°C. This temperature, the normal freezing point of water, is lower than the triple point because of the presence of dissolved air in the water (which accounts for a lowering of 0.0025°C) and because of the effect of an increase in total pressure on the

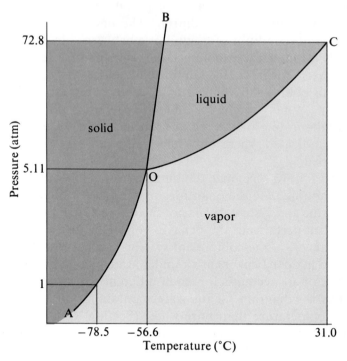

Figure 6.5   Pressure–temperature diagram for carbon dioxide (not drawn to scale).

solid–liquid equilibrium (which accounts for an additional lowering of 0.0075°C).

The slope of the melting point (or freezing point) curve, *BO*, shows that the freezing point decreases as the pressure is increased. This is observed for only a few substances such as antimony, bismuth, and water; it indicates an unusual situation where the liquid expands upon freezing. At 0°C, a mole of water occupies 18.019 cc, and a mole of ice occupies 19.651 cc. Thus there is an expansion at 0°C and 1 atm when 1 mole of liquid water freezes into ice. An increase in pressure on the system at 0°C would oppose this expansion and the freezing process. Hence, the freezing point of water is lowered as the total pressure is increased. In Figure 6.4, the slope of the line *BO* is exaggerated; as noted previously, the triple point–freezing point lowering due to a change in total pressure from 4.58 mm to 760 mm is only 0.0075°C.

For materials that contract upon freezing (i.e., the solid phase is more dense than the liquid phase), the freezing point curve inclines in the opposite direction, and the freezing point is increased as the pressure is increased. Such is the case for most substances and is seen in the phase diagram for carbon dioxide in Figure 6.5.

The process whereby a solid goes directly into a vapor without going through the liquid state is known as **sublimation;** this process is, of course, reversible. The phase diagram for carbon dioxide is typical of that for substances that sublime at ordinary pressures rather than melt and then boil. The triple point of the carbon dioxide system is $-55.6°C$ at a pressure of 5.11 atm, and, therefore, liquid carbon dioxide exists only at pressures greater than 5.11 atm. When solid carbon dioxide (dry ice) is heated at 1 atm pressure, it is converted directly into gas at $-78.5°$ C; the **molar heat of sublimation** is the heat that must be added to a mole of solid to convert it into a gas.

6.9 Crystals

The orderly arrangement of atoms, ions, or molecules in a crystalline solid was discussed in Sections 3.10 and 3.15. The constituent particles of a crystal are arranged in a repeating three-dimensional pattern called a **crystal** (or **space**) **lattice.** The smallest section of a crystal lattice that can be used to describe the lattice is the **unit cell.** A crystal can be reproduced, in theory, by stacking its unit cells in three dimensions.

Crystal systems are classified according to the dimensions of the unit cell along its three axes (a, b, c) and the three angles between the axes (α, β, γ). Table 6.2 lists the unit cells of the seven crystal systems; these are illustrated in Figure 6.6. Crystals have the same symmetry as their constituent unit cells.

In illustrations of crystal lattices, dots are customarily used to indicate the positions of the constituent ions, atoms, or molecules. Seven such point lattices can be drawn by indicating dots at the corners of the unit

TABLE 6.2.
CRYSTAL SYSTEMS.

System	Cell Dimensions along the Axes	Angles	Examples
cubic	$a = b = c$	$\alpha = \beta = \gamma = 90°$	NaCl, PbS, CaO, Cu, Ag
tetragonal	$a = b \neq c$	$\alpha = \beta = \gamma = 90°$	SnO_2, MgF_2, MnO_2, Sn
orthorhombic	$a \neq b \neq c$	$\alpha = \beta = \gamma = 90°$	$HgCl_2$, Sb_2S_3, I_2, S
monoclinic	$a \neq b \neq c$	$\alpha = \gamma = 90°$; $\beta \neq 90°$	As_2S_3, B, S
triclinic	$a \neq b \neq c$	$\alpha \neq \beta \neq \gamma \neq 90°$	$CuSO_4 \cdot 5H_2O$, $CaSiO_3$, CuO
hexagonal	$a = b \neq c$	$\alpha = \beta = 90°$; $\gamma = 120°$	SiO_2, CuS, AgI, Zn, C
rhombohedral	$a = b = c$	$\alpha = \beta = \gamma \neq 90°$	Al_2O_3, Fe_2O_3, NiS, As, Bi

cells of the seven crystal systems. However, more lattices than this exist since it is possible to have points in other positions in addition to the corners. Thus three cubic lattices are known (Figure 6.7): simple cubic, body-centered cubic, and face-centered cubic. Altogether, there are 14 possible lattices in which each point is surrounded in an identical manner by other points.

Example 6.1 Nickel crystallizes in a face-centered cubic crystal; the edge of the unit cell is 3.52 Å. The atomic weight of nickel is 58.7, and its density is 8.94 g/cm³. From these data, calculate Avogadro's number.

Solution There are four nickel atoms in each unit cell. In counting the number of atoms per unit cell, one must keep in mind that atoms on corners, edges, or faces are shared with adjoining cells. Eight unit cells share each corner atom; two unit cells share each face-centered atom. There are

Figure 6.6 Crystal systems.

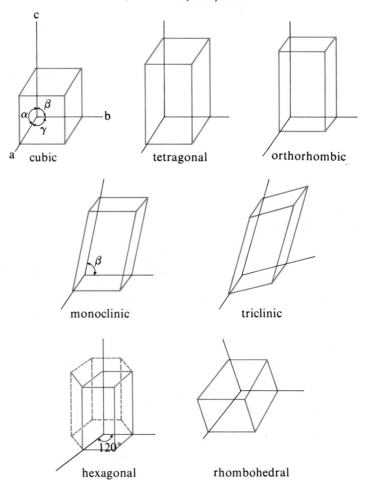

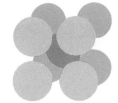

simple cubic   body-centered cubic   face-centered cubic

Figure 6.7   Cubic lattices.

eight corner atoms and six face-centered atoms in a face-centered cubic crystal; hence,

$$\text{(corners)}\quad 8 \times \tfrac{1}{8} = 1$$
$$\text{(faces)}\quad\ \ 6 \times \tfrac{1}{2} = 3$$

$$4 \text{ atoms/unit cell}$$

If we let N = Avogadro's number, the weight of one atom is $(58.7/N)$ g. The weight of one unit cell is $4\,(58.7/N)$ g. The volume of one unit cell is $(3.52 \times 10^{-8})^3\,\text{cm}^3$. The density of nickel is

$$\frac{4(58.7/N)\,\text{g}}{(3.52 \times 10^{-8})^3\,\text{cm}^3} = 8.94 \text{ g/cm}^3$$

Therefore $N = 6.02 \times 10^{23}$

An alternative solution follows:

$$?\,\text{atoms} = 58.7 \text{ g Ni} \left(\frac{1 \text{ cm}^3}{8.94 \text{ g Ni}}\right) \left(\frac{4 \text{ atoms}}{(3.52 \times 10^{-8})^3\,\text{cm}^3}\right)$$

$$= 6.02 \times 10^{23}$$

6.10   X-Ray Diffraction of Crystals

Much of what is known about the internal structure of crystals has been learned from X-ray diffraction experiments. X-rays are electromagnetic radiations of very short wavelength. They can be produced in a vacuum tube by the bombardment of a metal plate (the anode) with a stream of electrons moving with great velocity (a cathode ray).

Two waves that are in phase reinforce each other and produce a wave that is stronger than either of the original waves (Figure 6.8a). The re-

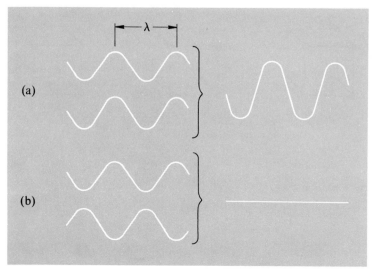

Figure 6.8 (a) Reinforcement of in-phase waves. (b) Destructive interference of out-of-phase waves.

sultant wave has a greater amplitude than either of the primary waves, but the wavelength, λ, remains the same. Two waves that are completely out of phase cancel each other; the resultant is of negligible intensity (Figure 6.8b).

Figure 6.9 illustrates the determination of crystal spacings by the use of X-rays of a single wavelength. The rays impinge upon parallel planes of the crystal at an angle ϕ; the angle of reflection equals the angle of incidence. Some of the rays are reflected from the upper plane, some from the second plane, and some from lower planes. A strong reflected beam will result only if all of the rays are in phase. In the illustration, the ray DFH travels farther than the ray ABC by an amount equal to $EF + FG$. These rays will be in phase at CH only if this difference equals

Figure 6.9   Derivation of the Bragg equation.

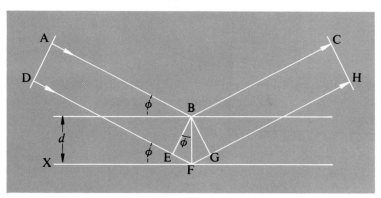

a whole number of wavelengths. Thus

$$EF + FG = n\lambda$$

where n is a simple integer.

The line BE is drawn perpendicular to DF. Angle BEF, therefore, equals 90 degrees. The sum of the other two angles (EBF and EFB) of the triangle BEF must also equal 90 degrees since the sum of the angles of any triangle equals 180 degrees.

$$\angle EBF + \angle EFB = 90°$$

Angle XFB is a right angle, and angle XFE is ϕ; therefore angle EFB is equal to 90 degrees minus ϕ. Consequently,

$$\angle EBF + (90° - \phi) = 90°$$

and angle EBF equals ϕ.

The sine of this angle, ϕ, is equal to EF/BF, and since BF is equal to d (the distance between the planes of the crystal),

$$\sin \phi = \frac{EF}{d}$$

or $$EF = d \sin \phi$$

Likewise, $$FG = d \sin \phi$$

and therefore,

$$EF + FG = 2d \sin \phi$$

or $$n\lambda = 2d \sin \phi$$

This equation was derived by William Henry Bragg and his son William Lawrence Bragg in 1913.

The Bragg equation can be rearranged:

$$\sin \phi = \frac{n\lambda}{2d}$$

Thus with X-rays of a definite wavelength, reflections at various angles will be observed for a given set of planes with a spacing equal to d. These reflections correspond to $n = 1, 2, 3$, etc., and are spoken of as a first order, second order, third order, etc. With each successive order, the angle ϕ increases, and the intensity of the reflected beam is observed to weaken.

Figure 6.10 is a schematic representation of an X-ray spectrometer. An X-ray beam, defined by a slit system, impinges on a crystal that is mounted on a turntable. A detector (photographic plate, ionization chamber, or Geiger counter) is positioned as shown in the figure. As the crystal is rotated, strong signals flash out as angles are passed that satisfy

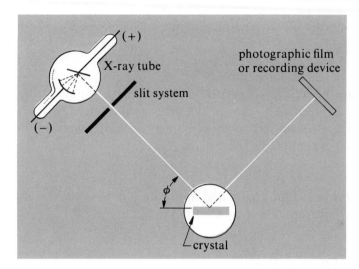

Figure 6.10   X-ray diffraction of crystals (schematic).

the Bragg equation. Any set of regularly positioned planes that contain atoms can give rise to reflections and not only those that form the faces of the unit cells. Thus the value of d is not necessarily the edge of the unit cell, although the two are always mathematically related.

Example 6.2   The diffraction of a crystal of barium with X-radiation of wavelength 2.29 Å gives a first order reflection at 27° 8′. What is the distance between the diffracted planes?

Solution   Substitution into the Bragg equation gives:

$$n\lambda = 2d \sin \phi$$
$$1(2.29 \text{ Å}) = 2d(0.456)$$
$$d = 2.51 \text{ Å}$$

6.11   Defect Structures

Few crystals are perfect; many have some type of lattice defects. **Dislocations** are crystal imperfections where planes of atoms are misaligned. For example, one type of dislocation is caused by the insertion, perpendicular to a face, of an extra plane of atoms part way through a crystal. Atoms in the part of the crystal containing the extra plane are compressed.

Point defects are caused by missing or misplaced ions. One type of defect consists of a cation that has been moved from its proper position (thus creating a vacancy) to a place between regular lattice sites (an **interstitial** position). Another type of point defect consists of a pair of vacancies—one cation and one anion; the ions for these lattice positions are missing from the structure completely. These defects do not alter the stoichiometry of the crystal.

Certain crystals are imperfect because their compositions are not stoichiometric. Thus samples of ferrous oxide, FeO, usually contain more oxygen atoms than iron atoms, whereas zinc oxide, ZnO, usually has an excess of zinc atoms over oxygen atoms. These departures from stoichiometry are usually quite small, on the order of 0.1%. There are several causes for **nonstoichiometry,** and in each, the electrical neutrality of the crystal is preserved. Extra metal *atoms* or nonmetal *atoms* may be included in interstitial positions between the *ions* of the crystal (such as extra Zn atoms in ZnO). In addition, metal *atoms* or nonmetal *atoms* may assume regular lattice positions in place of *ions;* in these cases, ionic vacancies exist in the crystal lattice so that the whole is electrically neutral. For example, in FeO oxygen atoms assume positions normally occupied by oxide ions, and there are missing Fe^{2+} ions so that a 1 to 1 cation–anion ratio is maintained. It is postulated that in some crystals of this type (e.g., KCl), electrons from the "extra" metal atoms occupy the holes created by the anion vacancies.

The presence of **impurities** frequently accounts for crystal defects. For example, a Mg^{2+} ion may occur in a lattice position in a NaCl crystal in place of a Na^+ ion; electrical neutrality requires that another Na^+ lattice position be vacant since the charge of the Mg^{2+} ion is twice that of the Na^+ ion. Arsenic or boron atoms are added to germanium crystals to create defect structures. Germanium, a group IV A element, has four valence electrons and forms a covalent crystal with a lattice similar to the diamond in which each Ge atom is bonded to four other Ge atoms. If an atom of boron, with three valence electrons, replaces a Ge atom in a germanium crystal, an electron "hole" results. The substitution of an arsenic atom (five valence electrons) for a Ge atom creates a structure with an extra electron over that required for the covalent bonding scheme.

Certain crystal defects account for the **semiconductivity** of some crystals. Semiconductors are materials of electrical conductivity intermediate between conductors and nonconductors. The conductivity of semiconductors, unlike that of conductors, increases as the temperature is increased and increases when the materials are illuminated. Semiconductors find use in photocells, transistors, and thermistors.

Perfect crystals of most semiconductors are insulators. The valence electrons in a crystal of germanium are used to form the covalent bonds that hold the crystal together; they are not like the mobile valence electrons of a metal. The conductivity of impure germanium is due to the motion of the extra electrons from impurities or the existence of "holes" that permit the electrons of the regular structure to move. Vacancies in ionic crystals permit the motion of ions, and this together with the motion of interstitial ions, accounts for the semiconductivity of these substances.

6.12   Born-Haber Cycle

The lattice energy (Section 3.4) is the energy *released* when isolated gaseous ions representing 1 mole of an ionic compound condense into a crystal lattice; it may also be defined as the energy *required* to disrupt 1 mole of a crystalline material and separate the resulting ions to infinite distance. Measurement of the lattice energy offers a means of evaluating the strength of the forces that hold a crystal together; this can be accomplished from thermochemical data by a method developed independently by Max Born and Fritz Haber in 1919.

To illustrate the Born-Haber cycle, we shall calculate the lattice energy of sodium chloride. If a value has a negative sign, the evolution of energy is indicated; a positive sign indicates the absorption of energy.

When a mole of crystalline NaCl is prepared from 1 gram atom of sodium metal and $\frac{1}{2}$ mole of chlorine gas, 98 kcal of heat is evolved ($-Q$).

$$Na(s) + \tfrac{1}{2}Cl_2(g) \rightarrow NaCl(s)$$

The total energy evolved in the following hypothetical preparation of sodium chloride, if the heat effect of each step is taken into account, should equal this experimentally determined 98 kcal.

(1) The heat of sublimation of sodium metal.

$$Na(s) \rightarrow Na(g) \qquad S = +26 \text{ kcal}$$

(2) The heat of dissociation of $Cl_2(g)$ into atoms ($\frac{1}{2}$ mole).

$$\tfrac{1}{2}Cl_2(g) \rightarrow Cl(g) \qquad \tfrac{1}{2}D = +29 \text{ kcal}$$

(3) The ionization energy of sodium (derived from the ionization potential).

$$Na(g) \rightarrow Na^+(g) + e^- \qquad I = +118 \text{ kcal}$$

(4) The electron affinity of chlorine.

$$Cl(g) + e^- \rightarrow Cl^-(g) \qquad -E = -88 \text{ kcal}$$

(5) The lattice energy of sodium chloride.

$$Na^+(g) + Cl^-(g) \rightarrow NaCl(s) \qquad -U$$

Thus the following equation is derived:

$$-Q = +S + \tfrac{1}{2}D + I - E - U$$

Or, if one solves for the lattice energy,

$$U = +Q + S + \tfrac{1}{2}D + I - E$$

Substituting the values for sodium chloride gives

$$U = +98 + 26 + 29 + 118 - 88$$
$$U = +183 \text{ kcal}$$

The Born-Haber cycle can be summarized schematically as follows:

$$Na(s) + \tfrac{1}{2}Cl_2(g) \xrightarrow{\ -Q\ } NaCl(s)$$

$$\downarrow +S \qquad \downarrow +\tfrac{1}{2}D \qquad\qquad\qquad \downarrow -U$$

$$Na(g) + Cl(g) \xrightarrow{\ +I\ -\ E\ } Na^+(g) + Cl^-(g)$$

SOME SUGGESTED READINGS

Addison, W. E., *Structural Principles of Inorganic Compounds,* New York, Wiley, 1961.

Azaroff, L. V., *Introduction to Solids,* New York, McGraw-Hill, 1960.

Evans, R. C., *An Introduction to Crystal Chemistry, 2nd ed.,* New York, Cambridge University Press, 1964 (paper).

Findlay, A., *The Phase Rule and Its Applications,* New York, Dover, 1951 (paper).

Frenkel, L., *Kinetic Theory of Liquids,* New York, Dover, 1955 (paper).

Hildebrand, J. H., *An Introduction to Molecular Kinetic Theory,* New York, Reinhold, 1964 (paper).

PROBLEMS

6.1 Briefly explain how and why each of the following gives an indication of the strength of the intermolecular forces of attraction: (a) critical temperature, (b) surface tension, (c) viscosity, (d) vapor pressure, (e) heat of vaporization, (f) heat of fusion, (g) normal boiling point, (h) molecular weight.

6.2 By the use of Trouton's rule, estimate the molar heat of vaporization of a compound, C_8H_{18}, that has a normal boiling point of 125.7°C.

6.3 Predict the normal boiling point of methylcyclohexane which has a molar heat of vaporization of 7.58 kcal/mole.

6.4 The experimentally determined specific heat of vaporization of toluene is 87.0 cal/g at its normal boiling point, 110.6°C. By the use of Trouton's rule, estimate the molecular weight of toluene.

6.5 Compare the heat effect observed when a gas expands (Joule-Thomson effect) with that observed in the process of evaporation.

6.6 Potassium crystallizes in the cubic system with a body-centered unit cell; the edge of the unit cell is 5.333 Å. (a) What is the closest approach of any two potassium atoms? (b) What is the density of potassium?

6.7 The dimensions of the unit cell (in angstrom units) and the axial angles are listed for five minerals in the following table. To what crystal system does each belong?

	a	b	c	α	β	γ
albite	7.94	12.90	7.12	90°	116°	90°
axinite	7.13	8.91	9.14	91° 51′	102° 52′	81° 57′
beryl	9.21	9.21	9.17	90°	90°	120°
topaz	4.64	8.78	8.37	90°	90°	90°
zircon	6.58	6.58	5.93	90°	90°	90°

6.8   In the X-ray diffraction of a tungsten crystal using X-rays of wavelength
      1.54 Å, a first-order reflection is shown at an angle of 29° 10'. What is the
      wavelength of X-rays that show this same reflection at an angle of 12° 57'?

6.9   (a) How many atoms are contained in one simple cubic unit cell?   (b) In
      one body-centered cubic unit cell?   (c) In one face-centered cubic unit cell?
      (d) Molybdenum crystallizes in a cubic system; the edge of the unit cell is
      3.15 Å. If the density of molybdenum is 10.2 g/cm^3, what type of cubic
      unit cell does molybdenum form?

6.10 Calculate the lattice energy of potassium chloride from the following data.
      For potassium, the ionization energy is 99 kcal/mole and the sublimation
      energy is 21 kcal/mole. For chlorine, the dissociation energy is 58 kcal/
      mole, and the electron affinity is −88 kcal/mole. The heat of formation of
      KCl is −104 kcal/mole.

6.11 A first-order reflection from a set of crystal planes is obtained at 21° 39'.
      What is $\emptyset$ for the second-order reflection from this same set of planes?

6.12 (a) Sodium chloride crystallizes in a cubic lattice with alternating Na$^+$
      and Cl$^-$ ions (see Figure 3.5). The distance between the center of a Na$^+$
      ion and the center of an adjacent Cl$^-$ ion (along an edge) is 2.819 Å. If we
      consider a unit cell with an edge equal to 2(2.819) Å, or 5.638 Å, how
      many ions of each kind are contained in the unit cell?   (b) Use the data
      from part (a) and the fact that the density of NaCl is 2.165 g/cm^3 to calcu-
      late the apparent molecular weight of NaCl to four significant figures.
      (c) The difference between the calculated value for the molecular weight
      of NaCl and the actual value (58.44) may be ascribed to a type of lattice
      defect in which sodium atoms replace some sodium ions in the crystal and
      an equal number of chloride ions are missing from lattice positions
      (vacancies). On the basis of your answer to (b), calculate the percentage
      of the anion sites that are vacant.

6.13 Nickel crystallizes in a face-centered cubic lattice. The density of nickel
      is 8.90 g/cm^3. What is the length of the edge of a unit cell?

6.14 Figure 6.4 is the phase diagram for water. Describe the phase changes
      that occur, and the approximate temperatures at which they occur, when
      water is heated from −10°C to 110°C (a) under a pressure of 1 mm, (b)
      under a pressure of 400 mm, and (c) under a pressure of 800 mm.

6.15 Figure 6.5 is the phase diagram for carbon dioxide. Describe the phase
      changes that occur, and the approximate pressures at which they occur,
      when the pressure on a CO$_2$ system is gradually increased (a) at a constant
      temperature of −60°C and (b) at a constant temperature of 0°C.

7

Oxygen and Hydrogen

Oxygen and hydrogen are probably the most important of all the elements. Oxygen is essential for the maintenance of life. Hydrogen forms more compounds than any other element (carbon is a close second). Water is the most common solvent and reaction medium. The classical acid-base scheme is based on water, and many analytical procedures depend upon the solubility of substances in water.

TABLE 7.1
ABUNDANCE OF THE ELEMENTS
(EARTH'S CRUST, BODIES OF WATER, AND ATMOSPHERE).

Rank	Element	Percent by Weight
1	O	49.2
2	Si	25.7
3	Al	7.5
4	Fe	4.7
5	Ca	3.4
6	Na	2.6
7	K	2.4
8	Mg	1.9
9	H	0.9
10	Ti	0.6
11	Cl	0.2
12	P	0.1
13	Mn	0.1
14	C	0.09
15	S	0.05
16	Ba	0.05
	all others	0.51

7.1   Occurrence and Preparation of Oxygen

Oxygen is the most abundant element (Table 7.1). Free oxygen makes up about 23.2% by weight of the atmosphere, or about 21.0% by volume. Water is approximately 89% oxygen, and most minerals contain oxygen in the combined state. Silica, SiO_2, is a common ingredient of many minerals and the chief constituent of sand. Silicon is second to oxygen in the order of natural abundance because of the widespread occurrence of silica. Other oxygen-containing minerals are oxides, sulfates, and carbonates. Oxygen is a constituent of the compounds that make up plant and animal matter; the human body is over 60% oxygen.

Oxygen is usually prepared in the laboratory by the thermal decomposition of certain oxygen-containing compounds. The oxides of metals of low reactivity (e.g., mercury, silver, and gold) decompose on heating to give oxygen and the free metals.

$$2HgO(s) \rightarrow 2Hg(l) + O_2(g)$$

Some higher oxides, upon heating, release only a part of their oxygen and go to lower oxides.

$$2PbO_2(s) \rightarrow 2PbO(s) + O_2(g)$$
$$3MnO_2(s) \rightarrow Mn_3O_4(s) + O_2(g)$$

Oxygen and the oxide ion are produced when the peroxide ion, O_2^{2-}, is heated.

$$2 \left[:\ddot{O}:\ddot{O}: \right]^{2-} \rightarrow 2 \left[:\ddot{O}: \right]^{2-} + O_2$$

Thus

$$2Na_2O_2(s) \rightarrow 2Na_2O(s) + O_2(g)$$
$$2BaO_2(s) \rightarrow 2BaO(s) + O_2(g)$$

(Note that PbO_2 and MnO_2 are not peroxides.) If sodium peroxide is added to water, oxygen and a solution of sodium hydroxide result.

$$2O_2^{2-}(aq) + 2H_2O \rightarrow 4OH^-(aq) + O_2(g)$$

Certain other compounds release all, or part, of their oxygen upon heating. Nitrates of the I A metals form nitrites.

$$2NaNO_3(l) \rightarrow 2NaNO_2(l) + O_2(g)$$

Potassium chlorate loses all of its oxygen; a catalyst (MnO_2) is generally used to lower the temperature required for this decomposition.

$$2KClO_3(s) \rightarrow 2KCl(s) + 3O_2(g)$$

Small amounts of pure oxygen are produced commercially by the electrolysis of water.

$$2H_2O \xrightarrow{\text{electrolysis}} 2H_2(g) + O_2(g)$$

Most of the oxygen produced industrially, however, is obtained from the liquefaction of air. The principal components of air are nitrogen (78% by volume) and oxygen (21% by volume). In the fractionation of liquid air, nitrogen (boiling point, $-196°C$) is boiled away from oxygen (boiling point, $-183°C$).

7.2 Properties of Oxygen

Oxygen is a colorless, odorless, and tasteless gas under ordinary conditions. The normal boiling point of oxygen is $-182.9°C$, and the normal melting point is $-218.4°C$; solid and liquid oxygen are pale blue in color. The critical temperature of oxygen is $-118°C$, and the critical pressure is 49.7 atm.

At STP, the density of oxygen gas is 1.429 g/liter. Approximately 31 ml of the gas will dissolve in 1 liter of water under ordinary conditions; evidently this small amount is enough to sustain fish and aquatic plant life under water.

There are three naturally occurring isotopes of oxygen: $^{16}_{8}O$ (99.759%), $^{18}_{8}O$ (0.204%), and $^{17}_{8}O$ (0.037%). The isotopes ^{14}O, ^{15}O, ^{19}O, and ^{20}O are artificial and unstable.

The structure of the O_2 molecule poses a problem. The Lewis structure, $:\ddot{O}::\ddot{O}:$, is incorrect because it fails to account for the observed paramagnetism of the oxygen molecule. The structure $:\dot{O}:\dot{O}:$ shows two unpaired electrons, but violates the octet principle and contains only a single bond between the oxygen atoms. Probably the best description is given by the method of molecular orbitals (Section 3.14) which accounts for a double bond as well as two unpaired electrons.

The reactions of oxygen are often more sluggish than would be predicted from the fact that oxygen is a very electronegative element (3.5), second in this property only to fluorine (4.0). The reason for this slowness is that the bond energy of oxygen is high (117.3 kcal/mole), and therefore reactions that require the oxygen-to-oxygen bond to be broken occur only at high temperatures. Many of these reactions are relatively highly exothermic and therefore produce enough heat to sustain themselves after having once been initiated by external heating.

Whether self-sustaining or not, most oxygen reactions occur at temperatures considerably higher than room temperature. The most facile reactions of oxygen are those in which the oxygen-to-oxygen bond of the O_2 molecule is not completely broken. Examples of this type of reaction are afforded by the reactions of oxygen in which peroxides are prepared.

All metals except the noble metals (Ag, Pt, and Au) react with oxygen; oxides of these noble metals are known but must be made indirectly. Three types of products result from the reactions of oxygen with metals: oxides, peroxides, and superoxides. The most reactive (and largest) metals of group I A, Cs, Rb, and K, react with oxygen to produce **superoxides.**

The superoxide ion, O_2^-, can be considered as arising from the addition of one electron to the $(\pi*2p)$ orbital of the oxygen molecule. Both the O_2 molecule and the O_2^- ion are paramagnetic. The O_2 molecule has two unpaired electrons; the O_2^- ion has only one unpaired electron and contains a $1\frac{1}{2}$ bond according to the molecular orbital theory (Section 3.14).

$$Cs(s) + O_2(g) \rightarrow CsO_2(s)$$

Sodium peroxide is produced by the reaction of sodium with oxygen.

$$2Na(s) + O_2(g) \rightarrow Na_2O_2(s)$$

The **peroxide ion**, O_2^{2-}, contains two additional electrons (in the $(\pi*2p)$ orbitals) over and above the O_2 molecule. The addition of these antibonding electrons reduces the number of bonds from two to one and also produces an ion that is diamagnetic.

Lithium metal does not form peroxides or superoxides presumably because O_2^{2-} or O_2^- ions cannot be arranged in a crystal lattice with the small Li^+ ion. When lithium is heated in the presence of oxygen, lithium oxide forms.

$$4Li(s) + O_2(g) \rightarrow 2Li_2O(s)$$

The **oxide ion**, $\ddot{\underset{\cdot\cdot}{O}}{}^{2-}$, is diamagnetic and isoelectronic with neon. Generally, oxides form at much higher temperatures than either peroxides or superoxides. The normal oxides of potassium, rubidium, and cesium can be obtained by heating oxygen with an excess of the metal.

With the exception of barium (which reacts with oxygen to yield barium peroxide), the remaining metals generally produce normal oxides in their reactions with oxygen.

$$2Mg(s) + O_2(g) \rightarrow 2MgO(s)$$
$$4Al(s) + 3O_2(g) \rightarrow 2Al_2O_3(s)$$

Analogous reactions can be written for the preparation of CaO, CuO, ZnO, PbO, and other oxides. The reaction of mercury and oxygen is reversible.

$$2Hg(l) + O_2(g) \rightleftharpoons 2HgO(s)$$

For metals that have more than one electrovalence number, the oxide produced generally depends upon the quantity of oxygen, the quantity of the metal, and the reaction conditions. Thus the reaction of iron and oxygen can be made to yield FeO (low pressure of oxygen, temperature above 600°C), Fe_3O_4 (finely divided iron, heated in air at 500°C), or Fe_2O_3 (iron heated in air at temperatures above 500°C). Hydrated Fe_2O_3 is iron rust.

Most of the nonmetals react with oxygen directly, with the notable exceptions of the noble gases and the group VII A elements; the oxides of this latter group must be prepared indirectly. The reaction of hydrogen produces water. Two oxides of carbon can be made depending upon the quantity of oxygen employed.

$$2C(s) + O_2(g) \rightarrow 2CO(g)$$
$$C(s) + O_2(g) \rightarrow CO_2(g)$$

In like manner, the product of the reaction of phosphorus and oxygen depends upon whether phosphorus is reacted in a limited oxygen supply (P_4O_6) or in excess oxygen (P_4O_{10}). Sulfur reacts to produce SO_2.

$$S(s) + O_2(g) \rightarrow SO_2(g)$$

The reaction of nitrogen with oxygen requires extremely high temperatures. The following reaction occurs in a high-energy electric arc.

$$N_2(g) + O_2(g) \rightarrow 2NO(g)$$

Additional important oxides of sulfur (e.g., SO_3) and nitrogen (e.g., NO_2 and N_2O_5) are prepared by means other than the direct combination of the elements. Lower oxides can be treated with oxygen to produce higher oxides. For example,

$$2Cu_2O(s) + O_2(g) \rightarrow 4CuO(s)$$
$$2CO(g) + O_2(g) \rightarrow 2CO_2(g)$$

Most reactions of compounds with oxygen, yield the same products that would be obtained if the individual elements comprising the compounds were reacted directly. Thus

$$2H_2S(g) + 3O_2(g) \rightarrow 2H_2O(g) + 2SO_2(g)$$
$$CS_2(l) + 3O_2(g) \rightarrow CO_2(g) + 2SO_2(g)$$
$$2C_2H_2(g) + 5O_2(g) \rightarrow 4CO_2(g) + 2H_2O(g)$$
$$C_2H_6O(l) + 3O_2(g) \rightarrow 2CO_2(g) + 3H_2O(g)$$

The reaction of zinc sulfide with oxygen illustrates a metallurgical process known as roasting; many sulfide ores are subjected to this procedure (Section 15.3).

$$2ZnS(s) + 3O_2(g) \rightarrow 2ZnO(s) + 2SO_2(g)$$

The products of the reaction of a hydrocarbon with oxygen depend upon the amount of oxygen supplied. Thus when natural gas (methane) is burned, three reactions can be identified.

$$CH_4(g) + O_2(g) \rightarrow C(s) + 2H_2O(g)$$
$$2CH_4(g) + 3O_2(g) \rightarrow 2CO(g) + 2H_2O(g)$$
$$CH_4(g) + 2O_2(g) \rightarrow CO_2(g) + 2H_2O(g)$$

7.3   Acidic and Alkaline Oxides

Many of the oxides of metals and nonmetals react with water to produce alkalies and acids. Thus the oxides of the group I A metals and calcium, strontium, and barium dissolve in water to produce hydroxides. All of these oxides are ionic; when one of them dissolves in water, it is the oxide ion that reacts.

$$O^{2-}(aq) + H_2O \rightarrow 2OH^-(aq)$$

Hydroxides of other metals exist, but these are insoluble and must be prepared by other methods. When heated, most hydroxides are converted to oxides.

$$Mg(OH)_2(s) \rightarrow MgO(s) + H_2O(g)$$

Many covalent, nonmetal oxides react with water to produce acids.

$$SO_3 + H_2O \rightarrow H_2SO_4$$
$$P_4O_{10} + 6H_2O \rightarrow 4H_3PO_4$$
$$Cl_2O + H_2O \rightarrow 2HClO$$
$$N_2O_5 + H_2O \rightarrow 2HNO_3$$
$$SO_2 + H_2O \rightarrow H_2SO_3$$

Most of the polyatomic anions listed in Table 3.8 are derived from acids that can be prepared in this manner. Binary acids, of course, are not derivable from oxides.

The oxides of metals, therefore, are frequently called **alkaline oxides,** and the oxides of the nonmetals are called **acidic oxides.** The oxides themselves can be made to undergo neutralization reactions. Thus barium sulfate can be prepared by the action of sulfuric acid on either barium hydroxide or barium oxide.

$$2H^+(aq) + SO_4^{2-}(aq) + Ba^{2+}(aq) + 2OH^-(aq) \rightarrow BaSO_4(s) + 2H_2O$$
$$2H^+(aq) + SO_4^{2-}(aq) + BaO(s) \rightarrow BaSO_4(s) + H_2O$$

The insoluble Fe_2O_3 will react with acids, even though it will not react with water to produce a hydroxide.

$$6H^+(aq) + Fe_2O_3(s) \rightarrow 2Fe^{3+}(aq) + 3H_2O$$

Oxides of nonmetals will neutralize alkalies. In the reaction with sodium hydroxide, SO_2 produces the same product as its counterpart H_2SO_3.

$$H_2SO_3(aq) + 2OH^-(aq) \rightarrow SO_3^{2-}(aq) + 2H_2O$$
$$SO_2(g) + 2OH^-(aq) \rightarrow SO_3^{2-}(aq) + H_2O$$

Some oxides react with both acids and alkalies. Such oxides are called **amphoteric** and are generally derived from elements in the center of the periodic table, on the borderline between the metals and the nonmetals.

$$ZnO(s) + 2OH^-(aq) + H_2O \rightarrow Zn(OH)_4^{2-}(aq)$$
$$\text{(zincate ion)}$$

$$ZnO(s) + 2H^+(aq) \rightarrow Zn^{2+}(aq) + H_2O$$

$$Al_2O_3(s) + 2OH^-(aq) + 3H_2O \rightarrow 2Al(OH)_4^-(aq)$$
$$\text{(aluminate ion)}$$

$$Al_2O_3(s) + 6H^+(aq) \rightarrow 2Al^{3+}(aq) + 3H_2O$$

7.4   Ozone

The existence of an element in more than one form in the same physical state is called **allotropy,** and the forms are called **allotropes.** A number of elements exhibit allotropy, for example, carbon, sulfur, and phosphorus. Oxygen exists in a triatomic form, ozone, in addition to the common diatomic modification.

The ozone molecule is diamagnetic and triangular in structure. Both oxygen-to-oxygen bonds have the same length (1.26 Å) which is intermediate between the double bond distance (1.10 Å) and the single bond distance (1.48 Å). Thus it is postulated that the O_3 molecule is a resonance hybrid:

Ozone is a pale blue gas with a characteristic odor; predictably, its density is $1\frac{1}{2}$ times that of O_2. The normal boiling point of ozone is $-112°C$, and the normal melting point is $-250°C$. It is slightly more soluble in water than is O_2.

Ozone is produced by passing a silent electric discharge through oxygen gas. The reaction proceeds through the dissociation of an O_2 molecule into oxygen atoms and the combination of an O atom with a second O_2 molecule.

$$117.3 \text{ kcal} + O_2 \rightarrow 2O$$
$$O_2 + O \rightarrow O_3 + 24.5 \text{ kcal}$$

The energy released in the second step, in which a new bond is formed, is not sufficient to compensate for the energy required by the first step, in which a bond is broken. Hence, the overall reaction for the preparation of ozone is endothermic:

$$68.4 \text{ kcal} + 3O_2 \rightarrow 2O_3$$

Ozone is highly reactive; it is explosive in the presence of substances that catalyze its decomposition or when warmed. Its higher reactivity, compared to diatomic oxygen, is consistent with its higher energy content.

7.5   Oxidation Numbers

The term oxidation was originally applied to reactions in which substances combined with oxygen.

$$2Zn(s) + O_2(g) \rightarrow 2ZnO(s)$$

Reduction was defined as the removal of oxygen from a substance.

$$ZnO(s) + C(s) \rightarrow Zn(g) + CO(g)$$

The meanings of the terms have gradually been broadened. At first, they were extended to include the gain and loss of other nonmetals in reactions that are obviously analogous to those involving oxygen.

$$Zn(s) + Cl_2(g) \rightarrow ZnCl_2(s)$$

$$2AgCl(s) + H_2(g) \rightarrow 2Ag(s) + 2HCl(g)$$

Today, even wider definitions of these terms are employed, and many more types of reactions are classified as oxidation-reduction reactions (Section 7.6). These enlarged definitions are based on the assignment of **oxidation numbers** to the atoms, combined or uncombined, that are involved in a given reaction.

The oxidation number of an atom in a binary electrovalent compound is the same as the charge on the ion derived from that atom (the electrovalence number). Thus the oxidation number of sodium in $NaCl$ is $1+$, and that of chlorine is $1-$. In K_2S, the oxidation number of potassium is $1+$ (a total of $2+$ for both potassium atoms), and the oxidation number of sulfur is $2-$. In Al_2O_3, the oxidation number of aluminum is $3+$ (total, $6+$), and that of oxygen is $2-$ (total, $6-$). Note that the sum of the oxidation numbers of the atoms of each compound equals zero; this is true of all compounds since they are electrically neutral.

By the use of some arbitrary rules, oxidation numbers can be assigned to the atoms of covalent compounds as well as those of electrovalent compounds derived from more than two elements. For example, if in the covalent compound SO_2 the oxidation number of oxygen is $2-$ (a total of $4-$ for the two oxygen atoms), then sulfur is arbitrarily assigned an oxidation number of $4+$. It must not be assumed that this number represents an actual charge on the sulfur atom or that the SO_2 molecule will break apart into monatomic ions under any circumstances, for neither is true.

Oxidation numbers are convenient and useful; this is the only justification for such an arbitrary concept. Later sections will show that oxidation numbers can be used to facilitate writing formulas, recognize and organize oxidation-reduction phenomena, balance oxidation-reduction equations, construct a simplified method for solving stoichiometric problems involving oxidation-reduction changes, and systematize the chemistry of the elements.

The following rules can be used to assign oxidation numbers.

1. Any uncombined atom, or any atom in a molecule of an element, is assigned an oxidation number of zero.

2. The sum of the oxidation numbers of the atoms in a compound is zero.

3. The oxidation number of a simple, monatomic ion is the same as the charge on the ion (electrovalence number). The sum of the oxidation numbers of the atoms comprising a polyatomic ion equals the charge on the ion.

4. The oxidation number of fluorine, the most electronegative element, is $1-$ in all fluorine-containing compounds.

5. In most oxygen-containing compounds, the oxidation number of oxygen is $2-$. There are a few exceptions. In peroxides, each oxygen has an oxidation number of $1-$. For example, the two oxygens of the peroxide ion, O_2^{2-}, are equivalent, and each must be assigned an oxidation number of $1-$ so that the sum equals the charge on the ion. In superoxides, O_2^{-}, each oxygen has an oxidation number of $\frac{1}{2}-$. In OF_2, the oxygen has an oxidation number of $2+$.

6. The oxidation number of hydrogen is $1+$ in all its compounds except the metallic hydrides (e.g., CaH_2 and NaH) in which hydrogen is in the $1-$ oxidation state.

The oxidation states of the constituent elements of most compounds can be determined through the use of these rules. The oxidation numbers of the atoms of H_3PO_4 must add up to zero. If each hydrogen is assigned $1+$ (total, $3+$) and each oxygen is assigned $2-$ (total, $8-$) the phosphorus must have an oxidation number of $5+$. The same conclusion can be reached by examining the ion derived from phosphoric acid, the phosphate ion, PO_4^{3-}. Here, the sum of the oxidation numbers must be the same as the charge on the ion, $3-$. Since each oxygen has an oxidation number of $2-$ (total, $8-$), the phosphorus must have an oxidation number of $5+$.

In the dichromate ion, $Cr_2O_7^{2-}$, the seven oxygen atoms have a combined oxidation number of $14+$. Since the charge on the ion is $2-$, the oxidation numbers of the two chromium atoms must add up to $12+$, and the oxidation number of chromium is $6+$. The usual practice is to report the oxidation state of an element in a compound on the basis of the oxidation number of a single atom. It would be misleading to say that oxygen is in an oxidation state of $2-$ in H_2O and $4-$ in SO_2; in both compounds, oxygen has an oxidation number of $2-$.

Fractional oxidation numbers are possible. Calculation of the oxidation number of iron in Fe_3O_4 gives a value of $2\frac{2}{3}+$. (Since the oxygens

add up to $8-$, the irons must add up to $8+$, and $8+$ divided by 3 is $2\frac{2}{3}+$.)
This compound can be considered to be formed from FeO and Fe_2O_3.
Hence, two iron atoms at $3+$ each and one iron atom at $2+$, average out
to $2\frac{2}{3}+$. When an element has a fractional oxidation number in a particular compound, this often means that the compound contains two (or
more) atoms of the element that are not perfectly equivalent.

Frequently, an element displays, in its compounds, a range of oxidation states. For example, in the compounds of nitrogen, this element
exhibits oxidation numbers of from $3-$ (e.g., in NH_3) to $5+$ (e.g., in
HNO_3). Since the number of valence electrons of an A family element
is the same as its group number, the highest positive charge (even a hypothetical one) that can logically be assigned to an A family element is
the same as its group number. The highest oxidation number of an A
family element is, therefore, its group number.

The lowest oxidation number of an A family element is its electrovalence number. Thus the highest oxidation number of sulfur (group
VI A) is $6+$ (e.g., in H_2SO_4) and the lowest oxidation number of sulfur
is $2-$ (e.g., in H_2S). The highest oxidation number of sodium (group I
A) is the same as the lowest oxidation number, $1+$. There are exceptions
to these generalizations, however (e.g., fluorine and oxygen).

7.6 Oxidation-Reduction Reactions

Oxidation and reduction may be defined on the basis of change in oxidation number. **Oxidation** is the process in which an atom undergoes
an algebraic increase in oxidation number and **reduction** is the process
in which an atom undergoes an algebraic decrease in oxidation number.
On this basis, oxidation-reduction is involved in the reaction

$$\overset{0}{S} + \overset{0}{O_2} \rightarrow \overset{4+\ 2-}{S\,O_2}$$

whereas oxidation-reduction is not involved in the reaction

$$\overset{4+\ 2-}{S\,O_2} + \overset{1+\ 2-}{H_2O} \rightarrow \overset{1+\ 4+\ 2-}{H_2\,S\,O_3}$$

The oxidation number of each type of atom is written above its symbol.
In the first reaction, sulfur is oxidized, and oxygen is reduced.

It is apparent from the manner in which oxidation numbers are assigned, that neither oxidation nor reduction can occur alone; furthermore, each process must occur to the same extent in a given reaction.
According to the rules by which oxidation numbers are assigned, the
sum of the oxidation numbers of any chemical species equals the charge
on that species (zero if the entire compound is considered). In any reaction, the sum of the charges of the reactant species (zero for reactions
involving only molecules) must equal the sum of the charges of the prod-

uct species (again zero for reactions involving only molecules). Charge conservation demands, therefore, that any oxidation (increase in oxidation number) be accompanied by a commensurate reduction (decrease in oxidation number).

Since one substance cannot be reduced unless another is simultaneously oxidized, the material that is reduced is responsible for the oxidation; as such it is called the **oxidizing agent** (or **oxidant**). Because of the interdependence of the two processes, the converse is also true: the material that is itself oxidized is the **reducing agent** (or **reductant**).

Equations for oxidation-reduction reactions are usually more difficult to balance than those for reactions that do not entail oxidation and reduction (such as neutralization reactions). It is advantageous to balance oxidation-reduction equations systematically, and oxidation numbers provide the basis for a system.

The **change-in-oxidation-number method** may be used to balance either molecular or ionic equations, and both applications will be illustrated. For clarity and simplicity, the physical state of the atoms, molecules, and ions will not be indicated in the examples that follow. In addition, the symbol H^+, instead of $H^+(aq)$ or H_3O^+, will be employed; it should be kept in mind, however, that all ions are hydrated in aqueous solution.

An example of oxidation-reduction is afforded by the reaction of nitric acid with hydrogen sulfide; the unbalanced equation for this change is:

$$HNO_3 + H_2S \rightarrow NO + S + H_2O$$

The oxidation number of the elements are calculated in order to identify those elements undergoing oxidation or reduction. Thus

$$\overset{5+}{H}\ \overset{}{N}\ \overset{}{O_3} + \overset{2-}{H_2\ S} \rightarrow \overset{2+}{N}\ \overset{}{O} + \overset{0}{S} + H_2O$$

In this example, nitrogen is reduced (5+ to 2+, a decrease of 3) and sulfur is oxidized (2– to 0, an increase of 2). The decrease in oxidation number must equal the increase in oxidation number. Thus it is necessary that two molecules of HNO_3 and two molecules of NO, as well as three molecules of H_2S and three atoms of S, be indicated. In this way the total increase in oxidation number will be 6 which will equal the total decrease in oxidation number of 6.

$$2HNO_3 + 3H_2S \rightarrow 2NO + 3S + H_2O$$

The equation is not yet balanced; the method takes care of only those materials that undergo oxidation-number changes; the coefficients for other materials must be supplied by inspection. In this example, there are now eight hydrogen atoms on the left, and therefore, four H_2O molecules must be indicated on the right.

$$2HNO_3 + 3H_2S \rightarrow 2NO + 3S + 4H_2O$$

The final, balanced, equation should be checked to ensure that there are as many atoms of each element on the left as there are on the right.

Nitric acid is frequently employed as an oxidizing agent, and it functions in this capacity in this reaction (the nitrogen of HNO_3 is reduced). The sulfur of H_2S is oxidized, and therefore, H_2S is acting as a reducing agent.

As another example, consider the reaction of permanganate ion and ferrous ion in acidic solution.

$$\overset{7+}{MnO_4^-} + \overset{2+}{Fe^{2+}} \quad H^+ \rightarrow \overset{2+}{Mn^{2+}} \rightarrow \overset{3+}{Fe^{3+}} + H_2O$$

Five iron ions (each of which increases by 1) must be taken to balance the decrease of 5 displayed by manganese.

$$MnO_4^- + 5Fe^{2+} + H^+ \rightarrow Mn^{2+} + 5Fe^{3+} + H_2O$$

The materials that undergo a change in oxidation number are now balanced and must not be changed; however, the H^+ and H_2O are not balanced. To make up the four oxygen atoms of the left side of this equation, four H_2O molecules are indicated on the right side. It follows, then, that the coefficient of H^+ must be 8 in order to balance the hydrogrens of the four H_2O molecules.

$$MnO_4^- + 5Fe^{2+} + 8H^+ \rightarrow Mn^{2+} + 5Fe^{3+} + 4H_2O$$

An ionic equation must indicate charge balance as well as mass balance. Since the algebraic sum of the charges on the left ($-1 + 10 + 8 = +17$) equals the net charge of the right ($+2 + 15 = +17$), the equation is properly balanced.

The steps used in balancing an oxidation-reduction equation are illustrated in the following, final, example.

$$\overset{0}{As} + \overset{1+}{OCl^-} + OH^- \rightarrow \overset{5+}{AsO_4^{3-}} + \overset{1-}{Cl^-} + H_2O$$

$$2As + 5OCl^- + OH^- \rightarrow 2AsO_4^{3-} + 5Cl^- + H_2O$$

$$2As + 5OCl^- + 6OH^- \rightarrow 2AsO_4^{3-} + 5Cl^- + 3H_2O$$

The net charge on each side of the final equation is $11-$.

Reactions in which electrons are transferred are clearly examples of oxidation-reduction reactions. In the reaction of sodium and chlorine, a sodium atom loses its valence electron to a chlorine atom.

$$\overset{0}{2Na} + \overset{0}{Cl_2} \rightarrow 2Na^+ + 2Cl^-$$

For simple ions, the oxidation number is the same as the charge on the ion. It follows, then, that electron loss represents a type of oxidation, and electron gain represents a type of reduction. This equation can be divided into two **partial equations** representing **half reactions.**

$$\text{Oxidation:} \quad 2Na \rightarrow 2Na^+ + 2e^-$$
$$\text{Reduction:} \quad 2e^- + Cl_2 \rightarrow 2Cl^-$$

The **ion-electron** method of balancing oxidation-reduction equations employs partial equations: one to represent the oxidation (in which electrons are lost) and one to represent the reduction (in which electrons are gained). The final equation is obtained by adding these two partial equations together in such a way that the number of electrons lost equals the number of electrons gained.

Most oxidation-reduction equations may be balanced by use of the ion-electron method, which is especially convenient for electrochemical reactions and reactions of ions in water solution. However, several misconceptions that can arise must be pointed out. Half reactions cannot occur alone, and partial equations do not represent complete chemical changes. Even in electrochemical cells, where the two half reactions take place at different electrodes, the two half reactions always occur simultaneously.

Whereas the partial equations probably represent an overall, if not detailed, view of the way an oxidation-reduction reaction occurs in an electrochemical cell, the same reaction in a beaker may not take place in this way at all. The method should *not* be interpreted as necessarily giving the correct mechanism by which a reaction occurs. It is, at times, difficult to recognize whether a given reaction is a legitimate example of an electron-exchange reaction. The reaction

$$\overset{4+}{S}O_3^{2-} + \overset{5+}{Cl}O_3^- \rightarrow \overset{6+}{S}O_4^{2-} + \overset{3+}{Cl}O_2^-$$

looks like an electron-exchange reaction, can be made to take place in an electrochemical cell, and can be balanced by the ion-electron method. However, this reaction has been shown to proceed by direct oxygen exchange (from ClO_3^- to SO_3^{2-}) and *not* by electron exchange.

Only those ions that are involved in the reaction are shown in the ion-electron method; unionized (or slightly ionized) species and insoluble substances that take part in the reaction are written in molecular form. In the example that follows, the equation for the reaction between dichromate ion and chloride ion in acid solution is used to illustrate the steps of the method.

1. Two skeleton partial equations for the half reactions are written, and the central element of each partial equation is balanced.

$$Cr_2O_7^{2-} \rightarrow 2Cr^{3+}$$
$$2Cl^- \rightarrow Cl_2$$

2. The hydrogen and oxygen atoms are then balanced. Since this reaction occurs in acid solution, H^+ and H_2O can be added where needed. For each oxygen atom that is needed, one H_2O molecule is added to the side of the partial equation that is deficient. The hydrogen is then brought into balance by the addition of H^+. Thus seven oxygens must be added to the right side of the first partial equation; the second partial equation is already in material balance.

$$14H^+ + Cr_2O_7^{2-} \longrightarrow 2Cr^{3+} + 7H_2O$$

$$2Cl^- \longrightarrow Cl_2$$

3. The next step is to balance the half reactions electrically. In the first partial equation, the net charge is $12+$ on the left side of the equation ($14+$ and $2-$) and $6+$ on the right side. Six electrons must be added to the left. The second equation is balanced electrically by the addition of two electrons to the right.

$$6e^- + 14H^+ + Cr_2O_7^{2-} \longrightarrow 2Cr^{3+} + 7H_2O$$

$$2Cl^- \longrightarrow Cl_2 + 2e^-$$

4. The number of electrons lost must equal the number of electrons gained. Therefore the oxidation equation is multiplied through by 3.

$$6e^- + 14H^+ + Cr_2O_7^{2-} \longrightarrow 2Cr^{3+} + 7H_2O$$

$$6Cl^- \longrightarrow 3Cl_2 + 6e^-$$

5. Addition of the two partial equations gives the final equation.

$$14H^+ + Cr_2O_7^{2-} + 6Cl^- \longrightarrow 2Cr^{3+} + 3Cl_2 + 7H_2O$$

These steps are illustrated, as follows, for the reaction in which As_4O_6 reacts with MnO_4^- to produce H_3AsO_4 and Mn^{2+}.

1. $$MnO_4^- \longrightarrow Mn^{2+}$$

$$As_4O_6 \longrightarrow 4H_3AsO_4$$

2. The first partial equation can be brought into material balance by the addition of $4H_2O$ to the right side and $8H^+$ to the left side. In the second partial equation, $10H_2O$ must be added to the left side to make up the needed 10 oxygens. If we stopped at this point, there would be 20 hydrogen atoms on the left and 12 on the right; therefore $8H^+$ must be added to the right.

$$8H^+ + MnO_4^- \longrightarrow Mn^{2+} + 4H_2O$$

$$10H_2O + As_4O_6 \longrightarrow 4H_3AsO_4 + 8H^+$$

3. To balance the net charges, electrons are added.

$$5e^- + 8H^+ + MnO_4^- \longrightarrow Mn^{2+} + 4H_2O$$

$$10H_2O + As_4O_6 \longrightarrow 4H_3AsO_4 + 8H^+ + 8e^-$$

4. The first partial equation must be multiplied through by eight and the second by five so that the same number of electrons are lost in the oxidation partial equation as are gained in the reduction.

$$40e^- + 64H^+ + 8MnO_4^- \rightarrow 8Mn^{2+} + 32H_2O$$

$$50H_2O + 5As_4O_6 \rightarrow 20H_3AsO_4 + 40H^+ + 40e^-$$

5. When these two partials are added, water molecules and hydrogen ions must be canceled as well as electrons. It is poor form to leave an equation with 64H$^+$ on the left and 40H$^+$ on the right.

$$24H^+ + 18H_2O + 5As_4O_6 + 8MnO_4^- \rightarrow 20H_3AsO_4 + 8Mn^{2+}$$

Equations for reactions that take place in alkaline solution are balanced in a slightly different manner from those that occur in acidic solution. All the steps are the same except the second one; H$^+$ cannot be be used to balance equations for alkaline reactions. In alkaline solution, MnO_4^- reacts with SO_3^{2-} to produce MnO_2 and SO_4^{2-}.

1. $$MnO_4^- \rightarrow MnO_2$$
$$SO_3^{2-} \rightarrow SO_4^{2-}$$

2. For reactions occurring in alkaline solution, OH$^-$ and H$_2$O are used to balance oxygen and hydrogen. For each oxygen that is needed, two OH$^-$ ions are added to the side of the partial equation that is deficient, and one H$_2$O molecule is added to the opposite side. For each hydrogen that is needed, one H$_2$O molecule is added to the side that is deficient, and one OH$^-$ ion is added to the opposite side.

$$2H_2O + MnO_4^- \rightarrow MnO_2 + 4OH^-$$
$$2OH^- + SO_3^{2-} \rightarrow SO_4^{2-} + H_2O$$

3. $$3e^- + 2H_2O + MnO_4^- \rightarrow MnO_2 + 4OH^-$$
$$2OH^- + SO_3^{2-} \rightarrow SO_4^{2-} + H_2O + 2e^-$$

4. $$6e^- + 4H_2O + 2MnO_4^- \rightarrow 2MnO_2 + 8OH^-$$
$$6OH^- + 3SO_3^{2-} \rightarrow 3SO_4^{2-} + 3H_2O + 6e^-$$

5. $$H_2O + 2MnO_4^- + 3SO_3^{2-} \rightarrow 2MnO_2 + 3SO_4^{2-} + 2OH^-$$

7.7 Equivalent Weights of Compounds

It is often covenient to use equivalent weights for stoichiometric calculations. The equivalent weight of a compound depends upon the type of reaction being considered. For neutralization reactions, **equivalent weights** are based on the fact that one proton reacts with one hydroxide ion.

$$H^+(aq) + OH^-(aq) \rightarrow H_2O$$

Thus the weight of an acid that supplies 1 gram molecular weight of H^+ is the gram equivalent weight of that acid. A gram equivalent weight of a hydroxide is the weight that will supply 1 gram mole of OH^-. It is obvious, then, that 1 gram equivalent of an acid will completely neutralize 1 gram equivalent of an alkali. Table 7.2 lists the equivalent weights of three acids and three hydroxides; these values can be derived by dividing the molecular weight of the compound by the number of replaceable hydrogens or hydroxyls per formula unit. In some instances, polyprotic acids undergo reactions where not all the hydrogens are neutralized; for such a reaction, the equivalent weight of the acid must be calculated on the basis of the number of hydrogens that are neutralized.

TABLE 7.2.
EQUIVALENT WEIGHTS OF SOME ACIDS AND BASES (COMPLETE NEUTRALIZATION).

Compound	Molecular Weight	Equivalent Weight
HNO_3	63.01	63.01
H_2SO_4	98.08	49.04
H_3PO_4	98.00	32.67
NaOH	40.00	40.00
$Ca(OH)_2$	74.09	37.05
$Al(OH)_3$	77.98	25.99

In an oxidation-reduction reaction, the total increase in oxidation number of one species must equal the total decrease in the oxidation number of another species. Therefore a system of equivalent weights for oxidizing and reducing agents is based on oxidation number changes. The equivalent weight of a compound functioning as an oxidizing or reducing agent is defined as the molecular weight of the compound divided by the total decrease or increase in oxidation number of all the atoms in one formula unit of the compound under consideration. Obviously, 1 gram equivalent weight of an oxidizing agent requires 1 gram equivalent weight of a reducing agent for complete reaction.

Thus in the reaction

$$\overset{0}{I_2} + 10 H \overset{5+}{N} O_3 \rightarrow 2 H \overset{5+}{I} O_3 + 10 \overset{4+}{N} O_2 + 4H_2O$$

each iodine atom undergoes an increase in oxidation number of 5, making a total increase of 10 per molecule of I_2. The molecular weight of I_2 is 253.81, and in this reaction, therefore, the equivalent weight of iodine is 253.81/10, or 25.381. In this reaction each nitrogen atom of HNO_3

undergoes a decrease in oxidation number of 1; therefore the equivalent weight of HNO_3 is the same as its molecular weight, 63.01.

The stoichiometric weight ratio of reductant (I_2) to oxidant (HNO_3) derived from equivalent weights is the same as that derived from the balanced chemical equation. Thus the balanced chemical equation for the reaction of I_2 and HNO_3 shows 1 mole of I_2, which is 10 equivalents, reacting with 10 moles of HNO_3, which is also 10 equivalents.

It is also possible to use half reactions to derive equivalent weights; the increase or decrease in oxidation number is the same as the number of electrons indicated as being lost or gained in the partial equations.

The equivalent weight of an oxidizing agent or a reducing agent is not invariant; for different reactions, a given compound may have different equivalent weights. When potassium permanganate serves as an oxidizing agent in acid solution, the partial equation for the reduction of permanganate ion is

$$5e^- + 8H^+ + \overset{7+}{Mn}O_4^- \rightarrow Mn^{2+} + H_2O$$

The equivalent weight of $KMnO_4$ for this reaction is the molecular weight (158.04) divided by the change in the oxidation number of Mn (5), or 31.61.

The partial equation for the use of $KMnO_4$ as an oxidizing agent in alkaline solution is

$$3e^- + 2H_2O + \overset{7+}{Mn}O_4^- \rightarrow \overset{4+}{Mn}O_2 + 4OH^-$$

Hence, the equivalent weight of $KMnO_4$ for this reaction is 158.04/3, or 52.68.

Some analytical determinations employ solutions containing a known concentration of a given oxidant or reductant. The concentrations of such solutions and the mathematical treatment of such analyses are usually based on equivalent weights. The preparation and use of these solutions are described in later chapters.

7.8 Hydrogen Peroxide

In addition to water, hydrogen and oxygen form a compound called hydrogen peroxide, H_2O_2. Under ordinary conditions, hydrogen peroxide is a liquid with a boiling point of 150.2°C and a melting point of -0.43°C. The molecule is diamagnetic and has the structure:

$$\overset{\displaystyle H}{:\!\ddot{O}\!:\!\ddot{O}\!:}$$
$$\underset{\displaystyle H}{}$$

The H—O—O bond angles are approximately 102°, and the four atoms are not coplanar; one hydrogen atom projects from the plane of the other three atoms at an angle of approximately 90°.

Hydrogen peroxide can be made by treating peroxides with acids.

$$BaO_2(s) + 2H^+(aq) + SO_4^{2-}(aq) \rightarrow BaSO_4(s) + H_2O_2(aq)$$

In this preparation, the barium sulfate, which is insoluble, can be removed by filtration.

Commercially, hydrogen peroxide is made by the electrolysis, under suitable conditions, of sulfuric acid or ammonium hydrogen sulfate. The peroxydisulfuric acid, $H_2S_2O_8$, produced in this process reacts with water to give hydrogen peroxide.

$$H_2S_2O_8 + 2H_2O \rightarrow 4H^+(aq) + 2SO_4^{2-}(aq) + H_2O_2(aq)$$

Hydrogen peroxide is also made commercially by the hydrogenation, oxidation, and subsequent reaction with water of an organic intermediate, 2-ethylanthraquinone.

The dilute solutions of hydrogen peroxide produced in the preceding processes are concentrated by distillation under reduced pressure (Section 6.4) since hydrogen peroxide readily decomposes.

$$2H_2O_2 \rightarrow 2H_2O + O_2$$

This decomposition, which is catalyzed by traces of heavy metal ions, is an example of an auto oxidation-reduction reaction. The oxygen of H_2O_2 has an oxidation number of $1-$; it is oxidized to an oxidation number of 0 in O_2 and is reduced to an oxidation number of $2-$ in H_2O.

Because the oxygen of H_2O_2 can be either oxidized or reduced, H_2O_2 can function as an oxidizing agent or a reducing agent. As an oxidizing agent, the oxygen of H_2O_2 is reduced to the normal $2-$ oxidation state.

$$2H^+(aq) + H_2O_2(aq) + 2I^-(aq) \rightarrow I_2(s) + 2H_2O$$
$$2OH^-(aq) + H_2O_2(aq) + Mn^{2+}(aq) \rightarrow MnO_2(s) + 2H_2O$$

Oxidations are often slow in acid solution; they generally occur more rapidly in alkaline solution.

Hydrogen peroxide only serves as a reducing agent with materials that are themselves strong oxidizing agents. In such reactions, the oxygen of the H_2O_2 is oxidized to O_2.

$$6H^+(aq) + 5H_2O_2(aq) + 2MnO_4^- \rightarrow 2Mn^{2+}(aq) + 5O_2(g) + 8H_2O$$

Reactions in which hydrogen peroxide functions as a reducing agent in alkaline solution are rarely encountered.

Hydrogen peroxide is a weak acid in water solution. One or two hydrogens of H_2O_2 can be neutralized by sodium hydroxide to produce either $NaHO_2$ (sodium hydroperoxide) or Na_2O_2 (sodium peroxide).

7.9 Occurrence and Preparation of Hydrogen

In the crust, bodies of water, and atmosphere of the earth, hydrogen constitutes less than 1% of the weight of the whole and ranks ninth of all elements in order of abundance (Table 7.1). The most important naturally occurring compound of hydrogen is water, which is the principal source of the element. Hydrogen forms a series of compounds with carbon known as the hydrocarbons; these occur in coal, natural gas, and petroleum. A few minerals, such as clay and certain hydrates, contain hydrogen. Compounds of hydrogen (with carbon, oxygen, and occasionally other elements) constitute the principal part of all plant and animal matter. Free hydrogen occurs in nature only in negligible amounts (e.g., as a component of volcanic gases).

The very reactive metals (Ca, Sr, Ba, and the group I A metals) react with water at room temperature to produce hydrogen and solutions of hydroxides.

$$2Na(s) + 2H_2O \rightarrow 2Na^+(aq) + 2OH^-(aq) + H_2(g)$$

$$Ca(s) + 2H_2O \rightarrow Ca^{2+}(aq) + 2OH^-(aq) + H_2(g)$$

At high temperatures, some additional metals, of slightly lower reactivity, will displace hydrogen from water (steam); in these cases, metal oxides (the anhydrides of hydroxides) are obtained instead of metal hydroxides.

$$Mg(s) + H_2O(g) \rightarrow MgO(s) + H_2(g)$$

The reaction of iron and steam serves as a commercial source of hydrogen.

$$3Fe(s) + 4H_2O(g) \rightarrow Fe_3O_4(s) + 4H_2(g)$$

A still longer list of metals (including, e.g., Mg, Al, Mn, Zn, Cr, Fe, Cd, Co, Ni, Sn, and Pb) will react with aqueous solutions of acids to produce hydrogen. This method is a convenient laboratory preparation, but it is too expensive to be of commercial importance. The very reactive metals react too violently to be useful.

$$Zn(s) + 2H^+(aq) \rightarrow Zn^{2+}(aq) + H_2(g)$$

$$Fe(s) + 2H^+(aq) \rightarrow Fe^{2+}(aq) + H_2(g)$$

$$2Al(s) + 6H^+(aq) \rightarrow 2Al^{3+}(aq) + 3H_2(g)$$

The anions of certain acids (e.g., nitric acid) react with the metals as well as hydrogen itself; such acids cannot be used to prepare pure hydrogen.

The reactions of metals and acids are examples of a type of oxidation-reduction reaction known as a **displacement reaction;** the metals are said to displace hydrogen from its compounds, the acids. Displacement reactions in which metals participate are often electron-exchange reactions. For example, in the reaction

$$Mg(s) + Cu^{2+}(aq) \rightarrow Mg^{2+}(aq) + Cu(s)$$

the more reactive metal, magnesium, loses its valence electrons to the ion of the lesser reactive metal, copper. Certain electrochemical determinations provide a measure of the tendency of a given metal toward electron loss and the tendency of a given metal ion toward electron gain; these **electrode potentials** are a topic of Chapter 9. The reactivities of some metals (e.g., Cu, Hg, Ag, and Au) is such that these metals do not displace hydrogen from acids.

Coke and steam react at high temperatures (1000°C) to produce a gaseous mixture known as water gas.

$$C(s) + H_2O(g) \rightarrow CO(g) + H_2(g)$$

This mixture is used as a fuel. Since it is difficult to separate hydrogen from carbon monoxide, the water gas is subjected to a second step if hydrogen alone is desired. Water gas, mixed with additional steam, is passed over a catalyst at a temperature of about 500°C; this converts the carbon monoxide into carbon dioxide.

$$CO(g) + H_2O(g) \rightarrow CO_2(g) + H_2(g)$$

The carbon dioxide and hydrogen are separated by taking advantage of the solubility of carbon dioxide in cold water under pressure.

Hydrocarbons react with steam, in the presence of suitable catalysts, to give mixtures of carbon monoxide and hydrogen.

$$CH_4(g) + H_2O(g) \rightarrow CO(g) + 3H_2(g)$$

The production of hydrogen and water gas from these reactions are industrially important.

Hydrogen is obtained from the catalytic decomposition of hydrocarbons at high temperatures.

$$CH_4(g) \rightarrow C(s) + 2H_2(g)$$

In gasoline refining, petroleum hydrocarbons are cracked into compounds of lower molecular weight; hydrogen is a by-product.

Very pure, but relatively expensive, hydrogen is commercially prepared by the electrolysis of water containing a small amount of sulfuric acid or sodium hydroxide.

$$2H_2O \xrightarrow{\text{electrolysis}} 2H_2(g) + O_2(g)$$

Hydrogen is a by-product (as is chlorine) in the industrial preparation of sodium hydroxide by the electrolysis of concentrated aqueous solutions of sodium chloride.

$$2Na^+(aq) + 2Cl^-(aq) + 2H_2O \xrightarrow{\text{electrolysis}}$$
$$2Na^+(aq) + 2OH^-(aq) + H_2(g) + Cl_2(g)$$

Certain metals and nonmetals displace hydrogen from alkaline solutions.

$$Zn(s) + 2OH^-(aq) + 2H_2O \longrightarrow H_2(g) + Zn(OH)_4^{2-}(aq)$$
$$\text{(zincate ion)}$$

$$2Al(s) + 2OH^-(aq) + 6H_2O \longrightarrow 3H_2(g) + 2Al(OH)_4^-(aq)$$
$$\text{(aluminate ion)}$$

$$Si(s) + 2OH^-(aq) + H_2O \longrightarrow 2H_2(g) + SiO_3^{2-}(aq)$$
$$\text{(silicate ion)}$$

7.10 Properties of Hydrogen

Hydrogen is a colorless, odorless, tasteless gas. It has the lowest density of any chemical substance; at STP, 1 liter of hydrogen weighs 0.0899 g. The two atoms of hydrogen of the H_2 molecule are joined by a single covalent bond, giving each atom a stable helium electronic configuration. The molecule is nonpolar; the weak nature of the intermolecular forces of attraction is indicated by the low normal boiling point ($-252.7°C$), the normal melting point ($-259.1°C$) and the critical temperature ($-240°C$ at a critical pressure of 12.8 atm). Hydrogen is virtually insoluble in water; approximately 2 ml of hydrogen will dissolve in 1 liter of water at room temperature and atmospheric pressure.

There are three isotopes of hydrogen. The most abundant isotope, $_1^1H$, constitutes 99.985% of naturally occurring hydrogen; deuterium, $_1^2H$ (or $_1^2D$) constitutes 0.015%; and the radioactive tritium, $_1^3H$ (or $_1^3T$) occurs only in trace amounts.

The electrons of a covalent bond have opposed spins. Nuclei of certain atoms also spin on their axes; when these are combined into diatomic molecules, two different molecular forms can exist. **Ortho hydrogen** is the form of molecular hydrogen in which the spins of the two nuclei are parallel (both clockwise or both counterclockwise); **para hydrogen** has nuclei of opposed spin (one clockwise and one counterclockwise). The two forms differ only slightly in physical properties (there is approximately a 0.1°C difference in boiling point and melting point) and are essentially identical in chemical characteristics. At low temperatures, the *para* form is the more stable; at room temperature and above, an equilibrium mixture of about three parts *ortho* to one part *para* exists. Other diatomic molecules, such as D_2, F_2, N_2, and Cl_2, exist in *ortho* and *para* forms.

The bond energy of the H—H bond is 103 kcal/mole. In the course of most reactions, this bond must be broken so that the H atoms can form new bonds with other atoms. Since this bond energy is relatively high, most of the reactions of hydrogen take place at elevated temperatures.

Hydrogen reacts with the metals of group IA and the heavier metals of group IIA (Ba, Sr, and Ca) to form **saltlike hydrides.** The hydride ion, H^-, of these compounds, is isoelectronic with helium and achieves this stable configuration by the addition of an electron from the metal. Since the electron affinity of hydrogen is low (0.7 ev), hydrogen reacts in this manner only with the most reactive metals

$$2Na(s) + H_2(g) \rightarrow 2NaH(s)$$
$$Ca(s) + H_2(g) \rightarrow CaH_2(s)$$

The saltlike hydrides react with water to form hydrogen.

$$H^- + H_2O \rightarrow H_2(g) + OH^-(aq)$$

With certain other metals, such as platinum palladium, and nickel, hydrogen forms **interstitial hydrides.** Many of these hydrides are non-stoichiometric, the apparent formulas of the hydrides depending upon the conditions under which they were prepared. Palladium can absorb up to 900 times its own volume of hydrogen. The interstitial hydrides resemble the metals from which they are derived; the crystal structures of the metals do not change (or change only slightly) as hydrogen is added. Whether these substances should be regarded as compounds is debatable; the name, interstitial hydrides, arises from the view that the hydrogen is only absorbed into the interstices of the metallic crystal.

However, magnetic studies indicate that electron pairing of some sort is involved in the formation of these hydrides. Many of the metals have unpaired electrons and, hence, are paramagnetic (Section 2.14). A grad-ual loss of paramagnetism is observed as the hydrides form from the metal. Since the electrons of molecular hydrogen are paired, these stud-ies imply that the hydrogen is incorporated into the crystal in atomic form. This would account for the catalytic activity of platinum, pal-ladium, nickel, and other metals for many reactions of hydrogen; if the H—H bond is broken, or even only weakened, the absorbed hydrogen should be much more reactive than ordinary H_2 gas.

Complex hydrides of boron and aluminum are important and useful compounds for chemical syntheses. Important examples are sodium borohydride and lithium aluminum hydride.

$$Na^+ \begin{bmatrix} H \\ H:\ddot{B}:H \\ H \end{bmatrix}^- \qquad Li^+ \begin{bmatrix} H \\ H:\ddot{Al}:H \\ H \end{bmatrix}^-$$

Since these compounds, as well as the saltlike hydrides, react with water to liberate hydrogen, they are prepared by reactions in ether.

$$4LiH + AlCl_3 \rightarrow Li[AlH_4] + 3LiCl$$

Hydrogen forms covalent compounds with most of the nonmetals. It reacts with the halogen to form colorless, covalent gases.

$$H_2(g) + Cl_2(g) \rightarrow 2HCl(g)$$

Reactions with fluorine or chlorine will take place at room temperature or below, but the reactions with the less reactive bromine or iodine require higher temperatures (400 to 600°C).

The reaction of hydrogen and oxygen is highly exothermic and is the basis of the high temperature (ca., 2800°C) produced by the oxy-hydrogen torch.

$$2H_2(g) + O_2(g) \rightarrow 2H_2O(g) + 115.6 \, kcal$$

or $$2H_2(g) + O_2(g) \rightarrow 2H_2O(l) + 136.6 \, kcal$$

The reaction with sulfur is more difficult and requires high temperatures.

$$H_2(g) + S(g) \rightarrow H_2S(g)$$

Hydrogen reacts with nitrogen at high pressures (300 to 1000 atm), at high temperatures (400 to 600°C), and in the presence of a catalyst to produce ammonia (Haber Process).

$$3H_2(g) + N_2(g) \rightarrow 2NH_3(g)$$

Hydrogen does not react readily with carbon, but at high temperatures, hydrogen can be made catalytically to react with finely divided carbon (Bergius process); hydrocarbons are produced.

$$2H_2(g) + C(g) \rightarrow CH_4(g)$$

The ionization potential of hydrogen is relatively high (13.60 ev). In none of the compounds formed between hydrogen and the nonmetals does hydrogen exist as positive ions; the bonding in all such compounds is covalent.

Hydrogen reacts with many metal oxides to produce water and the free metal.

$$CuO(s) + H_2(g) \rightarrow Cu(s) + H_2O(g)$$
$$WO_3(s) + 3H_2(g) \rightarrow W(s) + 3H_2O(g)$$
$$FeO(s) + H_2(g) \rightarrow Fe(s) + H_2O(g)$$

Certain of these reactions are employed in the metallurgy of oxide ores; for example, in the commercial production of tungsten metal, WO_3 is reduced to the free metal by hydrogen.

Carbon monoxide and hydrogen react at high temperatures and high pressures in the presence of a catalyst to produce methyl alcohol.

$$CO(g) + 2H_2(g) \rightarrow CH_3OH(g)$$

7.11 The Hydrogen Bond

The intermolecular attractions of certain hydrogen-containing compounds are unusually strong. These are compounds in which hydrogen is covalently bonded to highly electronegative elements of small atomic size. In these compounds, the electronegative element exerts such a strong attraction on the bonding electrons that the hydrogen is left with a significant δ^+ charge. In fact, the hydrogen is almost an exposed proton since this element has no screening electrons. The hydrogen of one molecule and a pair of unshared electrons on the electronegative atom of another molecule are mutually attracted and form what is called a **hydrogen bond.** Because of its small size, each hydrogen atom is capable of forming only one hydrogen bond. The association of HF, H_2O, and NH_3 by hydrogen bonds (indicated by dotted lines) can be roughly diagrammed as follows:

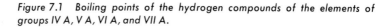

Unusual properties are characteristic of compounds in which hydrogen bonding occurs. In Figure 7.1 the normal boiling points of the hydrogen compounds of the elements of groups IV A, V A, VI A, and

Figure 7.1   Boiling points of the hydrogen compounds of the elements of groups IV A, V A, VI A, and VII A.

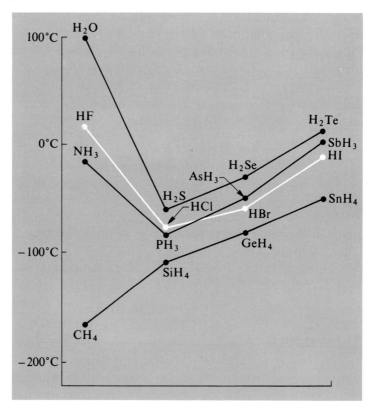

VII A are plotted. The series CH_4, SiH_4, GeH_4, and SnH_4 illustrates the expected trend in boiling points; the boiling point increases as the molecular weight increases (Section 6.4). However, the first member of each of the other three series of compounds has a boiling point that is 100 to 200 degrees higher than the boiling point that would be predicted on the basis of molecular weight alone. The boiling points of hydrogen fluoride, water, and ammonia are unusually high because of hydrogen bonding, which increases the difficulty in separating molecules from the liquid state. Methane, CH_4, does not form hydrogen bonds; the carbon of CH_4 has no unshared electron pair. In addition to high boiling points, compounds that are associated by hydrogen bonding have abnormally high melting points, heats of vaporization, heats of fusion, and viscosities; the crystalline solids of such compounds are unusually hard.

Hydrogen bonds are much stronger than ordinary van der Waals intermolecular attractions and have energies around 5 kcal/mole, which is about 5 to 10% as strong as average ionic or covalent bonds. The strength of the hydrogen bond depends in part upon the electronegativity of the element to which hydrogen is covalently bonded; the strength of the hydrogen bonds, $N—H\cdots N < O—H\cdots O < F—H\cdots F$, parallels the increasing electronegativity of the elements, $N < O < F$. The electronegativity of carbon is too low for carbon compounds to form hydrogen bonds readily. However, in certain compounds, the hydrogen bonded to a carbon can participate in intermolecular hydrogen bonding if highly electronegative groups are also bonded to the carbon; such hydrogen bonds are relatively weak, however. For example, the hydrogen of the chloroform molecule, $HCCl_3$, forms hydrogen bonds with an

electron pair of the oxygen of the acetone molecule, $CH_3\overset{\overset{\textstyle O}{\|}}{C}CH_3$,

$$
\begin{array}{ccc}
\text{Cl} & & \text{CH}_3 \\
| & & | \\
\text{Cl}-\text{C}-\text{H}\cdots\text{O}=\text{C} \\
| & & | \\
\text{Cl} & & \text{CH}_3
\end{array}
$$

and chloroform-acetone mixtures have higher boiling points than either pure component.

Another requirement for the formation of strong hydrogen bonds is that the element covalently bonded to the hydrogen must have a small atomic size. Really effective hydrogen bonds are formed only by fluorine, oxygen, and nitrogen compounds. Chlorine compounds form weak hydrogen bonds as evidenced by the slight displacement of the boiling point of HCl (Figure 7.1). Chlorine has approximately the same electronegativity as nitrogen; however, chlorine atoms are larger than nitrogen atoms, and the electron cloud of chlorine is, therefore, more diffuse than that of nitrogen.

An examination of Figure 7.1 will show that hydrogen bonding has a greater effect on the boiling point of water than on the boiling point of hydrogen fluoride. This is true even though the O—H⋯O bond is only about two-thirds as strong as the F—H⋯F bond. There are twice as many hydrogen bonds per molecule possible in water as there are in hydrogen fluoride. The oxygen of each water molecule has two hydrogen atoms and two electron pairs, and each molecule can, therefore, form hydrogen bonds with four other water molecules. The HF molecule has three free electron pairs that can bond with hydrogen atoms from other molecules, but only one hydrogen atom with which it can form a hydrogen bond; hence, a maximum average of two hydrogen bonds per molecule is possible in any aggregate of HF molecules.

There are other properties of water that are affected to an unusual degree by hydrogen bonding. The tetrahedral arrangement of the hydrogen atoms and the unshared electron pairs of oxygen in water (Section 3.13) cause the hydrogen bonds of the ice crystal to be arranged in this manner and leads to the open structure of the ice crystal. Ice, therefore, has a comparatively low density. In water at the freezing point, the molecules are arranged more closely together, and hence water has a higher density than ice—an unusual situation. It should be noted that H_2O molecules are associated by hydrogen bonds in the liquid state but not to the same extent, nor in the rigid manner, as they are associated in ice.

Hydrogen bonding also accounts for the unexpectedly high solubilities of some compounds containing oxygen, nitrogen, and fluorine in certain hydrogen-containing solvents, notably water. Thus ammonia and methanol dissolve in water through the formation of hydrogen bonds.

$$
\begin{array}{ccccc}
\text{H} & & & \text{H} & \\
| & & & | & \\
\text{H—N} \cdots \text{H—O} & & \text{H—C—O} \cdots \text{H—O} \\
| & | & & | \quad | & | \\
\text{H} & \text{H} & & \text{H} \ \text{H} & \text{H}
\end{array}
$$

In addition, certain oxygen-containing anions (e.g., sulfate, SO_4^{2-}) dissolve in water through the formation of hydrogen bonds.

The water molecule is polar and forms dipole-dipole interactions with certain other polar molecules. The essential difference between these interactions and the hydrogen bond is that the latter is much stronger and exerts a more pronounced effect upon the properties of the materials in which it occurs. Both of these intermolecular interactions are essentially electrostatic in character. The extra strength of the hydrogen bond comes about because of the highly concentrated positive charge on the hydrogen, owing to its small size and lack of screening electrons; this small size and effective charge of hydrogen attracts the electronegative element of another molecule strongly and permits it to approach closely. An extreme (and not typical) case is the HF_2^- ion, $F—H\cdots F^-$, in which the hydrogen is thought to be exactly midway between the two fluorine atoms. The hydrogen bond of the HF_2^- ion is so strong that this ion, formed from a fluoride ion and a HF molecule, can be considered as an entity in aqueous solution or in such crystalline materials as KHF_2.

Rather than the somewhat random arrangement of some polar molecules with the usual dipole-dipole attractions, there is some evidence that the hydrogen bond is directional. It is assumed, at least in certain cases, that the hydrogen atom of one molecule approaches the second molecule in the direction of the hybrid orbitals of the unshared electron pair (Section 3.12). This accounts for the tetrahedral structure observed in the ice crystal as well as the zig-zag arrangement of HF molecules in solid hydrogen fluoride.

$$H \diagup F \cdots H \diagdown \overset{}{\underset{F}{}} \cdots H \diagup F \cdots H \diagdown F$$

SOME SUGGESTED READINGS

Lavoisier, A., *Elements of Chemistry,* New York, Dover, 1965 (paper).

Pauling, L., *The Nature of the Chemical Bond,* Ithaca, N.Y., Cornell University Press, 1960.

Pimentel, G. C., and McClellan, A. L., *The Hydrogen Bond,* San Francisco, Freeman, 1960.

Weeks, M. E., and Leicester, H. M., *Discovery of the Elements, 6th ed.,* Easton, Penna., Chemical Education Publishing Co., 1956.

PROBLEMS

7.1 State the oxidation numbers of:

(a) P in H_3PO_3 (f) Sb in SbO_4^{3-}

(b) Ge in GeO_4^{4-} (g) B in $Na_2B_4O_7$

(c) As in $Mg_2As_2O_7$ (h) P in $Na_4P_2O_7$

(d) C in C_2H_4O (i) Mo in $H_2Mo_3O_{10}$

(e) S in $Na_2S_2O_3$ (j) Sn in $SnCl_6^{2-}$

7.2 Balance the following oxidation-reduction equations by the change-in-oxidation-number method:

(a) $Sb + H^+ + NO_3^- \rightarrow Sb_4O_6 + NO + H_2O$

(b) $S_2O_3^{2-} + I_2 \rightarrow S_4O_6^{2-} + I^-$

(c) $NaI + H_2SO_4 \rightarrow H_2S + I_2 + Na_2SO_4 + H_2O$

(d) $MnO_2 + HCl \rightarrow MnCl_2 + Cl_2 + H_2O$

(e) $As_4O_6 + Cl_2 + H_2O \rightarrow H_3AsO_4 + HCl$

(f) $Al + NaOH + H_2O \rightarrow NaAl(OH)_4 + H_2$

(g) $H^+ + I^- + IO_3^- \rightarrow I_2 + H_2O$

(h) $H^+ + AsO_3^{3-} + Zn \rightarrow AsH_3 + Zn^{2+} + H_2O$

(i) $Pt + H^+ + NO_3^- + Cl^- \rightarrow PtCl_6^{2-} + NO + H_2O$

(j) $MnO_4^- + H_2O_2 + H^+ \rightarrow Mn^{2+} + O_2 + H_2O$

7.3 Complete and balance the following oxidation-reduction equations by the ion-electron method. All of the reactions occur in acid solution.

(a) $Mn^{2+} + BiO_3^- \rightarrow MnO_4^- + Bi^{3+}$

(b) $MnO_4^- + H_2C_2O_4 \rightarrow Mn^{2+} + CO_2$

(c) $H_2O_2 + PbS \rightarrow H_2O + PbSO_4$

(d) $Cu + NO_3^- \rightarrow Cu^{2+} + NO$

(e) $BrO_3^- + Br^- \rightarrow Br_2$

(f) $Cr_2O_7^{2-} + H_2S \rightarrow Cr^{3+} + S$

(g) $IO_3^- + SO_3^{2-} \rightarrow I_2 + SO_4^{2-}$

(h) $P_4 + HClO \rightarrow H_3PO_4 + Cl^-$

(i) $Zn + NO_3^- \rightarrow Zn^{2+} + NH_4^+$

(j) $As_2S_3 + ClO_3^- \rightarrow H_3AsO_4 + S + Cl^-$

7.4 Complete and balance the following oxidation-reduction equations by the ion-electron method. All of the reactions occur in alkaline solution.

(a) $Bi(OH)_3 + Sn(OH)_4^{2-} \rightarrow Bi + Sn(OH)_6^{2-}$

(b) $Cr(OH)_3 + HO_2^- \rightarrow CrO_4^{2-} + H_2O$

(c) $MnO_4^- + ClO_2^- \rightarrow MnO_2 + ClO_4^-$

(d) $CrO_2^- + ClO^- \rightarrow CrO_4^{2-} + Cl^-$

(e) $Ag + CN^- + O_2 \rightarrow Ag(CN)_2^- + OH^-$

(f) $Zn + NO_3^- \rightarrow Zn(OH)_4^{2-} + NH_3$

(g) $NiO_2 + Fe \rightarrow Ni(OH)_2 + Fe(OH)_3$

(h) $Cl_2 \rightarrow ClO_3^- + Cl^-$

(i) $P_4 \rightarrow H_2PO_2^- + PH_3$

(j) $CrI_3 + Cl_2 \rightarrow CrO_4^{2-} + IO_3^- + Cl^-$

7.5 What is the equivalent weight of:

(a) $K_2Cr_2O_7$ when used in the reaction described in Problem 7.3(f).

(b) H_2O_2 when used in the reaction described in Problem 7.3(c).

(c) $H_2C_2O_4$ in the reaction: $CaO + H_2C_2O_4 \rightarrow CaC_2O_4 + H_2O$

(d) H_3PO_4 in the reaction: $2NaOH + H_3PO_4 \rightarrow Na_2HPO_4 + 2H_2O$

7.6 Complete and balance the following equations:

(a) $Al(OH)_3(s) \xrightarrow{heat}$ (d) $CO_2(g) + OH^-(aq) \rightarrow$

(b) $PbO(s) + H^+(aq) \rightarrow$ (e) $P_4O_{10}(s) + H_2O \rightarrow$

(c) $SO_2(g) + CaO(s) \rightarrow$ (f) $ZnO + OH^- + H_2O \rightarrow$

7.7 Write and balance equations for the complete combustion, in oxygen, of (a) $C_4H_{10}S$, (b) C_8H_{18}, and (c) C_5H_6O.

7.8 Write a balanced chemical equation for the reaction of each of the following with water: (a) Na_2O, (b) Na_2O_2, (c) NaH, (d) C, (e) Ca, (f) Cl_2O.

7.9 Write a balanced equation for the reaction that occurs when each of the following is heated: (a) HgO, (b) BaO_2, (c) $Ca(OH)_2$, (d) $NaNO_3$, (e) $KClO_3$.

7.10 For each of the following substances, write balanced chemical equations for the reaction with oxygen and the reaction with hydrogen: (a) Cu_2O, (b) K, (c) N_2, (d) C, (e) CO.

7.11 Starting with elements only, write a series of equations for the preparation of Na_2SO_3.

7.12 (a) Use Figure 7.1 to estimate what the normal boiling point of water would be if H_2O followed the trend established by H_2S, H_2Se, and H_2Te.

(b) By means of Trouton's rule (Section 6.5), calculate the molar heat of vaporization of water that would be expected on the basis of the boiling point from part (a). (c) The actual molar heat of vaporization of water is 9.72 kcal/mole. What explanation may be offered to account for the difference between the actual value and that derived from Trouton's rule?

7.13   In the vapor of methanol, CH_3OH, aggregates consisting of four methanol molecules have been identified. These tetramers are held together in a ring

$$\overset{\displaystyle O}{\underset{\displaystyle \|}{}}$$

structure by hydrogen bonding. Two formic acid molecules, $H-\overset{\overset{\displaystyle O}{\|}}{C}-OH$, may be joined together by hydrogen bonds, and such double molecules, or dimers, have been identified in formic acid vapor and in certain formic acid solutions. Diagram (a) the tetramer of methanol and (b) the dimer of formic acid.

7.14   The reaction of sodium tellurate, Na_2TeO_4, with hydrogen iodide, HI, yields tellurium and iodine. What are the equivalent weights of (a) Na_2TeO_4 and (b) HI in this reaction? (c) What quantity of HI is needed to react with 2.00 g Na_2TeO_4?

7.15   (a) Complete and balance the partial equation

$$[Co(NO_2)_6]^{3-} \longrightarrow Co^{2+} + NO_3^-$$

(b) What is the equivalent weight of $K_3[Co(NO_2)_6]$ with regard to this transformation? (c) This change can be brought about by reaction with MnO_4^- (which goes to Mn^{2+}). What quantity of $K_3[Co(NO_2)_6]$ will react with 1.00 mole of $KMnO_4$?

8

Solutions

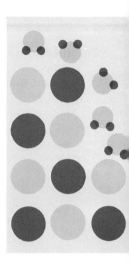

Most commonly encountered substances are mixtures, rather than pure substances. Mixtures may be classified as **heterogeneous** or **homogeneous.** A heterogeneous mixture consists of components in more than one phase, and the phase boundaries of most heterogeneous mixtures are easily distinguished. On the other hand, a homogeneous mixture, or **solution,** occurs in a single phase; it is impossible to distinguish particles of the components of a homogeneous mixture by ordinary visual means.

The composition of a mixture, unlike that of a compound, is continuously variable. For a hetergeneous mixture, there are no limits on this variability; for a solution, however, the composition may be varied only throughout a certain range (the limits of solubility).

8.1   Types of Solutions

Solutions may be classified according to their physical state, and gaseous, liquid, or solid solutions may be prepared. Gaseous solutions, of which air is an example, are mixtures of molecules of two or more gases. Dalton's law of partial pressures describes the behavior of gaseous solutions. Certain alloys are solid solutions; coinage silver is copper dissolved in silver, and brass is a solid solution of zinc in copper. Not all alloys, however, are solid solutions; some are heterogeneous mixtures, and some are intermetallic compounds. Liquid solutions are the most common and probably the most important to the chemist.

The component of a solution that is present in greatest quantity is usually called the **solvent**, and the other components are called **solutes.** Such terminology is loose and arbitrary. It is sometimes convenient to designate a component as the solvent even though it is present in only small amount; at other times, the assignment of the terms solute and solvent has little significance (e.g., in characterizing gaseous solutions).

212

Certain pairs of substances are miscible in all proportions. This is true of the constituents of all gaseous solutions and some pairs of components of liquid and solid solutions. However, for most materials, there is a limit on the amount of the substance that will dissolve in a given solvent. The **solubility** of a substance in a particular solvent at a specified temperature is the maximum amount of the solute that will dissolve in a definite amount of the solvent and produce a stable system.

For a given solution, the amount of solute dissolved in a unit volume of solution (or a unit amount of solvent) is the **concentration** of the solute. Solutions containing a relatively low concentration of solute are spoken of as **dilute** solutions; those of relatively high concentrations are called **concentrated** solutions.

If an excess of solute (more than will normally dissolve) is added to a quantity of a liquid solvent, an equilibrium is established between the pure solute and the dissolved solute.

$$\text{solute}_{(pure)} \rightleftharpoons \text{solute}_{(dissolved)}$$

The pure solute may be a solid, liquid, or gas. At equilibrium in such a system, the rate at which the pure solute dissolves equals the rate at which the dissolved solute comes out of solution. The concentration of the dissolved solute, therefore, is a constant. Such a solution is called a **saturated** solution, and the concentration of the solution is the solubility of the solute in question.

That such dynamic equilibria exist has been shown experimentally. If small crystals of a solid solute are placed in contact with a saturated solution of the solute, the crystals are observed to change in size and shape. Throughout this experiment, however, the concentration of the saturated solution does not change, nor does the quantity of excess solute decrease or increase.

An **unsaturated** solution has a lower concentration of solute than a saturated solution. Unsaturated solutions cannot exist in contact with excess solute. Instead, when pure solute is added to an unsaturated solution, some solute dissolves, and the concentration of the solution increases until equilibrium is attained and the solution is saturated.

It is sometimes possible to prepare a **supersaturated** solution, a metastable state. The concentration of solute in a supersaturated solution is higher than that of a saturated solution of the same solute. The additional solute, over that needed to saturate the solution, comes out of solution when pure solute is placed in contact with the supersaturated solution. The system quickly establishes a condition of equilibrium between solute and saturated solution.

Solutes exist in solution in molecular, atomic, or ionic dimensions, which is one reason for running chemical reactions in aqueous solution. Such reactions are usually rapid since: the reactants are in a small state of subdivision, the attractions between the particles (molecules, atoms, or ions) of the pure solute have been at least partially overcome, and these particles are free to move about through the solution. In addition, it is convenient to measure quantities of reactants volumetrically, which is possible when these reactants are in solution (Section 8.6). Because of their importance, liquid solutions containing gases, liquids, or solids as solutes will be the principal topic of this chapter.

8.2   The Solution Process

The molecules of a nonpolar covalent material, such as carbon tetrachloride, are held together by the weak fluctuating dipoles called van der Waals forces. On the other hand, polar covalent substances have relatively strong intermolecular attractions derived from the permanent dipoles of the molecules; the intermolecular attractions of water are unusually strong (Section 7.11). Nonpolar substances and polar substances are generally immiscible; for example, carbon tetrachloride is insoluble in water. The attraction of one water molecule for another water molecule is much greater than any attraction between a carbon tetrachloride molecule and a water molecule. Hence, carbon tetrachloride molecules are "squeezed out," and these two substances form a two-liquid-layer system.

Iodine is a nonpolar material and is soluble in carbon tetrachloride. The attractions between I_2 molecules in solid iodine are approximately of the same type and magnitude as those between CCl_4 molecules in pure carbon tetrachloride. Hence, significant I_2–CCl_4 attractions are possible, and iodine molecules can mix with carbon tetrachloride molecules. The resulting solution is a random molecular mixture.

Methyl alcohol, CH_3OH, like water, consists of polar molecules that are highly associated. In both pure liquids, the molecules are attracted to one another through hydrogen bonding.

$$
\begin{array}{ccc}
\text{H—O} \cdots \text{H—O} \cdots \text{H—O} & \qquad & \text{H—O} \cdots \text{H—O} \cdots \text{H—O} \\
\quad | \qquad\quad | \qquad\quad | & & \quad | \qquad\quad | \qquad\quad | \\
\text{H—C—H} \ \ \text{H—C—H} \ \ \text{H—C—H} & & \ \ \text{H} \qquad\quad \text{H} \qquad\quad \text{H} \\
\quad | \qquad\quad | \qquad\quad | & & \\
\text{H} \qquad\quad \text{H} \qquad\quad \text{H} & &
\end{array}
$$

Methyl alcohol and water are miscible in all proportions. In solutions of methyl alcohol in water, CH_3OH and H_2O molecules are associated through hydrogen bonding.

$$
\begin{array}{c}
\text{H—O} \cdots \text{H—O} \cdots \text{H—O} \\
\quad | \qquad\quad | \qquad\quad | \\
\text{H} \ \ \text{H—C—H} \ \ \text{H} \\
\qquad\quad | \\
\qquad\quad \text{H}
\end{array}
$$

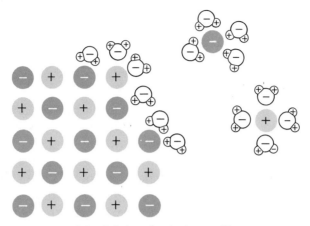

Figure 8.1   Solution of an ionic crystal in water.

Methyl alcohol does not dissolve in nonpolar solvents. The strong inter-molecular attractions of pure methyl alcohol are not overcome unless the solvent molecules can form attractions of equal, or almost equal, strength with the methyl alcohol molecules.

In general, then, polar materials dissolve only in polar solvents, and nonpolar substances are soluble in nonpolar solvents. This is the first rule of solubility: "like dissolves like." Network crystals, such as the diamond, in which the atoms comprising the crystal are held together by covalent bonds, are insoluble in all liquids. This crystalline structure is far too stable to be broken down by a solution process, and any potential solute–solvent attractions cannot approach the strength of the covalent bonding of the crystal.

Polar liquids (water, in particular) can function as solvents for many ionic compounds. The ions of the solute are electrostatically attracted by the polar solvent molecules—negative ions by the positive poles of the solvent molecules, positive ions by the negative poles of the solvent molecules. These ion–dipole attractions can be relatively strong. Figure 8.1 diagrams the solution of an ionic crystal in water. The ions in the center of the crystal are attracted equally in all directions by the oppositely charged ions of the crystal. The electrostatic attractions on the ions of the surface of the crystal, however, are unbalanced, and these are the ions that are exposed to the solvent molecules. Water molecules are attracted to the surface ions of the crystal, the positive ends of the water molecules to the anions and the negative ends of the water molecules to the cations. The ion–dipole attractions thus formed allow the ions to excape from the crystal and drift off into the liquid phase. The dissolved ions are **hydrated** and move through the solution surrounded by a sheath of water molecules; all ions are hydrated in water solution.

Certain covalent molecules with relatively high dipole moments dissolve in water to produce solutions of ions (see Section 3.17). For example, hydrogen chloride, which exists in the pure state as highly polar, covalent molecules, forms such aqueous solutions. When this substance is placed in water, the HCl molecules interact with the water molecules.

$$HCl(g) + H_2O \rightarrow H_3O^+(aq) + Cl^-(aq)$$

Both of the ions resulting from this reaction are, of course, hydrated.

A number of covalent compounds containing metals and nonmetals (e.g., aluminum chloride) also ionize in water solution. True cations with charges of 3+ or higher (such as Al^{3+}) seldom exist in pure compounds; aluminum chloride is a covalent compound. In addition, other species with relatively high ratios of charge to size (e.g., the very small Be^{2+} ion) form pure compounds that are largely covalent. The same factor that is principally responsible for the covalent character of these compounds (a high ratio of ionic charge to radius) also leads to the formation of very stable hydrated ions (Section 8.3).

$$BeCl_2(s) + 4H_2O \rightarrow Be(H_2O)_4^{2+}(aq) + 2Cl^-(aq)$$

8.3   Hydrates

The nature of the interactions between water molecules and ions in aqueous solution is a subject of extensive study. Negative ions in aqueous solution are hydrated by means of ion–dipole attractions or, where possible, by hydrogen bonding. Unless the positive ion itself contains hydrogen atoms (as, e.g., the ammonium ion, NH_4^+), hydrogen bonding between a positive ion and a water molecule is impossible.

Nevertheless, the attractions between water molecules and most metal cations are strong ones. At one time, coordinate covalent bonds were thought to bind these particles together into **complex ions,** such a bond being formed by the use of a vacant orbital of the metal cation and a pair of unshared electrons from the oxygen of a water molecule. This valence bond approach, especially when modified to take hybridized orbitals into account (Section 3.12), remains a useful one, but the ligand field theory and the molecular orbital theory (Section 16.4) offer interpretations that are more in agreement with the observed properties of these hydrated ions.

Most metal cations are hydrated by a definite number of water molecules; the most common number is six, although four is not rare. For sixfold coordination, the water molecules are arranged at the corners of a regular octahedron as illustrated in Figure 8.2 for the ion [Cr $(H_2O)_6]^{3+}$. Certain other molecules and anions (called **ligands**) form complex ions with metal cations (see Chapter 16). The number of ligands coordinated around the central ion is called the **coordination number,** or **ligancy,** of that ion. In aqueous solution, hydrated complex cations are undoubtedly further hydrated by additional water molecules that are hydrogen bonded to the coordinated water molecules; however,

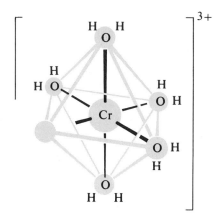

Figure 8.2 The hydrated Cr^{3+} ion.

the water molecules of the outer layers are much more loosely held than those of the inner coordination sphere.

Frequently, hydrated ions persist in the crystalline materials obtained by the evaporation of aqueous solutions of salts. Thus the solid compound $FeCl_3 \cdot 6H_2O$ is actually $[Fe(H_2O)_6]Cl_3$, and $[Fe(H_2O)_6]^{3+}$ ions can be identified in the crystal. Other examples of solid hydrates in which the water of hydration are coordinated to the cation are $[Co(H_2O)_6]Cl_2$, $[Cr(H_2O)_6]Cl_3$, and $[Be(H_2O)_4]Cl_2$.

Solid hydrates in which water molecules are coordinated to anions by hydrogen bonding are known but are not common. For example, in the compound $ZnSO_4 \cdot 7H_2O$, six water molecules are coordinated around the zinc ion, and the seventh is hydrogen bonded to the sulfate anion. Other examples include the analagous compounds $NiSO_4 \cdot 7H_2O$ and $CoSO_4 \cdot 7H_2O$ as well as $CuSO_4 \cdot 5H_2O$ which may be represented $[Cu(H_2O)_4]SO_4 \cdot H_2O$.

There are two other ways in which water can occur in a crystalline hydrate in addition to association with cation or anion. The water molecules may assume positions in the crystal lattice without being associated with a specific ion. Such is the case for the compound $BaCl_2 \cdot 2H_2O$; removal of the water from this compound destroys the crystal lattice. Or, the water molecules may occur between the layers or in the interstices of a crystal lattice; the hydrates of the zeolites, a group of silicate minerals, incorporate water in such a manner. Removal of zeolitic water from a hydrate changes the crystal very little, if at all.

8.4 Heat of Solution

When a solute dissolves in a solvent, energy is absorbed or evolved, the actual quantity per mole of solute depending upon the concentration of the final solution. Thus when a **heat of solution** is recorded, the number of moles of solvent used to dissolve 1 mole of solute in the determination of the heat effect must be indicated in some way. If no such distinction is made, it may be assumed that the heat of solution relates to a process in which 1 mole of solute is dissolved in an infinitely large quantity of solvent (heat of solution at infinite dilution); the heat of solution per mole of a given solute is virtually a constant when very dilute solutions are prepared.

The heat effect observed when a solution is prepared is the net result of the energy *required* to break apart certain chemical bonds or attractions (solute-solute and solvent-solvent) and the energy *released* by the formation of new ones (solute-solvent). Thus if an ionic solid (MX) dissolves in water, the heat of solution is a manifestation of the energy required to break apart the crystal lattice:

$$\text{energy}_1 + MX(s) \rightarrow M^+(g) + X^-(g)$$

and the energy liberated when the ions are hydrated:

$$M^+(g) + X^-(g) \rightarrow M^+(aq) + X^-(aq) + \text{energy}_2$$

The heat of hydration (energy_2) itself may be considered as the sum of two heat effects—the energy needed to break the hydrogen bonds between some of the solvent molecules and the energy released when these water molecules hydrate the ions of the solute. However, it is difficult experimentally to investigate these two effects separately.

If the heat of hydration (energy_2) is larger than the lattice energy (energy_1) for a given solute, then the overall solution process will be exothermic (ΔH, negative). On the other hand, if the lattice energy (energy_1) is larger than the hydration energy (energy_2) for a given solute, then heat will be absorbed when the solute dissolves in water; such is the case with the majority of ionic solutes.

The magnitude of the hydration energy of a salt depends upon the concentration of charge (ratio of charge to surface area) of its ions. In general, a high concentration of charge results when an ion has a small size, a high charge, or a combination of these two factors. Ions with high concentrations of charge attract water molecules strongly, and this leads to large heats of hydration. This is generally not reflected in the heat of solution because the same factor—high ionic charge concentrations—also leads to very stable crystal structures and consequently large lattice energies.

Similar considerations apply to the solution of nonionic materials. The lattice energies of molecular crystals are not so large as those of ionic crystals since the forces holding molecular crystals together are not so strong; however, solvation energies for such covalent materials are also of a low order. For molecular substances that dissolve in nonpolar solvents without ionization and without appreciable solute–solvent interaction, the heat of solution is endothermic and about the same magnitude as the heat of fusion of the solute.

Gases generally dissolve in liquids with the evolution of heat. Since no energy is required to separate the molecules of a gas, the predominant heat effect of such a solution process is the solvation of the gas molecules, and such is exothermic. The calculation of the heat of solution of hydrogen chloride gas in water, however, requires that the heat evolved by the formation of hydrated ions be reduced by the energy required for the ionization of the HCl molecules.

The effect of a temperature change on the solubility of a substance depends upon whether the heat of solution of the material is exothermic or endothermic. Suppose that a solute dissolves in water with the absorption of heat. The crystallization of this solute from a saturated solution would evolve a commensurate quantity of heat. We can represent the equilibrium between excess solid solute and saturated solution as

$$\text{energy} + \text{solute} + H_2O \rightleftharpoons \text{saturated solution}$$

The effect of adding heat to such a system can be predicted by means of a principle first proposed by Henri Le Chatelier in 1888. **Le Chatelier's principle** states that the application of a stress to a system in equilibrium results in the system reacting in such a way as to counteract the stress and establish a new equilibrium state. If the temperature of the system previously described is increased (energy added), the equilibrium point will shift to the right (the direction in which energy is absorbed), and hence more solute will dissolve. If the system is cooled, the point of equilibrium will shift to the left (the direction in which energy is evolved), and solute will precipitate out of solution. Hence, the solubility of materials that dissolve with the absorption of heat increases with increasing temperature; this is true of the solubility of most ionic solutes in water.

When a substance dissolves with the evolution of heat,

$$\text{solute} + H_2O \rightleftharpoons \text{saturated solution} + \text{energy}$$

Le Chatelier's principle indicates that the solubility of the solute increases when the temperature is lowered, and the solubility decreases when the temperature is raised. This is the case for all aqueous solutions of gases; warming a soft drink causes bubbles of carbon dioxide gas to come out of solution.

The solubility differential with respect to change in temperature depends upon the magnitude of the heat of solution. The solubilities of substances with small heats of solution do not change much with changes in temperature.

8.5   Pressure and Solubility

Changes in pressure ordinarily have little effect upon the solubility of solid and liquid solutes. However, increasing or decreasing the pressure on a solution containing a dissolved gas has a definite effect. William Henry in 1803 discovered that the amount of a gas that dissolves in a given quantity of a liquid, at constant temperature, is directly proportional to the partial pressure of a gas above the solution. **Henry's law** is valid only for dilute solutions and relatively low pressures. Gases that are extremely soluble generally react chemically with the solvent (e.g., the solution of hydrogen chloride gas in water); such solutions do not follow Henry's law.

Carbonated beverages are water solutions that are saturated with carbon dioxide gas. When a bottle of a carbonated beverage is opened, the pressure is relieved, and the solubility of the gas drops accordingly. Bubbles of CO_2 gas form and escape—a process known as effervescence.

The blood of deep sea divers becomes saturated with the nitrogen and oxygen of the air under the comparatively high pressures characteristic of the depths at which such divers work. If this pressure is relieved too rapidly, as by too rapid an ascent to the surface, the nitrogen comes out of solution rapidly and forms bubbles in the circulatory systems of the afflicted divers. This condition, known as the "bends," may be fatal. Since the dissolved oxygen in the blood can be utilized by the body, it causes no problem. This condition can be avoided by a slow ascent to the surface or by the use of a decompression chamber in which the pressure on the diver is slowly brought back to atmospheric. In these circumstances, the nitrogen slowly diffuses into the lungs from which it is exhaled. Another solution to the problem involves the use of an artificial atmosphere of helium and oxygen in place of air. Helium is much less soluble in blood than is nitrogen.

8.6   Concentration of Solutions

The concentration of solute in a solution may be expressed in several different ways.

1. The **weight percentage** of solute in a solution is 100 times the weight of solute divided by the *total* weight of the solution. Thus 100 g of a 10% aqueous solution of sulfuric acid contains 10 g of H_2SO_4 and 90 g of water. Notice that a solution of this concentration would contain 11 g of H_2SO_4 per 100 g of water. Volume percentages are not commonly employed; figures recorded as percentages should be understood to be based on weight unless specific notation to the contrary is made.

2. The **mole fraction,** X, of a component of a solution is the ratio of the number of moles of that component to the total number of moles of all components present in the solution (Section 5.10), Example 5.14). A 100 g sample of a 10% H_2SO_4 solution contains $10/98 = 0.10$ moles of H_2SO_4 and $90/18 = 5.0$ moles of H_2O. The mole fraction of H_2SO_4 is, therefore,

$$X_{H_2SO_4} = \frac{0.10}{5.0 + 0.10} = 0.020$$

Since the mole fractions of all of the components of a solution taken together must equal 1.00, $X_{H_2O} = 0.98$.

3. The **molarity,** *M,* of a solution is the number of moles of solute per liter of solution. Thus a $6M$ solution of sulfuric acid is prepared by taking 6 moles of H_2SO_4 ($6 \times 98.08 = 588.48$ g) and adding, with careful mixing, enough water to make exactly 1 liter of solution.

Notice that the definition is based on the total *volume* of the solution. When a liquid solution is prepared, the volume of the solution rarely equals the sum of the volumes of the pure components. Usually, the final volume of the solution is larger or smaller than the total of the volumes of the constituents. Hence, it is not practical to attempt to predict the amount of solvent that should be employed to prepare a given solution; rather, molar solutions (as well as others that are based on total volume) are generally prepared by the use of the volumetric flasks (Figure 8.3). In the preparation of a solution, the correct amount of solute is placed in the flask, and water is then added, with careful and constant mixing, until the solution fills the flask to the calibration mark on the neck.

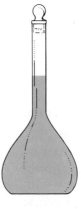

Figure 8.3 Volumetric flask.

It is a simple matter to calculate the quantity of solute present in a given sample of a solution when the concentration of the solution is expressed in terms of molarity. Concentrations defined on the basis of the total volume of solution have this decided advantage. Thus 1 liter of a $3M$ solution contains 3 moles of solute, 500 ml contains 1.5 moles, 250 ml contains 0.75 moles, and 100 ml contains 0.3 moles. A disadvantage, however, of basing concentrations on volume of solution is that such concentrations change slightly with temperature changes because of expansion or contraction of liquid solutions. For exact work, therefore, a solution should be prepared at the temperature at which it is to be used, and a volumetric flask calibrated for this temperature should be employed.

Example 8.1 What weight of concentrated nitric acid that is 70.0% HNO_3 should be used to prepare 250 ml of $2.00M$ HNO_3? If the density of the concentrated nitric acid is 1.42 g/ml, what volume of concentrated nitric acid should be used?

Solution The molecular weight of HNO_3 is 63.0, and therefore, $2(63.0) = 126.0$ g of HNO_3 should be contained in 1000 ml of $2.00M$ solution. In 100 g of concentrated nitric acid (70.0%), there would be 70.0 g HNO_3. Therefore

$$? \text{ g concd. } HNO_3 = 250 \text{ ml soln.} \left(\frac{126.0 \text{ g } HNO_3}{1000 \text{ ml soln.}}\right)\left(\frac{100.0 \text{ g concd.} HNO_3}{70.0 \text{ g } HNO_3}\right)$$

$$= 45.0 \text{ g concd.} HNO_3$$

To convert this into milliliters of concentrated acid,

$$? \text{ ml concd.} HNO_3 = 45.0 \text{ g concd.} HNO_3 \left(\frac{1.00 \text{ ml concd.} HNO_3}{1.42 \text{ g concd.} HNO_3}\right)$$

$$= 31.7 \text{ ml concd.} HNO_3$$

Example 8.2 What is the molarity of a 20.0% H_2SO_4 solution if the density of the solution is 1.14 g/ml?

Solution

$$? \text{ moles } H_2SO_4 = 1000 \text{ ml soln.} \left(\frac{1.14 \text{ g soln.}}{1.00 \text{ ml soln.}}\right)\left(\frac{20.0 \text{ g } H_2SO_4}{100 \text{ g soln.}}\right)$$

$$\left(\frac{1 \text{ mole } H_2SO_4}{98.08 \text{ g } H_2SO_4}\right)$$

$$= 2.32 \text{ moles } H_2SO_4$$

The solution is, therefore, $2.32M$.

4. The **normality,** N, of a solution is the number of gram equivalent weights of solute per liter of solution. The equivalent weight of a substance depends upon the reaction that the substance undergoes. Hence, the normality of a solution depends upon the use that is to be made of the solution. If sulfuric acid is to be used in a neutralization reaction, the equivalent weight of H_2SO_4 is one-half the molecular weight, or we can say that 1 mole of H_2SO_4 is 2 equiv (Section 7.7). Hence, a $1M$ solution of H_2SO_4 is $2N$.

For solutions of $KMnO_4$ that are to be employed in oxidation-reduction reactions in which the equivalent weight of $KMnO_4$ is $\frac{1}{5}$ the molecular weight (Section 7.7), the normality of a given solution is five times the molarity since 1 mole of $KMnO_4$ is 5 equiv. On the other hand, the normality of an NaOH solution, to be used in a neutralization reaction, is the same as its molarity since the equivalent weight of NaOH is the same as the molecular weight. The normality of a solution is always a simple whole number multiple (including 1) of the molarity of the solution.

Since the normality of a solution is based upon its total volume, the same volumetric technique is employed in the preparation of normal solutions as is used in the preparation of molar solutions. Similarly, the normality of a solution varies slightly with temperature.

Example 8.3 What weight of $K_2Cr_2O_7$ should be used to prepare 500.0 ml of $0.1000N$ solution if the dichromate ion functions as an oxidizing agent?

$$6e^- + 14H^+ + Cr_2O_7^{2-} \longrightarrow 2Cr^{3+} + 7H_2O$$

What is the molarity of this solution?

Solution The molecular weight of $K_2Cr_2O_7$ is 294.19, and according to the partial equation, the equivalent weight of $K_2Cr_2O_7$ is $\frac{1}{6}$ of the molecular weight, or 49.03. Thus

$$? \text{g } K_2Cr_2O_7 = 500 \text{ ml solution} \left(\frac{0.1\,(49.03)\text{ g } K_2Cr_2O_7}{1000 \text{ ml solution}} \right)$$

$$= 2.452 \text{ g } K_2Cr_2O_7$$

Since 1 equiv of $K_2Cr_2O_7$ is $\frac{1}{6}$ of a mole, this solution is $\frac{1}{6}(0.1)M$ or $0.1667\,M$.

5. The **molality,** m, of a solution is the number of moles of solute per 1000 g of solvent. Thus a $1m$ aqueous solution of sulfuric acid can be prepared by adding 1 mole (98.08 g) of H_2SO_4 to 1000 g of water. The final volume of a molal solution is of no importance, and $1m$ aqueous solutions of different solutes, each containing 1000 g of water, will have different volumes. However, these solutions all will have the same mole fractions of solute and solvent (see Examples 8.4 and 8.5 following).

The molality of a given solution does not vary with temperature since such solutions are prepared on the basis of the masses of the components and mass does not change with temperature changes. The molality of a *very dilute* aqueous solution is approximately the same as the molarity of the solution since 1000 g of water occupies approximately 1000 ml.

Example 8.4 What are the mole fractions of solute and solvent in a $1.0000m$ aqueous solution?

Solution The molecular weight of H_2O is 18.0153. Hence,

$$? \text{ moles } H_2O = 1000 \text{ g } H_2O \left(\frac{1 \text{ mole } H_2O}{18.0153 \text{ g } H_2O} \right) = 55.508 \text{ moles } H_2O$$

The total number of moles in a solution containing 1 mole of solute and 1000 g of H_2O is, therefore, $1 + 55.508 = 56.508$. Hence,

$$X_{H_2O} = \frac{55.508}{56.508} = 0.9823$$

$$X_{\text{solute}} = \frac{1.000}{56.508} = 0.0177$$

This last result could have been obtained by subtracting X_{H_2O} from 1.0000.

Example 8.5 What are the mole fractions of solute and solvent in a $1.0000m$ solution employing CCl_4 as a solvent?

Solution The molecular weight of CCl_4 is 153.823

$$? \text{ moles } CCl_4 = 1000 \text{ g } CCl_4 \left(\frac{1 \text{ mole } CCl_4}{153.823 \text{ g } CCl_4} \right) = 6.5009 \text{ moles } CCl_4$$

Thus

$$X_{CCl_4} = \frac{6.5009}{7.5009} = 0.8667$$

$$X_{solute} = \frac{1.0000}{7.5009} = 0.1333$$

Example 8.6 What is the molality of a 0.5000 M aqueous solution of sucrose ($C_{12}H_{22}O_{11}$) if the density of the solution is 1.0638 g/ml?

Solution The molecular weight of $C_{12}H_{22}O_{11}$ is 342.30 One liter of the solution weighs 1063.8 g and contains 342.30/2 = 171.15 g $C_{12}H_{22}O_{11}$ and (1063.8 − 171.2) = 892.6 g H_2O.

$$? \text{ moles } C_{12}H_{22}O_{11} = 1000 \text{ g } H_2O \frac{0.5 \text{ moles } C_{12}H_{22}O_{11}}{892.6 \text{ g } H_2O}$$

$$= 0.5601 \text{ moles } C_{12}H_{22}O_{11}$$

The solution is, therefore, 0.5601 m.

8.7 Volumetric Analysis

The concentration of a given solution is constant from sample to sample no matter how much of the solution is taken, but the actual quantity of solute in any sample is a different matter. Molar and normal concentrations state the amount of solute present in a liter of the solution. To determine the number of moles or the number of equivalents in a sample of a molar or normal solution, one must multiply the concentration of the solution by the volume, in liters, of the sample. Thus a $6M$ solution contains, by definition, 6 moles of solute in 1 liter of solution; 500 ml of this solution (0.5 liter) would contain 0.5(6) or 3 moles of solute; 100 ml of this solution (0.1 liter) would contain 0.1(6) or 0.6 mole of solute.

For a sample of a solution of volume V (*in liters*) and of molarity M or normality N:

$$V \times M = \text{number of moles of solute in sample}$$

$$V \times N = \text{number of equivalents of solute in sample}$$

Calculations for reactions that are run between substances in solution are simplified if the concentrations of the solutions are expressed in normalities. One equivalent weight of a substance will react with exactly 1 equivalent weight of another. Hence, n equivalents of 1 will react with exactly n equivalents of 2.

$$n_1 = n_2$$

But the number of equivalents of 1 in a sample of a solution of 1 is equal to the volume of the sample, in liters, times the normality of the solution.

$$n_1 = V_1 N_1 \quad \text{(volume in liters)}$$

Likewise,

$$n_2 = V_2 N_2 \qquad \text{(volume in liters)}$$

We can therefore derive the relationship

$$V_1 N_1 = V_2 N_2$$

Since a volume term appears on both sides of the equality, any units can be used to express V_1 and V_2 provided that both are expressed in the same units. This equation may be employed for calculations involving reactions between samples of two solutions.

Under some circumstances, another equation is useful. The number of equivalents in a sample is equal to the weight of the sample (g) divided by the equivalent weight (e) of the substance. Thus

$$n_2 = \frac{g_2}{e_2}$$

We can use this expression together with $n_1 = V_1 N_1$ to derive

$$V_1 N_1 = \frac{g_2}{e_2} \qquad \text{(volume in liters)}$$

If the volume is expressed in milliliters,

$$V_1 N_1 = \frac{1000\, g_2}{e_2} \qquad \text{(volume in milliliters)}$$

This expression is convenient for calculations for reactions between a weighed substance (2) and another (1) in solution. If sample 2 is impure, the actual weight of the reactive part of the sample is equal to the fractional purity (p_2) times the total weight of the sample (g_2); thus

$$V_1 N_1 = \frac{1000\, p_2 g_2}{e_2}$$

These equations are easily derived and need not be memorized.

Chemical analyses that employ solutions of exactly known concentrations are called **volumetric analyses;** in such determinations, a process known as **titration** is used. For example, the concentration of an acid solution could be measured by determining, through titration, the volume of an alkaline solution of known concentration (called a **standard solution**) necessary to neutralize a sample of the acid solution. The standard solution of alkali is placed in a graduated tube called a **buret.** The buret is fitted with a stopcock, or valve, at the lower end to permit the solution to be withdrawn in controlled amounts. A definite volume of the unknown acid solution is carefully measured into a flask and a few drops of a substance known as an indicator added. The standard alkali solution, from the buret, is added to the flask until the indicator changes color; throughout this addition, the contents of the flask are kept well mixed by swirling. At the **end point,** shown by the indicator, equivalent amounts of acid and alkali have been used. The volume of the standard alkali used is read from the buret, and the concentration of the acid is calculated as illustrated in Example 8.7.

Example 8.7   What is the normality of an acid solution if 50.00 ml of the solution requires 37.52 ml of 0.1429 N alkali for neutralization?

Solution

$$V_1 N_1 = V_2 N_2$$

$$(50.00 \text{ ml}) x = (37.52 \text{ ml})(0.1429 N)$$

$$x = 0.1702 N$$

Example 8.8   A 0.2676 g sample of a pure, solid acid dissolved in 100 ml of water requires 35.68 ml of 0.1190 N alkali for neutralization. What is the equivalent weight of the acid? What is the molecular weight of the acid if it is diprotic?

Solution

$$V_1 N_1 = \frac{g_2}{e_2} \qquad \text{(volume in liters)}$$

$$(0.03568)(0.1190) = \frac{0.2676}{x}$$

$$x = 63.03$$

Since the acid is diprotic, the equivalent weight is $\frac{1}{2}$ the molecular weight, and the molecular weight must be 126.06.

Example 8.9   A 0.4308 g sample of iron ore is dissolved in acid and the iron converted into the ferrous state. This solution is titrated against permanganate; the titration employs 32.31 ml of 0.1248 N $KMnO_4$ which oxidizes Fe^{2+} to Fe^{3+}. What is the percentage of iron in the ore?

Solution   Since the oxidation number of iron increases by 1 unit, the equivalent weight of iron is the same as the atomic weight, 55.85.

$$V_1 N_1 = \frac{p_2 g_2}{e_2} \qquad \text{(volume in liters)}$$

$$(0.03231)(0.1248) = \frac{x(0.4308)}{55.85}$$

$$x = 0.5228$$

The ore is 52.28% iron.

8.8   Vapor Pressure of Solutions

The vapor pressure of any solution (P_{total}) is the sum of the partial pressures of the components (p_A, p_B, etc.). Thus for a binary solution,

$$P_{total} = p_A + p_B$$

For **ideal solutions,** the partial pressure of each component can be calculated from the mole fraction of the component present in the solution
(X_A) and the vapor pressure of the pure component at the temperature
in question ($p_A°$). Thus

$$p_A = X_A p_A° \qquad p_B = X_B p_B°$$
$$P_{total} = X_A p_A° + X_B p_B°$$

In other words, ideal solutions have properties that are the weighted
averages of the properties of the components.   This relationship was
discovered by Francois Raoult in 1886 and is called **Raoult's law.**

Figure 8.4 illustrates partial pressure curves for components A and B
of ideal binary solutions as well as the total pressure curve which is, of

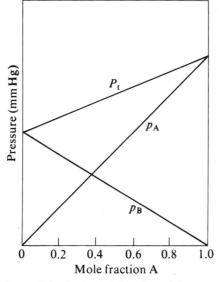

Figure 8.4   Typical total and partial vapor
pressure curves for solutions that follow
Raoult's law.

course, the sum of the two partial pressure curves.   A and B represent
liquids that are miscible in all proportions.   In the figure, pressures are
plotted versus mole fraction of A; since the mole fractions of A and B
must add up to 1.0, the mole fraction of B is easily derived from the scale
of the x axis.

Not all solutions are ideal.   The vapor pressures of some solutions
show negative deviations from Raoult's law (Figure 8.5); other nonideal
solutions show positive deviations (Figure 8.6).   The white lines of
Figures 8.5 and 8.6 are the partial pressure and total pressure curves calculated by means of Raoult's law.

In ideal solutions, the intermolecular attractions between the components (A–B attractions) are of the same magnitude as the intermolecu-

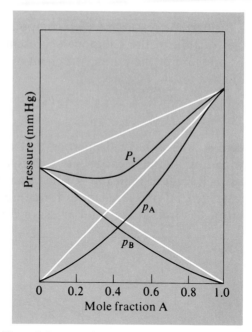

Figure 8.5 Typical total and partial vapor pressure curves for solutions that show negative deviations for Raoult's law. (White lines are based on Raoult's law.)

lar attractions found in the pure components (A–A attractions and B–B attractions). Consequently, no heat effect is observed when an ideal solution is prepared. Negative deviations are observed when the intermolecular attractions of the solution (A–B) are stronger than those of either of the pure components (A–A and B–B); hence, the escaping tendencies of the components are reduced when they are mixed. Such solutions generally have exothermic heats of solution. Positive deviations result when the pure components have stronger intermolecular attractions (A–A and B–B) than the mixture (A–B); heat is absorbed when such solutions are prepared.

Even though a pair of components does not form ideal solutions over the entire range of concentrations, most *dilute* solutions approach ideality. In Figures 8.5 and 8.6, this can be seen from the extreme right portion of the p_A curves where X_A approaches 1.0 or the extreme left portion of the p_B curves where X_B is close to 1.0.

Dilute solutions of *nonvolatile* molecular solutes generally follow Raoult's law. When the solute has a very low vapor pressure, the vapor pressure of the solution is almost entirely due to the solvent. If component A is the solvent and B is the solute, then

$$P_{total} = X_A p_A^{\circ}$$

or

$$P_{total} = (1 - X_B) p_A^{\circ}$$

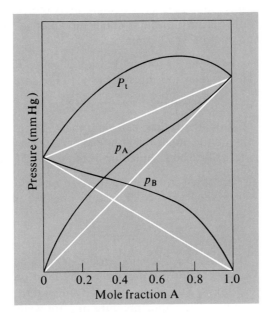

Figure 8.6 Typical total and partial vapor pressure curves for solutions that show positive deviations from Raoult's law. (White lines are based on Raoult's law.)

Hence, the vapor pressure of a solution prepared from 1 mole of a nonvolatile nonionizing solute and 99 moles of solvent would be lower by 1% than the vapor pressure of the pure solvent. This is because only 99% of the surface molecules in the solution are solvent molecules, and the escape of solvent molecules to the vapor phase would be lowered by a corresponding amount.

Raoult's law is only strictly applicable to this type of solution when the solution is dilute and solvent–solute interactions are unimportant. Under this condition, the particular nonvolatile solute does not matter. It is the number of dissolved solute particles per given quantity of solvent that determines the vapor pressure lowering not their size, shape, or weight. The properties of solutions containing nonvolatile solutes that are in ionic form are considered in Section 8.11.

Example 8.9 If heptane and octane form ideal solutions, what is the vapor pressure at 40°C of a solution containing 1.0 mole of heptane and 4.0 moles of octane? At 40°C, the vapor pressure of heptane is 92 mm, and the vapor pressure of octane, is 31 mm.

Solution

$$X_{\text{heptane}} = \tfrac{1}{5} \text{ and } X_{\text{octane}} = \tfrac{4}{5}$$

Hence,

$$P_{\text{total}} = \tfrac{1}{5}(92 \text{ mm}) + \tfrac{4}{5}(31 \text{ mm}) = 43 \text{ mm}$$

Example 8.10 Assuming ideality, calculate the vapor pressure of a 1.00*m* solution of a nonvolatile molecular solute in water at 50°C. The vapor pressure of water at 50°C is 92.5 mm.

Solution From Example 8.4, the mole fraction of water in a 1.00*m* solution is 0.982. Hence, the vapor pressure of a 1.00*m* solution at 50°C is

$$0.982\,(92.5 \text{ mm}) = 90.8 \text{ mm}$$

Example 8.11 Assuming ideality, calculate the vapor pressure of a 1.00*m* solution of a nonvolatile molecular solute in carbon tetrachloride at 50°C. The vapor pressure of carbon tetrachloride at 50°C is 317 mm.

Solution From Example 8.5, the mole fraction of carbon tetrachloride in a 1.00*m* solution is 0.867. Hence, the vapor pressure of a 1.00*m* solution at 50°C is

$$0.867\,(317 \text{ mm}) = 275 \text{ mm}$$

Example 8.12 A solution is prepared from 2.00 g of a nonvolatile solute and 90.10 g of water. The vapor pressure of the solution, at 60°C, is 147.4 mm. According to Raoult's law, what is the approximate molecular weight of the solute? The vapor pressure of pure water at 60°C is 148.9 mm.

Solution

$$P_t = X_A p_A^\circ$$
$$147.4 \text{ mm} = X_A\,(148.9 \text{ mm})$$
$$X_A = 0.990$$

The amount of water employed in the preparation of the solution (90.10 g) is 5.000 moles. Hence, the mole fraction of water in the solution is given by

$$X_A = \frac{n_A}{n_A + n_B}$$
$$0.990 = \frac{5.000}{5.000 + n_B}$$
$$n_B = 0.0505 \text{ moles}$$

Thus the 2.00 g of solute used in the solution represents 0.0505 moles.

$$?\,g = 1.00 \text{ mole}\,\frac{2.00 \text{ g}}{0.0505 \text{ mole}} = 39.6 \text{ g}$$

8.9 Boiling Point and Freezing Point of Solutions

The effect of a dissolved nonvolatile solute on the vapor pressure of a liquid is difficult to measure, but the consequences of this vapor pressure depression—elevation of the boiling point and depression of the freezing point—are relatively easily determined with considerable accuracy.

The boiling point of a liquid is defined as the temperature at which the vapor pressure of the liquid is equal to the prevailing atmospheric pressure; boiling points measured under 760 mm pressure are termed normal boiling points (Section 6.4). Since the addition of a nonvolatile solute decreases the vapor pressure of a liquid, a solution will not boil at the normal boiling point of the solvent. It is necessary to increase the temperature above this point in order to attain a vapor pressure over the solution of 760 mm. Hence, the boiling point of a solution containing a nonvolatile molecular solute is higher than that of the pure solvent, and the elevation is proportional to the concentration of solute in the solution.

This effect is illustrated by the vapor pressure curves plotted in Figure 8.7. The extent to which the vapor pressure curve of the solution lies below the vapor pressure curve of the solvent is proportional to the mole

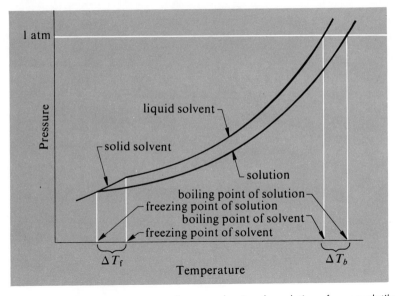

Figure 8.7   Vapor pressure curves of a pure solvent and a solution of a nonvolatile solute (not drawn to scale).

fraction of solute in the solution. The elevation of the boiling point, ΔT_b, follows from this displacement of the vapor pressure curve; for a given solvent, it is a constant for all solutions of the same concentration.

Concentrations are customarily expressed in molalities, rather than mole fractions, for problems involving boiling point elevations. For example, the boiling point of a $1m$ aqueous solution is 0.512°C higher than the boiling point of water. Table 8.1 lists molal boiling point elevation constants for several solvents. The boiling point of a $0.5m$ solution would be expected to be elevated by an amount equal to $\frac{1}{2}$ the molal constant. Thus the boiling point elevation, ΔT_b, of a solution can be calculated by multiplying the molal boiling point elevation constant of the solvent, K_b, by the molality of the solution, m.

$$\Delta T_b = mK_b$$

In reality, this relationship is only approximate; a more exact statement would require that the concentration be expressed in mole fraction of solute, not in molality. However, molalities of *dilute* solutions are proportional (at least with sufficient accuracy) to mole fractions of solute, and since Raoult's law only describes the behavior of most real solutions satisfactorily if they are dilute, the use of molalities in these calculations is justified.

TABLE 8.1.
MOLAL BOILING POINT ELEVATION AND FREEZING POINT DEPRESSION CONSTANTS.

Solvent	Boiling Point (°C)	K_b (°/m)	Freezing Point (°C)	K_f (°/m)
acetic acid	118.1	3.07	16.6	3.90
benzene	80.1	2.53	5.5	5.12
camphor	—	—	179.	39.7
carbon tetrachloride	76.8	5.02	−22.8	29.8
chloroform	61.2	3.63	−63.5	4.68
ethyl alcohol	78.4	1.22	−114.6	1.99
naphthalene	—	—	80.2	6.80
water	100.0	0.512	0.0	1.86

The mole fraction of solute in a solution, X_B, is

$$X_B = \frac{n_B}{n_A + n_B}$$

where n_B is the number of moles of solute, and n_A is the number of moles of solvent. If the solution is dilute, the number of moles of solute is negligible in comparison with the number of moles of solvent, and the denominator may be simplified by dropping the term n_B.

$$X_B \approx \frac{n_B}{n_A}$$

The molality of the solution, m, is the number of moles of solute per 1000 g of solvent. If the molecular weight of the solvent is M_A, $n_A = 1000/M_A$, and thus

$$X_B \approx \frac{m}{1000/M_A} \approx \frac{M_A}{1000} m$$

Hence, there is a direct relation between molality and mole fraction of solute for dilute solutions.

The freezing point of a solvent is the temperature at which the vapor pressure of the solid solvent and liquid solvent are equal. In Figure 8.7, the vapor pressure curves of the liquid solvent and the solid solvent intersect at the freezing point of the solvent. At this temperature, however, the vapor pressure of the solution is lower than the equilibrium vapor pressure of the pure solvent. The vapor pressure curve of the solution intersects the vapor pressure curve of the solid solvent at a lower temperature, and hence the freezing point of the solution is lower than that of the pure solvent. As in the case of boiling point elevations, freezing point depressions depend upon the concentration of the solution and the solvent employed. Molal freezing point depression constants for some solvents are listed in Table 8.1, and the freezing point depression, ΔT_f, of a solution can be calculated from the molality of the solution and the constant for the solvent, K_f.

$$\Delta T_f = mK_f$$

This statement assumes that the solute does not form a solid solution with the solvent and that the solid obtained, upon freezing, is pure solvent. If this is not the case, the relationship is not valid.

The following problems illustrate the use of these relations—for boiling point elevation and freezing point depression—in calculations of the boiling points and freezing points of solutions and, more importantly, the molecular weights of solutes.

> *Example 8.13* What is the boiling point and freezing point of a solution prepared by dissolving 2.40 g of biphenyl ($C_{12}H_{10}$) in 75.0 g of benzene? The molecular weight of biphenyl is 154.
>
> *Solution* The molality of the solution is
>
> $$? \text{ moles } C_{12}H_{10} = 1000 \text{ g benzene} \left(\frac{2.40 \text{ g } C_{12}H_{10}}{75.0 \text{ g benzene}}\right) \left(\frac{1 \text{ mole } C_{12}H_{10}}{154 \text{ g } C_{12}H_{10}}\right)$$
>
> $$= 0.208 \text{ mole } C_{12}H_{10}$$
>
> The boiling point elevation is
>
> $$? \, ^\circ C = 0.208 \, m \, C_{12}H_{10} \left(\frac{2.53 ^\circ C}{1 \, m \, C_{12}H_{10}}\right) = 0.526 ^\circ C$$
>
> The boiling point of the solution is
>
> $$80.1 ^\circ C + 0.5 ^\circ C = 80.6 ^\circ C$$
>
> The freezing point depression is
>
> $$? \, ^\circ C = 0.208 \, m \, C_{12}H_{10} \left(\frac{5.12 ^\circ C}{1 \, m \, C_{12}H_{10}}\right) = 1.06 ^\circ C$$

The freezing point of the solution is

$$5.5°C - 1.1°C = 4.4°C$$

Example 8.14   A solution prepared from 0.300 g of an unknown non-volatile solute in 30.0 g carbon tetrachloride has a boiling point 0.392°C higher than that of pure CCl_4. What is the molecular weight of the solute?

Solution K_b for CCl_4 is 5.02°C, and the molality of the solution is therefore

$$?m = 0.392°C \left(\frac{1m}{5.02°C}\right) = 0.0781m$$

Thus 1000 g of CCl_4 would contain 0.0781 moles of solute. The molecular weight of the solute is, therefore

$$?g = 1 \text{ mole solute} \left(\frac{1000 \text{ g } CCl_4}{0.0781 \text{ mole solute}}\right) \left(\frac{0.300 \text{ g solute}}{30.0 \text{ g } CCl_4}\right)$$

$$= 128 \text{ g}$$

8.10   Distillation

A solution of a nonvolatile solute can be separated into its components by **simple distillation.** Such a procedure consists of boiling away the volatile solvent from the solute. The solvent is obtained by condensing the vapor, and the solute is the residue remaining after the distillation.

A solution of two volatile components that follows Raoult's law (Figure 8.4) can be separated into its components by a process known as **fractional distillation.** According to Raoult's law, each component contributes to the vapor pressure of the solution in proportion to its mole fraction times its vapor pressure in the pure state. Let us assume that, at the temperature of the experiment, component A has a vapor pressure of 200 mm and component B has a vapor pressure of 400 mm; for a solution with a mole fraction of B equal to 0.60, the total vapor pressure is

$$P_t = X_A p_A° + X_B p_B°$$

$$= 0.40(200 \text{ mm}) + 0.60(400 \text{ mm})$$

$$= 80 \text{ mm} + 240 \text{ mm}$$

$$= 320 \text{ mm}$$

The composition of the *vapor* in equilibrium with this solution can be calculated by comparing the partial pressure of each component with the total vapor pressure of the solution (Section 5.10). Thus in the vapor,

$$X_{A,vapor} = \frac{80 \text{ mm}}{320 \text{ mm}} = 0.25 \qquad X_{B,vapor} = \frac{240 \text{ mm}}{320 \text{ mm}} = 0.75$$

Hence, a solution of concentration $X_B = 0.60$ would be in equilibrium with a vapor of concentration $X_{B,vapor} = 0.75$. For ideal solutions, the vapor is always richer than the liquid in the more volatile component (which is this instance in B—it has the higher vapor pressure).

In a distillation of a solution of A and B, the vapor coming off, and being condensed, is richer in B than the liquid remaining behind. The actual composition of vapor and liquid change as the distillation proceeds, but at any given time this generalization is true. By collecting the condensed vapor in several fractions and subjecting these fractions to repeated distillations, eventually the components of the original mixture can be obtained in substantially pure form.

For systems that deviate from Raoult's law, the situation is somewhat different. If the deviation is positive (Figure 8.6), there is a maximum in the total vapor pressure curve corresponding to a solution, of definite composition, that has a vapor pressure higher than either of the pure components. This means that such a solution, a **minimum-boiling azeotrope,** will boil at a lower temperature than either of the two pure components. Ethyl alcohol and water form a minimum boiling azeotrope that contains 4.0 weight percent water and has a normal boiling point of 78.17°C (ethyl alcohol and water boil at 78.3°C and 100°C, respectively).

If a system shows a negative deviation from Raoult's law (Figure 8.5), there will be a minimum in the P_{total} curve. The solution that has a concentration corresponding to this minimum will have a vapor pressure, at any given temperature, lower than either pure component. Thus this solution boils at a temperature *higher* than either pure component and is called a **maximum-boiling azeotrope.** Hydrochloric acid and water form such an azeotrope containing 20.22 weight percent HCl and boiling at 108.6° (pure HCl has a boiling point of −80°C).

The vapor in equilibrium with a maximum- or minimum-boiling azeotrope is of the same concentration as the liquid; hence, azeotropes, like pure substances, distill without change. Fractional distillation of a solution containing components that form an azeotrope will eventually produce one pure component and the azeotrope but not both pure components.

8.11   Solutions of Electrolytes

Solutes may be classified according to the ability of their aqueous solutions to conduct electricity (Section 9.2). The electrical conductivity of a solution depends upon the presence of ions; pure water, itself, is very slightly ionized and is a poor conductor (Section 14.2). An **electrolyte** is a solute of a solution that is a better electrical conductor than the parent solvent alone; in solution, such a solute exists (in whole or in part) as ions. Covalent solutes that are exclusively molecular in solution, and hence do nothing to enhance the conductivity of the solvent, are called **nonelectrolytes.**

Electrolytes may be further divided into two groups: **strong electrolytes** and **weak electrolytes.** The conductivity of a $1m$ solution of a weak electrolyte is much inferior to the conductivity of a $1m$ solution of a strong electrolyte. Weak electrolytes are covalent materials that are incompletely dissociated into ions in solution; strong electrolytes are essentially completely ionic in solution.

In 1887, Svante Arrhenius proposed his "chemical theory of electrolytes." In addition to data from electrical conductivity experiments, a principal source of evidence advanced by Arrhenius in support of his theory was derived from studies of the deviations from Raoult's law exhibited by solutions of electrolytes. The freezing points of *very dilute* solutions of electrolytes are lowered more than those of ideal solutions of nonelectrolytes with corresponding concentrations. The freezing point depression for a dilute solution of a salt such as $NaCl$ or $AgNO_3$ is approximately twice that of a solution of a nonelectrolyte with a similar molal concentration; the depression for a dilute solution of a salt such as K_2SO_4 or $BaCl_2$ is approximately three times as great as "expected" (see Table 8.2).

Arrhenius explained these results on the basis of the supposition that electrolytes are dissociated into ions in solution, $NaCl$ and $AgNO_3$ forming two ions (Na^+, Cl^- and Ag^+, NO_3^-) per "molecule," whereas K_2SO_4 and $BaCl_2$ form three ions ($2K^+$, SO_4^{2-} and Ba^{2+}, $2Cl^-$) per "molecule." Today we know that these salts are ionic even when pure; "molecules" of these materials do not exist. Substances of this type are, therefore, completely ionic in solution and are strong electrolytes. Similar deviations are observed for boiling point elevations.

TABLE 8.2
OBSERVED FREEZING POINT DEPRESSIONS FOR SOME AQUEOUS SOLUTIONS COMPARED TO CALCULATED DEPRESSIONS.[a]

Solute	Concentration of Solution		
	0.001 m	0.01 m	0.1 m
nonelectrolyte	0.00186°C	0.0186°C	0.186°C
sucrose	0.00186	0.0186	0.188
2 ions/formula	0.00372	0.0372	0.372
NaCl	0.00366	0.0360	0.348
3 ions/formula	0.00558	0.0588	0.588
K_2SO_4	0.00528	0.0501	0.432
4 ions/formula	0.00744	0.0744	0.744
$K_3[Fe(CN)_6]$	0.00710	0.0626	0.530

[a]Calculated on the assumptions that K_f for water is 1.86°C/molal over the entire range of concentrations, the salts are 100% ionic in solution, and the ions act independently of one another in their effect on the freezing point of the solution.

Theoretically, the net effect on the freezing point or boiling point depends only on the number of nonvolatile particles in solution and not on their nature. The question, then, is not why the deviations for these salt solutions are larger than those expected for solutions of nondissociating solutes; it is, rather, why the deviations are not *exactly* twice the "expected" in the case of solutions of salts containing two ions per formula unit or three times the "expected" in the case of solutions of salts containing three ions per formula unit. This will be the topic of Section 8.12.

The hydroxides of the group IA metals are ionic crystalline materials, are water soluble, and are strong electrolytes; $Ba(OH)_2$, $Sr(OH)_2$, and $Ca(OH)_2$* are only moderately soluble in water, but they too are strong electrolytes.

We have previously noted that certain covalent substances are ionized in water solution—a process more in harmony with Arrhenius' original views. Perchloric acid is completely ionic in water solution; it is virtually impossible to detect undissociated $HClO_4$ molecules.

$$H_2O + HClO_4 \rightarrow H_3O^+ + ClO_4^-$$

Other acids, though covalent when pure, are strong electrolytes in aqueous solution; the common ones that may be considered ionic in solutions of $1M$ concentration or less are $HClO_4$, HCl, HBr, HI, HNO_3, and H_2SO_4**.

Some covalent materials may be ionized to a lesser extent in water and are classed as weak electrolytes—for example, acetic acid, $HC_2H_3O_2$:

$$H_2O + HC_2H_3O_2 \rightleftharpoons H_3O^+ + C_2H_3O_2^-$$

A $0.01m$ solution of acetic acid is approximately 4% ionic at room temperature; at any given time, 96% of the acetic acid present in the solution is in molecular form. This process is reversible and therefore a double arrow is shown in the preceding equation. In the solution, molecules are constantly dissociating into ions at the same rate that ions, upon interionic contact, are re-forming molecules. Thus this reversible system is in a state of chemical equilibrium; such equilibria are the topic of Chapter 14. Most acids are weak electrolytes.

Some covalent compounds, of which ammonia is the most common example, react with water to produce hydroxide ions.

$$NH_3 + H_2O \rightleftharpoons NH_4^+ + OH^-$$

Thus it is possible to have alkaline solutions of weak electrolytes.

Most salts are ionic compounds; such substances, if soluble, are strong electrolytes in aqueous solution. A number of covalent compounds con-

---

*There is some evidence that in nearly saturated solutions of these compounds dissociation may be incomplete. Thus fairly large concentrations of the ion $CaOH^+$, as well as Ca^{2+} and OH^-, have been identified in such solutions, presumably from the dissociations: $Ca(OH)_2 \rightarrow CaOH^+ + OH^-$ and $CaOH^+ \rightleftharpoons Ca^{2+} + OH^-$.

**The first ionization only: $H_2O + H_2SO_4 \rightarrow H_3O^+ + HSO_4^-$.

taining metals and nonmetals (e.g., aluminum chloride, Section 8.2) are ionized virtually completely in water solution and are classed as strong electrolytes. A small number of covalent compounds of metals, however, dissolve in water but are not ionized completely; as such, they are weak electrolytes. Thus mercuric chloride solutions contain $HgCl_2$ molecules in addition to $HgCl^+$, Hg^{2+}, and Cl^- ions and other more complicated species.

8.12 Interionic Attractions in Solution

The **van't Hoff factor,** i, may be defined as the ratio of the observed freezing point depression for a solution (ΔT_f) to the depression calculated from the molality of the solution and the molal freezing point constant for the solvent (mK_f).

$$i = \frac{\Delta T_f}{mK_f}$$

Since a similar relation is used for boiling point elevations,

$$i = \frac{\Delta T_b}{mK_b}$$

we shall use unspecified ΔT and K in the discussion that follows.

If we rearrange the expression

$$\Delta T = imK$$

the significance of the i factor, which was named for Jacobus van't Hoff who first employed it, becomes clear. The expressions of Section 8.9, $\Delta T = mK$, were derived on the assumption that the solute *does not dissociate* ($i = 1$).

When dissociation of the solute occurs, it is necessary to correct the molality of the solution for freezing point and boiling point calculations. Thus if AB is a strong electrolyte and therefore dissociates completely in solution, in a $0.001m$ solution of AB there would be 0.001 moles of A^+ and 0.001 moles of B^- contained in 1000 g of water. On the assumption that each ion acts independently in its effect on the boiling point and freezing point, the effective concentration of this hypothetical solution would be $0.002m$. Hence, in this simplified example, $i = 2$, $m = 0.001$, and

$$\Delta T = 2(0.001m)K$$

Inspection of the i values recorded in Table 8.3 (which were derived from freezing point determinations) reveals that they do not exactly equal the number of ions per formula unit for each of the strong electrolytes listed. Thus for $0.001m$ solutions, the i value of NaCl is 1.97 (not 2), of K_2SO_4 is 2.84 (not 3), and of $K_3[Fe(CN)_6]$ is 3.82 (not 4). Furthermore, the i value changes with concentration of the solution approaching

TABLE 8.3.
VAN'T HOFF FACTOR, i, FOR VARIOUS STRONG ELECTROLYTES IN
SOLUTION.[a]

Electrolyte	Concentration of Solution		
	0.001 m	0.01 m	0.1 m
NaCl	1.97	1.94	1.87
MgSO$_4$	1.82	1.53	1.21
K$_2$SO$_4$	2.84	2.69	2.32
K$_3$[Fe(CN)$_6$]	3.82	3.36	2.85

[a] From freezing point determinations.

the value expected for complete dissociation as the solution becomes more and more dilute.

In 1923, Peter Debye and Erich Hückel proposed a quantitative theory to explain the behavior of dilute solutions of electrolytes.* According to the **Debye-Hückel theory,** there are interionic attractions in solutions of electrolytes so that the ions are not completely independent of one another as is the case for uncharged molecules in solution. (As has been noted in Section 8.8, solute–solute interactions cause deviations from Raoult's law.) Thus the electrical forces that operate between the oppositely charged ions reduce the effectiveness of these ions.

The i values in Table 8.3 show that the interionic attractions in solutions of MgSO$_4$ produce a stronger effect than those in solutions of NaCl of corresponding concentration even though both of these solutes contain 2 moles of ions per mole of compound; thus for 0.001 m NaCl, i = 1.97, whereas for 0.001 m MgSO$_4$, i = 1.82. This is because the ions of magnesium sulfate are both doubly charged (Mg^{2+}, SO^{2-}), whereas the ions of sodium chloride are but singly charged (Na$^+$, Cl$^-$), and hence the interionic attractions are stronger in solutions of magnesium sulfate.

The effect of dilution upon i values can also be explained on the basis of these interionic attractions. As a solution is diluted, the ions become farther and farther apart, their influence upon one another diminishes accordingly, and the i factor approaches its limiting value. Hence, in *very* dilute solutions, the Debye-Hückel effect is negligible, and the ions essentially behave independently.

Interionic attractions, therefore, make a solution behave as though its ion concentrations were less than they actually are. The **activity** of an

*It should be noted that the Debye-Hückel theory accounts only for the behavior of dilute solutions of electrolytes. Concentrated solutions are imperfectly understood at present. Among the factors that have been postulated to explain the anomolous behavior of concentrated solutions are the lack of sufficient water to hydrate the ions and the presence of ion pairs and ion triplets (ions closely associated with one another).

ion, a, is defined as the "effective concentration" of that ion; it is related to the actual concentration of the ion, c, by an **activity coefficient, γ.**

$$a = \gamma c$$

The activity coefficient is always less than 1 and approaches unity as the concentration of the solution decreases. The calculation of activity coefficients from experimental data is complicated. It is important to recognize that the activity of a given ion depends upon the concentrations of all ions present in the solution whether they are all derived from the same compound or not, since all ions can enter into interionic attractions.

Some characteristics of solutes are summarized in Table 8.4.

TABLE 8.4.
CHARACTERISTICS OF SOLUTES.

Solute	Form of Solute in $1\,m$ Solution	van't Hoff Factor for ΔT_f; Dilute Solutions of Molality, m $\Delta t_f = iK_f m$	Examples
nonelectrolytes	molecules	$i = 1$	$C_{12}H_{22}O_{11}$ (sucrose) CON_2H_4 (urea) $C_3H_5(OH)_3$ (glycerol)
strong electrolytes	ions	$i \approx n^a$	NaCl KOH
weak electrolytes	molecules and ions	$1 < i < n^a$	$HC_2H_3O_2$ NH_3 $HgCl_2$

[a] n = number of moles of ions per mole of solute.

SOME SUGGESTED READINGS

Dreisbach, D., *Liquids and Solutions,* Boston, Houghton Mifflin, 1966 (paper).

Hildebrand, J. H., and Scott, R. L., *Regular Solutions,* Englewood Cliffs, N.J., Prentice-Hall, 1962.

Hildebrand, J. H., and Scott, R. L., *The Solubility of Nonelectrolytes,* New York, Dover, 1964 (paper).

Hunt, J. P., *Metal Ions in Aqueous Solution,* New York, Benjamin, 1963 (paper).

PROBLEMS

8.1 Henry's law may be stated as $K = p/X$, where p is the partial pressure of the gas over a saturated solution, X is the mole fraction of the dissolved gas, and K is a constant. The value of K for nitrogen at 20°C is 5.75 × 10^7. How many grams of nitrogen dissolve in 100 g of water at 20°C if the pressure of nitrogen over the solution is 760 mm?

8.2 Describe an experiment that can be run at a single temperature to determine whether the solubility of a given salt increases or decreases with an increase in temperature.

8.3 What volume of concentrated hydrochloric acid should be used to prepare 500 ml of $0.100\,M$ HCl? The concentrated acid is 37.4% HCl and has a density of 1.19 g/ml.

8.4 What is the molarity of concentrated nitric acid if the acid is 70.0% HNO_3 and has a density of 1.42 g/ml?

8.5 A 10.0% solution of $AgNO_3$ has a density of 1.09 g/ml. What is the (a) molarity and (b) molality of this solution?

8.6 What is the mathematical relationship between the molarity and molality of a solution?

8.7 (a) What is the molarity of a $0.10N$ H_3PO_4 solution (calculated on the basis of complete neutralization of the acid)? (b) What is the normality of a $3.0M$ H_2SO_4 solution based on complete neutralization of the acid? (c) A potassium chlorate solution for use in a reaction in which $KClO_3$ is transformed into KCl is labeled $0.090N$. What is the molarity of the solution?

8.8 A 1.00 g sample containing oxalic acid, $H_2C_2O_4$, requires 17.8 ml of $0.300N$ NaOH for neutralization. Find the percentage oxalic acid in the material.

8.9 Potassium bromate, $KBrO_3$, reacts with hydrazine, N_2H_4, in acid solution.

$$2BrO_3^-(aq) + 3N_2H_4(aq) \longrightarrow 2Br^-(aq) + 3N_2(g) + 6H_2O$$

What percentage of a solution is hydrazine if a 1.00 g sample of this material requires 25.0 ml of $0.130N$ potassium bromate solution for complete reaction?

8.10 A 0.378 g sample of an alkali requires 150 ml of $0.0300N$ H_2SO_4 for neutralization. What is the equivalent weight of the alkali?

8.11 A solution is to be analyzed for concentration of Ca^{2+}. The calcium ion present in a 5.00 ml sample of the solution is precipitated as calcium oxalate, CaC_2O_4. The precipitate is removed by filtration, washed, and dissolved in hot dilute sulfuric acid. The resulting solution is titrated with potassium permanganate

$$16H^+ + 2MnO_4^- + 5C_2O_4^{2-} \longrightarrow 10CO_2 + 2Mn^{2+} + 8H_2O$$

and requires 35.0 ml of $0.100N$ $KMnO_4$. What is the concentration of Ca^{2+} (in g/ml) in the original solution?

8.12 Benzene, C_6H_6, and toluene, C_7H_8, form ideal solutions. At 50°C, the vapor pressure of benzene is 268 mm and that of toluene is 92.6 mm. (a)

What is the vapor pressure, at 50°C, of a solution prepared from 39.0 g of benzene and 23.0 g of toluene? (b) What is the composition of the vapor (mole fraction of benzene) in equilibrium with the solution of part (a) at 50°C?

8.13 A solution containing 19.1 g of chloroform, $CHCl_3$, and 2.32 g of acetone, C_3H_6O, has a vapor pressure of 265 mm at 35°C. At the same temperature, the vapor pressures of pure chloroform and pure acetone are 301 mm and 346 mm, respectively. (a) What would be the vapor pressure of a chloroform–acetone solution of this concentration if these substances formed ideal solutions? (b) Does the vapor pressure of this solution show a positive or negative deviation from Raoult's law? (c) Is heat evolved or absorbed when this solution is prepared? (d) Do chloroform and acetone form a maximum- or minimum-boiling azeotrope?

8.14 What is the vapor pressure at 100°C of a solution containing 150 g of urea, CON_2H_4, and 450 g of water? Assume that urea functions as a non-volatile, nondissociating solute in water solution.

8.15 The freezing point of a solution prepared by dissolving 0.140 g of a non-volatile, nondissociating solute in 10.0 g of benzene is 4.68°C. What is the molecular weight of the solute?

8.16 What weight of urea, CON_2H_4, should be added to 50.0 g of water to produce a solution that freezes at −10.0°C?

8.17 A solution containing 5.10 g of a nonvolatile, nondissociating solute in 250 g of CCl_4 boils at 78.0°C. What is the molecular weight of the solute?

8.18 What is the expected freezing point of a 10.0% solution of naphthalene, $C_{10}H_8$, in benzene?

8.19 In 0.100m solution, the weak acid HX is 15.0% ionized. Calculate the expected freezing point of this solution.

8.20 The i factor for the freezing point of a 0.01m solution of acetic acid in water is 1.02, whereas the i factor for the freezing point of a 0.01m solution of acetic acid in benzene is approximately 0.5. Acetic acid has the structure

$$
\begin{array}{ccc}
\text{H} & & \text{O} \\
| & & \nearrow \\
\text{H}-\text{C}-\text{C} & & \\
| & & \searrow \\
\text{H} & & \text{O}-\text{H}
\end{array}
$$

and only the hydrogen bonded to oxygen is acidic. Explain the results of the freezing point determinations.

8.21 A solution containing 1.85 g of $Mg(NO_3)_2$ and 125 g of water freezes at −0.474°C. What is the van't Hoff factor, i, for the freezing point of this solution?

9

Electrochemistry

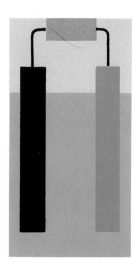

The relations between chemical change and electrical energy are of theoretical and practical importance. Chemical reactions may be used to produce electrical energy, or electrical energy may be used to bring about chemical transformations.

9.1   Metallic Conduction

An electric current is the flow of electric charge. In metals this charge is carried by electrons, and electrical conduction of this type is called **metallic** (or **electronic**) **conduction.** The current moves as a result of the application of electric force supplied by a battery or some other source of electrical energy, and it is necessary to have a complete circuit in order to have current flow.

Metallic crystals have been described in terms of mobile electron clouds permeating relatively fixed lattices of positive metal ions (Section 3.15). When electrons are forced into one end of a metal wire, the impressed electrons displace other electrons of the cloud at the point of entry. The displaced electrons, in turn, assume new positions by pushing neighboring electrons ahead, and this effect is transmitted down the length of the wire until electrons are forced out of the wire at the opposite end. The current source may be regarded as an electron pump, for it serves to force electrons into one end of the circuit and drain them off from the other end. At any one position in the wire, electrical neutrality is preserved since the rate of electrons in equals the rate of electrons out.

The analogy between the flow of electricity and the flow of a liquid is an old one; electricity was early described in terms of a current of "electric fluid." Conventions of long standing, which may be traced back to Benjamin Franklin (1747) and which were adopted before the electron was identified, ascribe a positive charge to this current. We shall interpret electrical circuits in terms of the movement of electrons. Remember, however, that conventional electric current is arbitrarily described as positive and as flowing in the opposite direction.

Quantity of electric charge is measured in **coulombs;** 1 coulomb is the charge carried by 6.2418×10^{18} electrons.* The rate of current flow is given by **amperes;** 1 amp is 1 coulomb/sec, and

$$I = Q/t \qquad \text{or} \qquad Q = I\,t$$

where I is the current in amperes; Q is coulombs of charge transported; and t is time in seconds.

The current is forced through the circuit by an electrical potential difference which is measured in **volts.** It takes 1 joule** of work to move 1 coulomb from a lower to a higher potential when the potential difference is 1 v. One volt, therefore, equals 1 joule/coulomb, and 1 volt coulomb is a unit of energy and equals 1 joule.

The higher the potential difference between two points in a given wire, the more current the wire will carry between those two points. Georg Ohm (1826) expressed the quantitative relation between potential difference, E, in volts and current, I, in amperes, as

$$I = E/R \qquad \text{or} \qquad E = I R$$

where the proportionality constant, R, of **Ohm's law** is called the resistance. Resistance is measured in **ohms;** 1 v is required to force a current of 1 amp through a resistance of 1 ohm.

Resistance to current flow in metals is probably caused by the vibration of the metal ions about their lattice positions; such vibrations interfere with the motion of the electrons and retard the flow of current. As the temperature is increased, the thermal motion of the metal ions is increased; hence, the resistance of metals increases, and metals become poorer conductors.

9.2 Electrolytic Conduction

Electrolytic conduction, in which the charge is carried by ions, will not occur unless the ions of the electrolyte are free to move. Hence, electrolytic conduction is exhibited principally by molten salts and by aqueous solutions of electrolytes. Furthermore, sustained current flow through an electrolytic conductor demands that chemical change accompany the movement of ions.

These principles of electrolytic conduction are best illustrated by reference to an electrolytic cell such as that diagrammed in Figure 9.1 for the electrolysis of molten NaCl between inert electrodes.† The current source pumps electrons into the left-hand electrode which therefore may

---

*One electrostatic unit of charge (esu) is the charge that will repel another like charge at a distance of 1 cm in a vacuum by a force of 1 dyne; 2.9979×10^9 esu $= 1$ coulomb.

**1 joule $= 10^7$ erg $= 2.3905 \times 10^{-1}$ cal. One erg is the work done when a force of 1 dyne acts through a distance of 1 cm; 1 erg $= 1$ dyne cm $= 1\,\mathrm{g\,cm^2/sec^2}$.

† Inert electrodes are not involved in electrode reactions.

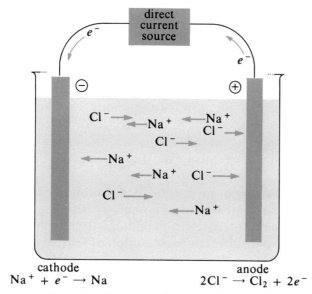

cathode
$$Na^+ + e^- \rightarrow Na$$

anode
$$2Cl^- \rightarrow Cl_2 + 2e^-$$

Figure 9.1   Electrolysis of molten sodium chloride.

be considered to be negatively charged; electrons are drained from the right-hand, positive, electrode. In the electric field thus produced, sodium ions (cations) are attracted toward the negative pole (cathode), and chloride ions (anions) are attracted toward the positive pole (anode). Electric charge, in electrolytic conduction, is carried by cations moving toward the **cathode** and anions moving in the opposite direction, toward the **anode.**

For a complete circuit, electrode reactions must accompany the movement of ions. At the cathode, some chemical species (not necessarily the charge carrier) must accept electrons and be reduced; at the anode, electrons must be removed from some chemical species which is consequently oxidized. The conventions relating to the terms anode and cathode are summarized in Table 9.1.

In the diagrammed cell, sodium ions are reduced at the cathode

$$Na^+ + e^- \rightarrow Na$$

and chloride ions are oxidized at the anode

$$2Cl^- \rightarrow Cl_2 + 2e^-$$

Proper addition of these two partial equations gives the reaction for the entire cell

$$2NaCl(l) \xrightarrow{\text{elec.}} 2Na(l) + Cl_2(g)$$

In the actual operation of the commercial cell used to produce metallic sodium, calcium chloride is added to lower the melting point of sodium chloride, and the cell is operated at a temperature of approximately 600°C. At this temperature, sodium metal is a liquid.

We can trace the flow of negative charge through the circuit of Figure 9.1 as follows. Electrons leave the current source and are pumped into the cathode where they are picked up by, and reduce, sodium ions which have been attracted to this negative electrode. Chloride ions move away from this pole, the cathode, toward the anode and thus carry negative charge in this direction. At the anode, electrons are removed from the chloride ions oxidizing them to chlorine gas; these electrons are pumped out of the cell by the current source. In this manner the circuit is completed.

Electrolytic conduction, then, rests on the mobility of ions, and anything that inhibits the motion of ions causes resistance to current flow. Factors that influence the electrical conductivity of solutions of electrolytes include interionic attractions, solvation of ions, and viscosity of the solvent; these factors rest on solute–solute attractions, solute–solvent attractions, and solvent–solvent attractions, respectively. The average kinetic energy of the solute ions increases as the temperature is raised, and therefore, the resistance of electrolytic conductors generally decreases as the temperature is raised (i.e., conduction increases). Furthermore, the effect of each of the three previously mentioned factors decreases as the temperature is increased.

At all times, electrical neutrality is preserved throughout all parts of the electrolytic liquid—there are as many cations per unit volume as there are anions.

9.3   Electrolysis

The electrolysis of molten sodium chloride serves as a commercial source of sodium metal and chlorine gas; analogous procedures are used to prepare other very active metals (such as potassium and calcium). When certain aqueous solutions are electrolyzed, however, water is involved in the electrode reactions rather than the ions derived from the

TABLE 9.1.
ELECTRODE CONVENTIONS.

	Cathode	Anode
ions attracted	cations	anions
direction of electron movement	into cell	out of cell
half reaction	reduction	oxidation
sign		
electrolysis cell	negative	positive
galvanic cell	positive	negative

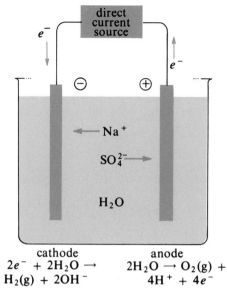

Figure 9.2 *Electrolysis of aqueous sodium sulfate.*

solute. Hence, the current-carrying ions are not necessarily discharged at the electrodes.

In the electrolysis of aqueous sodium sulfate, sodium ions move toward the cathode and sulfate ions move toward the anode (Figure 9.2). Both these ions are difficult to discharge. When this electrolysis is conducted between inert electrodes, hydrogen gas is evolved at the cathode, and the solution surrounding the electrode becomes alkaline. Reduction occurs at the cathode, but rather than the reduction of the sodium ion

$$e^- + Na^+ \rightarrow Na$$

the *net change* that occurs is the reduction of water

$$2e^- + 2H_2O \rightarrow H_2(g) + 2OH^-$$

Water is an extremely weak electrolyte; pure water is approximately $2 \times 10^{-7}\%$ ionized at 25°C

$$2H_2O \rightleftharpoons H_3O^+ + OH^-$$

or, more briefly,

$$H_2O \rightleftharpoons H^+ + OH^-$$

The exact mechanism of the cathode reaction in the electrolysis of aqueous Na_2SO_4 is not known. It may be that the hydrogen ions from water are discharged and that the reaction proceeds as follows

$$H_2O \rightleftharpoons H^+ + OH^-$$
$$2e^- + 2H^+ \rightarrow H_2(g)$$

Proper addition of these two steps gives the net change

$$2e^- + 2H_2O \rightarrow H_2(g) + 2OH^-$$

In general, water is reduced at the cathode (producing hydrogen gas and hydroxide ions) whenever the cation of the solute is difficult to reduce.

Oxidation occurs at the anode, and in the electrolysis of aqueous Na_2SO_4, the anions (SO_4^{2-}) that migrate toward the anode are difficult to oxidize

$$2SO_4^{2-} \rightarrow S_2O_8^{2-} + 2e^-$$

Therefore the oxidation of water occurs preferentially. The mode of this reaction may be

$$H_2O \rightleftharpoons H^+ + OH^-$$
$$4OH^- \rightarrow O_2(g) + 2H_2O + 4e^-$$

Multiplying the first equation by 4 and adding, we get the net change

$$2H_2O \rightarrow O_2(g) + 4H^+ + 4e^-$$

At the anode, the evolution of oxygen gas is observed, and the solution surrounding the pole becomes acidic. In general, water is oxidized at the anode (producing oxygen gas and hydrogen ions) whenever the anion of the solute is difficult to oxidize.

The complete reaction for the electrolysis of aqueous Na_2SO_4 may be obtained by adding the cathode and anode reactions

$$2[2e^- + 2H_2O \rightarrow H_2(g) + 2OH^-]$$
$$2H_2O \rightarrow O_2(g) + 4H^+ + 4e^-$$
$$\overline{}$$
$$6H_2O \rightarrow 2H_2(g) + O_2(g) + 4H^+ + 4OH^-$$

If the solution is mixed, the hydrogen and hydroxide ions produced neutralize one another, and the net change

$$2H_2O \xrightarrow{\text{elec.}} 2H_2(g) + O_2(g)$$

is merely the electrolysis of water. In the course of the electrolysis, the hydrogen ions migrate away from the anode, where they are produced, toward the cathode. In like manner, the hydroxide ions move toward the anode. These ions neutralize one another in the solution between the two electrodes.

The electrolysis of an aqueous solution of NaCl between inert electrodes serves as an example of a process in which the anion of the electrolyte is discharged, but the cation is not.

cathode: $2e^- + 2H_2O \rightarrow H_2(g) + 2OH^-$

anode: $2Cl^- \rightarrow Cl_2(g) + 2e^-$

$$\overline{}$$

$$2H_2O + 2Cl^- \rightarrow H_2(g) + Cl_2(g) + 2OH^-$$

Since the sodium ion remains in the solution unchanged, the reaction may be indicated

$$2H_2O + 2(Na^+, Cl^-) \xrightarrow[\text{elec.}]{} H_2(g) + Cl_2(g) + 2(Na^+, OH^-)$$

This process is a commercial source of hydrogen gas, chlorine gas, and, by evaporation of the solution left after electrolysis, sodium hydroxide.

In the electrolysis of a solution of $CuSO_4$ between inert electrodes (Figure 9.3), the current is carried by the Cu^{2+} and SO_4^{2-} ions. The current-carrying cations are discharged, but the anions are not.

cathode: $\qquad\qquad 2e^- + Cu^{2+} \longrightarrow Cu(s)$

$$2H_2O \longrightarrow O_2(g) + 4H^+ + 4e^-$$

$$2Cu^{2+} + 2H_2O \xrightarrow[\text{elec.}]{} O_2(g) + 2Cu(s) + 4H^+$$

It is, of course, possible to have both ions of the solute discharged during the electrolysis of an aqueous solution. An example is the electrolysis of $CuCl_2$ between inert electrodes.

cathode: $\qquad\qquad 2e^- + Cu^{2+} \longrightarrow Cu(s)$

anode: $\qquad\qquad 2Cl^- \longrightarrow Cl_2(g) + 2e^-$

$$Cu^{2+} + 2Cl^- \xrightarrow[\text{elec.}]{} Cu(s) + Cl_2(g)$$

It is also possible to have the electrode itself enter into an electrode reaction. If aqueous $CuSO_4$ is electrolyzed between copper electrodes,

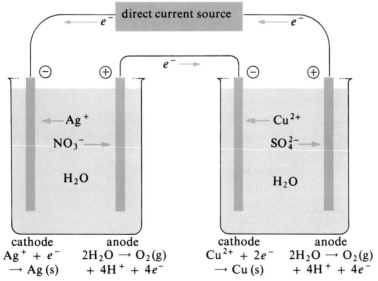

Figure 9.3 *Silver coulometer in series with a cell for electrolysis.*

Cu^{2+} ions are reduced at the cathode

$$2e^- + Cu^{2+} \longrightarrow Cu$$

but of the *three* possible anode oxidations

$$2SO_4^{2-} \longrightarrow 2S_2O_8^{2-} + 2e^-$$
$$2H_2O \longrightarrow O_2(g) + 4H^+ + 4e^-$$
$$Cu(s) \longrightarrow Cu^{2+} + 2e^-$$

the oxidation of the copper metal of the electrode is observed to occur. Hence, at the anode, copper from the electrode goes into solution as Cu^{2+} ions, and at the cathode, Cu^{2+} ions plate out as $Cu(s)$ on the electrode. This process is used to refine copper. Impure copper is used as the anode of an electrolytic cell, and a solution of $CuSO_4$ is electrolyzed; pure copper plates out on the cathode. Active electrodes are also used in electroplating processes; in silver plating, silver anodes are employed.

9.4 Faraday's Laws

The quantitative relationships between electricity and chemical change were first described by Michael Faraday. In 1832, he showed that the weight of a chemical substance liberated at an electrode is directly proportional to the amount of current passed through the cell. In 1833, he stated that the weights of different substances produced by a given amount of current are proportional to the equivalent weights of the substances.

Faraday's laws are readily interpreted by reference to the electrolysis of molten sodium chloride. The change at the cathode requires one electron for every sodium ion reduced.

$$Na^+ + e^- \longrightarrow Na$$

If Avogadro's number of electrons (1 mole) are consumed at this electrode, 22.9898 g of sodium metal (1 gram atom) is produced. The corresponding quantity of electricity is called the **faraday** (F) and has been found to equal 96,487 coulombs (for ordinary problem work, this value is customarily rounded off to 96,500 coulombs). If 2 F of electricity (2 moles of electrons) are used, 2 gram atoms of sodium are produced; 0.5 F would liberate 0.5 gram atom of sodium. Since the charge on the sodium ion is 1+, the equivalent weight of sodium is the same as the atomic weight.

In the same time that electrons equivalent to 1F are added to the cathode, that same number of electrons are removed from the anode.

$$2Cl^- \longrightarrow Cl_2 + 2e^-$$

The removal of 1 mole of electrons from this anode would result in the discharge of 35.453 g of chloride ion (1 gram atom), producing 0.5 mole of chlorine gas (1 gram equivalent). If 2 F of electricity flows through the cell, 2 gram atoms of chloride ion are discharged.

One faraday, then, will liberate 1 gram equivalent of an element or a compound. Rather than use equivalent weights, however, it is possible to interpret electrode reactions in terms of gram atoms, moles, and faradays. Thus the anode oxidation of the hydroxide ion,

$$4OH^- \rightarrow O_2(g) + 2H_2O + 4e^-$$

may be read: four hydroxide ions produce one oxygen molecule, two water molecules, and four electrons, or 4 moles of hydroxide ion produce 1 mole of oxygen and 2 moles of water when 4 faradays of electricity is passed through the cell.

In Figure 9.3, two electrolytic cells are set up in series; electricity passes through one cell first and then through the other before returning to the current source. If silver nitrate is electrolyzed in one of the cells, the cathode reaction is

$$Ag^+ + e^- \rightarrow Ag(s)$$

and metallic silver is plated out on the electrode used for the electrolysis. By weighing the electrode before and after the electrolysis, one can determine the quantity of silver plated out and hence the number of coulombs that has been passed through the cell. One faraday would plate out 107.870 g of silver; therefore, 1 coulomb is equivalent to

$$107.870/96,487 = 1.1180 \times 10^{-3} \text{g of silver}$$

The same number of coulombs pass through both cells in a given time when these cells are arranged in series. Therefore the number of coulombs used in an electrolysis may be determined through the addition, in series, of this **silver coulometer** to the circuit of the experimental cell.

Example 9.1 The charge on a single electron is 1.6021×10^{-19} coulomb. Calculate Avogadro's number from the fact that 1 F = 96,487 coulombs.

Solution

$$? \text{ electrons} = 9.6487 \times 10^4 \text{ coulombs} \left(\frac{1 \text{ electron}}{1.6021 \times 10^{-19} \text{ coulombs}} \right)$$

$$= 6.0225 \times 10^{23} \text{ electrons}$$

Example 9.2 In the electrolysis of $CuSO_4$, what weight of copper is plated out on the cathode by a current of 0.750 amp flowing for 10.0 min?

Solution The number of faradays employed may be calculated as follows

$$? F = 10.0 \text{ min} \left(\frac{60 \text{ sec}}{1 \text{ min}} \right) \left(\frac{0.75 \text{ coulombs}}{1 \text{ sec}} \right) \left(\frac{1 \text{ F}}{96,500 \text{ coulombs}} \right)$$

$$= 0.00466 \text{ F}$$

The cathode reaction is $Cu^{2+}(aq) + 2e^- \rightarrow Cu(s)$, and therefore 2 F plate out 63.5 g Cu(s)

$$? \text{g Cu} = 0.00466 \text{ F} \left(\frac{63.5 \text{ g Cu(s)}}{2F} \right) = 0.148 \text{ g Cu(s)}$$

Example 9.3 (a) What volume of $O_2(g)$, at STP, is liberated at the anode in the electrolysis of $CuSO_4$ described in Example 9.2? (b) If 100 ml of $1.00 M$ $CuSO_4$ is employed in the cell, what is the $H^+(aq)$ concentration at the end of the electrolysis? Assume that there is no volume change for the solution during the experiment and that the anode reaction is $2H_2O \longrightarrow 4H^+(aq) + O_2(g) + 4e^-$

Solution (a) Four faradays produce 22.4 liters of $O_2(g)$ at STP.

$$? \text{ liters } O_2(g) = 0.00466 \text{ F} \left(\frac{22.4 \text{ liters } O_2(g)}{4 \text{ F}} \right) = 0.0261 \text{ liters } O_2(g)$$

(b) Four faradays also produce 4 moles of $H^+(aq)$

$$? \text{ moles } H^+(aq) = 0.00466 \text{ F} \left(\frac{1 \text{ mole } H^+(aq)}{1 \text{ F}} \right) = 0.00466 \text{ moles } H^+(aq)$$

The small contribution of $H^+(aq)$ from the ionization of water may be ignored, and we may assume that there are 0.00466 moles $H^+(aq)$ in 100 ml of solution.

$$? \text{ moles } H^+(aq) = 1000 \text{ ml solution} \left(\frac{0.00466 \text{ moles } H^+(aq)}{100 \text{ ml solution}} \right)$$

$$= 0.0466 \text{ moles } H^+(aq)$$

The solution is therefore $0.0466 M$ in hydrogen ion.

Example 9.4 (a) What weight of copper is plated out in the electrolysis of $CuSO_4$ in the same time that it takes to deposit 1.00 g of Ag in a silver coulometer that is arranged in series with the $CuSO_4$ cell? (b) If a current of 1.00 amp is used, how many minutes are required to plate out this quantity of copper?

Solution (a) From the electrode reactions, we see that 2 F deposit 63.5 g Cu and 1 F deposits 107.9 g Ag.

$$? \text{ g Cu} = 1.00 \text{ g Ag} \left(\frac{1 \text{ F}}{107.9 \text{ g Ag}} \right) \left(\frac{63.5 \text{ g Cu}}{2 \text{ F}} \right) = 0.294 \text{ g Cu}$$

(b)

$$? \text{ min} = 1.00 \text{ g Ag} \left(\frac{96,500 \text{ coulombs}}{107.9 \text{ g Ag}} \right) \left(\frac{1 \text{ sec}}{1 \text{ coulomb}} \right) \left(\frac{1 \text{ min}}{60 \text{ sec}} \right) = 14.9 \text{ min}$$

9.5 Electrolytic Conductance

A material with a high electrical resistance is a poor electrical conductor; the ability of a substance to conduct electrical current is inversely related to that substance's electrical resistance. **Conductance** is defined as the reciprocal of resistance and has the units of reciprocal ohms (1/ohm). From Ohm's law,

$$R = \frac{E}{I}$$

and

$$\text{conductance} = \frac{1}{R} = \frac{I}{E}$$

Therefore the conductance of a given solution is equal to the amount of current flowing when a potential drop of 1 v is applied to the electrodes.

Conductance measurements are made using alternating current to minimize the effect of electrode reactions. A generator of alternating current (a.c.) reverses the direction of current flow at regular intervals of time. The usual house current is 60 cycle a.c. (120 reversals/sec); the alternating current used in conductance measurements is approximately 1000 cycle a.c.

The conductance of a given solution will vary with the cell dimensions —the area of the electrodes and the distance between them. **Specific conductance,** κ, is defined so that measurements will be comparable; it is the conductance of 1 cm^3 of solution when a potential of 1 v is applied between electrodes 1 cm apart and has the units 1/ohm cm. It is not necessary to construct a cell of these exact dimensions in order to determine specific conductances. By measuring the resistance of a solution of known κ in an experimental cell, one can calculate the cell constant, k,

$$\kappa = \frac{k}{R}$$

and by means of this constant convert resistances measured in that cell into specific conductances. Since resistance varies with temperature, conductance varies with temperature. It is necessary to measure conductances under constant conditions of temperature, and this value should be recorded with the measurements.

Still another factor must be taken into account before the conductances of two or more solutions may be compared conveniently—the charges of the solute ions. At 25°C, the specific conductance of 0.001 M NaCl is 1.07×10^{-4}/ohm cm, and the specific conductance of 0.001 M CuSO$_4$ is 2.30×10^{-4}/ohm cm. Under similar conditions, 0.001 moles of Na$^+$ and 0.001 moles of Cl$^-$ ions are capable of carrying only half the current that can be carried by 0.001 moles of Cu^{2+} ions and 0.001 moles of SO$_4^{2-}$ ions. Therefore comparisons should be made between solutions of corresponding normality, rather than corresponding molarity. Thus a 0.001 M (0.001 N) solution of NaCl should be compared with a 0.0005 M (0.001 N) solution of CuSO$_4$ or a 0.0005 M (0.001 N) solution of BaCl$_2$.

Equivalent conductance, Λ, is defined as the conductance of an entire solution containing 1 gram equivalent of solute between electrodes 1 cm apart. The equivalent weight of the solute can be obtained by dividing the molecular weight of the solute by the total positive charge represented in the formula of the compound. Equivalent conductance can be calculated from specific conductance by

$$\Lambda = \frac{1000}{C} \kappa$$

where C is the number of gram equivalents of solute per liter of solution; Λ has the units cm^2/ohm equivalent. Notice that the equivalent conductance of a solution measures the conductance of a collection of cations equal to Avogadro's number of positive charges plus a collection of anions equal to Avogadro's number of negative charges. Thus the equivalent conductance of $0.1 N$ NaCl would represent the conductance of 10 liters of solution between electrodes 1 cm apart; the equivalent conductance of $0.01 N$ NaCl represents the conductance of 100 liters of solution between electrodes 1 cm apart.

TABLE 9.2.
EQUIVALENT CONDUCTANCES, Λ, OF VARIOUS ELECTROLYTES AT 25°C (IN CM^2/OHM EQUIVALENT).

Electrolyte	Concentration (equivalents/liter)			
	0.000	0.001	0.010	0.100
NaCl	126.5	123.7	118.5	106.7
KCl	149.9	147.0	141.3	129.0
BaCl$_2$	140.0	134.3	123.9	105.2
CuSO$_4$	133.0	115.2	83.3	50.5

An examination of the data of Table 9.2 shows that the equivalent conductance of solutions of a given electrolyte, for example, NaCl, increases with decreasing concentration and approaches a limiting value, Λ_0, at infinite dilution. One might expect that the equivalent conductance of any NaCl solution would be a constant since a constant number of ions is involved in any equivalent conductance determination. The reason for the variation of equivalent conductance with concentration is provided by the Debye-Hückel theory.

Owing to interionic attraction, any ion has a diffuse atmosphere of oppositely charged ions surrounding it; its motion in an electric field is therefore retarded. At infinite dilution, the ions are far enough apart to act independently of one another, and theoretically this ion-drag effect is eliminated. These interionic attractions increase as the ionic charges increase, and thus the decrease in equivalent conductance with increasing concentration is *proportionately* greater for solutions of BaCl$_2$ than for solutions of NaCl and greater still for solutions of CuSO$_4$.

Equivalent conductance measurements provide a method for the determination of the **degree of dissociation** (α) of a weak electrolyte in solution. In a solution of a weak electrolyte such as acetic acid

$$H_2O + HC_2H_3O_2 \rightleftharpoons H_3O^+ + C_2H_3O_2^-$$

the fraction of the compound in ionic form increases as the solution is diluted; weak electrolytes are theoretically 100% ionic at infinite dilution. At ordinary concentrations, the concentrations of ions in solutions of weak electrolytes are so small that interionic-attraction effects may be ignored. The undissociated compound has no conductance since it is uncharged, and the equivalent conductance of a solution is due entirely to the fraction of the compound in ionic form. Since Λ_0 is the equivalent conductance that represents complete dissociation,

$$\Lambda = \alpha \Lambda_0$$

or

$$\alpha = \frac{\Lambda}{\Lambda_0}$$

Example 9.5 A conductance cell filled with $0.0200 M$ KCl has a resistance of 163.3 ohms at 25°C. When filled with $0.0500 M$ $AgNO_3$, it had a resistance of 78.5 ohms. The specific conductance of $0.0200 M$ KCl is 2.768×10^{-3}/ohm cm. (a) What is the specific conductance of $0.0500 M$ $AgNO_3$? (b) What is the equivalent conductance of this solution?

Solution   (a) The cell constant may be determined by

$$\kappa = \frac{k}{R}$$

$$k = \kappa R = (2.768 \times 10^{-3}/\text{ohm cm})(163.3 \text{ ohm}) = 0.4520/\text{cm}$$

For $0.0500 M$ $AgNO_3$,

$$\kappa = \frac{0.4520/\text{cm}}{78.5 \text{ ohm}} = 5.76 \times 10^{-3}/\text{ohm cm}$$

(b)

$$\Lambda = \frac{1000}{C} \kappa = \frac{1000 \text{ cm}^3\, 5.76 \times 10^{-3}/\text{ohm cm}}{5.00 \times 10^{-2} \text{ equiv}} = 115 \text{ cm}^2/\text{ohm equiv}$$

Example 9.6 At 25°C, the equivalent conductance of $0.100 M$ $HC_2H_3O_2$ is 5.2 cm^2/ohm equivalent; Λ_0 for acetic acid is 390.7 cm^2/ohm equiv. What is the degree of dissociation of $0.100 M$ $HC_2H_3O_2$ at 25°C?

Solution

$$\alpha = \frac{\Lambda}{\Lambda_0}$$

$$\alpha = \frac{5.2 \text{ cm}^2/\text{ohm equiv}}{390.7 \text{ cm}^2/\text{ohm equiv}}$$

$$\alpha = 0.013$$

At 25°C, $0.100 M$ acetic acid is 1.3% ionized.

9.6   Voltaic Cells

A cell that is used as a source of electrical energy is called a **voltaic,** or **galvanic, cell** after Alessandro Volta (1800) or Luigi Galvani (1780) who first experimented with the conversion of chemical energy into electrical energy.

The reaction between metallic zinc and copper(II) ions in solution is illustrative of a spontaneous change in which electrons are transferred.

$$Zn(s) + Cu^{2+}(aq) \rightarrow Zn^{2+}(aq) + Cu(s)$$

The exact mechanism by which electron transfer occurs is not known; however, we may represent the above reaction as a combination of two half reactions.

$$Zn(s) \rightarrow Zn^{2+}(aq) + 2e^-$$
$$Cu^{2+}(aq) + 2e^- \rightarrow Cu(s)$$

In a voltaic cell, these half reactions are made to occur at different electrodes so that the transfer of electrons takes place through the external electrical circuit rather than directly between zinc metal and copper(II) ions.

The cell diagrammed in Figure 9.4 is designed to make use of this reaction to produce an electric current. The half cell on the left contains a zinc metal electrode and $ZnSO_4$ solution; the half cell on the right consists of a copper metal electrode in a solution of $CuSO_4$. The half cells are separated by a porous partition that prevents the mechanical mixing of the solutions in each half cell but permits the passage of ions under the influence of the flow of electricity.

When the zinc and copper electrodes are joined by a wire, electrons flow from the zinc electrode to the copper electrode. At the zinc electrode, the zinc metal is *oxidized* to zinc ions; this electrode is the **anode,** and the electrons that are the product of the oxidation *leave* the cell from

Figure 9.4   The Daniell Cell.

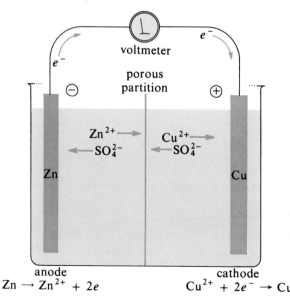

anode   cathode
$Zn \rightarrow Zn^{2+} + 2e$ $Cu^{2+} + 2e^- \rightarrow Cu$

this pole (Table 9.1). The electrons travel the external circuit to the copper electrode where they are used in the reduction of copper(II) ions to metallic copper; the copper thus produced plates out on the electrode. The copper electrode is the **cathode**; here, electrons *enter* the cell, and *reduction* occurs.

Since electrons are produced at the zinc electrode, this anode is designated as the negative pole. Electrons travel from the negative pole to the positive pole in the external circuit of any voltaic cell when the cell is operating. The cathode, where electrons are used in the electrode reaction, is therefore the positive pole. Within the cell, the movement of ions completes the electric circuit. At first glance, it is surprising that anions, being negatively charged, should travel toward an anode that is the negative electrode. Conversely, cations, which carry a positive charge, travel toward the cathode which is the positive pole.

Careful consideration of the electrode reactions provides the answer to this apparent anomaly. At the anode, zinc ions are being produced and electrons left behind in the metal. At all times, the electrical neutrality of the solution is maintained; in the solution surrounding the electrode, there must be as much negative charge from anions as there is positive charge from cations. Hence, SO_4^{2-} ions move toward the anode to neutralize the effect of the Zn^{2+} ions being produced. At the same time, zinc ions move away from the anode toward the cathode. At the cathode, electrons are being used to reduce Cu^{2+} ions to copper metal. While the Cu^{2+} ions are being discharged, more Cu^{2+} ions move into the region surrounding the cathode to take the place of the ions being removed. If this did not occur, a surplus of SO_4^{2-} ions would build up around the cathode.

The porous partition is added to prevent mechanical mixing of the solutions of the half cells. If Cu^{2+} ions came into contact with the zinc metal electrode, electrons would be transferred directly rather than through the circuit. In the normal operation of the cell, this "short circuit" does not occur because the Cu^{2+} ions move in a direction away from the zinc electrode.

Actually, this cell would work if a solution of an electrolyte other than $ZnSO_4$ were used in the anode compartment, and if a metal other than copper were used for the cathode. However, the substitutes must be chosen so that the electrolyte in the anode compartment does not react with the zinc electrode and the cathode does not react with Cu^{2+} ions.

9.7   Electromotive Force

If $1m$ $ZnSO_4$ and $1m$ $CuSO_4$ solutions are employed in the Daniell cell, the cell may be represented by the notation

$$Zn(s) \,|\, Zn^{2+}(1m) \,|\, Cu^{2+}(1m) \,|\, Cu(s)$$

where the vertical lines represent phase boundaries. The voltage of a voltaic cell depends upon the concentrations of the materials used in the construction of the cell (Section 9.9). Standard voltages are determined at 25°C for cells with all reactants and products at unit activity (Section 9.8). For our discussion, we shall make the assumption that the activity of ions may be represented by their molal concentrations and the activity of gases by their pressures in atmospheres. Hence, according to this approximation, a standard cell would contain ions at $1m$ concentrations and gases at 1 atm pressures. In the cell notations that follow, concentrations will be indicated only if they deviate from standard.

The voltage of a cell gives a measure of the force with which electrons are pumped around the circuit—the **electromotive force** (emf)—and a measure of the vigor with which the oxidation-reduction reaction of the cell occurs. The emf must be determined in a reversible manner if it is to be a true indication of the maximum work obtainable from the process and thus accurately reflect the tendency of the cell reaction to occur spontaneously.

Reversibility implies that, at any time, the cell reaction may be reversed by the application of an equal and opposite emf. Measurement is accomplished by the use of a potentiometer, and the cell potential is balanced by a measured potential from the potentiometer. If an appreciable current flows during measurement, the voltage measured, E, will be reduced by an amount, IR, equal to the product of the amount of current flowing, I, and the resistance of the cell, R. In addition, current flow produces concentration effects around the electrodes which affect the measured emf.

In the Daniell cell, a small source of irreversibility is introduced by the liquid junction between the $ZnSO_4$ and $CuSO_4$ solutions. When the cell discharges, Zn^{2+} ions move across the junction to the right toward the cathode; when the cell is reversed (i.e., acts as an electrolytic cell), Cu^{2+} ions move across the junction in the opposite direction. Thus the cell is inherently not reversible. This effect may be minimized by employing a salt bridge (Figure 9.5). A tube filled with a concentrated solution of a salt (usually KCl) is used to connect the two half cells so that most of the current is carried across the junction by K^+ and Cl^- ions. When a salt bridge is used, the Daniell cell is diagrammed with a double bar in the center.

$$Zn \mid Zn^{2+} \parallel Cu^{2+} \mid Cu$$

A standard emf is given the symbol $E°$, and the $E°$ for the Daniell cell is 1.10 v.

Faraday's laws apply to the cell reactions of voltaic, as well as electrolytic cells. One precaution must be observed, however. Electricity is generated by the simultaneous oxidation and reduction half reactions

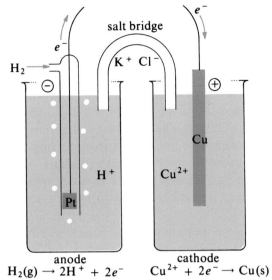

anode
$$H_2(g) \rightarrow 2H^+ + 2e^-$$

cathode
$$Cu^{2+} + 2e^- \rightarrow Cu(s)$$

Figure 9.5 Standard Hydrogen Electrode and a Cu^{2+}/Cu Electrode.

occurring at the anode and cathode, respectively; both must occur if the cell is to deliver current. Two faradays of electricity will be produced, therefore, by the oxidation of 1 gram atom of zinc at the anode *as well as* the reduction of 1 mole of Cu^{2+} ions at the cathode. The partial equations

cathode: $\qquad 2e^- + Cu^{2+} \rightarrow Cu$

anode: $\qquad Zn \rightarrow Zn^{2+}e^-$

read in terms of gram atoms and moles, represent the flow of two times Avogadro's number of electrons or the production of $2F$ of electricity.

The quantity of electrical energy, in joules, produced by a cell is the product of the quantity of electricity delivered, in coulombs, and the emf of the cell, in volts (see Section 9.1). The energy *produced* by the reaction between 1 gram atom of zinc metal and 1 mole of copper(II) ions may be calculated as follows

$$-2\,(96,500 \text{ coulombs})(1.10 \text{ v}) = -212,000 \text{ joules}$$

or since 1 cal = 4.184 joule,

$$\frac{-212,000 \text{ joule}}{4.18 \text{ joule/cal}} = -50,800 \text{ cal}$$

We can interpret this in terms of a function of the system called the **Gibbs free energy**, G^* (Section 11.9). The energy released by the reaction

---

*This function was named in honor of J. Willard Gibbs, who developed the application of thermodynamic principles to chemistry.

is attributed to a change in the free energy content of the system, ΔG, and since energy is lost relative to the system, this is a negative quantity.

$$\Delta G = -nFE$$

where n is the number of faradays, F is the value of the faraday in appropriate units and E is the emf in volts. If F is expressed as 96,487 coulombs, ΔG is obtained in joules; if F is used as 23,061 cal/v, ΔG is obtained in calories. The change in Gibbs free energy represents the maximum *net* work that can be derived from a chemical change carried out reversibly at constant temperature and pressure—that is, the work in excess of that due to any volume change that occurs in the course of the reaction. A change in free energy derived from a standard emf, $E°$, is given the symbol $\Delta G°$.

For any spontaneous reaction ΔG is negative. Hence, only if E is positive will the cell reaction be spontaneous and serve as a source of electrical energy.

9.8 Electrode Potentials

In order to catalog the emf's of a large number of voltaic cells, it is not necessary to measure and record the emf of each cell; the same end can be realized by tabulating the potentials of a smaller number of half cells and using these to calculate cell emf's. However, since it is impossible to determine the absolute value of the potential of only one electrode, a relative scale has been established by assigning a value of zero to the voltage of a standard reference electrode and expressing all half-cell potentials relative to this reference electrode.

The reference electrode used is the standard hydrogen electrode (Figure 9.5) which consists of hydrogen gas, at 1 atm pressure, bubbling over the surface of a platinum electrode (coated with platinum black) that is immersed in an acid solution containing hydrogen ion at unit activity.

$$Pt \mid H_2 \mid H^+$$

If a cell is constructed with a standard hydrogen electrode coupled to a standard Cu^{2+}/Cu electrode, the measured emf of the cell is 0.34 v. Since the copper electrode is the *positive* electrode of the cell, the **electrode potential** of the Cu^{2+}/Cu half cell is assigned the value +0.34 v. In a cell formed by combining a standard hydrogen electrode with a standard Zn^{2+}/Zn electrode, the latter electrode is negative and the cell generates a voltage of 0.76 v. Since the zinc electrode is *negative* with respect to the hydrogen electrode, the electrode potential of the Zn^{2+}/Zn electrode is assigned the value −0.76 v. The difference between +0.34 v and −0.76 v is, of course, 1.10 v—which agrees with the measured potential difference of the standard Daniell cell.

Notice that electrode potentials are expressed relative to the reaction

$2e^- + 2H^+ \rightleftharpoons H_2$. The negative sign on the Zn^{2+}/Zn electrode potential means, therefore, that Zn^{2+} ions are less active electron acceptors than H^+ ions; it does not mean that it is impossible to derive electricity from a hydrogen-zinc cell. The positive sign on the Cu^{2+}/Cu electrode potential means merely that Cu^{2+} ions are more active electron acceptors than H^+ ions. The difference between the two electrode potentials of any cell gives the potential difference of the cell.

How can we correlate values of electrode potentials with half-cell reactions and spontaneity of chemical change? We wish to preserve the notation that ΔG is negative, and E is positive, for any spontaneous change. Therefore let us say that the cell reaction corresponding to the Cu^{2+}/Cu electrode potential is spontaneous since the potential is positive, and that the reaction corresponding to the Zn^{2+}/Zn electrode potential is nonspontaneous since this potential is negative.

In the hydrogen-copper cell, the copper electrode is positive; hence, it is the cathode, and Cu^{2+} ions are reduced at this electrode. We diagram the cell with the oxidation half reaction on the left and the reduction half reaction on the right

$$Pt \mid H_2 \mid H^+ \parallel Cu^{2+} \mid Cu$$

which implies the reaction

$$H_2 + Cu^{2+} \rightarrow 2H^+ + Cu \qquad E° = +0.34 \text{ v}$$

In the hydrogen-zinc cell, the zinc electrode is the negative electrode; hence, it is the anode. In a spontaneously discharging cell, zinc metal is oxidized. The nonspontaneous change for the Zn^{2+}/Zn electrode is, therefore, reduction. The electrode potential would, in theory, be derivable from the cell

$$Pt \mid H_2 \mid H^+ \parallel Zn^{2+} \mid Zn$$

which implies the reaction

$$H_2 + Zn^{2+} \rightarrow 2H^+ + Zn \qquad E° = -0.76 \text{ v}$$

This reaction is the reverse of that which occurs in a spontaneously discharging cell.

Determination of the emf and the cell reaction of the zinc-copper cell through the use of electrode potentials and the corresponding reactions proceeds as follows. The cell may be diagrammed

$$Zn \mid Zn^{2+} \parallel Cu^{2+} \mid Cu$$

With the oxidation indicated on the left and the reduction indicated on the right, the cell potential may be calculated

$$E° = E°_{\text{right}} - E°_{\text{left}}$$

We may subtract the chemical equations as well as the electrode potentials

$$H_2 + Cu^{2+} \rightarrow 2H^+ + Cu \qquad E^\circ_{right} = +0.34 \text{ v}$$
$$-[H_2 + Zn^{2+} \rightarrow 2H^+ + Zn] \qquad -[E^\circ_{left} = -0.76 \text{ v}]$$

$$\overline{Cu^{2+} - Zn^{2+} \rightarrow Cu - Zn \qquad E^\circ = +1.10 \text{ v}}$$

or, if we rearrange terms,

$$Zn + Cu^{2+} \rightarrow Zn^{2+} + Cu \qquad E^\circ = +1.10 \text{ v}$$

Notice that had the cell been diagrammed in reverse order, then the reverse reaction would have been obtained as well as a final E^0 for the cell of -1.10 v; this would indicate a nonspontaneous change.

Another way of using half-cell potentials involves defining the terms **oxidation potential** and **reduction potential.** Such a potential is given a sign depending upon whether the half reaction it describes is written as an oxidation or a reduction. Electrode potentials are equal to reduction potentials. Thus the reduction potential of the Cu^{2+}/Cu half cell is

$$2e^- + Cu^{2+} \rightarrow Cu \qquad E^\circ = +0.34 \text{ v}$$

and the oxidation potential is

$$Cu \rightarrow Cu^{2+} + 2e^- \qquad E^\circ_{ox} = -0.34 \text{ v}$$

The reduction and oxidation potentials for the Zn^{2+}/Zn half cell are

$$2e^- + Zn^{2+} \rightarrow Zn \qquad E^\circ = -0.76 \text{ v}$$
$$Zn \rightarrow Zn^{2+} + 2e^- \qquad E^\circ_{ox} = +0.76 \text{ v}$$

In a standard Daniell cell, the zinc is oxidized and Cu^{2+} ions are reduced. Therefore, we may calculate the emf of such a cell by adding the oxidation potential of the Zn^{2+}/Zn half cell and the reduction potential of the Cu^{2+}/Cu half cell.

$$2e^- + Cu^{2+} \rightarrow Cu \qquad E^\circ = +0.34 \text{ v}$$
$$Zn \rightarrow Zn^{2+} + 2e^- \qquad E^\circ_{ox} = +0.76 \text{ v}$$

$$\overline{Zn + Cu^{2+} \rightarrow Zn^{2+} + Cu \qquad E^\circ = +1.10 \text{ v}}$$

Hydrogen and H^+ are usually not included in the partial equations used in conjunction with oxidation potentials or reduction potentials. It is understood that the values of the potentials are derived by setting the potential of the half reaction $2e^- + 2H^+ \rightleftharpoons H_2$ equal to zero in either direction.

The preceding definition of electrode potentials agrees with that suggested by the International Union of Pure and Applied Chemistry (IUPAC) meeting in Stockholm in 1953. Care must be exercised in reading earlier works since, prior to 1953, the common American practice was to tabulate oxidation potentials rather than electrode potentials. A list of standard electrode potentials is recorded in Table 9.3.

The two conventions are easily reconciled. For example, the cell

$$Cu \mid Cu^{2+} \parallel Ag^+ \mid Ag$$

has an experimentally determined $E°$ of $+0.46$ v. The equation for the observed cell reaction is

$$Cu + 2Ag^+ \rightarrow Cu^{2+} + 2Ag \qquad E° = +0.46 \text{ v}$$

TABLE 9.3.
STANDARD ELECTRODE POTENTIALS AT 25°C.[a]

Half reaction	$E°$ (volts)	
$Li^+ + e^- \rightarrow Li$	-3.045	BEST REDUCING AGENT
$K^+ + e^- \rightleftharpoons K$	-2.925	
$Ba^{2+} + 2e^- \rightarrow Ba$	-2.906	
$Ca^{2+} + 2e^- \rightleftharpoons Ca$	-2.866	
$Na^+ + e^- \rightleftharpoons Na$	-2.714	
$Mg^{2+} + 2e^- \rightleftharpoons Mg$	-2.363	
$Al^{3+} + 3e^- \rightleftharpoons Al$	-1.662	
$2H_2O + 2e^- \rightleftharpoons H_2 + 2OH^-$	-0.82806	
$Zn^{2+} + 2e^- \rightleftharpoons Zn$	-0.7628	
$Cr^{3+} + 3e^- \rightleftharpoons Cr$	-0.744	
$Fe^{2+} + 2e^- \rightleftharpoons Fe$	-0.4402	
$Cd^{2+} + 2e^- \rightleftharpoons Cd$	-0.4029	
$Ni^{2+} + 2e^- \rightleftharpoons Ni$	-0.250	
$Sn^{2+} + 2e^- \rightleftharpoons Sn$	-0.136	
$Pb^{2+} + 2e^- \rightleftharpoons Pb$	-0.126	
$2H^+ + 2e^- \rightleftharpoons H_2$	0	
$Cu^{2+} + 2e^- \rightleftharpoons Cu$	$+0.337$	
$Cu^+ + e^- \rightleftharpoons Cu$	$+0.521$	
$I_2 + 2e^- \rightleftharpoons 2I^-$	$+0.5355$	
$Fe^{3+} + e^- \rightleftharpoons Fe^{2+}$	$+0.771$	
$Ag^+ + e^- \rightleftharpoons Ag$	$+0.7991$	
$Br_2 + 2e^- \rightleftharpoons 2Br^-$	$+1.0652$	
$O_2 + 4H^+ + 4e^- \rightleftharpoons 2H_2O$	$+1.229$	
$Cr_2O_7^{2-} + 14H^+ + 6e^- \rightleftharpoons 2Cr^{3+} + 7H_2O$	$+1.33$	
$Cl_2 + 2e^- \rightleftharpoons 2Cl^-$	$+1.3595$	
$MnO_4^- + 8H^+ + 5e^- \rightleftharpoons Mn^{2+} + 4H_2O$	$+1.51$	STRONG OXIDIZING AGENT
$F_2 + 2e^- \rightleftharpoons 2F^-$	$+2.87$	

[a] Data from A. J. de Bethune and N. A. Swendeman Loud "Table of Electrode Potentials and Temperature Coefficients," pp. 414–424 in *Encyclopedia of Electrochemistry* (C. A. Hampel, editor), Reinhold, New York, 1964 and from A. J. de Bethune and N. A. Swendeman Loud *Standard Aqueous Electrode Potentials and Temperature Coefficients,* 19 pp., C. A. Hampel, publisher, Skokie, Illinois, 1964.

Since Cu is oxidized, the oxidation potential of copper is

$$Cu \rightarrow Cu^{2+} + 2e^- \qquad E_{ox}^{\circ} = -0.34 \text{ v}$$

By subtraction,

$$2e^- + 2Ag^+ \rightarrow 2Ag \qquad E^{\circ} = +0.80 \text{ v}$$

or

$$e^- + Ag^+ \rightarrow Ag \qquad E^{\circ} = +0.80 \text{ v}$$

and the reduction potential (or electrode potential) of the Ag^+/Ag electrode is $+0.80$ v. (Notice that the number of electrons lost or gained does not affect the value of the potential.)

The same result is obtained by means of electrode potentials:

$$E^{\circ} = E_{right}^{\circ} - E_{left}^{\circ}$$
$$+0.46 = E_{right}^{\circ} - (+0.34)$$
$$E_{right}^{\circ} = +0.80 \text{ v}$$

Electrode potentials may be subtracted to find cell emf's; however, two electrode potentials may *not* be combined directly to give a third *electrode* potential. The following electrode potentials are listed in Table 9.3.

$$2e^- + Fe^{2+} \rightarrow Fe \qquad E^{\circ} = -0.440\text{v} \qquad (1)$$
$$e^- + Fe^{3+} \rightarrow Fe^{2+} \qquad E^{\circ} = +0.771 \text{ v} \qquad (2)$$

The partial equation

$$3e^- + Fe^{3+} \rightarrow Fe \qquad (3)$$

is the sum of equations (1) and (2), but the electrode potential of (3) is not the sum of the other two.

A solution to the problem is provided by the fact that changes in free energy are additive in the same manner as changes in enthalpy (see the law of Hess, Section 4.9). Thus the ΔG° for half reaction (1) may be added to the ΔG° for half reaction (2) to give the ΔG° for half reaction (3). The electrode potential for (3) may then be found from ΔG° for (3). Thus

	E°	$\Delta G^{\circ} = -nFE^{\circ}$	
$2e^- + Fe^{2+} \rightarrow Fe$	-0.440	$-2(-0.440)F = +0.880\,F$	(1)
$e^- + Fe^{3+} \rightarrow Fe^{2+}$	$+0.771$	$-1(+0.771)F = -0.771\,F$	(2)
$3e^- + Fe^{3+} \rightarrow Fe$	—	$+0.109\,F$	(3)

In partial equation (3), $n = 3$. Since $\Delta G^{\circ} = -nFE^{\circ}$,

$$+0.109\,F = -(3)\,FE^{\circ}$$

$$E^{\circ} = \frac{+0.109\,F}{-3\,F} = -0.036 \text{ v}$$

9.9 Electrode Potentials and Concentration Changes

If we assign the Gibbs free energy of a *mole* of substance W in its standard state (unit activity) the symbol G_W°, the Gibbs free energy of a mole of this substance at another activity is given by the equation

$$G_W = G_W^\circ + RT \ln a_W$$

where R is the gas constant, T is the absolute temperature, and $\ln a_W$ is the natural logarithm of the activity of W*. For w moles of material

$$wG_W = wG_W^\circ + wRT \ln a_W$$

or
$$wG_W = wG_W^\circ + RT \ln (a_W)^w \tag{4}$$

The absolute values of free energies are not known; however, changes in free energies can be determined. For the hypothetical reaction

$$w\,W + x\,X \longrightarrow y\,Y + z\,Z$$

the change in free energy is given by the equation

$$\Delta G = yG_Y + zG_Z - (wG_W + xG_X) \tag{5}$$

In like manner,

$$\Delta G^\circ = yG_Y^\circ + zG_Z^\circ - (wG_W^\circ + xG_X^\circ) \tag{6}$$

By substituting expressions similar to (4) into equation (5), we get

$$\Delta G = yG_Y^\circ + RT \ln (a_Y)^y + zG_Z^\circ + RT \ln (a_Z)^z$$
$$- wG_W^\circ - RT \ln (a_W)^w - xG_X^\circ - RT \ln (a_X)^x$$

Combining terms, we get

$$\Delta G = yG_Y^\circ + zG_Z^\circ - wG_W^\circ - xG_X^\circ + RT \ln \left(\frac{(a_Y)^y (a_Z)^z}{(a_W)^w (a_X)^x} \right)$$

From equation (6),

$$\Delta G = \Delta G^\circ + RT \ln \left(\frac{(a_Y)^y (a_Z)^z}{(a_W)^w (a_X)^x} \right) \tag{7}$$

In Section 9.7, the expressions

$$\Delta G = -nFE \qquad \text{and} \qquad \Delta G^\circ = -nFE^\circ$$

were derived. By substitution of these expressions into equation (7), we get

$$-nFE = -nFE^\circ + RT \ln \left(\frac{(a_Y)^y (a_Z)^z}{(a_W)^w (a_X)^x} \right)$$

*The natural logarithm of the activity of W is equal to 2.303 log a_W.

and division by $-nF$ gives

$$E = E° - \frac{RT}{nF} \ln \left(\frac{(a_Y)^y (a_Z)^z}{(a_W)^w (a_X)^x}\right)$$

If we substitute the appropriate values of the constants and convert the natural logarithm into a logarithm to the base 10, at 25°C,

$$E = E° - \frac{0.05916}{n} \log \left(\frac{(a_Y)^y (a_Z)^z}{(a_W)^w (a_X)^x}\right)$$

This is called the **Nernst equation** after Walther Nernst who developed a similar equation (using concentrations instead of activities) in 1889. When all substances are present at an activity of 1, the logarithm term is equal to zero, and $E = E°$.

The Nernst equation may be used to calculate electrode potentials of electrodes in which all species are not present at unit activity, or it may be used to determine the voltage of a cell constructed from nonstandard electrodes. From the cell voltage, thus calculated, the ΔG for any cell reaction may be calculated.

Example 9.7 What is the electrode potential of a Zn^{2+}/Zn electrode in which the concentration of Zn^{2+} ions is $0.1m$?

Solution We shall assume that the concentration of zinc ion (given the notation $[Zn^{2+}]$) is equal to the activity of zinc ion. The activities of solid species are taken as unity. The partial equation

$$2e^- + Zn^{2+} \rightarrow Zn(s)$$

shows two electrons gained. Therefore

$$E = E° - \frac{0.0592}{2} \log \left(\frac{1}{[Zn^{2+}]}\right)$$

$E°$ for the Zn^{2+}/Zn electrode is -0.76 v.

$$E = -0.76 - \frac{0.0592}{2} \log \left(\frac{1}{0.1}\right)$$

$$E = -0.76 - 0.0296(1) = -0.79 \text{ v}$$

Example 9.8 (a) What is the potential for the cell

$$Ni \mid Ni^{2+} (0.01m) \parallel Cl^- (0.2m) \mid Cl_2 (1 \text{ atm}) \mid Pt$$

(b) What is ΔG for the cell reaction?

Solution (a) Two faradays of electricity are involved in the cell reaction

$$Ni + Cl_2 \rightarrow Ni^{2+} + 2Cl^-$$

and therefore $n = 2$. $E°$ for the cell, calculated from the standard electrode potentials, is $+1.61$ v. The activity of a gas at 1 atm pressure is taken as unity.

$$E = E° - \frac{0.0592}{2} \log\left(\frac{[Cl^-]^2 [Ni^{2+}]}{[Cl_2]}\right)$$

$$E = +1.61 - \frac{0.0592}{2} \log\left(\frac{(0.2)^2 (0.01)}{(1)}\right)$$

$$E = +1.61 - 0.0296 \log (0.0004)$$

$$E = +1.61 + 0.10 = +1.71 \text{ v}$$

(b)

$$\Delta G = -nFE$$

$$\Delta G = -2(23,100 \text{ cal/v})(1.71 \text{ v}) = -79,000 \text{ cal}$$

Example 9.9 What is the E of the cell

$$Sn \mid Sn^{2+}(a = 1.000) \parallel Pb^{2+}(a = 0.001) \mid Pb$$

Solution The following may be obtained from a table of standard electrode potentials

$$Sn \longrightarrow Sn^{2+} + 2e^- \qquad E°_{ox} = +0.136 \text{ v}$$

$$2e^- + Pb^{2+} \longrightarrow Pb \qquad E° = -0.126 \text{ v}$$

Thus the reaction in a standard cell is

$$Sn + Pb^{2+} \longrightarrow Sn^{2+} + Pb \qquad E° = +0.010 \text{ v}$$

For the cell as diagrammed in the problem,

$$E = E° - \frac{0.0592}{2} \log\left(\frac{[Sn^{2+}]}{[Pb^{2+}]}\right)$$

$$E = +0.010 - \frac{0.0592}{2} \log\left(\frac{1.000}{0.001}\right)$$

$$E = +0.010 - 0.0296 (3)$$

$$= +0.010 - 0.089 = -0.079 \text{ v}$$

This result means that the cell will not function in the manner implied by the diagram. Instead, it would operate in the reverse order and in a direction opposite to that of the standard cell. The cell is properly diagrammed

$$Pb \mid Pb^{2+}(a = 0.001) \parallel Sn^{2+}(a = 1.000) \mid Sn$$

and the reaction of the cell is

$$Pb + Sn^{2+} \longrightarrow Pb^{2+} + Sn \qquad E = +0.079 \text{ v}$$

From this example, we see that concentration effects can sometimes reverse the direction that a reaction is expected to take.

9.10 Concentration Cells

Since an electrode potential depends upon the concentration of the ions used in the electrode, a cell may be constructed from two electrodes composed of the same materials but differing in concentration of ions. For example,

$$Cu \mid Cu^{2+}(a = 0.01) \parallel Cu^{2+}(a = 0.10) \mid Cu$$

From the partial equation,

$$2e^- + Cu^{2+} \rightleftharpoons Cu \qquad E^\circ = +0.34 \text{ v}$$

and Le Chatelier's principle (Section 8.4), we can predict that *increasing* the concentration of Cu^{2+} ions would drive the reaction to the right and raise the reduction potential, whereas *decreasing* the concentration of Cu^{2+} ions would drive the reaction to the left and raise the oxidation potential (or, lower the reduction potential). Hence in the cell diagrammed, the left electrode would have the stronger tendency for oxidation and the right would have the stronger tendency for reduction. The "reaction" of the cell is

$$Cu + Cu^{2+}(a = 0.10) \rightarrow Cu^{2+}(a = 0.01) + Cu$$

E° for this cell is zero since the same electrode is involved in each half cell. Then

$$E = 0.00 - \frac{0.0592}{2} \log\left(\frac{0.01}{0.10}\right)$$

$$E = -0.0296\,(-1) = +0.0296 \text{ v}$$

9.11 Applications of Half-Cell Potentials

Electrode potentials may be used to make qualitative, as well as quantitative, predictions about the course of many oxidation-reduction reactions as well as electrochemical processes. Table 9.3 is constructed with the most positive electrode potential (greatest tendency for reduction) at the bottom; the half reactions are shown as reductions. Hence, if a pair of electrodes is combined to make a voltaic cell, the reduction half reaction (cathode) of the cell will be that listed for the electrode of the pair that stands lower in the table, and the oxidation half reaction will be the reverse of that shown for the electrode of the pair that stands higher in the table. The E° for the cell may be obtained, therefore, by reversing the sign of the upper electrode potential and adding the two half-cell potentials. Appropriate changes must be made, by means of the Nernst equation, for cells in which all substances are not present at unit activity. It must be kept in mind that electrode potentials are determined under reversible conditions. The measured voltage of a spontaneously discharging voltaic cell will not equal the calculated electromotive force for the cell since in the production of an electric current, the cell is operating in an irreversible manner (Section 9.7).

The cell emf calculated by means of electrode potentials is the maximum voltage that the cell can develop and may be determined by the application of a measured external voltage of a magnitude that will just stop the flow of electrons. If an external voltage infinitesimally greater than that which the cell develops is applied, the cell will run in the reverse direction; electrolysis will occur. Electrode potentials, therefore, give the minimum voltage necessary for electrolysis.

In practice, however, it is found that a higher voltage than calculated must be applied to effect electrolysis. Part of the increased voltage is required to overcome the electrical resistance of the cell, and the remainder is needed to overcome two additional effects. The first is called **concentration polarization** and is caused by the changes in the concentration of the electrolyte around the electrodes as the electrolysis proceeds, and ions are removed or produced. The concentration gradient set up within the cell is, in effect, a concentration cell of the type discussed in Section 9.10 and produces a back emf opposing the applied voltage. Concentration polarization can be reduced by stirring the electrolyte during the course of the electrolysis.

The other effect that makes the voltage required for an electrolysis higher than the reversible emf is called **overvoltage.** Overvoltage is caused by a slow rate of reaction at the electrodes so that an excess applied voltage is required to make the electrolysis proceed at an appreciable rate. Overvoltages for the deposition of metals are low, but those required for the liberation of hydrogen gas or oxygen gas are appreciable, vary with the material used for the electrode, and may amount to a volt or more.

Electrolysis is an important procedure for the quantitative analysis of ores, alloys, and other metal-containing compounds and mixtures. For the electrolysis of any neutral aqueous solution, the half reaction

$$2e^- + 2H_2O \rightleftharpoons H_2(g) + 2OH^- \qquad E = -0.414 \text{ v}$$

must be taken into account in the consideration of what reduction occurs at the cathode. Ions or molecules should be discharged at the cathode in order of decreasing value of electrode potential—most positive value (lowest on the table) first—as the voltage is increased. One would predict it to be impossible to reduce any species with an electrode potential more negative than -0.414 v, the reduction potential for water. However, because of the high hydrogen overvoltage, it is possible to plate out, on the cathode, metals that have electrode potentials more negative than that for the reduction of water—down to, and including, zinc ($E° = -0.763$ v).

For the electrolysis of any neutral aqueous solution, the half reaction

$$4e^- + 4H^+ + O_2(g) \rightleftharpoons 2H_2O \qquad E = +0.815 \text{ v}$$

must be considered, written in reverse order, as an oxidation that could occur at the anode. One would predict that the oxidations at the anode would proceed in inverse order of electrode potentials—most negative (highest on the table) first—and that it would be impossible to oxidize any species with an electrode potential more positive than $+0.815$ v. Unlike the H_2O/H_2 electrode, however, the O_2/H_2O electrode is highly irreversible and values obtained experimentally are not subject to exact theoretical treatment. Furthermore, high overvoltages are required for the liberation of oxygen. Thus the oxidation of chloride ion to chlorine gas takes place in the electrolysis of aqueous solutions of chlorides.

$$2e^- + Cl_2(g) \rightleftharpoons 2Cl^- \qquad E° = +1.36 \text{ v}$$

The overvoltage of chlorine (the Cl_2/Cl^- couple is reversible) is less than the overvoltage of oxygen.

The products of electrolysis vary with the concentration of ions in the solution since the half-cell emf's are dependent upon concentrations. For example, the electrolysis of *dilute* solutions of chlorides yields oxygen at the anode rather than chlorine. Furthermore, after the primary electrode reactions in which electrons are transferred, secondary reactions may occur. Thus if chlorine is liberated in an alkaline solution, ClO^- or ClO_3^- ions are formed from the reaction of the chlorine with the hydroxide ions; if chlorine is liberated on a silver anode, $AgCl$ is formed.

Example 9.10 A solution is 1m in each of the following: $AgNO_3$, $Cu(NO_3)_2$, $Fe(NO_3)_2$, and $NaNO_3$. In the electrolysis of this solution, between inert electrodes, the voltage is gradually increased. What would be the order in which materials would plate out on the cathode, and at what voltage would each be discharged? Assume that the overvoltage of oxygen is 0.600 v, the overvoltage of hydrogen is 0.300 v, and that the solution is neutral. Ignore concentration polarization and cell resistance.

Solution The only species at the anode (which is inert) are the nitrate ion and water. Since it is impossible to oxidize the nitrate ion, water will be oxidized:

$$2H_2O \rightarrow O_2(g) + 4H^+ + 4e^- \qquad E_{ox} = -0.815 \text{ v}$$

If the overvoltage of oxygen is taken into account, the half-cell potential for the *oxidation* is -1.415 v.

The following reductions are possible at the cathode:

$$e^- + Na^+ \rightarrow Na \qquad E° = -2.714 \text{ v}$$
$$2e^- + Fe^{2+} \rightarrow Fe \qquad E° = -0.440 \text{ v}$$
$$2e^- + Cu^{2+} \rightarrow Cu \qquad E° = +0.337 \text{ v}$$
$$e^- + Ag^+ \rightarrow Ag \qquad E° = +0.799 \text{ v}$$

In addition the reduction of water

$$2e^- + 2H_2O \rightarrow H_2(g) + 2OH^- \qquad E = -0.414 \text{ v}$$

must be considered. If the overvoltage of hydrogen is taken into account, the reduction potential for water is -0.714 v.

The silver will plate out first. The voltage at which this will occur will be equal to the oxidation potential of water (-1.415 v) plus the reduction potential of Ag ($+0.799$ v), or -0.616 v. (The values are negative, since the voltage is applied.) After the silver has been removed, the copper will plate out at a voltage of -1.088 v, followed by the iron at a voltage of -1.855 v. The reduction of water (half cell potential $= -0.714$ v) will occur before the reduction of sodium ions (half cell potential $= -2.714$ v). Hence at a voltage of 2.129 v, hydrogen will be evolved at the cathode. Sodium ions can be reduced only in the absence of water, that is, the electrolysis of molten sodium salts.

Electrode potentials are also useful for the evaluation of chemical reactions that take place outside of electrochemical cells. The half reactions of Table 9.3 are listed as reductions, from left to right, with the oxidized form of the element, molecule or ion accepting electrons to produce the reduced form:

$$\text{oxidant} + ne^- \rightleftharpoons \text{reductant}$$

Because of the way in which the table is constructed (greatest tendency for reduction at the bottom), any reduced form, at unit activity, should be able to reduce the oxidized form, at unit activity, of a half reaction listed below in the table (with a more positive $E°$). This is in agreement with the prediction of the course of voltaic cell reactions. Thus the species with the greatest tendency toward oxidation (best reducing agent) is the reduced form of the half reaction at the top of the table (Li in Table 9.3); the oxidized form of the half reaction at the bottom of the table (F$_2$ in Table 9.3) has the greatest tendency to be itself reduced (best oxidizing agent).

On this basis, displacement reactions (Section 7.6 and 7.9) are readily interpreted. The two half reactions

$$2e + Mg^{2+} \rightleftharpoons Mg \qquad E° = -2.363 \text{ v}$$
$$e^- + Ag^+ \rightleftharpoons Ag \qquad E° = +0.799 \text{ v}$$

would lead one to predict that magnesium metal would displace silver from its compounds.

$$Mg(s) + Ag^+(aq) \rightarrow Mg^{2+}(aq) + Ag(s)$$

Displacement reactions involving nonmetals are also encountered.

$$2e^- + I_2 \rightleftharpoons 2I^- \qquad E° = +0.536 \text{ v}$$
$$2e^- + Cl_2 \rightleftharpoons 2Cl^- \qquad E° = +1.360 \text{ v}$$

From these half reactions, one would predict

$$Cl_2(g) + 2I^-(aq) \rightarrow 2Cl^-(aq) + I_2(s)$$

There are several factors that must be kept in mind when using a table of electrode potentials to predict the course of a chemical reaction. Because E changes with changes in concentration, many presumably unfavored reactions can be made to occur by altering the concentrations of the reacting species or by running the reaction in a solution of different acidity or alkalinity. In addition, some theoretically favored reactions proceed at such a slow rate that they are of no practical consequence.

Correct use of the table also demands that all pertinent half reactions of a given element be considered before making a prediction. On the basis of the half reactions

$$3e^- + Fe^{3+} \rightleftharpoons Fe \qquad E° = -0.036 \text{ v}$$
$$2e^- + 2H^+ \rightleftharpoons H_2 \qquad E° = 0.000 \text{ v}$$

one would predict that the products of the reaction of iron with acids would be hydrogen gas and Fe^{3+} ions ($E°$ for the complete reaction, +0.036 v). However, the oxidation state iron(II) lies between metallic iron and the oxidation state iron(III). Once an iron atom has lost two electrons and becomes a Fe^{2+} ion, further oxidation is opposed.

$$e^- + Fe^{3+} \rightleftharpoons Fe^{2+} \qquad E° = +0.771 \text{ v}$$

Thus the reaction of iron metal and acids yields Fe^{2+} ions only. This fact could have been predicted by an examination of the half reaction

$$2e^- + Fe^{2+} \rightleftharpoons Fe \qquad E° = -0.440 \text{ v}$$

The $E°$ for the production of Fe^{2+} ions from the reaction of iron metal and acids (+0.440 v) is greater than that for the production of Fe^{3+} ions (+0.336 v), and hence the former is favored.

We may summarize the electrode potentials for iron and its ions as follows.

$$Fe^{3+} \xrightarrow{+0.771 \text{ v}} Fe^{2+} \xrightarrow{-0.440 \text{ v}} Fe$$
$$\underset{-0.036 \text{ v}}{\underline{\phantom{Fe^{3+}\xrightarrow{\qquad\qquad} Fe^{2+}\xrightarrow{\qquad} Fe}}}$$

The preceding predictions are immediately evident from this diagram.

Another pitfall to be avoided is the existance of oxidation states that are unstable due to disproportionation. The electrode potentials for copper and its ions may be summarized:

$$Cu^{2+} \xrightarrow{+0.153 \text{ v}} Cu^+ \xrightarrow{+0.521} Cu$$
$$\underset{+0.337 \text{ v}}{\underline{\phantom{Cu^{2+}\xrightarrow{\qquad\qquad} Cu^+\xrightarrow{\qquad} Cu}}}$$

From this we see that the Cu^+ ion is not a very stable one. In water, Cu^+ ions disproportionate to copper metal and Cu^{2+} ions.

$$2Cu^+(aq) \rightarrow Cu(s) + Cu^{2+}(aq)$$

The $E°$ for this reaction is $+0.521 - 0.153 = +0.368$ v. Species instable toward disproportionation may be readily recognized by the fact that the electrode potential for the reduction to the next lower oxidation state is more positive than the electrode potential for the couple with the next higher oxidation state. An inspection of the diagram for iron and its ions shows that the Fe^{2+} ion is stable toward such disproportionation.

9.12 Some Commercial Voltaic Cells

Several voltaic cells are of commercial importance. The **dry cell** (Figure 9.6) consists of a zinc metal container (which serves as the anode) filled with a moist paste of ammonium chloride and zinc chloride and containing a graphite electrode (the cathode) surrounded by manganese

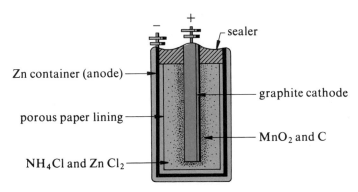

Figure 9.6 The Dry Cell.

dioxide. The electrode reactions are complex, but they may be approximately represented by

cathode: $\quad 2e^- + 2MnO_2 + 2NH_4^+ \rightarrow Mn_2O_3 + H_2O + 2NH_3$

anode: $\quad\quad\quad\quad\quad\quad\quad Zn \rightarrow Zn^{2+} + 2e^-$

The dry cell generates a voltage of approximately 1.25 to 1.50 v.

A newer type of dry cell which has found use in small electrical devices (such as hearing aids) consists of a zinc container as the anode, a carbon rod as the cathode, and moist mercury(II) oxide mixed with potassium hydroxide as the electrolyte. A lining of porous paper keeps the electrolyte separated from the zinc anode. The cell has a potential of approximately 1.35 v.

cathode: $\quad 2e^- + HgO + H_2O \rightarrow Hg + 2OH^-$

anode: $\quad\quad\quad Zn + 2OH^- \rightarrow Zn(OH)_2 + 2e^-$

The **lead storage cell** consists of a lead cathode and a grid of lead packed with lead dioxide as the anode. The electrolyte is sulfuric acid, and the half-cell reactions are

cathode: $2e^- + PbO_2(s) + SO_4^{2-} + 4H^+ \longrightarrow PbSO_4(s) + 2H_2O$

anode: $Pb(s) + SO_4^{2-} \longrightarrow PbSO_4(s) + 2e^-$

In practice, a lead storage cell is made of a number of Cathode plates and a number of anode plates arranged alternately and joined to increase the current obtainable; one cell gives a potential of approximately 2 v. A storage battery consists of three or six such cells joined in series to produce a 6- or a 12-volt battery.

The electrode reactions of the storage battery can be reversed by the application of an external current source, and in this manner, the battery can be recharged. Since sulfuric acid is consumed as the storage battery delivers current, the state of charge of the battery can be determined by measuring the density of the battery electrolyte.

The **nickel-cadmium storage cell** has a longer life than the lead storage cell but is more expensive to manufacture.

cathode: $2e^- + NiO_2(s) + 2H_2O \longrightarrow Ni(OH)_2 + 2OH^-$

anode: $Cd(s) + 2OH^- \longrightarrow Cd(OH)_2 + 2e^-$

The potential of each cell of a nickel-cadmium battery is approximately 1.4 v, and the battery is rechargeable.

9.13   Fuel Cells

Electrical cells that are designed to convert the energy from the combustion of fuels such as hydrogen, carbon monoxide, or methane directly into electrical energy are called fuel cells. Since, in theory, 100% of the free energy released by a combustion (ΔG) should be obtainable from an efficient fuel cell, extensive research into their development is currently being undertaken. Although approximately only 60 to 70% efficiency has been realized as yet, present fuel cells are about twice as efficient as processes in which the heat of combustion is used to generate electricity by mechanical means.

In a typical fuel cell, hydrogen and oxygen are bubbled through porous carbon electrodes into concentrated aqueous sodium hydroxide or potassium hydroxide.

$$C \mid H_2(g) \mid OH^- \mid O_2(g) \mid C$$

The gaseous materials are consumed and are continuously supplied. The electrode reactions are

cathode: $4e^- + O_2(g) + 2H_2O \longrightarrow 4OH^-$

anode: $2H_2(g) + 4OH^- \longrightarrow 4H_2O + 4e^-$

The complete cell reaction is

$$2H_2(g) + O_2(g) \longrightarrow 2H_2O(l)$$

The cell is maintained at an elevated temperature, and the water produced by the cell reaction evaporates as it is formed.

Research in the design of fuel cells is currently being directed toward lowering the cost of the processes. Another problem involves the development of electrodes with catalytic surfaces that will cause the half-cell reactions to occur rapidly.

SOME SUGGESTED READINGS

Denaro, A. R., *Elementary Electrochemistry*, Washington, D.C., Butterworth, 1965 (paper).

Gurney, R. W., *Ions in Solution*, New York, Dover, 1962 (paper).

Gurney, R. W., *Ionic Processes in Solution*, New York, Dover, 1962 (paper).

Latimer, W. M., *Oxidation Potentials*, 2nd ed., Englewood Cliffs, N. J., Prentice-Hall, 1952.

Leveson, L. L., *Introduction to Electroanalysis*, Washington, D.C., Butterworth, 1964 (paper).

MacInnes, D. A., *The Principles of Electrochemistry*, New York, Dover, 1961 (paper).

Murray, R. E., and Reilley, C. N., *Electroanalytical Principles*, New York, Wiley, 1964 (paper).

Reynolds, W. L., and Lumbry, R. W., *Mechanisms of Electron Transfer*, New York, Ronald, 1966.

Tunney, T. A., *Oxidation Mechanisms*, Washington, D.C., Butterworth, 1965.

PROBLEMS

9.1   The equivalent conductance of $0.100 M$ NaCl is 106.7 cm^2/ohm equivalent at 25°C. A cell with electrodes that are 2.00 cm^2 in surface area and 10.0 cm apart is filled with $0.100 M$ NaCl. How much current will flow when the potential difference between the electrodes is 50.0 v?

9.2   A conductance cell is filled with $0.100 M$ KCl (specific conductance, κ, 1.29×10^{-2}/ohm cm) at 25°C and the measured resistance is 93.6 ohms. When the cell is filled with $0.0100 M$ CaCl$_2$, the measured resistance is 522.2 ohms at 25°C. What are the specific and equivalent conductances of the calcium chloride solution?

9.3   Barium sulfate is only slightly soluble in water, and a saturated solution of BaSO$_4$ may be regarded as infinitely dilute. The equivalent conductance of BaSO$_4$ at infinite dilution, Λ_0, (estimated from the equivalent conductances of solutions of other sulfates and other barium salts) is 143 cm^2/ohm equivalent. The specific conductance, κ, of a saturated solution of BaSO$_4$ is 2.85×10^{-6}/ohm cm after correction for the conductance of pure water. What is the solubility of BaSO$_4$ in moles per liter?

9.4   At 25°C, the equivalent conductance of $0.00100 M$ acetic acid is 49.2 cm^2/ohm equivalent. The equivalent conductance at infinite dilution of HC$_2$H$_3$O$_2$ is 390.7 cm^2/ohm equivalent. What is the degree of dissociation, α, of acetic acid in $0.00100 M$ solution?

9.5   In 0.00500 M solution, acetic acid is 5.8% dissociated at 25°C. If Λ_0 for $HC_2H_3O_2$ is 390.7 cm^2/ohm equivalent, what is the specific conductance, κ, of 0.00500 M $HC_2H_3O_2$?

9.6   Magnesium metal is prepared by the electrolysis of anhydrous molten $MgCl_2$. (a) How many grams of magnesium would be prepared by using a current of 8.00 amp for 5.00 hours? (b) What volume of chlorine (measured at STP) would be produced in (a)?

9.7   How many grams of sodium would be produced by the electrolysis of anhydrous molten NaCl in the same time that it takes to liberate 100 liters of chlorine gas (measured at STP)?

9.8   Aluminum is produced by the electrolysis of molten aluminum oxide, Al_2O_3. The electrode reactions are

$$\text{cathode:} \quad 3e^- + Al^{3+} \longrightarrow Al$$
$$\text{anode:} \quad C + 2O^{2-} \longrightarrow CO_2 + 4e^-$$

In the process, the carbon of which the anode is composed is gradually consumed by the anode reaction. What is the weight loss of the anode when 1.00 lb of aluminum is prepared?

9.9   How long will it take to produce 1.00 kg of aluminum by means of the process described in 9.8 if a current of 10.0 amp is used?

9.10 What is the concentration of Ni^{2+} remaining in solution after the electrolysis of 100 ml of 0.500 M $NiSO_4$ solution when one uses a current of 1.50 amp for 1.00 hour? Assume that the volume of the solution does not change during the course of the electrolysis.

9.11 What is the equivalent weight of a metal if a current of 0.250 amp will cause 0.108 g of the metal to plate out of a solution undergoing electrolysis in 40.0 minutes?

9.12 Sketch the following voltaic cell:

$$Mg \mid Mg^{2+} \parallel Ni^{2+} \mid Ni$$

On your diagram indicate (a) the signs of the electrodes, (b) the cathode and anode, (c) the directions of motion of the ions, (d) the direction of motion of electrons in the circuit, (e) the electrode reactions, and (f) the cell voltage.

9.13 Sketch a cell for the electrolysis of aqueous $NiSO_4$ between inert electrodes. On the diagram label (a) the cathode and anode, (b) the signs of the electrodes, (c) the directions of motion of the ions, (d) the direction in which electrons move, and (e) the electrode reactions.

9.14 From the substances listed in Table 9.3, select (a) an oxidizing agent capable of oxidizing Sn to Sn^{2+} but not Ag to Ag^+, (b) an oxidizing agent capable of oxidizing I^- to I_2 but not Br^- to Br_2, (c) a reducing agent capable of reducing Zn^{2+} to Zn but not Mg^{2+} to Mg, and (d) a reducing agent capable of reducing Br_2 to Br^- but not Cu^{2+} to Cu.

9.15 Predict whether or not each of the following reactions will occur spontaneously, and write a balanced chemical equation for each reaction that is predicted to occur. Assume that each reactant and product is present at unit activity in aqueous solution. (a) Cd^{2+} reduced to Cd by Ni, (b) Sn oxidized to Sn^{2+} by Cu^{2+} ion, (c) I_2 reduced to I^- by Ag metal, (d) MnO_4^- reduced to Mn^{2+} by Br^-, (e) Cr^{3+} oxidized to $Cr_2O_7^{2-}$ by MnO_4^-.

9.16 From the standard electrode potentials

$$3e^- + Au^{3+} \longrightarrow Au \qquad E° = +1.50 \text{ v}$$
$$e^- + Au^+ \longrightarrow Au \qquad E° = +1.69 \text{ v}$$

calculate the potential for the half reaction

$$2e^- + Au^{3+} \longrightarrow Au^+$$

What conclusions can be drawn regarding the stability of the Au^+ ion in water solution?

9.17 From the standard electrode potentials

$$3e^- + Ce^{3+} \longrightarrow Ce \qquad E° = -2.48 \text{ v}$$
$$e^- + Ce^{4+} \longrightarrow Ce^{3+} \qquad E° = +1.61 \text{ v}$$

calculate the potential for the half reaction

$$4e^- + Ce^{4+} \longrightarrow Ce$$

9.18 The following electrode potentials correspond to half reactions that occur in neutral solution (in which the concentration of H^+ (aq) and the concentration of OH^- (aq) each equal $1.0 \times 10^{-7} M$).

$$2e^- + H_2O \longrightarrow 2OH^- + H_2 \qquad E = -0.414 \text{ v}$$
$$4e^- + 4H^+ + O_2 \longrightarrow 2H_2O \qquad E = +0.815 \text{ v}$$

If each of the gas pressures is maintained at exactly 1 atm, what are the standard electrode potentials for these half reactions? Assume that unit activity of H^+ and of OH^- is $1.0 M$.

9.19 What is the electrode potential of

$$5e^- + 8H^+ + MnO_4^- \longrightarrow Mn^{2+} + 4H_2O$$

with H^+ (aq) present in a concentration of $4.00 M$ and other species at unit activity? Assume that unit activity of H^+ is $1.00 M$. $E°$ for the half reaction is $+1.51$ v.

9.20 (a) What is the potential for the cell

$$Co \mid Co^{2+}(0.010m) \parallel Pd^{2+}(0.500m) \mid Pd$$

(b) What is ΔG for the cell reaction? $E°$ for Co^{2+}/Co is -0.28 v and for Pd^{2+}/Pd is $+0.99$ v.

9.21 What potential will a concentration cell develop if a standard Cl_2/Cl^- half cell is connected to another Cl_2/Cl^- half cell in which the pressure of Cl_2 gas is 2.0 atm and the concentration of Cl^- ions is $0.10m$? (b) Which electrode is the cathode? (c) Indicate the cell notation for this concentration cell.

10

The Nonmetals

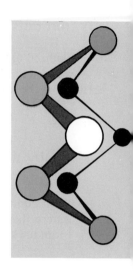

The very important nonmetals hydrogen and oxygen have been discussed in Chapter 7. In this chapter, we shall survey the chemistry of the remaining nonmetals.

THE NOBLE GASES

The outstanding characteristic of the noble gases is their *almost* total lack of chemical reactivity. Until 1962, no true compounds of these elements were known, and hence they were called the "inert gases." At the present, only a few compounds of the heavier elements of the family have been prepared.

10.1 Properties of the Noble Gases

The low order of chemical reactivity of the group 0 elements is explained by their exceptionally stable electronic structures (Section 2.17). Helium has a complete $n = 1$ shell ($1s^2$); the outermost shell of each of the other noble gases consists of eight electrons arranged in the configuration $ns^2 np^6$ where n, the principal quantum number, is the same as the number of the period in which the element is found.

The atoms of a group 0 element have no tendency to combine to form polyatomic molecules; each element occurs in nature as a colorless monatomic gas. The low melting points and boiling points of these elements (Table 10.1) illustrate the weak nature of the forces of attraction between the atoms of a given element—van der Waals forces caused by the motion of electrons (Section 3.10). Furthermore, each element has a melting point that lies close to its boiling point. Thus the elements exist as liquids over very narrow temperature ranges, and the forces of attraction of a crystal must be very similar to those of the corresponding liquid.

Within the group, the boiling point and melting point increase with increasing atomic number. This trend is expected since the strength of van der Waals forces depends upon the number of electrons in the atoms. In addition, the size of the atom increases with increasing atomic number and the outer electrons become slightly less tightly held—a factor which makes for stronger van der Waals forces. This last effect is also shown by the ionization energies of the noble gases; the ionization potentials decrease in a regular fashion from helium to radon (Section 3.2).

All of the noble gases occur in the atmosphere (Table 10.1), and Ne, Ar, Kr, and Xe are by-products of the fractionation of liquid air. Certain natural gas deposits (located principally in the United States) contain a higher percentage of helium than is found in air; these constitute the major commercial source of helium. Radon, used in cancer therapy, is a product of the radioactive decay of radium. Radon itself is radioactive with a half life of 3.82 days. (The half life is the period of time that it takes for half of the radioactive material to disappear.)

Cryogenics is the study of phenomena that occur at extremely low temperatures. Liquid helium may be cooled to an extremely low temperature by pumping away helium vapor from the evaporating liquid, and temperatures below $1°K$ have been reached in this manner. (Temperatures close to $0.001°K$ have been obtained by other techniques applied after initial cooling by helium evaporation.)

When liquid helium (helium I; normal boiling point, $4.2°K$) is cooled below $2.18°K$, a new form of helium (helium II) is obtained. Whereas

*The period of time that it takes for half of the radioactive material to disappear.

TABLE 10.1.
MELTING POINTS, BOILING POINTS, AND OCCURRENCE OF THE NOBLE GASES.

Gas	Melting Point ($°C$)	Boiling Point ($°C$)	Abundance in Atmosphere (Volume %)*
He	* *	-268.9	5×10^{-4}
Ne	-248.6	-245.9	2×10^{-3}
Ar	-189.3	-185.8	0.94
Kr	-157	-152.9	1×10^{-4}
Xe	-112	-107.1	9×10^{-6}
Rn	-71	-61.8	trace

*Dry air at sea level.
** $-272.2°C$ at 26 atm pressure.

helium I has properties characteristic of ordinary liquids, helium II has such remarkable properties that it has been called a "fourth state of matter" or a "degenerate gas." Among the unusual properties of helium II are: an extremely low viscosity (about 1/1000 that of hydrogen *gas*), an extremely high thermal conductivity (about 600 times that of copper at room temperature), and a peculiar flow phenomenon in which the liquid climbs up the walls of the container and over the top, flows down the outside, and drips off the bottom. Helium II is produced only from ^4_2He, not from ^3_2He (which constitutes 1.4×10^{-3} % of natural helium).

It has long been known that the heavier noble gases (Ar, Kr, and Xe) form what are called **clathrates.** These are substances that are produced when a material such as hydroquinone, $C_6H_4(OH)_2$, is crystallized under a high pressure of the noble gas. In the crystallization, atoms of the gas are trapped in cavities formed by the molecules of the hydroquinone crystal. These same noble gases form hydrates, which are highly unstable solids; these hydrates are made by a similar procedure and may also be clathrates. Whether such materials should be classed as chemical compounds is questionable.

However, the noble gases of higher atomic weight do form a few true chemical compounds. The first such compound reported (1962) was xenon hexafluoroplatinate, $XePtF_6$, a yellow solid; an analogous compound xenon hexafluororhodate, $XeRhF_6$, has also been reported. Direct reaction of xenon and fluorine at 400°C yields xenon tetrafluoride, XeF_4, a colorless cyrstalline solid that melts at approximately 90°C. Under other conditions, xenon difluoride, XeF_2, and xenon hexafluoride, XeF_6, may be prepared; these compounds are also solids. The xenon fluorides react readily with water and produce oxygen-containing compounds (such as XeO_3, $XeOF_4$, $Xe(OH)_4$, and $XeO_2(OH)_4$) that are considerably less stable than the fluorides. The preparations of radon tetrafluoride, RnF_4, and krypton tetrafluoride, KrF_4, have also been reported.

It is significant that, thus far, only compounds of Kr, Xe, and Rn have been prepared; these are the noble gases of largest size and lowest ionization energy. In addition, the only binary compounds that have been prepared involve the two most electronegative elements—fluorine and oxygen. There is some evidence that the compound $XePtF_6$ may be an ionic compound formed of Xe^+ and PtF_6^- ions.

The geometric structure of the compound XeF_4 has been determined. The compound is square planar with a Xe—F bond distance of 1.93Å. This configuration can be accounted for by assuming that the compound is bonded through sp^3d^2 hybridized orbitals (octahedral) of xenon with two of the hybridized orbitals occupied by unshared pairs of electrons (see Section 3.13 and Figure 10.1).

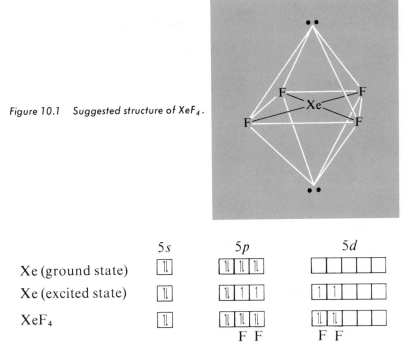

Figure 10.1   Suggested structure of XeF₄.

	5s	5p	5d
Xe (ground state)			
Xe (excited state)			
XeF₄			

THE HALOGENS

The elements of group VIIA, fluorine, chlorine, bromine iodine, and astatine, are called the **halogens**. These elements, with the exception of astatine, occur extensively in nature in the form of halide salts (particularly in sea water); the name "halogen" is derived from Greek and means "salt former." Astatine probably occurs in nature, in extremely small amounts, as a short-lived intermediate of natural radioactive decay processes (Section 18.2). However, most of our meager information about the chemistry of astatine comes from the study of the small amounts of a radioactive isotope of this element prepared by nuclear transmutation reactions. This element will be omitted from the discussion that follows.

10.2   Group Properties

The electronic configurations of the halogens are listed in Table 10.2; each halogen atom has one electron less than the noble gas following it in the periodic classification. Hence, there is a marked tendency on the part of a halogen atom to attain a noble-gas configuration either by electron transfer in an ionic compound

$$Na^+ \quad :\ddot{I}:^-$$

TABLE 10.2.
ELECTRONIC CONFIGURATIONS OF THE HALOGENS.

Element	Z	1s	2s	2p	3s	3p	3d	4s	4p	4d	4f	5s	5p	5d	6s	6p
F	9	2	2	5												
Cl	17	2	2	6	2	5										
Br	35	2	2	6	2	6	10	2	5							
I	53	2	2	6	2	6	10	2	6	10		2	5			
At	85	2	2	6	2	6	10	2	6	10	14	2	6	10	2	5

or by electron sharing in a covalent compound

$$H : \overset{..}{\underset{..}{Br}} :$$

Under ordinary conditions, these elements exist as diatomic molecules with a single covalent bond joining the atoms of the molecule

$$: \overset{..}{\underset{..}{Cl}} : \overset{..}{\underset{..}{Cl}} :$$

Positive oxidation states exist for all of the elements other than fluorine (Section 10.8).

Some properties of the halogens are summarized in Table 10.3. Most of the properties listed increase or decrease in a regular fashion within the halogen series arranged according to increasing atomic number. Each halogen is the most active nonmetal of its period; the halogen of each period has a high ionization potential, second only in magnitude to the noble gas of the period.

Within the halogen series, the ionization potential varies inversely with atomic radius. It is easier to remove an electron from an iodine atom than from a fluorine atom because the iodine atom is so much larger than the fluorine atom; in some of its reactions, iodine appears as

TABLE 10.3.
SOME PROPERTIES OF THE HALOGENS

	F_2	Cl_2	Br_2	I_2
Color	pale yellow	yellow-green	red-brown	violet-black
melting point (°C)	−218	−101	−7	+113
boiling point (°C)	−188	−35	+59	+183
atomic radius (Å)	0.72	0.99	1.14	1.33
ionic radius, X^- (Å)	1.36	1.81	1.95	2.16
first ionization potential (ev)	17.4	13.0	11.8	10.4
electron affinity (ev)	3.6	3.8	3.5	3.2
electronegativity	4.0	3.0	2.8	2.5
bond energy (kcal/mole)	37	58	46	36

a unipositive ion. Within any group of the periodic classification, metallic properties increase with increase in atomic number. The existence of compounds in which iodine exhibits cationic behavior illustrates the appearance of weak metallic character in group VIIA; presumably, astatine is more metallic than iodine.

The molecules of a given halogen are attracted to one another by van der Waals forces—the temporary dipoles caused by electron displacements within the molecules. Of all the halogens, the iodine molecule is largest, has the most electrons, and is more polarizable; it is not surprising that the intermolecular attractions are strongest in this element and that iodine has the highest melting point and boiling point. Under ordinary conditions, I_2 is a solid, Br_2 is a liquid, and Cl_2 and F_2 are gases.

Fluorine is the most active of all the nonmetals and has the highest electronegativity. Its great tendency to be reduced to the $1-$ oxidation state makes it the strongest oxidizing agent known. The electronegativity of the halogens decreases in the order $F > Cl > Br > I$, and the oxidizing power of the halogens decreases proportionately.

TABLE 10.4.
STANDARD ELECTRODE POTENTIALS OF THE HALOGENS (VOLTS).

$$2e^- + I_2 \rightleftharpoons 2I^- \qquad E° = +0.54 \text{ v}$$
$$2e^- + Br_2 \rightleftharpoons 2Br^- \qquad E° = +1.07 \text{ v}$$
$$2e^- + Cl_2 \rightleftharpoons 2Cl^- \qquad E° = +1.36 \text{ v}$$
$$2e^- + F_2 \rightleftharpoons 2F^- \qquad E° = +2.87 \text{ v}$$

The values for electron affinity and bond energy of the halogens listed in Table 10.3 each show a maximum at chlorine. This may appear surprising in view of the trend in electronegativities, the electrode potentials (Table 10.4), and the experimentally observed oxidizing abilities of the halogens. The reasons for the comparatively low electron affinity of fluorine and for the relatively low F—F bond energy are not completely understood; it is thought that the repulsions of the nonbonding electrons in the small fluorine atom are responsible for these effects.

Recall that electrode potentials refer to processes occurring in water solution in which all materials are present at unit activity. On this basis, the superior oxidizing ability of fluorine in comparison to the other halogens can be explained, in spite of fluorine's relatively low electron affinity, by consideration of the several steps involved in the conversion of the free halogens to halide ions in water solution. These are summarized in Table 10.5.

In the first step, heat is *absorbed* in the dissociation of the halogen molecules into gaseous halogen atoms. The enthalpy of dissociation of

TABLE 10.5.
ENTHALPIES OF SOME HALOGEN REACTIONS (kcal).

Reaction		F_2	Cl_2	Br_2	I_2
X_2(standard state)	$\longrightarrow 2X(g)$	+37	+58	+53	+51
$2X(g) + 2e^-(g)$	$\longrightarrow 2X^-(g)$	-167	-174	-163	-149
$2X^-(g)$	$\longrightarrow 2X^-(aq)$	-246	-178	-162	-144
X_2(standard state) $+ 2e^-(g) \rightarrow 2X^-(aq)$		-376	-294	-272	-242

iodine includes the energy needed to convert $I_2(s)$ to $I_2(g)$ as well as the bond energy of I_2, and the enthalpy of dissociation of bromine includes the heat needed to convert $Br_2(l)$ to $Br_2(g)$. In the second step, heat is *evolved* (the election affinity) by the formation of the gaseous halide ion. In the third step, heat is *evolved* by the hydration of the ions. The fluoride ion, which is the smallest of all the halide ions and has the highest charge density, has the highest enthalpy of hydration.

For each of the halogens, the algebraic sum of the enthalpies listed in Table 10.5 gives a measure of the vigor of the formation of the halide ion in water solution. It should be noted that the final equation of Table 10.5 involves gaseous electrons; however, the enthalpy values relating to this equation are adequate for the purpose of comparison. It is obvious that the high enthalpy of hydration of the fluoride ion (and to a lesser extent the low enthalpy of dissociation of the fluorine molecule) more than compensate for the difference in electron affinity. Therefore in water solution, fluorine is the most easily reduced halogen and consequently the strongest oxidizing agent.

In anhydrous reactions, fluorine is again the most reactive halogen; this is shown by the enthalpies of formation of the halides. The values listed in Table 10.6 are the heat effects when 1 mole of each of the compounds listed is prepared from the elements in their standard states (25°C). In each series, more heat is liberated in the preparation of the fluoride than in the production of any other halide, and the values decline in the expected order. The relatively low energy of the F—F bond (energy that is absorbed in the preparation) coupled with the relatively

TABLE 10.6.
ENTHALPIES OF FORMATION OF SOME HALIDES (kcal/mole).

	X = F	X = Cl	X = Br	X = I
NaX(s)	-136.0	-98.2	-86.3	-69.5
KX(s)	-134.5	-104.2	-94.2	-78.9
HX(g)	-64.2	-22.1	-8.7	$+6.2$

high energies of the short, strong bonds that fluorine forms with most other nonmetals (energy evolved) is believed to explain this effect for the covalent halides. Crystalline fluorides have high lattice energies because the F^- ion is relatively small and has a high charge density.

The relative oxidizing ability of the halogens may be observed in displacement reactions. Thus fluorine can displace chlorine, bromine, and iodine from their salts; chlorine can displace bromine and iodine from their salts; and bromine can displace iodine from iodides.

$$F_2(g) + 2NaCl(s) \longrightarrow 2NaF(s) + Cl_2(g)$$
$$Cl_2(g) + 2Br^-(aq) \longrightarrow 2Cl^-(aq) + Br_2(l)$$
$$Br_2(l) + 2I^-(aq) \longrightarrow 2Br^-(aq) + I_2(s)$$

10.3 Preparation of the Halogens

The principal natural sources of the halogens are listed in Table 10.7. Since fluorine is the most active known oxidizing agent, the preparation of elementary fluorine from a fluoride cannot be accomplished merely by chemical means. Instead, fluorine must be prepared by an electrochemical process. Furthermore, since the oxidation of water is easier to accomplish than the oxidation of the fluoride ion, the electrolysis must be carried out under anhydrous conditions. In actual practice, anhydrous molten potassium hydrogen fluoride, KHF_2, is electrolyzed between carbon electrodes in a nickel or copper vessel.

$$2KHF_2(l) \xrightarrow[\text{heat}]{\text{elec.}} H_2(g) + F_2(g) + 2KF(l)$$

In the process, the nickel or copper container reacts with fluorine, and the fluoride coating thus formed protects the metal from further reaction. The KHF_2 for the electrolysis is prepared from KF and HF. Hydrogen fluoride is commercially derived from fluorospar, CaF_2, (Section 10.5), and KF is the product of the reaction of K_2CO_3 and HF.

The principal industrial source of chlorine is the electrolysis of aqueous sodium chloride, from which sodium hydroxide and hydrogen are also products (Section 9.3).

$$2Na^+(aq) + 2Cl^-(aq) + 2H_2O \xrightarrow{\text{elec.}}$$
$$H_2(g) + Cl_2(g) + 2Na^+(aq) + 2OH^-(aq)$$

Smaller quantities of chlorine are produced by the electrolysis of anhydrous molten sodium chloride (Section 9.2).

$$2NaCl(l) \xrightarrow{\text{elec.}} 2Na(l) + Cl_2(g)$$

Bromine is commercially prepared by the oxidation of the bromide ion of salt brines or sea water with chlorine as the oxidizing agent.

TABLE 10.7.
OCCURRENCE OF THE HALOGENS.

Element	Percent of Earth's Crust	Occurrence
fluorine	0.1	CaF_2(fluorspar), Na_3AlF_6 (cryolite)
chlorine	0.2	Cl^- (sea water and underground brines) $NaCl$ (rock salt)
bromine	0.001	Br^- (sea water, underground brines, solid salt beds)
iodine	0.001	I^- (oil-well brines, sea water) $NaIO_3$, $NaIO_4$ (impurities in Chilean saltpeter, $NaNO_3$)

$$Cl_2(g) + 2Br^-(aq) \longrightarrow 2Cl^-(aq) + Br_2(l)$$

In the United States, the principal commercial source of iodine is the iodide ion found in oil-well brines; free iodine is obtained by chlorine displacement.

$$Cl_2(g) + 2I^-(aq) \longrightarrow 2Cl^-(aq) + I_2(s)$$

In addition, iodine is commercially obtained from the iodate impurity found in Chilean nitrates; sodium bisulfite is used to reduce the iodate ion.

$$2IO_3^-(aq) + 5HSO_3^-(aq) \longrightarrow I_2(s) + 5SO_4^{2-}(aq) + 3H^+(aq) + H_2O$$

With the exception of fluorine (which must be prepared electrochemically), the free halogens are usually prepared in the laboratory by the action of oxidizing agents on aqueous solutions of the hydrogen halides or solutions containing the sodium halides and sulfuric acid.

From a table of standard electrode potentials, we can get an approximate idea of what oxidizing agents will satisfactorily oxidize a given halide ion. Thus any couple with a standard electrode potential more positive than +1.36 should oxidize chloride ion as well as bromide ion ($E° = +1.07$ v) and iodide ion ($E° = +0.54$ v). Recall, however, that standard electrode potentials are listed for half reactions at 25°C with all materials at unit activity. Thus even though the standard electrode potential of $MnO_2 \longrightarrow Mn^{2+}$ is only +1.23 v, MnO_2 is capable of oxidizing the chloride ion if concentrated HCl is used (rather than HCl at unit activity) and if the reaction is heated (Section 9.9). In actual practice, $KMnO_4$, $K_2Cr_2O_7$, PbO_2, and MnO_2 are frequently used to prepare the free halogens from halide ions.

$$MnO_2(s) + 4H^+(aq) + 2Cl^-(aq) \longrightarrow Mn^{2+}(aq) + Cl_2(g) + 2H_2O$$
$$2MnO_4^-(aq) + 16H^+(aq) + 10Br^-(aq) \longrightarrow 2Mn^{2+}(aq) + 5Br_2(l) + 8H_2O$$
$$Cr_2O_7^{2-}(aq) + 14H^+(aq) + 6I^-(aq) \longrightarrow 2Cr^{3+}(aq) + 3I_2(s) + 7H_2O.$$

Some of the reactions of the halogens are summarized in Table 10.8.

TABLE 10.8.
SOME REACTIONS OF THE HALOGENS (X_2 = F_2, Cl_2, Br_2, OR I_2).

General Reaction	Remarks
$nX_2 + 2M \rightarrow 2MX_n$	F_2, Cl_2 with practically all metals; Br_2, I_2 with all except noble metals
$X_2 + H_2 \rightarrow 2HX$	
$3X_2 + 2P \rightarrow 2PX_3$	With excess P; similar reactions with As, Sb, and Bi
$5X_2 + 2P \rightarrow 2PX_5$	With excess X_2, but not with I_2; SbF_5, $SbCl_5$, AsF_5, $AsCl_5$, and BiF_5 may be similarly prepared
$X_2 + 2S \rightarrow S_2X_2$	With Cl_2, Br_2
$X_2 + H_2O \rightarrow H^+ + X^- + HOX$	Not with F_2
$2X_2 + 2H_2O \rightarrow 4H^+ + 4X^- + O_2$	F_2 rapidly; Cl_2, Br_2 slowly in sunlight
$X_2 + H_2S \rightarrow 2HX + S$	
$X_2 + CO \rightarrow COX_2$	Cl_2, Br_2
$X_2 + SO_2 \rightarrow SO_2X_2$	F_2, Cl_2
$X_2 + 2X'^- \rightarrow X'_2 + 2X^-$	$F_2 > Cl_2 > Br_2 > I_2$
$X_2 + X'_2 \rightarrow 2XX'$	Formation of the interhalogen compounds (all except IF)

10.4 The Interhalogen Compounds

Since the free halogens all exist as diatomic molecules, it is not surprising that interhalogen compounds of formula XX' (such as BrCl) are produced when two halogens are reacted; all possible combinations are known except IF. In addition, ClF_3, BrF_3, ICl_3, BrF_5, IF_5 and IF_7 may be prepared by direct combination of the elements. Notice that the maximum number of covalent bonds formed by each element in this series of compounds increases as the size of the central atom increases (ClF_3, BrF_5, and IF_7). Furthermore, this maximum is exhibited in the compound in which the central halogen atom is bonded to fluorine (the most electronegative and smallest halogen).

The bonding in the higher interhalogen compounds must violate the octet principle. It has been suggested that the bonding in ClF_3 uses hybridized sp^3d orbitals of chlorine with three of these orbitals used to bond fluorine atoms and the remaining two orbitals occupied by unshared electron pairs (Section 3.13).

	3s	3p	3d
Cl (ground state)	⇅	⇅ ⇅ ↑	☐☐☐☐☐
Cl (excited state)	⇅	⇅ ↑ ↑	↑ ☐☐☐☐
ClF_3	⇅	⇅ ⇅ ⇅	⇅ ☐☐☐☐
		F F	F

The use of sp^3d orbitals for bonding leads to compounds in which the bonds are directed to the apieces of a trigonal bipyramid and experimental evidence bears out this geometric configuration, in somewhat distorted form, for ClF_3.

In like manner, it has been suggested that BrF_5 is bonded through the hybridized sp^3d^2 (octahedral) orbitals of bromine with one of the orbitals being occupied by an unshared electron pair. The structure of IF_7 is believed to have the form of a pentagonal bipyramid and be bonded through sp^3d^3 hybridized orbitals. These configurations are illustrated in Figure 10.2.

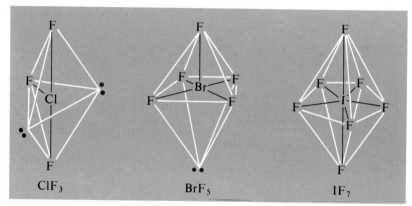

Figure 10.2   Geometric configurations of some interhalogen compounds.

The weak metallic character of iodine is seen in the electrochemical behavior of pure molten ICl. Presumably, this compound ionizes as follows:

$$2ICl \rightleftharpoons I^+ + ICl_2^-$$

10.5   The Hydrogen Halides

Each of the hydrogen halides may be prepared by the direct reaction of hydrogen with the corresponding free halogen; the vigor of the reaction decreases markedly from fluorine to iodine.

Both HF and HCl are made industrially by the action of warm concentrated sulfuric acid on the corresponding naturally occuring halide, CaF_2 and NaCl.

$$CaF_2(s) + H_2SO_4(l) \rightarrow CaSO_4(s) + 2HF(g)$$
$$NaCl(s) + H_2SO_4(l) \rightarrow NaHSO_4(s) + HCl(g)$$

All of the hydrogen halides are colorless gases at room temperature; sulfuric acid, on the other hand, is a high-boiling liquid. Thus the foregoing reactions are examples of a general method for the preparation of a volatile acid from its salts by means of a nonvolatile acid. At higher temperatures (ca., 500°C), further reaction occurs between $NaHSO_4$ and $NaCl$.

$$NaCl(s) + NaHSO_4(l) \rightarrow HCl(g) + Na_2SO_4(s)$$

Hydrogen bromide and hydrogen iodide cannot be made by the action of concentrated sulfuric acid on bromides and iodides because hot, concentrated sulfuric acid oxidizes these anions to the free halogens. The bromide and iodide ions are easier to oxidize than the fluoride and chloride ions.

$$2NaBr(s) + 2H_2SO_4(l) \rightarrow Br_2(g) + SO_2(g) + Na_2SO_4(s) + 2H_2O(g)$$

Since the iodide ion is a stronger reducing agent (more easily oxidized) than the bromide ion, S and H_2S, as well as SO_2, are obtained as reduction products from the reaction of NaI with hot concentrated sulfuric acid.

$$2NaI(s) + H_2SO_4(l) \rightarrow I_2(g) + SO_2(g) + Na_2SO_4(s) + H_2O(g)$$
$$6NaI(s) + 4H_2SO_4(l) \rightarrow 3I_2(g) + S(s) + 3Na_2SO_4(s) + 4H_2O(g)$$
$$8NaI(s) + 5H_2SO_4(l) \rightarrow 4I_2(g) + H_2S(g) + 4Na_2SO_4(s) + 4H_2O(g)$$

Pure HBr or HI can be obtained by the action of phosphoric acid on NaBr or NaI; phosphoric acid is an essentially nonvolatile acid and is a poor oxidizing agent.

$$NaBr(s) + H_3PO_4(l) \rightarrow HBr(g) + NaH_2PO_4(s)$$
$$NaI(s) + H_3PO_4(l) \rightarrow HI(g) + NaH_2PO_4(s)$$

The hydrogen halides may be prepared by the reaction of water on the appropriate phosphorus trihalide.

$$PX_3 + 3H_2O \rightarrow 3HX(g) + H_3PO_3(aq)$$

Convenient laboratory preparations of HBr and HI have been developed in which red phosphorus, bromine or iodine, and a limited amount of water are employed and in which no attempt is made to isolate the phosphorus trihalide intermediate.

A convenient method for preparing aqueous hydrogen iodide involves the reduction of a water suspension of iodine by means of hydrogen sulfide gas.

$$H_2S(g) + I_2(s) \rightarrow 2H^+(aq) + 2I^-(aq) + S(s)$$

All of the hydrogen halides are very soluble in water, and the water solutions are called the *hydrohalic acids*; for example, a water solution of hydrogen iodide is called hydroiodic acid. Hydrogen iodide, hydrogen bromide, and hydrogen chloride are monomolecular gases and are essentially completely dissociated in water. On the other hand, hydrogen fluoride is an associated substance (as a result of hydrogen bonding), and hydrogen fluoride gas appears to consist of aggregates up to $(HF)_5$ (Section 7.11). In water solution, hydrogen fluoride is a weak acid; the H—F bond is much stronger than any other H—X bond and is therefore more difficult to break. In dilute aqueous solutions, HF molecules are strongly hydrogen bonded to water molecules

$$\begin{array}{c} H \\ \diagdown \\ \end{array} O{-}H{-}{-}{-}F{-}H \qquad \text{and} \qquad \begin{array}{c} H \\ \diagdown \\ \diagup \\ H \end{array} O{-}{-}{-}H{-}F,$$

and the acid ionizes according to the equation

$$HF(aq) \rightleftharpoons H^+(aq) + F^-(aq)$$

In more concentrated aqueous solution, hydrogen fluoride is thought to occur in dimeric form (through hydrogen bonding): $\begin{array}{c} H \\ \diagdown \end{array} O{-}{-}{-}H{-}F$ and the acid probably dissociates according to the equation

$$(HF)_2(aq) \rightleftharpoons H^+(aq) + HF_2^-(aq)$$

Hydrofluoric acid reacts with silica, SiO_2, and glass.

$$SiO_2(s) + 6HF(aq) \rightarrow 2H^+(aq) + SiF_6^{2-}(aq) + 2H_2O$$

When warmed, the reaction is

$$SiO_2(g) + 4HF(aq) \rightarrow SiF_4(g) + 2H_2O(g)$$

For this reason, hydrofluoric acid must be stored in wax or plastic containers instead of glass bottles.

The fluorosilicate ion, SiF_6^{2-}, is an example of a large group of complex ions formed by the halide ions. Halo complexes are formed by most metals (with the notable exceptions of the group IA, group IIA, and lanthanide metals) and with some nonmetals (e.g., BF_4^-). The formulas of these complex ions are most commonly of the types $(MX_4)^{n-4}$ and $(MX_6)^{n-6}$ where n is the oxidation number of the central atom of the complex.

10.6   The Metal Halides

The character of the bonding in metal halides varies widely as do the physical properties of these compounds. A metal that has a low ionization energy generally forms halides that are highly ionic and consequently have high melting and boiling points. On the other hand, metals that have comparatively high ionization energies react, particularly with halogens of low electron affinity, to form halides in which the bonding has a high degree of covalent character; such compounds have comparatively low melting points and boiling points. In general, the high-melting halides are, in the fused state, better conductors of electricity than are the low-melting compounds.

The metal halides serve as convincing examples of the validity of Fajan's rules (Section 3.8). Since fluorine is the most electronegative of the halogens, its compounds are generally highly polar, and the fluoride of a given metal is usually the most ionic of the halides of that metal. This is borne out by the melting points of the sodium halides:

NaF	NaCl	NaBr	NaI
993°C	801°C	755°C	651°C

This series is typical; the degree of covalent character increases with increasing size of the halide ion and decreasing electronegativity of the halogen.

Covalent character also increases as the size of the cation decreases; the melting points of the chlorides of the group IIA metals are:

$BeCl_2$	$MgCl_2$	$CaCl_2$	$SrCl_2$	$BaCl_2$
440°C	708°C	772°C	873°C	962°C

A high charge on the cation also leads to enhanced covalence as illustrated by the melting points of the compounds listed below.

$SnCl_2$	$SnCl_4$	$SbCl_3$	$SbCl_5$
246°C	−33°C	73.4°C	2.8°C

Lastly, compounds containing cations that are isoelectronic with noble gases are more ionic than compounds with cations that are not; to be valid, comparisons must be made between compounds in which the cations both have similar charges and sizes. This is approximately true for the following two pairs of compounds which are listed together with their melting points.

$MgCl_2$	$CuCl_2$	$SrCl_2$	$HgCl_2$
708°C	498°C	873°C	276°C

In each pair, the cation of the chloride listed on the left has a noble-gas electronic configuration.

The water solubility of fluorides is considerably different from that of the chlorides, bromides, and iodides. The fluorides of lithium, the group IIA metals, and the lanthanides are only slightly soluble, whereas the other halides of these metals are relatively soluble.

Most chlorides, bromides, and iodides are soluble in water. The cations that form slightly soluble compounds with these halide ions include silver, mercury(I), lead(II), and thallium(I).

The insolubility of the silver salts of Cl^-, Br^-, and I^- is the basis of a common test for these halide ions; AgCl is white, AgBr is cream, and AgI is yellow. The silver halide precipitates may be formed by the addition of a solution of silver nitrate to a solution containing the appropriate halide ion. Silver iodide is insoluble in excess ammonia;

however, AgCl readily dissolves to form the $Ag(NH_3)_2^+$ complex ion (Section 16.1), and AgBr dissolves with difficulty. Silver fluoride is soluble; generally, MgF_2 or CaF_2 precipitates are used to confirm the presence of the fluoride ion in a solution.

If the iodide ion, in aqueous solution, is oxidized to iodine (the usual procedure employs chlorine), the I_2 can be extracted by carbon tetrachloride, which forms a two-liquid-layer system with water. The I_2 solution, in CCl_4, is violet colored. In the corresponding test for the bromide ion, the Br_2–CCl_4 solution is brown.

10.7 Iodimetry and Iodometry

The half reaction

$$2e^- + I_2 \rightleftharpoons 2I^- \qquad E° = +0.54 \text{ v}$$

is a very useful one in analytical chemistry. In a table of standard electrode potentials, there are many half reactions that stand above this one (with $E°$ values less positive than $+0.54$ v). Therefore there are many substances, such as S^{2-}, Sn^{2+}, SO_3^{2-}, As_2O_3, and $S_2O_3^{2-}$, that can reduce I_2 to I^-. Use is made of this fact in an analytical procedure called **iodimetry** in which a standard solution of iodine is used to titrate a reducing agent such as sodium thiosulfate, $Na_2S_2O_3$.

Iodine is only very slightly soluble in water. However, in the presence of the iodide ion, the solubility is significantly increased by the reaction

$$I_2(s) + I^-(aq) \longrightarrow I_3^-(aq)$$

and standard iodine solutions are always prepared by dissolving iodine in potassium iodide solutions.

Therefore the titration of thiosulfate ion with a standard iodine solution actually proceeds by the reaction

$$2S_2O_3^{2-}(aq) + I_3^-(aq) \longrightarrow S_4O_6^{2-}(aq) + 3I^-(aq)$$

It is, however, more convenient to consider the reaction to be

$$2S_2O_3^{2-}(aq) + I_2(aq) \longrightarrow S_4O_6^{2-}(aq) + 2I^-(aq)$$

The two equations differ formally only by one I^- on each side.

Iodine and starch form an intense-blue addition compound *in the presence of iodide ion*; the iodide ion alone has no visible effect on starch. Therefore a starch solution, which is capable of detecting iodine in concentrations as low as 10^{-5} M, is used as an indicator for iodimetric titrations.

In a typical analysis, a sodium thiosulfate solution, to which a small quantity of starch solution has been added, is titrated with a standard iodine solution. As the iodine solution is added, the $S_2O_3^{2-}$ ion is oxidized to the tetrathionate ion ($S_4O_6^{2-}$) and the I_2 is reduced to I^-. When one drop of iodine solution is added in excess of that needed for the oxidation of the $S_2O_3^{2-}$ ion, the blue color of the iodine–starch compound appears and signifies the end point of the titration.

From the position of the I_2/I^- half reaction in the table of standard electrode potentials, we can see that there are many substances capable of oxidizing I^- to I_2 (such as MnO_4^-, $Cr_2O_7^{2-}$, Fe^{3+}, and Ce^{4+}). The half reactions for these substances stand below the I_2/I^- half reaction and have $E°$ values more positive than $+0.54$ v. A procedure called **iodometry** is used to analyze solutions of these oxidizing agents.

Iodometry involves reacting the oxidizing agent with an excess of potassium iodide; iodine is liberated in a quantity equivalent to the oxidant being determined, and the iodine is titrated against a standard thiosulfate solution with starch as an indicator (see Example 10.1). The reactions of iodide ion and the iodine are usually rapid and proceed without side effects. The titrations are generally conducted in dilute acid.

Paper that is coated with a mixture of starch and KI (starch-iodide paper) is frequently used in a qualitative test for an oxidant. The oxidation of the iodide ion produces iodine that reacts with the starch and causes the test paper to turn blue.

Example 10.1   A 1.20 g sample of H_2O_2 solution is reacted with excess KI (acid solution, molybdate catalyst).

$$2H^+(aq) + H_2O_2(aq) + 2I^-(aq) \rightarrow I_2(aq) + 2H_2O \qquad (1)$$

The iodine produced by this reaction is titrated with standard $Na_2S_2O_3$.

$$2S_2O_3^{2-}(aq) + I_2(aq) \rightarrow S_4O_6^{2-}(aq) + 2I^-(aq) \qquad (2)$$

Near the end of the titration, when the color of the I_2 has started to fade, a few milliliters of starch solution is added and the titration is continued until the blue color of the iodine–starch complex just disappears. The titration requires 21.0 ml of 0.100N $Na_2S_2O_3$. What is the weight percent of H_2O_2 in the original peroxide solution?

Solution   The number of equivalents of $S_2O_3^{2-}$ used in the titration is

$$? \text{ equiv } S_2O_3^{2-} = 21.0 \text{ ml } S_2O_3^{2-} \text{ soln.} \left(\frac{0.100 \text{ equiv } S_2O_3^{2-}}{1000 \text{ ml } S_2O_3^{2-} \text{ soln.}} \right)$$

$$= 0.00210 \text{ equiv } S_2O_3^{2-}$$

The number of equivalents of I_2 produced in reaction (1) is the same as the number of equivalents of $S_2O_3^{2-}$ consumed in reaction (2), and the number of equivalents of iodine produced equals the number of equivalents of H_2O_2 present in the original sample of H_2O_2 solution (0.00210 equiv).

In reaction (1), the total change in oxidation number for the peroxide is $2-$. Since the molecular weight of H_2O_2 is 34.0, the equivalent weight of H_2O_2 is 34.0/2, or 17.0.

$$? \text{ g } H_2O_2 = 100 \text{ g } H_2O_2 \text{ soln.} \left(\frac{0.00210 \text{ equiv } H_2O_2}{1.20 \text{ g } H_2O_2 \text{ soln.}}\right)\left(\frac{17.0 \text{ g } H_2O_2}{1 \text{ equiv } H_2O_2}\right)$$

$$= 2.98 \text{ g } H_2O_2$$

The solution is 2.98% hydrogen peroxide.

10.8   Oxyacids of the Halogens

The known oxyacids of the halogens are listed in Table 10.9 (electronic formulas are given in Figure 10.3). The acids of chlorine, and their salts, are the most important of these compounds. Fluorine does not form oxyacids.

The hypohalous acids (HOX) are weak acids; they exist in aqueous solution but cannot be prepared in pure form. The hypohalous acids are produced in low concentrations by the reactions of the free halogens and water.

$$X_2 + H_2O \rightarrow H^+(aq) + X^-(aq) + HOX(aq)$$

This reaction may be driven to the right, and the yield of HOX increased, by the addition of Ag_2O or HgO to the reaction mixture (Section 12.10). These oxides precipitate the X^- ion and remove $H^+(aq)$.

$$2X_2 + Ag_2O(s) + H_2O \rightarrow 2AgX(s) + 2HOX(aq)$$

$$2X_2 + 4HgO(s) + H_2O \rightarrow HgX_2 \cdot 3HgO(s) + 2HOX(aq)$$

Solutions of sodium hypochlorite, used commercially in cotton bleaching (e.g., Chlorox), are prepared by electrolyzing cold sodium chloride solutions as in the preparation of chlorine (Section 10.3). In this process, however, the products of the electrolysis are not kept separate; rather, the electrolyte is vigorously mixed so that the chlorine produced at the anode reacts with the hydroxide ion produced at the cathode.

**TABLE 10.9
OXYHALOGEN ACIDS**

Oxidation State of the Halogen	Formula of Acid			Name of Acid	Name of Anion Derived from Acid
1+	HOCl	HOBr	HOI	hypohalous acid	hypohalite ion
3+	$HClO_2$	—	—	halous acid	halite ion
5+	$HClO_3^a$	$HBrO_3^a$	HIO_3^a	halic acid	halate ion
7+	$HClO_4^a$	—	$\begin{cases} HIO_4 \\ H_4I_2O_9 \\ H_5IO_6 \end{cases}$	perhalic acid	perhalate ion

^{a}Strong acids.

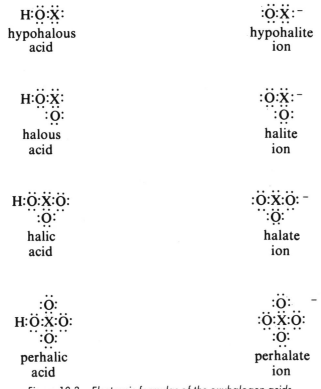

Figure 10.3   *Electronic formulas of the oxyhalogen acids.*

anode: $2Cl^- \rightarrow Cl_2 + 2e^-$

cathode: $2e^- + 2H_2O \rightarrow 2OH^- + H_2$

                  $Cl_2 + 2OH^- \rightarrow OCl^- + Cl^- + H_2O$

The overall equation for the entire process is

$$Cl^- + H_2O \xrightarrow[\text{cold}]{\text{elec.}} OCl^- + H_2$$

The only halous acid known is chlorous acid ($HClO_2$). It cannot be isolated in pure form, and even in aqueous solution it decomposes rapidly. Chlorous acid is a weak acid, but it is stronger than hypochlorous. Chlorites are comparatively stable in alkaline solution and may be prepared by passing chlorine dioxide gas (a very reactive odd-electron molecule) into a solution of an alkali.

$$2ClO_2(g) + 2OH^-(aq) \rightarrow ClO_2^-(aq) + ClO_3^-(aq) + H_2O$$

A better preparation, in which no chlorate ion is produced, is the reaction of ClO_2 with an alkaline solution of sodium peroxide (which forms the hydroperoxide ion, HO_2^-, in water).

$$2ClO_2(g) + HO_2^-(aq) + OH^-(aq) \rightarrow 2ClO_2^-(aq) + O_2(g) + H_2O$$

Solid chlorites are dangerous chemicals; they detonate when heated and are explosive in contact with combustible material.

The hypohalite ions are unstable and disproportionate, especially when warmed.

$$3XO^- \rightarrow XO_3^- + 2X^-$$

Thus if a free halogen is added to a hot, concentrated solution of alkali, the corresponding halide and halate ions are produced rather than the halide and hypohalite ions.

$$3X_2 + 6OH^-(aq) \rightarrow 5X^-(aq) + XO_3^-(aq) + 3H_2O$$

The chlorates are commercially prepared by the electrolysis of hot, concentrated solutions of chlorides (instead of the cold solutions used for the electrochemical preparation of the hypochlorites). The electrolyte is stirred vigorously so that the chlorine produced at the anode reacts with the hydroxide ion that is a product of the reduction at the cathode.

anode: $\qquad 2Cl^- \rightarrow Cl_2 + 2e^-$

cathode: $\quad 2e^- + 2H_2O \rightarrow 2OH^- + H_2$

$$3Cl_2 + 6OH^- \rightarrow 5Cl^- + ClO_3^- + 3H_2O$$

If the three foregoing equations are added, after the first two equations have each been multiplied through by 3, the equation for the overall process is obtained.

$$Cl^- + 3H_2O \xrightarrow[\text{hot}]{\text{elec.}} ClO_3^- + 3H_2$$

The chlorate crystalliyes from the concentrated solution employed as the electrolyte of the cell. Whereas chlorates are generally water soluble, they are much less soluble than the corresponding chlorides.

Solutions of a halic acid can be prepared by adding sulfuric acid to a solution of the barium salt of the acid.

$$Ba^{2+}(aq) + 2XO_3^-(aq) + 2H^+(aq) + SO_4^{2-}(aq) \rightarrow BaSO_4(s)$$
$$+ 2H^+(aq) + 2XO_3^-(aq)$$

Pure $HBrO_3$ or $HClO_3$ cannot be isolated from aqueous solutions because of decomposition. Iodic acid, HIO_3, however, can be obtained as a white solid; this acid is generally prepared by oxidizing iodine with concentrated nitric acid. All of the halic acids are strong.

Chlorine dioxide, which is used in the preparation of chlorites, may be prepared by the reaction of a chlorate with sulfuric acid; this preparation, however, is dangerous. A safer procedure is the reduction of a chlorate, in aqueous solution, by sulfur dioxide gas.

$$2ClO_3^-(aq) + SO_2(g) \rightarrow ClO_2(g) + SO_4^{2-}(aq)$$

The halate salts decompose upon heating in a variety of ways. At high temperatures, and particularly in the presence of a catalyst, chlorates decompose into chlorides and oxygen (Section 7.1).

$$2KClO_3(s) \xrightarrow[\text{MnO}_2]{\text{heat}} 2KCl(s) + 3O_2(g)$$

At more moderate temperatures, in the absence of a catalyst, the decomposition yields perchlorates and chlorides.

$$4KClO_3(s) \xrightarrow{\text{heat}} 3KClO_4(s) + KCl(s)$$

The decompositions of bromates and iodates are not as clean cut. Depending upon the salt, various mixtures are obtained, and products include the free halogens, oxygen, halide salts, and metal oxides. Perbromic acid and perbromates are not known, but the periodate is obtained as one of the products of the thermal decomposition of certain iodates.

Perchlorate salts are made by the controlled thermal decomposition of a chlorate or by the electrolysis of a cold solution of a chlorate. The free acid, a clear hygroscopic liquid, may be prepared by distilling a mixture of a perchlorate salt with concentrated sulfuric acid. A number of crystalline hydrates of perchloric acid are known. The compound $HClO_4 \cdot H_2O$ is of interest; the lattice positions of the crystal are occupied by H_3O^+ and ClO_4^- ions, and the solid is isomorphous (of the same crystalline structure) with NH_4ClO_4.

TABLE 10.10
STANDARD ELECTRODE POTENTIALS OF OXYHALOGEN COMPOUNDS (VOLTS).

Half Reaction		X = Cl	X = Br	X = I
ACID SOLUTION				
$2e^- + HOX + H^+$	$\rightleftharpoons X^- + H_2O$	+1.49	+1.33	+0.99
$4e^- + HOXO + 3H^+$	$\rightleftharpoons X^- + 2H_2O$	+1.56	—	—
$6e^- + XO_3^- + 6H^+$	$\rightleftharpoons X^- + 3H_2O$	+1.45	+1.45	+1.09
$8e^- + XO_4^- + 8H^+$	$\rightleftharpoons X^- + 4H_2O$	+1.38	—	?
$8e^- + H_5XO_6 + 7H^+$	$\rightleftharpoons X^- + 6H_2O$	—	—	~+1.24
ALKALINE SOLUTION				
$2e^- + XO^- + H_2O$	$\rightleftharpoons X^- + 2OH^-$	+0.88	+0.76	+0.49
$4e^- + XO_2^- + 2H_2O$	$\rightleftharpoons X^- + 4OH^-$	+0.77	—	—
$6e^- + XO_3^- + 3H_2O$	$\rightleftharpoons X^- + 6OH^-$	+0.62	+0.61	+0.26
$8e^- + XO_4^- + 4H_2O$	$\rightleftharpoons X^- + 8OH^-$	+0.55	—	?
$8e^- + H_3XO_6^{2-} + 3H_2O$	$\rightleftharpoons X^- + 9OH^-$	—	—	~+0.37

A series of periodates is known; in general, they are made by the oxidation of iodates. The acids HIO_4, $H_4I_2O_9$, and H_5IO_6 have been prepared, and salts of the hypothetical acid H_3IO_5 exist. There is enough room around an iodine atom for more than four oxygen atoms in contrast to the situation existing in the chlorine series in which ClO_4^- is the only perchlorate ion known. The ClO_4^- and IO_4^- ions are tetrahedral, whereas the IO_6^{5-} ion is octahedral (Figure 10.4).

One of the outstanding characteristics of the oxyhalogen anions and acids is their ability to function as oxidizing agents. The oxidation state of the halogen-containing product of a reaction in which one of these

Figure 10.4   Geometric configurations of some oxyhalogen anions.

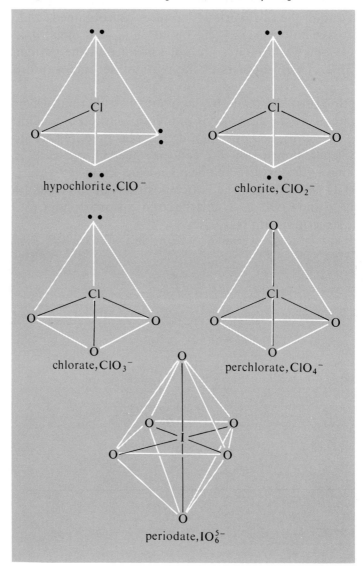

TABLE 10.11.
ELECTRONIC CONFIGURATIONS OF THE GROUP VI A ELEMENTS.

Element	Z	1s	2s	2p	3s	3p	3d	4s	4p	4d	4f	5s	5p	5d	6s	6p
O	8	2	2	4												
S	16	2	2	6	2	4										
Se	34	2	2	6	2	6	10	2	4							
Te	52	2	2	6	2	6	10	2	6	10		2	4			
Po	84	2	2	6	2	6	10	2	6	10	14	2	6	10	2	4

compounds is used as an oxidizing agent depends upon the specific re-action. However, an idea of the relative oxidizing strength of each of the acids and ions may be obtained from the data of Table 10.10 in which $E°$ values are recorded for reductions to the corresponding halide ions. In general, these compounds are stronger oxidizing agents in acid solu-tion (as acids) than the corresponding salts are in alkaline solution. For the anions, the oxidizing power decreases with increase in the oxidation number of the halogen (with the exception of the $H_3IO_6^{2-}$ ion).

SULFUR, SELENIUM, AND TELLURIUM

Group VI A includes oxygen, sulfur, selenium, tellurium, and po-lonium. The chemistry of oxygen, the most important and most abun-dant element of the group, has been discussed in Chapter 7. Polonium is produced by the radioactive disintegration of radium, and all of the iso-topes of polonium are radioactive. The most abundant isotope, ^{210}Po, has a half life of only 138.7 days and not much is known definitely about the chemistry of this element.

10.9 Group Properties

The electronic configurations of the group VI A elements are listed in Table 10.11: each element is two electrons short of a noble gas structure. Hence, these elements attain a noble-gas electronic configuration in the formation of ionic compounds by accepting two electrons per atom.

$$2Na^+ \quad :\ddot{\underset{..}{S}}:^{2-}$$

The elements also acquire noble-gas configurations through covalent-bond formation.

$$H:\ddot{\underset{..}{Se}}:$$
$$H$$

Certain properties of the group VI A elements are summarized in Table 10.12. Each member of the group is a less active nonmetal than the halogen of its period. The electronegativities of the elements decrease, in the expected manner, with increasing atomic number. Oxygen is the second most electronegative element (fluorine is first); sulfur is about as electronegative as iodine. Thus the oxides of most metals are ionic, whereas the sulfides, selenides, and tellurides of only the most active metals (such as the I A and II A metals) are truly ionic compounds.

TABLE 10.12.
SOME PROPERTIES OF THE GROUP VI A ELEMENTS.

	Oxygen	Sulfur	Selenium	Tellurium
color	colorless	yellow	red to black	silver-white
molecular formula	O_2	S_8 rings	Se_8 rings $(Se)_n$ chains	$(Te)_n$ chains
melting point (°C)	−218.4	119	217	452
boiling point (°C)	−182.9	444.6	688	1390
atomic radius (Å)	0.74	1.04	1.17	1.37
ionic radius (2− ion) (Å)	1.40	1.84	1.98	2.21
first ionization potential (ev)	13.6	10.4	9.8	9.0
electronegativity	3.5	2.5	2.4	2.1
bond energy (single bonds) (kcal/mole)	33	51	44	33

The group VI A elements are predominately nonmetallic in chemical behavior; however, metallic characteristics appear in the heavier members of the group. The trend in increasing metallic character parallels, as expected, increasing atomic number, increasing atomic radius, and decreasing ionization potential. Polonium is the most metallic member of the group; it appears to be capable of forming a Po^{2+} ion that exists in aqueous solution, and the 2− state of polonium (e.g., in H_2Po) is unstable. Whereas tellurium is essentially nonmetallic in character, unstable salts of tellurium with anions of strong acids have been reported. The ordinary form of tellurium is metallic, and selenium exists in both metallic and nonmetallic crystalline modifications.

Sulfur, selenium, and tellurium exist in positive oxidation states in compounds in which they are combined with more electronegative elements (such as oxygen and the halogens); oxygen is considered to have a positive oxidation number only in the few compounds that it forms with fluorine. For sulfur, selenium, and tellurium, the oxidation states of 4+ and 6+ are particularly important.

The electrode potentials listed in Table 10.13 give an idea of the strength of the group VI A elements as oxidizing agents. Oxygen is a strong oxidizing agent, but there is a striking decrease in this property

TABLE 10.13. STANDARD ELECTRODE POTENTIALS OF THE GROUP VI A ELEMENTS IN ACID SOLUTION.		
$2e^- + 2H^+ + Te \rightleftharpoons H_2Te$	E°	$= -0.72$ v
$2e^- + 2H^+ + Se \rightleftharpoons H_2Se$	E°	$= -0.40$ v
$2e^- + 2H^+ + S \rightleftharpoons H_2S$	E°	$= +0.14$ v
$4e^- + 4H^+ + O_2 \rightleftharpoons 2H_2O$	E°	$= +1.23$ v

from oxygen to tellurium; in fact, H_2Te and H_2Se are better *reducing* agents than hydrogen. Compare the values listed in Table 10.13 with those for the halogens in Table 10.4.

10.10 The Elements

All the members of this group exist in more than one allotropic modification. For a given element, the difference may be in molecular complexity (O_2 and O_3 for oxygen, Section 7.4), in crystalline form, or in both of these factors.

The most important solid modifications of sulfur belong to the rhombic and monoclinic crystal systems (Section 6.9). The crystals of both allotropes are built up from S_8 molecules. These molecules are in the form of puckered, eight-membered rings of S atoms in which the S atoms are bonded to each other by single covalent bonds and the S—S—S bond angle is about 105° (Figure 10.5). In chemical equations, therefore, elementary sulfur should be indicated by the formula S_8. However, the usual practice is to designate sulfur by the symbol S; this practice leads to less complicated equations that are nevertheless stoichiometrically valid.

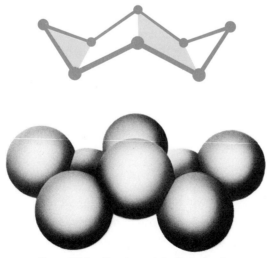

Figure 10.5   Structure of the S_8 molecule.

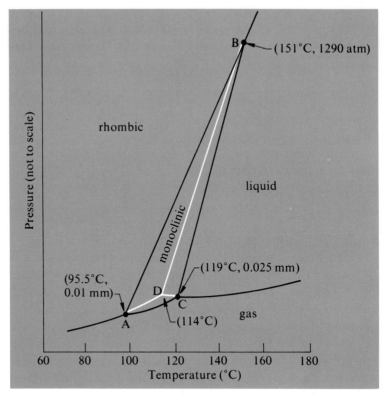

Figure 10.6   Phase diagram for sulfur.

The phase diagram for sulfur is shown in Figure 10.6. The rhombic form of sulfur is the stable modification under ordinary conditions of temperature and pressure. Any point that falls within the triangle ABC of the diagram describes a set of temperature and pressure conditions under which monoclinic sulfur is the stable modification. If rhombic sulfur is heated under its own vapor pressure, it slowly undergoes a transition to monoclinic sulfur at 95.5°C, and the monoclinic sulfur, upon continued heating, melts at 119°C. The transition from one solid form to another is slow; rapid heating of the rhombic form causes it to melt, without going through the monoclinic form at 114°C (lines AD, DC, and DB of Figure 10.6). There are three triple points (A, B, and C) and one metastable triple point (between rhombic, liquid, and gas at point D).

Liquid sulfur undergoes a series of changes as its temperature is increased. At the melting point, liquid sulfur is a light yellow, mobile liquid consisting principally of S_8 molecules. Upon continued heating, the sulfur changes into a red-brown, highly viscous material. The viscosity reaches a maximum between 160 and 200°C; upon further heating (up to the boiling point at 444.6°C), the viscosity of the liquid decreases. It is believed that the viscosity effect is caused by the dissociation of the

S_8 rings and the formation of long chains of S atoms; at temperatures approaching the boiling point, it appears that these chains break into fragments. If sulfur is heated to approximately 200°C and then poured into cold water, a red-brown rubbery mass called plastic sulfur is obtained. It is assumed that plastic sulfur consists mainly of long chains of sulfur atoms, and the X-ray analysis of plastic sulfur has shown that it has a molecular structure characteristic of fibers. At room temperature, plastic sulfur, which is a supercooled liquid, slowly crystallizes and the S_8 rings re-form. Sulfur vapor has been shown to consist of S_8, S_6, S_4, and S_2 molecules; S_2 is paramagnetic, like O_2.

The stable modification of selenium at room temperature is a gray, metallic, hexagonal form, the crystals of which are constructed of zigzag chains of selenium atoms. It is this form that is used in photoelectric cells; the normally low electrical conductivity of hexagonal selenium is increased about 200 times by exposure of the element to light. There are two monoclinic forms of selenium, both red, and one of these has been shown to be made up of Se_8 rings that are similar to S_8 rings. In addition, amorphous forms of selenium have been described.

The common form of tellurium consists of silver-white, metallic hexagonal crystals built up from zigzag chains of tellurium atoms. A black, amorphous form of tellurium exists.

The two modifications of polonium that have been reported belong to the cubic and rhombohedral systems.

The principal forms in which sulfur, selenium, and tellurium occur in nature are listed in Table 10.14. Sulfur is obtained from large under-

| | | **TABLE 10.14.** |
| | | **OCCURRENCE OF SULFUR, SELENIUM, AND TELLURIUM.** |

Element	Percent of Earth's Crust	Occurrence
sulfur	0.05	Native
		FeS_2 (pyrite), PbS (galena), HgS (cinnabar), ZnS (sphalerite), Cu_2S (chalcocite), $CuFeS_2$ (chalcopyrite)
		$CaSO_4 \cdot 2 H_2O$ (gypsum), $BaSO_4$ (barite), $MgSO_4 \cdot 7 H_2O$ (epsomite)
selenium	9×10^{-6}	Small amounts of Se in some S deposits
		Rare minerals: Cu_2Se, PbSe, Ag_2Se
		Low concentrations in sulfide ores of Cu, Fe, Pb, Ni
tellurium	2×10^{-7}	Small amounts of Te in some S deposits
		Rare minerals: $AuTe_2$, PbTe, Ag_2Te, Au_2Te, Cu_2Te
		Low concentrations in sulfide ores of Cu, Fe

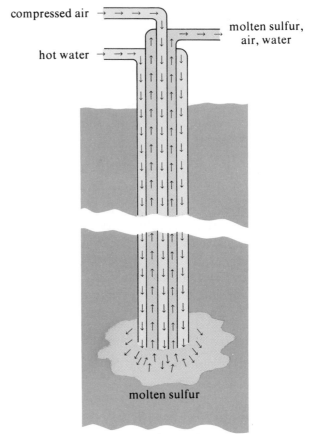

Figure 10.7   The Frasch process.

ground beds of the free element by the **Frasch process** (Figure 10.7). The sulfur is melted underground by water that is heated to approximately 170°C under pressure and forced down to the deposits. A froth of sulfur, air, and water is forced to the surface by hot, compressed air. The sulfur thus obtained is about 99.5% pure.

The principal commercial source of both selenium and tellurium is the anode sludge obtained from the electrolytic refining of copper (Section 15.5).

Some reactions of sulfur, selenium, and tellurium are summarized in Table 10.15.

10.11   Hydrogen Compounds and Derivatives

The hydrogen compounds of sulfur, selenium, and tellurium can be prepared by the direct combination of the elements at elevated temperatures. However, direct combination is not a satisfactory laboratory

TABLE 10.15.
SOME REACTIONS OF SULFUR, SELENIUM, AND TELLURIUM.

Reaction of Sulfur	Remarks
$nS + mM \rightarrow M_mS_n$	Se, Te react similarly with many metals (not noble metals)
$nS + S^{2-} \rightarrow S_{n+1}^{2-}$	For S and Te, $n = 1$ to 5; for Se, $n = 1$ to 4
$S + H_2 \rightarrow H_2S$	S > Se > Te; elevated temperatures; compounds are better prepared by action of dilute HCl on sulfides, selenides, or tellurides
$S + O_2 \rightarrow SO_2$	S > Se > Te; dioxides of Se and Te are easier to prepare with a mixture of $O_2 + NO_2$
$S + 3F_2 \rightarrow SF_6$	S, Se, Te with excess F_2
$S + 2F_2 \rightarrow SF_4$	S, Se; TeF_4 is made indirectly ($TeF_6 + Te$)
$2S + X_2 \rightarrow S_2X_2$	S, Se; $X_2 = Cl_2$ or Br_2
$S + 2X_2 \rightarrow SX_4$	S, Se, Te with excess Cl_2; Se, Te with excess Br_2; Te with excess I_2
$S_2Cl_2 + Cl_2 \rightarrow 2SCl_2$	SCl_2 only, SBr_2 unknown; $SeCl_2$, $SeBr_2$ (only in vapor state); $TeCl_2$, $TeBr_2$ are made by thermal decomposition of higher halides
$S + 4HNO_3 \rightarrow SO_2 + 4NO_2 + 2H_2O$	Hot, concentrated nitric acid; S yields mixtures of SO_2 and SO_4^{2-}; Se yields H_2SeO_3 ($SeO_2 \cdot H_2O$); Te yields $2TeO_2 \cdot HNO_3$

source of the compounds; in addition to the inconvenience of this method of preparation, H_2S, H_2Se, and H_2Te are unstable at high temperatures, and the products are contaminated by starting materials.

The hydrogen compounds are readily obtained by the action of dilute acid on sulfides, selenides, and tellurides; for example;

$$FeS(s) + 2H^+(aq) \rightarrow Fe^{2+}(aq) + H_2S(g)$$

The reaction of thioacetamide with water is a convenient laboratory source of H_2S.

(thioacetamide)   (acetamide)

Hydrogen sulfide, hydrogen selenide, and hydrogen telluride are colorless, unpleasant-smelling, highly poisonous gases; they are composed of angular molecules, similar to the water molecule (Figure 3.18). The physical properties of water are out of line in comparison to those of H_2S, H_2Se, and H_2Te because of the extensive hydrogen bonding that occurs between water molecules (Section 7.11).

Hydrogen sulfide reacts with oxygen to yield water and either SO_2 or free S depending upon the amount of oxygen employed. The combustion of H_2Se or H_2Te in oxygen produces water and either Se or Te.

The compounds H_2S, H_2Se, and H_2Te are all moderately soluble in water and are weak acids in aqueous solution. The trend in acid strength parallels that of the hydrogen halides—the element of highest atomic number forming the strongest acid. Thus H_2Te is the strongest acid, and H_2S is the weakest acid of the group. The acids are diprotic and ionize in two steps.

$$H_2S(aq) \rightleftharpoons H^+(aq) + HS^-(aq)$$
$$HS^-(aq) \rightleftharpoons H^+(aq) + S^{2-}(aq)$$

The aqueous hydrogen sulfide system is discussed in Section 14.10.

The sulfides of the group I A and group II A metals are water soluble. The sulfides of the remaining metals are either very slightly soluble or decompose in the presence of water to form slightly soluble hydroxides.

$$Al_2S_3(s) + 6H_2O \longrightarrow 2Al(OH)_3(s) + 3H_2S(g)$$

Precipitation of the slightly soluble sulfides, under varying conditions, is extensively used in analytical procedures for the separation and identification of cations in solution (Section 14.11). An analytical test for the sulfide ion consists of generating H_2S gas by the addition of acid to the sulfide; the H_2S may be identified by its odor or by the formation of insoluble, black PbS on a filter paper wet with a solution of a soluble Pb^{2+} salt.

$$Pb^{2+}(aq) + H_2S(g) \longrightarrow PbS(s) + 2H^+(aq)$$

Sulfur dissolves in solutions of soluble sulfides and forms a mixture of polysulfide anions.

$$S^{2-}(aq) + nS(s) \longrightarrow S_{n+1}^{2-}(aq)$$

Polyselenide and polytelluride ions can be prepared by analogous reactions. For sulfur, ions varying in complexity from S_2^{2-} to S_6^{2-} have been prepared; Se_5^{2-} and Te_6^{2-} are the highest polyselenides and polytellurides known. The atoms of a polysulfide ion are joined into chains by single covalent bonds.

$$\left[\begin{array}{cc} \ddot{S} & \ddot{S} \\ & \ddot{S} & \ddot{S} \end{array} \right]^{2-}$$

The structure of the disulfide ion, S_2^{2-}, is similar to that of the peroxide ion (Section 7.8). The mineral pyrite, FeS_2, is iron(II) disulfide.

At room temperature, polysulfides decompose in acid solution to yield mainly H_2S and free S; however, careful treatment of a polysulfide solution with concentrated HCl at $-15°C$ yields H_2S_2, H_2S_3, and small quantities of higher homologs. The hydrogen polysulfides are unstable, yellow oils.

10.12 The 4+ Oxidation State

The important compounds in which sulfur appears in a 4+ oxidation state are sulfur dioxide (SO_2), sulfurous acid (H_2SO_3), and the salts of sulfurous acid—the sulfites. Both selenium and tellurium form compounds analogous to those of sulfur.

Sulfur dioxide is commercially obtained by burning sulfur

$$S(s) + O_2(g) \rightarrow SO_2(g)$$

or by roasting sulfide ores (such as ZnS, PbS, Cu_2S, and FeS_2) in air (Section 15.3)

$$2ZnS(s) + 3O_2(g) \rightarrow 2ZnO(s) + 2SO_2(g)$$

Sulfur dioxide is a colorless gas. It has a sharp, irritating odor and is somewhat poisonous. The molecules of SO_2 are angular, and the structure of the compound may be represented as a resonance hybrid (Section 3.11). The polar nature of the SO_2 molecule is reflected in the ease with which sulfur dioxide may be liquefied. Sulfur dioxide liquefies at $-10°C$ (the normal boiling point) under a pressure of 1 atm, and at 20°C, a pressure of about 3 atm will liquefy the gas. It is this property of SO_2 that makes the compound useful as a refrigerant.

Sulfur dioxide is moderately soluble in water—producing solutions of sulfurous acid, H_2SO_3. The acid is not very stable, and pure H_2SO_3 cannot be isolated. The extent of the reaction between dissolved SO_2 molecules and water is not known; probably both H_2SO_3 and SO_2 molecules exist in the solution in equilibrium.

$$SO_2(aq) + H_2O \rightleftharpoons H_2SO_3(aq)$$

Sulfurous acid is a weak, diprotic acid.

$$H_2SO_3(aq) \rightleftharpoons H^+(aq) + HSO_3^-(aq)$$
or $$SO_2(aq) + H_2O \rightleftharpoons H^+(aq) + HSO_3^-(aq)$$
and $$HSO_3^-(aq) \rightleftharpoons H^+(aq) + SO_3^{2-}(aq)$$

Therefore sulfurous acid forms two series of salts: normal salts (e.g., Na_2SO_3, sodium sulfite) and acid salts (e.g., $NaHSO_3$, sodium bisulfite or sodium hydrogen sulfite).

Sulfites are often prepared by bubbling SO_2 gas through a solution of a hydroxide.

$$2OH^- + SO_2(g) \rightarrow SO_3^{2-}(aq) + H_2O$$

If the addition is continued, acid sulfites are produced.

$$H_2O + SO_3^{2-}(aq) + SO_2(g) \rightarrow 2HSO_3^-(aq)$$

The salts of sulfurous acid can be isolated from solution.

Since sulfurous acid is unstable, the addition of an acid to a sulfite, or an acid sulfite, liberates SO_2 gas; this is a convenient way to prepare the gas in the laboratory.

$$SO_3^{2-}(aq) + 2H^+(aq) \rightarrow SO_2(g) + H_2O$$

Sulfur dioxide, sulfurous acid, and sulfites can function as mild oxidizing agents; however, reactions in which these compounds react as reducing agents (and are oxidized to the sulfate ion, SO_4^{2-}) are more numerous and more important. Many substances (such as potassium permanganate, potassium dichromate, chlorine, and bromine) oxidize sulfite to sulfate. In fact, sulfites are usually contaminated by traces of sulfates because of oxidation by the oxygen of the air.

$$2SO_3^{2-} + O_2(g) \rightarrow 2SO_4^{2-}$$

Sulfites may be identified by the production of SO_2 gas upon acidification and by oxidation to the sulfate ion,

$$6H^+(aq) + 5SO_3^{2-}(aq) + 2MnO_4^-(aq) \rightarrow 5SO_4^{2-}(aq) +$$
$$2Mn^{2+}(aq) + 3H_2O$$

followed by the precipitation of the sulfate as the insoluble barium salt.

$$Ba^{2+}(aq) + SO_4^{2-}(aq) \rightarrow BaSO_4(s)$$

The dioxides of selenium and tellurium may be prepared by direct combination of the elements with oxygen; however, SeO_2 and TeO_2 are usually made by heating the product obtained from the oxidation of selenium or tellurium by concentrated nitric acid (see Table 10.15). Both SeO_2 and TeO_2 are white solids.

Selenous acid, H_2SeO_3, is formed when the very soluble SeO_2 is dissolved in water; it is a weak, diprotic acid and may be obtained in pure form by the evaporation of a solution of SeO_2. Tellurium dioxide is only slightly soluble in water, and pure H_2TeO_3 has never been prepared. Consequently, only very dilute solutions of tellurous acid have been studied.

Tellurium dioxide, as well as selenium dioxide, will dissolve in aqueous solutions of hydroxides to produce tellurites and selenites. If an excess of the dioxide is employed, the corresponding acid salt is obtained.

The selenium and tellurium compounds of the $4+$ oxidation state are better oxidizing agents, and poorer reducing agents, than the corresponding sulfur compounds: SeO_2 is a good oxidizing agent and is employed in certain organic syntheses.

10.13 The 6+ Oxidation State

Sulfur trioxide is produced when sulfur dioxide reacts with atmospheric oxygen. Since the reaction is very slow at ordinary temperatures, the commercial preparation is conducted at elevated temperatures (400 to 700°C) and in the presence of a catalyst (such as divanadium pentoxide or spongy platinum).

$$2SO_2(g) + O_2(g) \rightarrow 2SO_3(g)$$

Sulfur trioxide is a volatile material (boiling point, 44.8°C); in the gas phase it consists of single molecules that are planar, triangular in form with O—S—O bond angles of 120°. The electronic structure of the molecule may be represented as a resonance hybrid:

$$
\begin{array}{ccccc}
:\!\ddot{O}\!: & & :\!\ddot{O}\!: & & :\!\ddot{O}\!: \\
\ddot{S} & \leftrightarrow & .\!\overset{..}{S} & \leftrightarrow & \overset{..}{S}. \\
:\!\ddot{O}\!:\ :\!\ddot{O}\!: & & \cdot\!\ddot{O}\!:\ :\!\ddot{O}\!: & & :\!\ddot{O}\!:\ :\!\ddot{O}\!\cdot \\
\end{array}
$$

The compound exists in at least three solid modifications that are formed by the condensation of SO_3 units into larger molecules called polymers. The commercial product, which is a variable mixture of two forms of the compound, is a colorless solid that melts at approximately 40°C.

Sulfur trioxide is an extremely reactive substance and a strong oxidizing agent. It is the anhydride of sulfuric acid, H_2SO_4, and reacts vigorously with water to produce the acid and with metallic oxides to produce sulfates (Section 7.3).

Sulfuric acid is an important industrial chemical. Most sulfuric acid is made by the **contact process** in which SO_2 is catalytically oxidized to SO_3 in the manner previously described. The SO_3 vapor is bubbled through H_2SO_4 and pyrosulfuric acid ($H_2S_2O_7$) is formed.

$$SO_3(g) + H_2SO_4(l) \rightarrow H_2S_2O_7(l)$$

Water is then added to the pyrosulfuric acid to give sulfuric acid of the desired concentration.

$$H_2S_2O_7(l) + H_2O \rightarrow 2H_2SO_4(l)$$

This procedure, in which pyrosulfuric acid is formed, is easier to control than the direct reaction of SO_3 with water.

The **lead chamber process** is an older method for the manufacture of sulfuric acid. Sulfur dioxide, oxygen, water vapor, and oxides of nitrogen are mixed in a lead-lined chamber. The reactions are complex and not completely understood, but it is recognized that nitrosylsulfuric acid, $HOSO_2(ONO)$, is formed as an intermediate and that this compound then reacts with water to form sulfuric acid. We may summarize the process by the simplified equations

$$2SO_2(g) + NO(g) + NO_2(g) + O_2(g) + H_2O(g) \rightarrow$$
$$2HOSO_2(ONO)(s)$$

$$2HOSO_2(ONO)(s) + H_2O(g) \rightarrow$$
$$2H_2SO_4(l) + NO(g) + NO_2(g)$$

The oxides of nitrogen are regenerated and are used over and over again. The sulfuric acid produced by the lead chamber process has a concentration of only 60 to 78% and is less pure than that made by the contact process.

Sulfuric acid is a colorless, oily liquid that freezes at 10.4°C and begins to boil at approximately 290°C with decomposition into water and sulfur trioxide. The electronic structure of sulfuric acid may be represented as

$$\ddot{\mathrm{O}}:$$
$$\mathrm{H} : \ddot{\mathrm{O}} : \overset{..}{\mathrm{S}} : \ddot{\mathrm{O}} : \mathrm{H}$$
$$: \ddot{\mathrm{O}} :$$

However, the S—O bond distance of H_2SO_4 is shorter than an ordinary S—O single bond and indicates that these bonds have some double-bond character. Resonance structures containing double bonds can be drawn for H_2SO_4 by assuming that two of the $3d$ orbitals of sulfur, as well as the $3s$ and $3p$ orbitals, are involved in bond formation. The H_2SO_4 molecule, as well as the sulfate ion, is tetrahedral (Figure 10.8).

When concentrated sulfuric acid is added to water, a great deal of heat is evolved; this heat effect may be because of the formation of the hydronium ion, H_3O^+. Sulfuric acid has a strong affinity for water and forms a series of hydrates (such as $H_2SO_4 \cdot H_2O$, $H_2SO_4 \cdot 2H_2O$, and $H_2SO_4 \cdot 4H_2O$). Thus sulfuric acid is used as a drying agent, and gases that do not react with H_2SO_4 may be dried by being bubbled through the acid. The dehydrating power of sulfuric acid is also seen in the charring action of the acid on carbohydrates.

$$C_{12}H_{22}O_{11}(s) \xrightarrow{\ H_2SO_4\ } 12C(s) + 11H_2O(g)$$
$$\text{sucrose}$$

In aqueous solution, sulfuric acid ionizes in two steps.

$$H_2SO_4 \rightarrow H^+(aq) + HSO_4^-(aq)$$
$$HSO_4^-(aq) \rightleftharpoons H^+(aq) + SO_4^{2-}(aq)$$

Sulfuric acid is a strong electrolyte as far as the first dissociation is concerned; however, the second dissociation is not complete. The acid forms two series of salts: normal salts (such as sodium sulfate, Na_2SO_4) and acid salts (such as sodium bisulfate, $NaHSO_4$). Most sulfates are

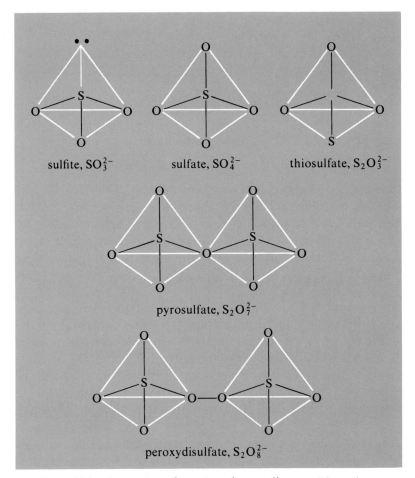

Figure 10.8   Geometric configurations of some sulfur-containing anions.

soluble in water. However, barium sulfate ($BaSO_4$), strontium sulfate ($SrSO_4$), and lead sulfate ($PbSO_4$) exhibit very low solubility, and calcium sulfate ($CaSO_4$), mercury(I) sulfate (Hg_2SO_4), and silver sulfate (Ag_2SO_4) are but slightly soluble. The formation of white, insoluble barium sulfate, the least soluble of the substances listed, is commonly used as a laboratory test for the sulfate ion.

Since sulfuric acid has a relatively high boiling point (or decomposition temperature), it is used to secure more volatile acids from their salts. This use is illustrated by the preparations of HF and HCl (Section 10.5) as well as the preparation of HNO_3 (Section 10.20).

Sulfuric acid at unit concentration and 25°C is not a particularly good oxidizing agent (note the relatively low standard electrode potential in Table 10.16); however, hot, concentrated sulfuric acid is a moderately effective oxidizing agent. The oxidizing ability of hot, concentrated H_2SO_4 on bromides and iodides has already been noted (Section 10.5).

TABLE 10.16.
STANDARD ELECTRODE POTENTIALS OF SULFURIC, SELENIC, AND
TELLURIC ACIDS.

$$2e^- + 4H^+ + SO_4^{2-} \rightleftharpoons H_2SO_3 + H_2O \qquad E° = +0.17 \text{ v}$$
$$2e^- + 4H^+ + SeO_4^{2-} \rightleftharpoons H_2SeO_3 + H_2O \qquad E° = +1.15 \text{ v}$$
$$2e^- + 2H^+ + H_6TeO_6 \rightleftharpoons TeO_2 + 4H_2O \qquad E° = +1.02 \text{ v}$$

This reagent will also oxidize many nonmetals.

$$C(s) + 2H_2SO_4(l) \rightarrow CO_2(g) + 2SO_2(g) + 2H_2O(g)$$

Most metals are oxidized by hot, concentrated sulfuric acid including those metals of relatively low reactivity that are not oxidized by hydronium ion. For example, copper will not displace hydrogen from aqueous acids; copper metal is, however, oxidized by hot, concentrated sulfuric acid although hydrogen gas is not a product of the reaction.

$$Cu(s) + 2H_2SO_4(l) \rightarrow CuSO_4(s) + SO_2(g) + 2H_2O(g)$$

Selenic acid, H_2SeO_4, is prepared by the oxidization of selenous acid, H_2SeO_3, and selenates may be prepared by the oxidation of the corresponding selenites. Selenium trioxide, the acid anhydride of selenic acid, is not very stable and decomposes to SeO_2 and O_2 on warming. Low yields of SeO_3 mixed with SeO_2 are produced when an electric discharge is passed through selenium vapor and oxygen; the trioxide may also be prepared by the reaction of potassium selenate, K_2SeO_4, and SO_3.

Selenic acid is very similar to sulfuric acid. In aqueous solution, the first dissociation of H_2SeO_4 is strong and the second dissociation weak. The acid forms normal and acid salts. Crystalline selenates are in most cases isomorphous with the corresponding sulfates. Like the sulfate ion, the selenate ion is tetrahedral.

Telluric acid is prepared by the action of vigorous oxidizing agents on elementary tellurium. Unlike H_2SO_4 and H_2SeO_4, the formula of telluric acid is H_6TeO_6 which may be regarded as a hydrated form of the nonexistent H_2TeO_4. No compound of formula H_2TeO_4 has ever been prepared although salts of an acid corresponding to this formula exist. Tellurium, like iodine (Section 10.8), is a large atom and can accommodate six oxygen atoms, and telluric acid, like IO_6^{5-}, is octahedral (Figure 10.4). Telluric acid is not very similar to sulfuric acid, and H_6TeO_6 functions in aqueous solution as a very weak diprotic acid. If H_6TeO_6 is heated to approximately 350°C, water is driven off and solid tellurium trioxide results. This compound is not very water soluble but reacts with alkalies to produce tellurates.

Both selenic and telluric acids are stronger oxidizing agents than sulfuric acid (Table 10.16) although the reactions of H_2SeO_4 and H_6TeO_6 often proceed slowly.

There are other acids of sulfur in which the sulfur has an oxidation number of 6+. Pyrosulfuric acid (or disulfuric acid) has been mentioned as the product of the reaction of 1 mole of SO_3 with 1 mole of H_2SO_4. The electronic structure of this compound may be represented as

$$\text{H:}\ddot{\text{O}}\text{:}\ddot{\text{S}}\text{:}\ddot{\text{O}}\text{:}\ddot{\text{S}}\text{:}\ddot{\text{O}}\text{:H}$$

The geometric configuration of $H_2S_2O_7$ consists of two tetrahedra joined through an oxygen atom common to both tetrahedra (Figure 10.8). Pyrosulfuric acid is a stronger oxidizing agent and a stronger dehydrating agent than sulfuric acid.

A peroxy acid is an acid that contains a peroxide group ($-O-O-$) somewhere in the molecule. Two peroxy acids of sulfur exist: peroxymonosulfuric acid (H_2SO_5) and peroxydisulfuric acid ($H_2S_2O_8$).

$$\text{H:}\ddot{\text{O}}\text{:}\ddot{\text{O}}\text{:}\ddot{\text{S}}\text{:}\ddot{\text{O}}\text{:H} \qquad \text{H:}\ddot{\text{O}}\text{:}\ddot{\text{S}}\text{:}\ddot{\text{O}}\text{:}\ddot{\text{O}}\text{:}\ddot{\text{S}}\text{:}\ddot{\text{O}}\text{:H}$$

The molecule of peroxydisulfuric acid has been shown to consist of two tetrahedra joined by an O—O bond (Figure 10.8).

Peroxydisulfuric acid is prepared by the electrolysis of moderately concentrated solutions of sulfuric acid (50 to 70%) at temperatures below room temperature (5 to 10°C). Potassium and ammonium salts of this acid are prepared by the electrolysis of the corresponding acid sulfates. The anode reaction in these electrolyses may be represented by the partial equation

$$2HSO_4^- \rightarrow S_2O_8^{2-} + 2H^+ + 2e^-$$

The reaction of peroxydisulfuric acid with water yields peroxymonosulfuric acid.

$$H_2S_2O_8 + H_2O \rightarrow H_2SO_5 + H_2SO_4$$

Upon further hydrolysis, H_2SO_5 is decomposed into hydrogen peroxide and H_2SO_4.

$$H_2SO_5 + H_2O \rightarrow H_2SO_4 + H_2O_2$$

The acids may also be prepared by the reaction of 1 mole of hydrogen peroxide with 1 or 2 moles of chlorosulfonic acid, $HOSO_2Cl$ (the product of the reaction of SO_3 and HCl).

Both peroxymonosulfuric acid and peroxydisulfuric acid are low melting solids. The first ionization of peroxydisulfuric acid is strong. The peroxydisulfate ion is one of the strongest oxidizing agents known.

$$2e^- + S_2O_8^{2-} \rightleftharpoons 2SO_4^{2-} \qquad E° = +2.01 \text{ v}$$

The oxidations, however, are slow and are usually catalyzed by Ag^+ ions. In both peroxy acids, sulfur is assumed to be in its highest oxidation state $(6+)$. However, the oxygen atoms of the peroxide grouping are each assigned an oxidation number of $1-$, and in the course of an oxidation, it is the peroxide oxygens that change oxidation state (from $1-$ to $2-$).

There is another significant group of sulfur-containing anions. The most important representative of the group is the thiosulfate ion, $S_2O_3{}^{2-}$.

$$\left[\begin{array}{c} :\ddot{O}: \\ :\ddot{O}:\ddot{S}:\ddot{O}: \\ :\ddot{S}: \end{array} \right]^{2-}$$

This tetrahedral ion may be regarded as a sulfate ion in which one oxygen atom has been replaced by a sulfur atom. In fact, the prefix "thio-" is used when the species to be named may be considered to be derived from the compound described by the base name by replacing an oxygen atom by a sulfur atom. Thus CNO^- is the cyanate ion—CNS^- is the thiocyanate ion; $CO(NH_2)_2$ is urea—$CS(NH_2)_2$ is thiourea.

Thiosulfates may be prepared by the reaction of sulfur with sulfites in aqueous solution.

$$SO_3^{2-}(aq) + S(s) \rightarrow S_2O_3^{2-}(aq)$$

The corresponding acid does not exist. Upon acidification, thiosulfates decompose to elementary sulfur and SO_2 gas.

$$S_2O_3^{2-}(aq) + 2H^+(aq) \rightarrow S(s) + SO_2(g) + H_2O$$

The two sulfur atoms of the thiosulfate ion are not equivalent. This has been shown by the reactions of a compound derived from sulfite and radioactive sulfur, $^{35}_{16}S$. When a compound thus prepared is decomposed by acidification, all of the activity ends in the elementary sulfur.

$$SO_3^{2-}(aq) + {}^{35}S(s) \rightarrow {}^{35}SSO_3^{2-}(aq)$$
$$^{35}SSO_3^{2-}(aq) + 2H^+(aq) \rightarrow {}^{35}S(s) + SO_2(g) + H_2O$$

Hence, the central sulfur atom is generally assigned an oxidation number of $6+$ (as in the sulfate ion), and the coordinated sulfur is usually assigned an oxidation number of $2-$ (as the oxidation number of the oxygen it replaces); the average oxidation state of sulfur in the ion is $2+$.

The thiosulfate ion is readily oxidized to the tetrathionate ion, $S_4O_6^{2-}$; use is made of this transformation in iodometric analysis (Section 10.7). The tetrathionate ion may be regarded as an analog of the peroxydisulfate ion, $S_2O_8^{2-}$, in which the peroxide group $(—O—O—)$ is replaced by a disulfide group $(—S—S—)$. Other thionate ions exist—for example the dithionate ion, $S_2O_6^{2-}$, and the trithionate ion, $S_3O_6^{2-}$; the latter is structurally similar to the pyrosulfate ion, $S_2O_7^{2-}$, with a sulfur atom replacing the central oxygen atom.

THE GROUP V A ELEMENTS

The elements of group V A—nitrogen, phosphorus, arsenic, antimony, and bismuth—collectively show a wider range of properties than is exhibited by either the elements of group VI A or the elements of group VII A.

10.14 Group Properties

Within any group of the periodic classification, metallic character increases (and nonmetallic character decreases) with increasing atomic number, atomic weight, and atomic size. This trend is particularly striking in group V A. Thus the electronegativities and first ionization potentials of the elements in the group decrease from values typical of a nonmetal (N) to those characteristic of a metal (Bi); these values are listed in Table 10.17. Nitrogen and phosphorus are generally regarded as nonmetals, arsenic and antimony as semimetals or metalloids, and bismuth as a metal. Bismuth, however, is not strongly metallic; its electrical and heat conductivities are low.

TABLE 10.17
SOME PROPERTIES OF THE GROUP V A ELEMENTS.

	Nitrogen	Phosphorus	Arsenic	Antimony	Bismuth
color	colorless	white, red, black	gray metallic, yellow	gray metallic, yellow	gray metallic
molecular formula	N_2	P_4 (white) P_n (black)	As_n (metallic) As_4 (yellow)	Sb_n (metallic) Sb_4 (yellow)	Bi_n
melting point (°C)	−210	44.1 (white)	814 (metallic) (36 atm)	630.5 (metallic)	271
boiling point (°C)	−195.8	280	633 (sublimes)	1325	1560
atomic radius (Å)	0.74	1.10	1.21	1.41	1.52
ionic radius (Å)	1.4 (N^{3-})	1.85 (P^{3-})		0.92 (Sb^{3+})	1.08 (Bi^{3+})
first ionization potential (ev)	14.5	11.0	10.0	8.6	8.0
electronegativity	3.0	2.1	2.0	1.9	1.9

TABLE 10.18.
ELECTRONIC CONFIGURATIONS OF THE GROUP V A ELEMENTS.

Element	Z	1s	2s	2p	3s	3p	3d	4s	4p	4d	4f	5s	5p	5d	6s	6p
N	7	2	2	3												
P	15	2	2	6	2	3										
As	33	2	2	6	2	6	10	2	3							
Sb	51	2	2	6	2	6	10	2	6	10		2	3			
Bi	83	2	2	6	2	6	10	2	6	10	14	2	6	10	2	3

The electronic configurations of the elements are listed in Table 10.18. Each element has three electrons less than the noble gas of its period, and the formation of trinegative ions might be expected. Nitrogen forms the nitride ion, N^{3-}, in combination with certain reactive metals; phosphorus forms the phosphide ion, P^{3-}, less readily. The remaining elements of the group, however, have lower electronegativities and are more metallic than nitrogen and phosphorus; hence, arsenic, antimony, and bismuth have no tendency to form comparable anions.

The loss of electrons and consequent formation of cations, which is characteristic of metals, is observed for the heavier members of the group. High ionization potentials prohibit the loss of all five valence electrons by any element; therefore, 5+ ions do not exist, and the 5+ oxidation state is only attained through covalent bonding. In addition, most of the compounds in which the group V A elements appear in the 3+ oxidation state are covalent. However, antimony and bismuth form some truly ionic compounds, such as BiF_3, $Sb_2(SO_4)_3$, and $Bi(ClO_4)_3 \cdot 5H_2O$. The 3+ ions of antimony and bismuth react with water to form antimonyl and bismuthyl ions (SbO^+ and BiO^+) as well as hydrated forms of these ions (e.g., $Bi(OH)_2^+$).

$$Bi^{3+}(aq) + H_2O \rightleftharpoons BiO^+(aq) + 2H^+(aq)$$

Nitrogen, phosphorus, and arsenic do not form simple cations.

An ion that has a pair of s electrons in the outer shell is called an **inert-pair ion**; Sb^{3+} and Bi^{3+} are examples of this type of ion. The inert-pair configuration $(\cdots(n-1)s^2(n-1)p^6(n-1)d^{10}ns^2)$, like the pseudo-noble-gas configuration $(\cdots ns^2np^6nd^{10})$, is not so stable nor so common as the noble-gas configuration $(\cdots ns^2np^6)$.

The oxides of the group V A elements become less acidic, and more basic, as the metallic character of the element increases. Thus N_2O_3, P_4O_6, and As_4O_6 are acidic oxides; they dissolve in water to form acids, and they dissolve in solutions of alkalies to form salts of these acids. The compound Sb_4O_6 is amphoteric; it will dissolve in hydrochloric acid as well as sodium hydroxide. The comparable oxide of bismuth is strictly basic; Bi_2O_3 is not soluble in alkalies, but the compound will dissolve in acids to produce bismuth salts.

All of the oxides in which the elements exhibit a 5+ oxidation state are acidic, but the acidity declines markedly from N_2O_5 to Bi_2O_5. In addition, the stability of the 5+ oxidation state decreases with increasing atomic number; Bi_2O_5 is extremely unstable and has never been prepared in a pure state.

The halides of the elements, in the series from nitrogen to bismuth, exhibit properties that reflect the increasing ionic character of the compounds. This trend is, of course, a result of the increasing metallic character of the group V A elements in this series.

Many of the properties of nitrogen are out of line when compared with those of the other V A elements; this is characteristic of the first members of the groups of the periodic classification. Nitrogen is the smallest and the most electronegative atom of group V A; however, free nitrogen, N_2, has a low order of chemical reactivity (Section 10.15). In fact, phosphorus is more reactive toward oxygen than is nitrogen; phosphorus is the only member of group V A that does not occur free in nature.

Nitrogen (electronic configuration, $1s^2 2s^2 2p^1 2p^1 2p^1$) has no completely unoccupied orbital in its valence level. Consequently, the maximum covalence exhibited by nitrogen is four (e.g., in NH_4^+). In the valence levels of the other V A elements, there are empty d orbitals which may be utilized in covalent bond formation. Hence, "expanded shell" species, such as PCl_5, PF_6^-, AsF_5, $SbCl_5$, $SbCl_6^-$, and $BiCl_5^{2-}$, are known for phosphorus, arsenic, antimony, and bismuth.

For the group as a whole, the 3−, 3+, and 5+ oxidation states are most common, the importance, and stability, of the 5+ and 3− states declining from the lighter to the heavier elements. Nitrogen, however, appears in every oxidation state from 3− to 5+. Nitrogen also shows a much greater tendency toward the formation of multiple bonds (e.g., in the cyanide ion, $C{\equiv}N^-$) than does any other V A element.

10.15 The Elements

Nitrogen constitutes about 78% by volume of the earth's atmosphere and is produced commercially by the fractional distillation of liquid air. Very pure nitrogen is conveniently prepared by heating an aqueous solution saturated with ammonium chloride and sodium nitrite,

$$NH_4^+(aq) + NO_2^-(aq) \rightarrow N_2(g) + H_2O$$

or by the thermal decomposition of certain nitrogen-containing compounds such as sodium azide.

$$2NaN_3(s) \rightarrow 2Na(s) + 3N_2(g)$$

Phosphorus is industrially prepared by heating a mixture of phosphate rock, sand, and coke in an electric furnace.

$$2Ca_3(PO_4)_2(s) + 6SiO_2(s) \rightarrow 6CaSiO_3(l) + P_4O_{10}(g)$$
$$P_4O_{10}(g) + 10C(s) \rightarrow P_4(g) + 10CO(g)$$

The calcium silicate is withdrawn, as a molten slag, from the bottom of the furnace, and the product gases are passed through water which condenses the phosphorus vapor into a white solid.

Arsenic, antimony, and bismuth are obtained by carbon reduction of their oxides at elevated temperatures.

$$As_4O_6(s) + 6C(s) \rightarrow As_4(g) + 6CO(g)$$

An important industrial source of the oxides is the flue dusts obtained from the processes used in the production of certain metals, notably copper and lead. In addition, the oxides are obtained by roasting the sulfide ores of the elements in air; for example,

$$2Sb_2S_3(s) + 6O_2(g) \rightarrow Sb_4O_6(g) + 6SO_2(g)$$

The ore arsenopyrite is decomposed by heating in the absence of air.

$$4FeAsS(s) \rightarrow 4FeS(s) + As_4(g)$$

Stibnite may be reduced by iron at high temperatures.

$$Sb_2S_3(s) + 3Fe(s) \rightarrow 3FeS(l) + 2Sb(l)$$

Although arsenic, antimony, and bismuth all occur as native ores, only the deposits of native bismuth are large enough to be of commercial importance. The principal natural sources of the group V A elements are listed in Table 10.19.

Phosphorus, arsenic, and antimony occur in allotropic modifications. There are three important forms of phosphorus: white, red, and black. White phosphorus, a waxy solid, is obtained by condensing phosphorus vapor. Crystals of white phosphorus are formed from P_4 molecules (Figure 10.9) in which each phosphorus atom has an unshared pair of electrons and completes its octet by forming single covalent bonds with the other three phosphorus atoms of the molecule.

Figure 10.9   Structure of the P_4 molecule.

TABLE 10.19.
OCCURRENCE OF THE GROUP V A ELEMENTS.

Element	Percent of Earth's Crust	Occurrence
nitrogen	0.0046 (0.03 including atmosphere)	N_2 (atmosphere) $NaNO_3$ (Chilean saltpeter)
phosphorus	0.12	$Ca_3(PO_4)_2$ (phosphate rock), $Ca_5(PO_4)_3F$ and $Ca_5(PO_4)_3Cl$ (apatite)
arsenic	5×10^{-4}	FeAsS (arsenopyrite), As_4S_4 (realgar), As_2S_3 (orpiment), As_4O_6 (arsenolite); native As; in ores of Cu, Pb, Co, Ni, Zn, Sn, Ag, and Au
antimony	5×10^{-5}	Sb_2S_3 (stibnite), Sb_4O_6 (senarmontite); native Sb; in ores of Cu, Pb, Ag, and Hg
bismuth	1×10^{-5}	Bi_2S_3 (bismuthinite), Bi_2O_3 (bismite); native Bi; in ores of Cu, Pb, Sn, Co, Ni, Ag, and Au

White phosphorus is soluble in a number of nonpolar solvents (e.g., benzene, carbon disulfide, and ethyl ether). In such solutions, in liquid white phosphorus, and in phosphorus vapor, the element exists as P_4 molecules. At temperatures above 800°C, a slight dissociation of the P_4 molecules of the vapor into P_2 molecules is observed; these latter molecules are assumed to have a structure similar to that of the N_2 molecule

$$: P \!:\!:\!: P :$$

White phosphorus is the most reactive form of the element and is stored under water to protect it from atmospheric oxygen.

Red phosphorus may be prepared by heating white phosphorus to about 250°C in the absence of air. It is a polymeric material in which many phosphorus atoms are joined in a network, but the details of the structure of red phosphorus are not known. Red phosphorus is not soluble in common solvents and is considerably less reactive than the white variety. It does not react with oxygen at room temperature.

Black phosphorus, a less common allotrope, is made by subjecting the element to very high pressures or by a slow crystallization of liquid white phosphorus in the presence of mercury as a catalyst and a seed of black phosphorus. Crystalline black phosphorus consists of layers of phosphorus atoms covalently joined into a network (Figure 10.10). The dis-

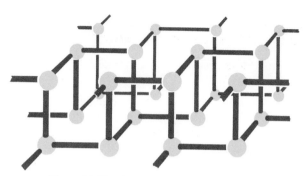

Figure 10.10   Structure of black phosphorus.

tance between phosphorus atoms of adjacent layers is much greater than the distance between bonded phosphorus atoms of the same layer; it is assumed that the layers are held together by comparatively weak van der Waals forces. Hence, black phosphorus is a flaky material much like graphite, (which also has a layer-type crystal, Section 10.23), and like graphite, black phosphorus is an electrical conductor. Black phosphorus is the least soluble and least reactive form of the element.

Arsenic and antimony exist in soft, yellow, nonmetallic modifications which are thought to be formed from tetrahedral As_4 and Sb_4 molecules analogous to the P_4 molecules of white phosphorus. These yellow forms may be obtained by the rapid condensation of vapors and are soluble in carbon disulfide. They are unstable and are readily converted into stable, gray, metallic modifications.

Bismuth commonly occurs as a light gray metal with a reddish cast; the element does not exist in a yellow modification. The metallic modifications of arsenic, antimony, and bismuth are comparatively soft and brittle and have a metallic luster. Their crystalline structures are similar to that of black phosphorus, and they are electrical conductors.

Free nitrogen is surprisingly unreactive partly because of the great strength of the bonding in the N_2 molecule. The structure of N_2 may be represented as

$$:N:::N:$$

The molecular orbital designation is given in Section 3.14; the nitrogen atoms of the molecule are assumed to be held together by a σ bond and two π bonds. The bond energy of N_2 is very high ($+225$ kcal/mole), and any reaction in which the nitrogen atoms are separated must provide this large quantity of energy. Consequently, many compounds of nitrogen are endothermic—even those with comparatively strong bonding.

Not every molecule containing a triple bond is unreactive. Carbon monoxide is isoelectronic with nitrogen

$$:C:::O:$$

and the bond energy of CO (+225.8 kcal/mole) is even larger than that of nitrogen. Yet CO is a moderately reactive molecule. The reactions of CO, however, utilize the unshared electron pair of the carbon atom of the molecule as, for example, in the formation of nickel carbonyl.

$$Ni + 4CO \rightarrow Ni(CO)_4$$

Nitrogen, which is a nonpolar molecule, does not react in this way.

The ionization potential of the N_2 *molecule* is considerably larger than the ionization potential of the CO *molecule*. Removal of a single electron from N_2 results in a species, N_2^+, in which the bond length is longer than that of N_2, whereas the same procedure applied to CO produces an ion, CO^+, that has a shorter bond length than that of the parent molecule, CO. This is interpreted to mean that the most loosely held electron in N_2 is an electron of a π bond, whereas the most loosely held electron in CO is not one directly involved in bond formation.

Many molecules containing triple bonds react by serving as donors of π electrons in reactions known as addition reactions. For example, hydrogen adds to acetylene, $H:C:::C:H$, to form ethene, $H_2C::CH_2$

$$H-C\equiv C-H + H_2 \rightarrow \begin{array}{c} H \\ \diagdown \\ C=C \\ \diagup \\ H \end{array}\begin{array}{c} H \\ \diagup \\ \\ \diagdown \\ H \end{array}$$

Nitrogen is not known to function in this manner.

10.16 Nitrides and Phosphides

Elementary nitrogen reacts with a number of metals at high temperatures. It forms ionic compounds that contain the N^{3-} ion with lithium, the group II A metals, cadmium, and zinc. These **ionic nitrides** are high-melting, white, crystalline solids; they readily react with water to yield ammonia and hydroxides.

$$Li_3N(s) + 3H_2O \rightarrow 3Li^+(aq) + 3OH^-(aq) + NH_3(g)$$
$$Ca_3N_2(s) + 6H_2O \rightarrow 3Ca^{2+}(aq) + 6OH^-(aq) + 2NH_3(g)$$

Interstitial nitrides may be made, at elevated temperatures, from many transition metals, in powdered form, and nitrogen or ammonia. These substances, such as VN, Fe_4N, W_2N, and TiN, contain nitrogen atoms in the interstices of the metal lattices; they frequently deviate slightly from exact stoichiometry. Interstitial nitrides have extremely high melting points, resemble metals in appearance, are good electrical conductors, are very hard, and are chemically inert.

Covalent nitrides include such compounds as S_4N_4, P_3N_5, Si_3N_4, Sn_3N_4, BN, and AlN. Some of these compounds are molecular in form; others are materials in which a large number of the constituent atoms are covalently joined into a crystal lattice. Aluminum nitride and boron nitride, which are representative of the latter type of compound, may be prepared by the reaction of the elements at high temperatures; AlN and BN react with water (BN only at red heat) to give ammonia and Al_2O_3 or B_2O_3. Since one B atom and one N atom may be considered to be equivalent to two C atoms, BN may be considered to be isoelectronic with carbon, and the compound is known in two crystalline modifications—one resembling graphite and another extremely hard form similar to the diamond.

Many metals unite with white phosphorus directly to form phosphides; these compounds have not been so well characterized as the nitrides. The bonding of the phosphides of the I A and II A metals (such as Na_3P, Ca_3P_2, and K_2P_5) must have considerable ionic character, but the existence of the P^{3-} ion has not been firmly established. Such compounds readily hydrolyze to produce phosphine, PH_3.

$$Ca_3P_2(s) + 6H_2O \rightarrow 3Ca^{2+}(aq) + 6OH^-(aq) + 2PH_3(g)$$

Covalent phosphides of the III A metals are known (BP, AlP, etc.). Many transition elements form phosphides (e.g., FeP, Fe_2P, Co_2P_5, RuP, and OsP_2); these materials are gray-black, semimetallic substances that are electrical conductors and are insoluble in water.

Arsenides, stibnides, and bismuthides are known, but they are progressively more difficult to prepare. Undoubtedly, these compounds are not ionic, even those formed from the I A and II A metals.

10.17 Hydrogen Compounds

The group V A elements all form hydrogen compounds, the most important of which is ammonia, NH_3. Large quantities of ammonia are commercially prepared by the direct union of the elements (**Haber process**).

$$N_2(g) + 3H_2(g) \rightarrow 2NH_3(g) + 22.1 \text{ kcal}$$

Ammonia is the only hydrogen compound of the V A elements that can be prepared directly. The reaction is conducted under high pressures (from 100 to 1000 atm), at a temperature of approximately 1000°C, and in the presence of a catalyst. One catalyst, so employed, consists of finely divided iron and Fe_3O_4 containing small amounts of K_2O and Al_2O_3 (Section 12.3).

Smaller quantities of ammonia are produced as a by-product in the manufacture of coke by the destructive distillation of coal.

Ammonia was formerly produced by the reaction of calcium cyanamide, CaNCN, with steam under pressure.

$$CaNCN(s) + 3H_2O(g) \rightarrow CaCO_3(s) + 2NH_3(g)$$

However, the Haber process has largely displaced this method as a source of ammonia, and calcium cyanamide is produced chiefly as a fertilizer and as a raw material in the manufacture of certain nitrogen-containing organic compounds. Calcium cyanamide is produced in a two step process. Calcium carbide, CaC_2, is made by the reaction of CaO and coke in an electric furnace

$$CaO(s) + 3C(s) \rightarrow CaC_2(s) + CO(g)$$

and the calcium carbide is reacted with relatively pure nitrogen at approximately 1000°C to produce calcium cyanamide.

$$CaC_2(s) + N_2(g) \rightarrow CaNCN(s) + C(s)$$

In the laboratory, ammonia is conveniently prepared by the hydrolysis of nitrides (Section 10.16) or by heating an ammonium salt with a strong alkali (such as NaOH or $Ca(OH)_2$) either dry or in solution.

$$NH_4^+(aq) + OH^-(aq) \rightarrow NH_3(g) + H_2O$$

The ammonia molecule is trigonal pyramidal with the nitrogen atom at the apex (Section 3.13), and the compound is associated through hydrogen bonding in the liquid and solid states (Section 7.11). Liquid ammonia chemistry is discussed in Section 13.2. Ammonia forms many complex ions (e.g., $Ag(NH_3)_2^+$, $Cu(NH_3)_4^{2+}$, and $Cr(NH_3)_6^{3+}$) through the unshared electron pair on nitrogen or through ion-dipole attractions (Sections 14.12 and 16.1).

Aqueous solutions of ammonia are alkaline (Sections 13.3 and 14.1).

$$NH_3(aq) + H_2O \rightarrow NH_4^+(aq) + OH^-(aq)$$

In solution, or as a dry gas, ammonia reacts with acids to produce ammonium salts.

$$NH_3(g) + HCl(g) \rightarrow NH_4Cl(s)$$

The ammonium ion is tetrahedral.

Nitrogen is formed when ammonia is burned in pure oxygen.

$$4NH_3(g) + 3O_2(g) \rightarrow 2N_2(g) + 6H_2O(g)$$

However, when a mixture of ammonia and air is passed over platinum gauze at 1000°C, nitric oxide, NO, is produced.

$$4NH_3(g) + 5O_2(g) \rightarrow 4NO(g) + 6H_2O(g)$$

Hydrazine, N_2H_4, has the structure

$$H:\ddot{N}:\ddot{N}:H$$
$$\ddot{H}\ \ddot{H}$$

The compound, which is a liquid, may be prepared by oxidizing ammonia with sodium hypochlorite. It is less basic than ammonia but does form cations in which either one proton or two protons are bonded to the free electron pairs of the molecule (e.g., $(N_2H_5)Cl$ and $(N_2H_6)Cl_2$). Hydrazine is a strong reducing agent and has found some use in rocket fuels. A closely related substance, hydroxylamine, NH_2OH,

$$H:\overset{\cdot\cdot}{\underset{H}{N}}:\overset{\cdot\cdot}{\underset{\cdot\cdot}{O}}:H$$

is likewise a weak base and forms salts such as $(NH_3OH)Cl$.

Hydrazoic acid, HN_3, a weak acid, is prepared by distilling an acidified solution of an azide. Sodium azide, NaN_3, may be obtained by the oxidation of molten sodium amide, $NaNH_2$, by N_2O.

$$NaNH_2(l) + N_2O(g) \rightarrow NaN_3(l) + NaOH(l) + NH_3(g)$$

Azides, particularly those of the heavy metals (such as $Pb(N_3)_2$), are explosive. The axide ion is linear,

$$[:\overset{\cdot\cdot}{N}::N::\overset{\cdot\cdot}{N}:]^-$$

Phosphine, PH_3, a very poisonous, colorless gas is prepared by the hydrolysis of phosphides or by the reaction of white phosphorus with concentrated solutions of alkalies.

$$P_4(s) + 3OH^-(aq) + 3H_2O \rightarrow PH_3(g) + 3H_2PO_2^-(aq)$$
$$\text{hypophosphite ion}$$

The PH_3 molecule is pyramidal, similar to the NH_3 molecule; however, unlike NH_3, the compound is not associated in the liquid state.

The gas is only sparingly soluble in water; such solutions are not alkaline and decompose to yield phosphorus, hydrogen, and other products. Phosphonium compounds, analogous to ammonium compounds, can be prepared by reacting anhydrous phosphine gas with the anhydrous hydrogen halides.

$$PH_3(g) + HI(g) \rightarrow PH_4I(s)$$

Phosphine is, however, much less basic than ammonia, and phosphonium compounds are unstable. They decompose at relatively low temperatures, or in aqueous solution, to yield phosphine and the acid halide.

Diphosphine, P_2H_4, is generally formed along with phosphine in the preparations of the latter compound. It is spontaneously flammable. Diphosphine has no basic properties in contrast to its nitrogen analog, hydrazine. Nitrogen and phosphorus are the only V A elements that form hydrides of general formula M_2H_4.

Arsine (AsH_3), stibine (SbH_3), and bismuthine (BiH_3) are extremely poisonous gases that may be produced by the hydrolysis of arsenides, stibnides, and bismuthides (e.g., Na_3As, Zn_3Sb_2, and Mg_3Bi_2). The yields of the hydrogen compounds become poorer with increasing molecular weight, and very poor yields of bismuthine are obtained by this method. The stability of the hydrogen compounds declines in the series from NH_3 to BiH_3, and bismuthine is very unstable decomposing to the elements at room temperature. Consequently, bismuthine is poorly characterized. Arsine and stibine may be similarly decomposed by warming.

Compounds of these V A elements in higher oxidation states may be reduced by reactive metals in sulfuric acid solution to prepare the corresponding hydrogen compounds.

$$H_3AsO_3(aq) + 6H^+(aq) + 3Zn(s) \rightarrow AsH_3(g) + 3Zn^{2+}(aq) + 3H_2O$$

In the Marsh test for arsenic or antimony, arsine or stibine is generated by metal reduction, and the gas is thermally decomposed to form an arsenic or antimony mirror on a hot surface.

Arsine, stibine, and bismuthine have no basic properties and do not form salts with acids.

10.18 Halogen Compounds

The halogen compounds of the group V A elements are listed in Table 10.20. Nitrogen forms only four halides that have been obtained in a pure condition: NF_3, N_2F_2, N_2F_4, and NCl_3. Both nitrogen trifluoride and dinitrogen difluoride are obtained when ammonium fluoride dissolved in anhydrous hydrogen fluoride is electrolyzed. Dinitrogen tetrafluoride is best obtained by the reaction

$$2NF_3(g) + Cu(s) \rightarrow N_2F_4(g) + CuF_2(s)$$

The direct fluorination of ammonia, with nitrogen gas as a diluent, produces NF_3 when fluorine is in excess or all three nitrogen fluoride gases when an excess of ammonia is employed.

TABLE 10.20.
BINARY HALOGEN COMPOUNDS OF THE GROUP V A ELEMENTS.

Nitrogen	Phosphorus	Arsenic	Antimony	Bismuth
NF_3	PF_3	AsF_3	SbF_3	BiF_3
N_2F_2	PF_5	AsF_5	SbF_5	BiF_5
N_2F_4				
NCl_3	PCl_3	$AsCl_3$	$SbCl_3$	$BiCl_3$
	PCl_5		$SbCl_5$	
	P_2Cl_4			
	PBr_3	$AsBr_3$	$SbBr_3$	$BiBr_3$
	PBr_5			
	PI_3	AsI_3	SbI_3	BiI_3
	P_2I_4			

Nitrogen trifluoride is a very stable compound. It does not react with water and has no basic properties. The fluorine atoms, which are highly electronegative, withdraw electron density away from the nitrogen atom; hence, the unshared electron pair of the nitrogen atom is not a reactive site.

$$F—\ddot{N}—F$$
$$|$$
$$F$$

Isomers are substances that have the same molecular formula but differ in the way the constituent atoms are arranged into molecules. Dinitrogen difluoride exists in two isomeric forms.

trans   *cis*

The double bond, a σ bond and a π bond, between the two nitrogen atoms prevents free rotation about the nitrogen-nitrogen axis. In the *cis* isomer, both fluorine atoms are on the same side of the doubly bonded nitrogen atoms, whereas in the more stable *trans* isomer, the fluorine atoms are on opposite sides; both molecules are planar.

Nitrogen trichloride, a yellow liquid, is prepared by the chlorination of ammonium chloride in acid solution. In contrast to NF_3, NCl_3 is very reactive, sometimes explosively so. It readily reacts with water

$$NCl_3(l) + 3H_2O \rightarrow NH_3(g) + 3HOCl(aq)$$

Two series of nitrogen oxyhalides are known: the nitrosyl halides, XNO (X = F, Cl, and Br), and the nitryl halides, XNO_2 (X = F and Cl). These compounds are relatively unstable and are very reactive.

The principal halides of phosphorus, arsenic, antimony, and bismuth are trihalides and pentahalides. In addition to those listed in Table 10.20, several mixed halides are known (e.g., PF_2Cl, $PFBr_2$, PF_3Cl_2, and SbF_3Cl_2).

All of the simple trihalides may be prepared by direct halogenation using an excess of the V A element. However, PF_3 is best prepared by an exchange reaction between PCl_3 and a fluoride (such as AsF_3, ZnF_2, or PbF_2).

$$2PCl_3(l) + 3PbF_2(s) \rightarrow 2PF_3(g) + 3PbCl_2(s)$$

Molecules of the trihalides are trigonal pyramidal like NH_3 and PH_3.

The trihalides undergo hydrolysis:

$$PCl_3(l) + 3H_2O \longrightarrow H_3PO_3(aq) + 3H^+(aq) + 3Cl^-(aq)$$
$$AsCl_3(l) + 3H_2O \longrightarrow H_3AsO_3(aq) + 3H^+(aq) + 3Cl^-(aq)$$
$$SbCl_3(s) + H_2O \longrightarrow SbOCl(s) + 2H^+(aq) + 2Cl^-(aq)$$
$$BiCl_3(s) + H_2O \longrightarrow BiOCl(s) + 2H^+(aq) + 2Cl^-(aq)$$

In these reactions, the V A elements appear in 3+ oxidation states; in the hydrolysis of NCl_3, nitrogen functions in a 3− oxidation state and appears to be more electronegative than chlorine.

The pentahalides may be prepared by direct reaction of the elements using an excess of the halogen and by the reaction of the halogen with the trihalide.

$$PCl_3(l) + Cl_2(g) \longrightarrow PCl_5(s)$$

All of the pentahalides of phosphorus are known with the exception of the pentaiodide; presumably, there is not enough room around a phosphorus atom to accommodate five large iodine atoms. In addition, AsF_5, SbF_5, BiF_5, and $SbCl_5$ have been prepared.

The pentahalides are trigonal bipyramidal molecules (sp^3d hybridization) in the gaseous and liquid state (Figure 10.11). The crystal lattice of $SbCl_5$ consists of such molecules; however, solid PCl_5 and PBr_5 form

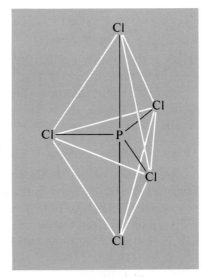

Figure 10.11   Structure of the gaseous PCl₅ molecule.

ionic lattices composed of PCl_4^+ and PCl_6^- and PBr_4^+ and Br^-, respectively. Apparently, it is impossible to pack six bromine atoms around a phosphorus atom since PBr_6^- does not form. The cations are tetrahedral (sp^3) and the PCl_6^- ion is octahedral (sp^3d^2); see Figure 10.12.

The phosphorus pentahalides undergo hydrolysis in two steps; for example,

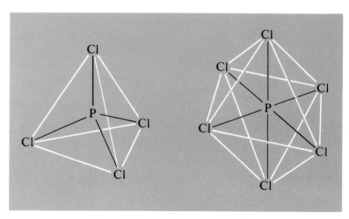

Figure 10.12   Structures of PCl$_4^+$ and PCl$_6^-$.

$$PCl_5(s) + H_2O \rightarrow POCl_3(l) + 2H^+(aq) + 2Cl^-(aq)$$

$$POCl_3(l) + 3H_2O \rightarrow H_3PO_4(aq) + 3H^+(aq) + 3Cl^-(aq)$$

The most important oxyhalides of phosphorus are the phosphoryl halides, POX$_3$ (X = F, Cl, or Br). These compounds may be prepared by the hydrolysis of the appropriate pentahalide in a limited amount of water or by the reaction of the trihalide with oxygen.

$$2PCl_3(l) + O_2(g) \rightarrow 2POCl_3(l)$$

Molecules of the phosphoryl halides have a PX$_3$ grouping arranged as a trigonal pyramid with an oxygen atom bonded to the phosphorus atom thus forming a distorted tetrahedron.

Antimony and bismuth form antimonyl and bismuthyl halides (e.g., SbOCl and BiOCl), but only one oxyhalide of arsenic has been prepared, AsOF$_3$.

10.19   Sulfides

The sulfides of the V A elements are listed in Table 10.21; other sulfides have been reported, but their existence is questioned. Tetranitrogen tetrasulfide, N$_4$S$_4$, is obtained by the reaction of anhydrous ammonia with either disulfur dichloride, S$_2$Cl$_2$, or sulfur dichloride, SCl$_2$; it is a yellow-orange crystalline solid.

TABLE 10.21.
SULFIDES OF THE V A ELEMENTS.

Nitrogen	Phosphorus	Arsenic	Antimony	Bismuth
N$_4$S$_4$	P$_4$S$_3$	As$_4$S$_3$	Sb$_2$S$_3$	Bi$_2$S$_3$
	P$_4$S$_5$	As$_4$S$_4$	Sb$_2$S$_5$	
	P$_4$S$_7$	As$_2$S$_3$		
	P$_4$S$_{10}$	As$_2$S$_5$		

With the exception of N_4S_4, all of the sulfides listed in Table 10.21 may be prepared by the direct reaction of the elements. Each of the four phosphorus sulfides is a yellow crystalline material; P_4S_3 is used in the manufacture of strike-anywhere matches.

The sulfides of bismuth and antimony, as well as As_2S_3 and As_2S_5, may be precipitated from acidic solutions of appropriate compounds of these V A elements by hydrogen sulfide; As_2S_3 and As_2S_5 are yellow; Sb_2S_3 is orange-red to black; As_2S_5 is orange; and Bi_2S_3 is dark brown. The arsenic and antimony sulfides are dissolved by excess sulfide ion to form thio anions; the 3+ compounds form the thioarsenite, AsS_3^{3-}, and thioantimonite, SbS_3^{3-}, ions, and the 5+ compounds form the thioarsenate, AsS_4^{3-}, and the thioantimonate, SbS_4^{3-}, ions. Bismuth sulfide, Bi_2S_3, is not dissolved by sulfide ion. The formation of thio anions is used in qualitative analysis to effect separations of sulfide precipitates (Section 14.12).

10.20   Oxides and Oxyacids of Nitrogen

Oxides are known for every oxidation state of nitrogen from 1+ to 5+. Nitrous oxide (or dinitrogen oxide), N_2O, is prepared by gently heating molten ammonium nitrate.

$$NH_4NO_3(l) \rightarrow N_2O(g) + 2H_2O(g)$$

It is a colorless gas and is relatively unreactive. However, at temperatures around 500°C, nitrous oxide decomposes to nitrogen and oxygen, and hence, N_2O supports combustion. Molecules of N_2O are linear, and the electronic structure of the compound may be represented as a resonance hybrid.

$$:\ddot{N}::N::\ddot{O}: \leftrightarrow :N:::N:\ddot{O}:$$

Nitric oxide (or nitrogen oxide), NO, may be prepared by the direct reaction of the elements at high temperatures.

$$N_2(g) + O_2(g) \rightarrow 2NO(g)$$

The reaction is endothermic ($\Delta H = +21.6$ kcal/mole), but even at 3000°C, the yield of NO is only approximately 4%. In a successful preparation, the hot gases from the reaction must be rapidly cooled to prevent the decomposition of NO back into nitrogen and oxygen. By this reaction, atmospheric nitrogen is fixed during lightning storms, and the reaction serves as the basis of the **arc process** of nitrogen fixation in which an electric arc is used to provide the high temperatures necessary for the direct combination of nitrogen and oxygen. As a commercial source of NO, the arc process has been supplanted by the catalytic oxidation of ammonia from the Haber process (Section 10.17).

Nitric oxide is conveniently prepared in the laboratory by the reaction of copper and dilute nitric acid.

$$3Cu(s) + 8H^+(aq) + 2NO_3^-(aq) \rightarrow 3Cu^{2+}(aq) + 2NO(g) + 4H_2O$$

The NO molecule contains an odd number of electrons, which means that one electron must be unpaired; for this reason, NO is paramagnetic. The electronic structure of the molecule may be represented by the resonance forms

$$:\dot{N}:\ddot{O}: \leftrightarrow :\ddot{N}::\dot{O}:$$

However, the structure is best described by the method of molecular orbitals (Section 3.14). Whereas odd-electron molecules are generally very reactive and highly colored, nitric oxide is only moderately reactive and is a colorless gas (condensing to a blue liquid and blue solid at low temperatures). In addition, NO shows little tendency to associate into N_2O_2 molecules by electron pairing.

Nitric oxide readily forms the nitrosonium ion, NO^+, through the loss of an electron, and ionic compounds containing this ion are known (such as $NO^+HSO_4^-$, $NO^+ClO_4^-$, and $NO^+BF_4^-$). It reacts instantly with oxygen at room temperature to form nitrogen dioxide.

$$2NO(g) + O_2(g) \rightarrow 2NO_2(g)$$

Dinitrogen trioxide, N_2O_3, forms as a blue liquid when an equimolar mixture of nitric oxide and nitrogen dioxide is cooled to $-20°C$.

$$NO(g) + NO_2(g) \rightarrow N_2O_3(l)$$

The compound is unstable under ordinary conditions and decomposes into NO and NO_2. Both NO and NO_2 are odd-electron molecules; N_2O_3 is formed by electron pairing, and the N_2O_3 molecule is thought to contain a N—N bond. It is the anhydride of nitrous acid, HNO_2, and dissolves in aqueous alkali to produce the nitrite ion, NO_2^-.

Nitrogen dioxide, NO_2, and dinitrogen tetroxide, N_2O_4, exist in equilibrium with each other.

$$2NO_2 \rightleftharpoons N_2O_4$$

Nitrogen dioxide consists of odd-electron molecules, is paramagnetic, and is brown in color; the dimer, in which the electrons are paired, is diamagnetic and colorless. In the solid state, the oxide is colorless and consists of pure N_2O_4. The liquid is yellow in color and consists of a dilute solution of NO_2 in N_2O_4. As the temperature is raised, the gas contains more and more NO_2 and becomes deeper and deeper brown in color. At $135°C$, approximately 99% of the mixture is NO_2.

Nitrogen dioxide molecules are angular.

The structure of N_2O_4 is thought to be planar with two NO_2 units joined by a N—N bond.

Nitrogen dioxide is produced by the reaction of nitric oxide with oxygen. In the laboratory, the compound is conveniently prepared by heating lead nitrate.

$$2Pb(NO_3)_2(s) \rightarrow 2PbO(s) + 4NO_2(g) + O_2(g)$$

Dinitrogen pentoxide, N_2O_5, is the acid anhydride of nitric acid from which it may be prepared by dehydration using phosphorus (V) oxide.

$$4HNO_3(g) + P_4O_{10}(s) \rightarrow 4HPO_3(s) + N_2O_5(g)$$

The compound is a colorless, crystalline material that sublimes at 32.5°C. The vapor consists of N_2O_5 molecules which are thought to be planar with the two nitrogen atoms joined through an oxygen atom (O_2NONO_2).

The electronic structure of the molecule may be represented as a resonance hybrid between

$$\ddot{O} \qquad \ddot{O}$$
$$N:\ddot{O}:N$$
$$\ddot{O} \qquad \ddot{O}$$

and other equivalent structures with different arrangements of the double bonds. The compound is unstable in the vapor state and decomposes according to the equation

$$2N_2O_5(g) \rightarrow 4NO_2(g) + O_2(g)$$

Crystals of N_2O_5 are composed of nitronium, NO_2^+, and nitrate, NO_3^-, ions; the compound is dissociated into these two ions in solutions in anhydrous sulfuric acid, nitric acid, and phosphoric acid. The nitrate ion is triangular planar. The nitronium ion is linear; it is isoelectronic with CO_2 and may be considered as a nitrogen dioxide molecule minus the odd electron. The ion is probably a reaction intermediate in certain reactions of nitric acid in the presence of sulfuric acid (nitrations) and ionic nitronium compounds have been prepared (e.g., $NO_2^+ClO_4^-$, $NO_2^+BF_4^-$, $NO_2^+Pf_6^-$).

There is chemical and spectroscopic evidence for the existence of NO_3 and N_2O_6. However, these substances have not been isolated in the pure condition.

The most important oxyacid of nitrogen is nitric acid, HNO_3, in which nitrogen exhibits an oxidation number of 5+. Commercially, nitric acid is produced by the **Ostwald process.** Nitric oxide, from the catalytic oxidation of ammonia, is reacted with oxygen to form nitrogen dioxide. This gas, together with excess oxygen, is passed into a tower where it reacts with warm water.

$$3NO_2(g) + H_2O \rightarrow 2H^+(aq) + 2NO_3^-(aq) + NO(g)$$

The excess oxygen converts the NO from the preceding reaction into NO_2, which reacts with water as before. In this manner, the nitric oxide is eventually completely converted into nitric acid. The product of the Ostwald process is about 70% HNO_3 and is known as concentrated nitric acid; more concentrated solutions may be prepared from it by distillation.

Pure nitric acid is a colorless liquid that boils at 83°C. It may be prepared in the laboratory by heating sodium nitrate with concentrated sulfuric acid.

$$NaNO_3(s) + H_2SO_4(l) \rightarrow NaHSO_4(s) + HNO_3(g)$$

This preparation (from Chilean saltpeter) is a minor commercial source of the acid.

The HNO_3 molecule is planar and may be represented as a resonance hybrid.

Nitric acid is a strong acid, almost completely dissociated in aqueous solution. Most of the salts of nitric acid, the nitrates, are very soluble in water. The nitrate ion is triangular planar.

Nitric acid is a powerful oxidizing agent; it oxidizes most nonmetals (generally to oxides or oxyacids of their highest oxidation state) and all metals with the exception of a few of the noble metals. Many unreactive metals, such as silver and copper, that do not react to yield hydrogen with nonoxidizing acids, such as HCl, dissolve in nitric acid.

In nitric acid oxidations, hydrogen is almost never obtained; instead, a variety of nitrogen-containing compounds, of lower oxidation state, is produced (Table 10.22). The product to which HNO_3 is reduced depends upon the concentration of the acid, the temperature, and the nature of the material being oxidized. Generally, a mixture of products is obtained, but the principal product, in many cases, is NO when dilute HNO_3 is employed and the nitrogen (IV) oxides when concentrated HNO_3 is used.

dilute:

$$3Cu(s) + 8H^+(aq) + 2NO_3^-(aq) \rightarrow 3Cu^{2+}(aq) + 2NO(g) + 4H_2O$$

concentrated:

$$Cu(s) + 4H^+(aq) + 2NO_3^-(aq) \rightarrow Cu^{2+}(aq) + 2NO_2(g) + 2H_2O$$

In some instances, however, strong reducing agents are known to produce almost pure compounds of nitrogen in lower oxidation states; for example, the reaction of zinc and dilute nitric acid yields NH_3 as the reduction product of HNO_3.

TABLE 10.22. STANDARD ELECTRODE POTENTIALS FOR REDUCTIONS OF THE NITRATE ION.	
$e^- + 2H^+ + NO_3^- \rightleftharpoons NO_2 + H_2O$	$E^\circ = +0.80 \text{ v}$
$8e^- + 10H^+ + NO_3^- \rightleftharpoons NH_4^+ + 3H_2O$	$E^\circ = +0.88 \text{ v}$
$2e^- + 3H^+ + NO_3^- \rightleftharpoons HNO_2 + H_2O$	$E^\circ = +0.94 \text{ v}$
$3e^- + 4H^+ + NO_3^- \rightleftharpoons NO + 2H_2O$	$E^\circ = +0.96 \text{ v}$
$8e^- + 10H^+ + 2NO_3^- \rightleftharpoons N_2O + 5H_2O$	$E^\circ = +1.12 \text{ v}$
$10e^- + 6H^+ + 2NO_3^- \rightleftharpoons N_2 + 6H_2O$	$E^\circ = +1.25 \text{ v}$

The half reactions for the reduction of the nitrate ion in acid solution (Table 10.22) show the E° values to be strongly dependent upon the H^+ (aq) concentration. This concentration dependence is experimentally observed; below a concentration of $2M$, nitric acid has little more oxidizing power than solutions of HCl of corresponding concentration.

Pure nitrous acid, HNO_2, has never been isolated, but a solution of this acid may be prepared by adding an equimolar mixture of NO and NO_2 to water.

$$NO(g) + NO_2(g) + H_2O \rightleftharpoons 2HNO_2(aq)$$

The reaction is exothermic and reversible; when warmed, nitrous acid decomposes, and the NO_2, thus produced, reacts with water to give nitric acid. The overall reaction may be indicated

$$3HNO_2(aq) \rightarrow H^+(aq) + NO_3^-(aq) + H_2O + 2NO(g)$$

Consequently, solutions of the acid are usually prepared by adding a strong acid to a cold aqueous solution of a nitrite.

$$H^+(aq) + NO_2^-(aq) \rightarrow HNO_2(aq)$$

The acid is weak and may function as an oxidizing agent or a reducing agent. The electronic structure may be represented as

Nitrites are prepared by the addition of NO and NO_2 to solutions of alkalies. The nitrites of the I A metals are formed when the nitrates are heated, or they may be prepared by heating the nitrate with a reducing agent, such as lead, iron, or coke.

$$NaNO_3(l) + C(s) \rightarrow NaNO_2(l) + CO(g)$$

The nitrite ion is angular.

$$\left[:\overset{..}{O}: \quad \overset{\overset{..}{N}.}{} \quad :\overset{..}{O}: \right]^{-} \leftrightarrow \left[:\overset{..}{O}: \quad \overset{.\overset{..}{N}}{} \quad :\overset{..}{O}: \right]^{-}$$

Hyponitrous acid, $H_2N_2O_2$, is a relatively unimportant oxyacid of nitrogen. It is a very weak acid and readily decomposes to yield nitrous oxide.

$$H_2N_2O_2(aq) \rightarrow H_2O + N_2O(g)$$

Although nitrous oxide is formally the acid anhydride of hyponitrous acid, neither the acid nor its salts may be prepared from N_2O.

10.21   Oxides and Oxyacids of Phosphorus, Arsenic, Antimony, and Bismuth

When white phosphorus is burned in a limited supply of air, the chief product is phosphorus(III) oxide (or phosphor*ous* oxide), P_4O_6. It is a colorless material that melts at 23.8°C. The combustion of phosphorus in excess oxygen yields phosphorus (V) oxide (or phosphor*ic* oxide), P_4O_{10}, a white powder that sublimes at approximately 360°C. The structures of these molecules are based on P_4 tetrahedra (Figure 10.13). Before the true molecular structures of these compounds were known, empirical formulas were used; consequently, the compounds are often designated as P_2O_3, phosphorus trioxide, and P_2O_5, phosphorus pentox-

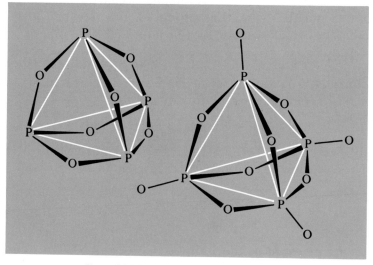

Figure 10.13   Structures of P_4O_6 and P_4O_{10}.

ide. Phosphorus(V) oxide exists in three crystalline modifications, two of which are polymeric. When P_4O_6 is heated above 210°C, red phosphorus and a third oxide, $(PO_2)_n$, are formed; $(PO_2)_n$ is a polymeric material and is relatively unimportant.

Phosphorus(V) oxide has a great affinity for water and is a very effective drying agent. By the addition of the proper amount of water to P_4O_{10}, any one of a number of phosphoric acids may be obtained. Significant reactions are

$$nP_4O_{10} + 2nH_2O \longrightarrow 4(HPO_3)_n$$
metaphosphoric acid

$$P_4O_{10} + 4H_2O \longrightarrow 2H_4P_2O_7$$
pyrophosphoric acid

$$P_4O_{10} + 6H_2O \longrightarrow 4H_3PO_4$$
orthophosphoric acid

The most important acid of phosphorus in the 5+ state is orthophosphoric acid (or merely phosphoric acid). It is obtained commercially by the complete hydration of P_4O_{10} or by treating phosphate rock with sulfuric acid.

$$Ca_3(PO_4)_2(s) + 3H_2SO_4(l) \longrightarrow 2H_3PO_4(l) + 3CaSO_4(s)$$

The compound is a colorless solid but is generally sold as an 85% solution. It is a weak, triprotic acid without effective oxidizing power.

$$H_3PO_4(aq) \rightleftharpoons H^+(aq) + H_2PO_4^-(aq)$$
$$H_2PO_4^-(aq) \rightleftharpoons H^+(aq) + HPO_4^{2-}(aq)$$
$$HPO_4^{2-}(aq) \rightleftharpoons H^+(aq) + PO_4^{3-}(aq)$$

Hence, three series of salts may be derived from H_3PO_4: the dihydrogen phosphates, the monohydrogen phosphates, and the normal phosphates; the product of a given neutralization depends upon the stoichiometric ratio of H_3PO_4 to alkali.

Pyrophosphoric and metaphosphoric acids are examples of condensed phosphoric acids. Not only may they be prepared by the limited hydration of P_4O_{10}, but also by the condensation of two or more molecules of H_3PO_4 with the elimination of water. For example, at 215°C,

$$2H_3PO_4(l) \longrightarrow H_4P_2O_7(l) + H_2O(g)$$

and stronger dehydration, at 325°C,

$$nH_3PO_4(l) \longrightarrow (HPO_3)_n(l) + nH_2O(g)$$

On standing in water, the condensed phosphoric acids revert to orthophosphoric acid.

The phosphate ion is tetrahedral, and the pyrophosphate ion consists of two PO_4 tetrahedra joined through a common oxygen atom (Figure

10.14). Metaphosphoric acid is in reality a mixture of many polymeric species (hence the formula $(HPO_3)_n$); the basis of each, however, is PO_4 tetrahedra joined by bridge oxygen atoms. Salts of many condensed phosphoric acids have been prepared, but all of the corresponding acids have not been isolated.

Phosphor*ous* acid, H_3PO_3, may be prepared by adding P_4O_6 to cold water,

$$P_4O_6(s) + 6H_2O \rightarrow 4H_3PO_3(aq)$$

or by the hydrolysis of PCl_3 (Section 10.18). Condensed phosphorous acids also exist. Even though the H_3PO_3 molecule contains three hydrogen atoms, phosphorous acid is a weak, *diprotic* acid and is probably better formulated as $H_2(HPO_3)$.

$$H_2(HPO_3)(aq) \rightleftharpoons H^+(aq) + H(HPO_3)^-(aq)$$
$$H(HPO_3)^-(aq) \rightleftharpoons H^+(aq) + HPO_3^{2-}(aq)$$

The sodium salts NaH_2PO_3 and Na_2HPO_3 are known, but it is impossible to prepare Na_3PO_3.

Solutions of salts of hypophosphorous acid, H_3PO_2, are prepared by boiling white phosphorus with solutions of alkalies (Section 10.17). The acid, which is a colorless crystalline material, may be obtained by treating a solution of barium hypophosphite with sulfuric acid, removing the precipitated barium sulfate by filtration, and evaporating the solution. Hypophosphorous acid is a weak monoprotic acid; hence the formula of the compound is sometimes written $H(H_2PO_2)$.

$$H(H_2PO_2)(aq) \rightleftharpoons H^+(aq) + H_2PO_2^-(aq)$$

Phosphorous acid, hypophosphorous acid, and the salts of these acids are poor oxidizing agents. However, they have strong reducing properties, the acids being oxidized to H_3PO_4 and the anions being oxidized to PO_4^{3-}.

The numbers of protons released by orthophosphoric, phosphorous, and hypophosphorous acids may be explained by the electronic structures of these compounds.

|orthophosphoric acid|phosphorous acid|hypophosphorous acid|

Only the hydrogen atoms bonded to oxygen atoms dissociate, whereas those bonded to a phosphorus atoms are not acidic. In each of these acids, as in the anions derived from them, the four groups are disposed around the phosphorus atom in a tetrahedral manner (Figure 10.14).

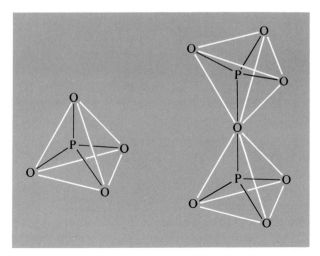

Figure 10.14   Structures of PO_4^{3-} and $P_2O_7^{4-}$.

When arsenic, antimony, or bismuth are burned in air, the 3+ oxides are formed; 5+ oxides of these elements are not obtained by direct union. Arsenic(III) oxide, As_4O_6, and antimony(III) oxide, Sb_4O_6, have molecular structures similar to that of P_4O_6 (Figure 10.13). Bismuth(III) oxide, the most ionic of the V A oxides, does not exist in discrete molecules in the crystalline state and is usually represented by the empirical formula Bi_2O_3. The 3+ oxides of arsenic and antimony are white solids; bismuth(III) oxide is yellow.

Arsenic(III) oxide is slightly soluble in water, and solutions of the very weak acid, arsenious acid, may be thus produced. It is not known whether the acid is in the meta- form, $HAsO_2$, or some more highly hydrated form, and the acid, in solution, is usually assigned the ortho-structure, H_3AsO_3. The pure "acid" is probably the hydrated oxide. A wide variety of arsenites is known; some of them are poorly characterized. The majority of the known salts are metaarsenites (e.g., $NaAsO_2$), but orthoarsenites (such as $Cu(HAsO_3)$ and Na_3AsO_3) as well as arsenites presumably derived from condensed arsenious acids are known.

Arsenic(III) oxide, although predominantly an acidic oxide, is somewhat amphoteric. It readily dissolves in solutions of hydroxides to produce arsenites. It less readily dissolves in concentrated acid to yield AsO^+ or $As(OH)_2^+$; dilution reprecipitates the oxide.

Antimony(III) oxide is practically insoluble in water. This oxide is amphoteric; it dissolves in acids to give antimonyl salts (such as $(SbO)_2SO_4$ and $SbONO_3$), and it dissolves in alkalies to give antimonites (e.g., $NaSbO_2$). Orthoantimonites and pyroantimonites, as well as metaantimonites, are known. Free antimonous acid is unknown; acidification of a solution of an antimonite yields only the hydrated oxide.

Bismuth(III) oxide, a yellow solid insoluble in water, has no acidic characteristics. It will not dissolve in alkalies but is soluble in acids. Evaporation of these acidic solutions yields Bi^{3+} salts (e.g., $Bi(NO_3)_3$). However, if these solutions are diluted, or if Bi^{3+} salts are dissolved in water, bismuthyl salts precipitate (such as $BiONO_3$, $BiOCl$, and $(BiO)_2SO_4$). Most bismuthyl compounds are insoluble. The addition of OH^- to a solution of a bismuth salt precipitates $Bi(OH)_3$; this is a true hydroxide, and no similar compound of arsenic or antimony is known. Under different conditions, bismuthyl hydroxide, $BiO(OH)$, can be prepared.

The structures of the $5+$ oxides of arsenic and antimony are not known and empirical formulas (As_2O_5 and Sb_2O_5) are employed. These compounds are acidic oxides and possess no amphoteric characteristics. Arsenic(V) oxide, a white solid, is prepared by heating orthoarsenic acid; this acid is obtained as a crystalline hydrate, $2H_3AsO_4 \cdot H_2O$, by evaporation of the solution resulting from the action of concentrated nitric acid on As_4O_6 or arsenic. Arsenic(V) oxide readily dissolves in water to produce arsenic acid, a weak triprotic acid. Metaarsenic acid, $HAsO_2$, and pyroarsenic acid, $H_4As_2O_7$, may be prepared by heating orthoarsenic acid; they revert to the ortho- form in water. The arsenates, which may be prepared by neutralizing arsenic acid or by dissolving As_2O_5 in alkali, resemble phosphates in crystal form and solubility.

Antimony(V) oxide is prepared in a manner analogous to that employed in the preparation of As_2O_5. The reaction of concentrated nitric acid and either Sb_4O_6 or antimony yields insoluble Sb_2O_5 hydrated by an indefinite number of water molecules. Heating this product produces Sb_2O_5, a yellow powder. Free antimonic acid is unknown, but antimonates may be produced by dissolving Sb_2O_5 in alkalies. Sodium antimonate, $NaSb(OH)_6$, is one of the least soluble salts of Na^+, and its formation is often used as a test for this ion. The antimonate ion ($Sb(OH)_6^-$) is octahedral in contrast to the tetrahedral AsO_4^{3-} and PO_4^{3-} ions; antimony is a large enough atom to accommodate six oxygen atoms.

Bismuth(V) oxide has never been prepared in the pure state; it is unstable and readily loses oxygen. The red-brown product obtained by the action of strong oxidizing agents (such as Cl_2, OCl^-, and $S_2O_8^{2-}$) on a suspension of Bi_2O_3 in an alkaline solution is thought to be impure Bi_2O_5. Bismuth(V) oxide dissolves in sodium hydroxide to produce a yellow-brown substance known as sodium bismuthate and assigned the formula $NaBiO_3$. This material, which may also be prepared by fusing Na_2O_2 and Bi_2O_3, is probably a mixture of oxides containing some Bi_2O_5. Bismuthic acid is not known.

In contrast to the phosphate ion, the arsenate ion and the antimonate ion are relatively good oxidizing agents in acidic solution. Sodium bismuthate, in acidic solution, is an extremely powerful oxidizing agent.

CARBON AND SILICON

Carbon, silicon, germanium, tin, and lead comprise group IV A. The compounds of carbon are more numerous than the compounds of any other element with the exception of hydrogen. In fact, approximately ten compounds that contain carbon are known for every one compound that does not. The chemistry of the compounds of carbon (most of which also contain hydrogen) is the subject of **organic chemistry** (Chapter 17).

10.22 Group Properties

The transition from nonmetallic character to metallic character with increasing atomic number that is exhibited by the elements of group V A is also evident in the chemistry of the IV A elements. Carbon is strictly a nonmetal (although graphite is an electrical conductor). Silicon is essentially a nonmetal in its chemical behavior; however, its electrical and physical properties are those of a semimetal. Germanium is a semimetal; its properties are more metallic than nonmetallic. Tin and lead are truly metallic, although some vestiges of nonmetallic character remain (e.g., the oxides and hydroxides of tin and lead are amphoteric).

Carbon exists in giant-molecule crystals with the atoms of the crystal held together by covalent bonds (Section 10.23). A large amount of energy is required to rupture some or all of these bonds in fusion or vaporization; hence, carbon has the highest melting point and boiling point of the family (Table 10.23). The heaviest member of the family, lead, exists in a typical metallic lattice. The crystalline forms of the intervening members show a transition between the two extremes displayed by carbon and lead, and this accounts for the trend in melting points and boiling points of the elements (Table 10.23).

The crystalline forms of silicon and germanium are similar to the diamond (Section 10.23); however, the bonds are not so strong as those

TABLE 10.23.
SOME PROPERTIES OF THE GROUP IV A ELEMENTS.

	Carbon	Silicon	Germanium	Tin	Lead
melting point (°C)	3570	1420	959	232	327
boiling point (°C)	4200	2355	2700	2360	1755
atomic radius (Å)	0.77	1.17	1.22	1.41	1.54
ionization potential (ev)					
first	11.3	8.1	8.1	7.3	7.4
second	24.4	16.3	15.9	14.5	15.0
third	47.9	33.5	34.1	30.5	32.0
fourth	64.5	45.1	45.5	39.4	42.1
electronegativity	2.5	1.8	1.8	1.8	1.8

in the diamond, and silicon and germanium are semiconductors (the diamond is not). Silicon and germanium may be used to prepare impurity semiconductors (Section 6.11) that are employed in transistors. Although one modification of tin has a diamond-type structure, the principal form of tin is metallic.

The electronic configurations of the elements are listed in Table 10.24. With the possible exception of carbon, the assumption of a noble-gas configuration through the formation of a $4-$ ion by electron gain is not observed; the electronegativities of the group IV A elements are generally low (Table 10.23). Carbon forms saltlike carbides with certain strongly metallic elements (Section 10.24); however, the bonding in these compounds probably has a significant degree of covalent character.

TABLE 10.24.
ELECTRONIC CONFIGURATIONS OF THE GROUP IV A ELEMENTS.

Element	Z	1s	2s	2p	3s	3p	3d	4s	4p	4d	4f	5s	5p	5d	6s	6p
C	6	2	2	2												
Si	14	2	2	6	2	2										
Ge	32	2	2	6	2	6	10	2	2							
Sn	50	2	2	6	2	6	10	2	6	10		2	2			
Pb	82	2	2	6	2	6	10	2	6	10	14	2	6	10	2	2

The ionization potentials of the elements (Table 10.23) show that the energy required for the removal of all four valence electrons from any given element is extremely high. Consequently, simple $4+$ ions of group IV A elements are unknown. Tin and lead, however, are capable of forming inert-pair ions by the loss of two electrons. Whereas Sn^{2+} compounds appear to be predominantly covalent in the pure state, compounds of Pb^{2+} (such as PbF_2, $PbCl_2$, and PbS) are ionic in the solid state, and both Sn^{2+} and Pb^{2+} ions exist in polar solvents.

In the majority of their compounds, the IV A elements are covalently bonded. Through the formation of four covalent bonds per atom, an element can attain the electronic configuration of the noble gas of its period. These bonds may be regarded as having been formed by the use of sp^3 hybrid orbitals, and compounds of the type AB_4 are tetrahedral. All of the carbon family elements can form such compounds, but only a few compounds of this type are known for lead (PbF_4, $PbCl_4$, and PbH_4) and they, with the exception of PbF_4, are unstable.

In the case of carbon, the formation of four covalent bonds saturates the valence level. However, the other members of the group have empty d orbitals available in their valence levels and can form species in which the atom of the IV A element exhibits a covalence greater than four. The ions SiF_6^{2-}, $GeCl_6^{2-}$, $SnBr_6^{2-}$, $Sn(OH)_6^{2-}$, $Pb(OH)_6^{2-}$, and $PbCl_6^{4-}$ utilize sp^3d^2 hybrid bonding orbitals; they are octahedral.

The most important way in which carbon differs from the remaining elements of group IV A (as well as from all other elements) is the pronounced ability of carbon to form compounds in which many carbon atoms are bonded to each other in chains or rings. This property, called **catenation,** is exhibited by other elements near carbon in the periodic classification (such as boron, nitrogen, phosphorus, sulfur, oxygen, silicon, germanium, and tin) but to a much lesser extent than carbon, and it is this property of carbon that makes for the large number of organic compounds.

In group IV A, the tendency for self-linkage diminishes markedly with increasing atomic number. The hydrides, which have the general formula E_nH_{2n+2} (where E is a group IV A element), illustrate this trend. There appears to be no limit to the number of carbon atoms that can bond together to form chains, and a very large number of hydrocarbons are known. For the other IV A elements, the most complex hydrides that have been prepared are Si_6H_{14}, Ge_8H_{18}, SnH_4, and PbH_4. The existance of plumbane, PbH_4, is questioned. The carbon-carbon single bond energy (82 kcal/mole) is much greater than that of the silicon-silicon bond (43 kcal/mole), the germanium-germanium bond (40 kcal/mole), or the tin-tin bond (37 kcal/mole).

In addition, carbon chains are much more stable than the chains of any other element. The reason for this difference in stability may be derived, in part, from a comparison of some bond energies:

C—C	82 kcal/mole	Si—Si	43 kcal/mole
C—O	84 kcal/mole	Si—O	89 kcal/mole
C—H	99 kcal/mole	Si—H	81 kcal/mole
C—Cl	78 kcal/mole	Si—Cl	86 kcal/mole
C—F	105 kcal/mole	Si—F	128 kcal/mole

The C—C bond energy is approximately of the same order of magnitude as the energies of the bond between carbon and other elements. The Si—Si bond, however, is weaker than the bonds that silicon forms with other elements.

Carbon has the ability to form multiple bonds with itself and with other nonmetals, in contrast to the other members of group IV A which do not participate in the formation of multiple bonds. Groupings such as $\diagdown C{=}C\diagdown$, $-C{\equiv}C-$, $-C{\equiv}N$, $\diagup C{=}O$, and $\diagup C{=}S$ are known for carbon but for no other IV A element, and the pronounced ability of carbon to form π bonds is another distinguishing characteristic of the element. Certain compounds of silicon appear to be similar to carbon compounds that contain multiple bonds; however, the similarity is only stoichiometric and not structural. Thus carbon dioxide is made up of molecules in which a central carbon atom is bonded by double bonds to two oxygen atoms,

$$\ddot{O}::C::\ddot{O}$$

whereas silicon dioxide forms a giant-molecule crystal in which silicon and oxygen atoms are joined together by single covalent bonds into a three-dimensional network. (Section 10.25).

Only the truly nonmetallic members of the family, carbon and silicon, will be treated in the sections that follow.

10.23   The Elements

Carbon constitutes approximately 0.03% of the earth's crust; in addition, the atmosphere contains 0.03% CO_2, by volume, and carbon is an important constituent of all plant and animal matter. The allotropes of carbon, diamond and graphite, as well as impure forms of the element such as coal (which also contains combined carbon) are naturally occurring. In combined form, the element occurs in compounds with hydrogen, called **hydrocarbons**, found in natural gas and petroleum, in the atmosphere as CO_2, and in carbonate minerals such as limestone ($CaCO_3$), dolomite ($CaCO_3 \cdot MgCO_3$), siderite ($FeCO_3$), witherite ($BaCO_3$), and malachite ($CuCO_3 \cdot Cu(OH)_2$).

In diamond, each carbon atom is bonded, through sp^3 hybrid orbitals, to four other carbon atoms arranged tetrahedrally (Figure 10.15). Strong bonds hold this network crystal together; furthermore, all of the valence electrons of each carbon atom are paired in bonding orbitals, and the valence level of each carbon atom can hold no more than eight electrons. Thus the diamond is extremely hard, high melting, stable, and a nonconductor of electricity.

Figure 10.15   Arrangement of atoms in a diamond crystal.

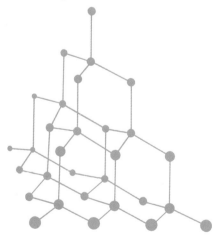

Whereas the diamond is a colorless, transparent material with a high refractivity, graphite is a soft, black solid with a slight metallic luster. The graphite crystal is composed of layers formed from hexagonal rings of carbon atoms (Figure 10.16). The layers are held together by relatively weak van der Waals forces, and the distance from carbon atom to carbon atom in adjacent planes is 3.40 Å as compared to a distance of 1.415 Å between bonded carbon atoms of a plane. Since it is easy for the layers to slide over one another, graphite is soft and has a slippery feel; it is less dense than diamond.

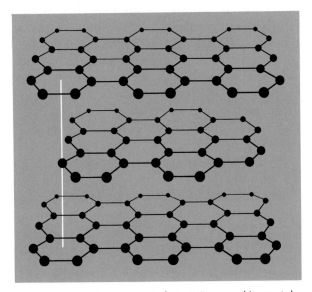

Figure 10.16   Arrangement of atoms in a graphite crystal.

The nature of the bonding in the layers of the graphite crystal accounts for some of the properties of this substance. Each carbon atom is bonded to three other carbon atoms, and all of the bonds are perfectly equivalent. The C—C bond distance in graphite (1.415 Å) compared to that in the diamond (1.54 Å) suggests that a degree of multiple bonding exists in the former, and graphite may be represented as a resonance hybrid (Figure 10.17) in which each bond is a $1\frac{1}{3}$ bond.

An alternative view is that each carbon atom forms three σ bonds, through sp^2 hybridization, with three other carbon atoms. This is consistent with the geometry observed for molecules containing sp^2 hybridized bonds since the three carbon atoms are disposed at the corners of an equilateral triangle. Such bonding accounts for three of the valence electrons of each carbon atom; the fourth electron, in a p orbital, is not involved in σ bond formation (Figure 10.18a). If only two adjacent atoms in a molecule had this electron arrangement, the additional p electrons would pair to form a π bond, and thus the atoms would be joined by a

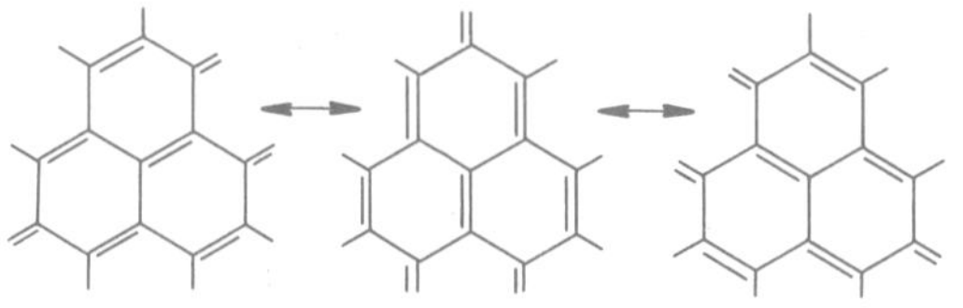

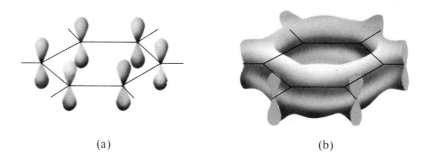

Figure 10.17   Resonance forms for a fragment of a
graphite layer.

double bond. However, in graphite, *each* carbon atom has an additional
p electron. The resonance forms depict the possibility of forming conventional double bonds in three ways, but in reality, all of the p electrons
interact to form one π molecular orbital which is best described as a
multicenter π orbital (Figure 10.18b). The electrons in this molecular
orbital belong to the molecule as a whole; they are not localized between
two atoms and are comparatively free to move throughout the entire
layer. It is this that gives the metallic luster to graphite and causes this
substance to be an electrical conductor. The conductivity is fairly large
in a direction parallel to the layers but is small in a direction perpendicular to the planes of the crystal.

Silicon, which constitutes approximately 28% of the earth's crust, is
the second most abundant element (oxygen is first). The element does
not occur free in nature; rather, it is found as silicon dioxide (sometimes
called silica) and in an enormous variety of silicate minerals.

Silicon is prepared by the reduction of silicon dioxide by coke, at high
temperatures, in an electric furnace.

$$SiO_2(l) + 2C(s) \longrightarrow Si(l) + 2CO(g)$$

If a larger quantity of carbon is employed, silicon carbide, (or "Car-
borundum"), SiC, is produced rather than silicon. The only known
modification of silicon has a structure similar to diamond. Crystalline
silicon is a gray, lustrous solid that is a semiconductor. The bonds in
silicon are not so strong as those in diamond, and the bonding electrons

Figure 10.18   Schematic representation of the formation of the multicenter π bond of a
graphite fragment. (σ bonds are shown as lines.)

(a)   (b)

are not so firmly localized. Evidently, in silicon, electrons may be thermally excited to a conductance band that is energetically close to the valence band (Section 3.15).

Very pure silicon, for use in transistors, is prepared by a series of steps. First, impure silicon is reacted with chlorine to produce $SiCl_4$. The tetrachloride, a volatile liquid, is purified by fractional distillation and then reduced, by hydrogen, to elementary silicon. This product is further purified by zone refining. In this process, a short section of one end of a silicon rod is melted, and this melted zone is caused to move slowly along the rod to the other end by the movement of the heater. Pure silicon crystallizes from the melt, and the impurities are swept along, in the melted zone, to one end of the rod which is subsequently sawed off and discarded.

10.24 Carbides and Silicides

A large number of carbides and silicides are known—the carbides having been much more extensively studied than the silicides. Carbides may be made by heating the metal or its oxide with carbon, carbon monoxide, or a hydrocarbon. As is the case with the hydrides and nitrides, carbides may be classified as **saltlike, interstitial,** or **covalent.**

The saltlike carbides may be divided into two types. The I A and II A metals, as well as Cu^+, Ag^+, Au^+, Zn^{2+}, and Cd^{2+}, form carbides that are believed to contain the acetylide ion, C_2^{2-}, which has the structure

$$[:C:::C:]^{2-}$$

Upon hydrolysis, acetylides yield acetylene, C_2H_2,

$$H:C:::C:H$$

$$CaC_2(s) + 2H_2O \rightarrow Ca(OH)_2(aq) + C_2H_2(g)$$

Beryllium carbide, Be_2C, and aluminum carbide, Al_4C_3, contain the methanide ion, C^{4-}, and yield methane,

$$\begin{array}{c} H \\ H:\overset{\cdot\cdot}{\underset{\cdot\cdot}{C}}:H \\ H \end{array}$$

upon hydrolysis.

$$Al_4C_3(s) + 12H_2O \rightarrow 4Al(OH)_3(s) + 3CH_4(g)$$

Interstitial carbides are formed by transition elements and consist of metallic lattices with carbon atoms in the interstices. These materials, such as TiC, TaC, W_2C, VC, and Mo_2C, are in general very hard, high melting, and chemically inert. They resemble metals in appearance and electrical conductivity.

For the formation of interstitial carbides, the interstices of the metallic crystal must be large enough to accommodate carbon atoms, and this requires that the metals have a radius greater than 1.3 Å. Some transition metals, with radii less than 1.3 Å, form carbides intermediate in character between the saltlike carbides and the interstitial carbides. The metal lattices of these substances, such as Fe_3C, Cr_3C_2, Co_3C, and Ni_3C, are distorted, and these materials are readily hydrolyzed.

Silicon carbide, produced by the reaction of SiO_2 and C, is a covalent carbide. It is hard, stable, and chemically inert. The silicon carbide crystal consists of a three-dimensional network formed from tetrahedra of alternating carbon and silicon atoms. Boron carbide, B_4C, which is even harder than silicon carbide, is made by the reduction of B_2O_3 by carbon in an electric furnace.

Silicon dissolves in almost all molten metals, and in many of these instances, definite compounds, called silicides, are produced. The compounds Mg_2Si, $CaSi_2$, Li_3Si, $FeSi$, Fe_2Si, Ni_2Si, $NiSi$, VSi_2, and $CoSi_3$ are among those known. Although probably none of the silicides are truly ionic, certain of them hydrolyze to produce hydrogen-silicon compounds, called **silicon hydrides** or **silanes**. This is not surprising since carbides of the interstital-iron type hydrolyze, and silicon compounds, in general, hydrolyze more readily than carbon compounds (Section 10.26).

The silanes are compounds of general formula Si_nH_{2n+2}, and compounds where n equals 1 to 6 are well characterized. The hydrolysis of Mg_2Si, by dilute acids, gives a mixture of silanes; for example,

$$Mg_2Si(s) + 4H^+(aq) \rightarrow 2Mg^{2+}(aq) + SiH_4(g)$$

The silanes structurally resemble the hydrocarbons called **alkanes** of formula C_nH_{2n+2} (Figure 10.19). However, there is presumably no limit on the number of carbon atoms that can join together to form alkanes, and the alkanes are much more stable than the silanes which are spontaneously flammable in air.

$$2Si_2H_6(g) + 7O_2(g) \rightarrow 4SiO_2(s) + 6H_2O(g)$$

Silicon hydrides containing multiple bonds, analogous to such hydrocarbons as acetylene, are unknown. The hydrocarbons are treated in Chapter 17.

10.25 Oxides and Oxyacids

Three oxides of carbon are well characterized: C_3O_2 (carbon suboxide); CO (carbon monoxide), and CO_2 (carbon dioxide). Carbon monoxide is formed by the combustion of carbon in a limited supply of oxygen at high temperatures (ca., 1000°C).

$$2C(s) + O_2(g) \rightarrow 2CO(g)$$

It is produced commercially in the water gas reaction (Section 7.9).

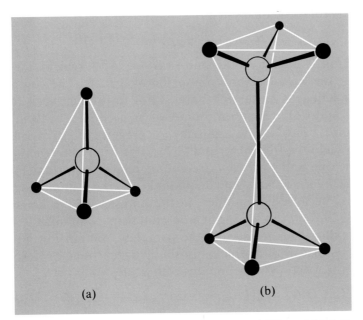

Figure 10.19   Arrangement of atoms in (a) CH₄ and SiH₄ and (b) C₂H₆ and Si₂H₆. Open circles, C or Si; black circles; H.

Carbon monoxide is isoelectronic with nitrogen (Section 10.15),

$$:C:::O:$$

with a σ bond and two π bonds joining the atoms. With certain transition metals and transition metal salts, carbon monoxide gives metal carbonyls in which the nonbonded electron pair of the carbon atom is used for bond formation. Nickel carbonyl, $Ni(CO)_4$, produced by the direct reaction of nickel metal and CO, consists of tetrahedral molecules in which a central nickel atom is bonded, through carbon, to four CO molecules. The bonding can be visualized as occurring through sp^3 hybrid orbitals of nickel. Thus the outer sublevels of nickel have the electronic configuration

In the carbonyl the electronic structure of nickel is

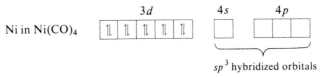

In like manner, the iron in $Fe(CO)_5$ exhibits dsp^3 hybridization (the molecule is trigonal bipyramidal), and the chromium in $Cr(CO)_6$ displays d^2sp^3 hybridization (octahedral molecules). The carbonyls are volatile, typically covalent materials and are diamagnetic.

Carbon monoxide burns in air.

$$2CO(g) + O_2(g) \rightarrow 2CO_2(g)$$

The reaction is highly exothermic ($\Delta H = -67.6$ kcal/mole) which accounts for the use of carbon monoxide as a fuel. The compound will react with halogens (in sunlight) and sulfur to produce such compounds as $COCl_2$ and COS. Carbon monoxide is used as a reducing agent in metallurgical processes; at high temperatures, it reacts with many metal oxides to yield the free metal and CO_2. The catalyzed reactions of carbon monoxide and hydrogen are commercially important for the production of hydrocarbons and methanol. Carbon monoxide is a poisonous gas because it combines, in the lungs, with the hemoglobin of the blood, thus preventing the hemoglobin from combining with oxygen.

Carbon dioxide is formed by the complete combustion of carbon or compounds of carbon (principally the hydrocarbons). It is also produced by the reaction of carbonates with acids,

$$CaCO_3(s) + 2H^+(aq) \rightarrow Ca^{2+}(aq) + CO_2(g) + H_2O$$

and by heating carbonates,

$$CaCO_3(s) \rightarrow CaO(s) + CO_2(g)$$

The molecule is linear and nonpolar; its electronic structure may be represented

$$\ddot{O}::C::\ddot{O}$$

In addition to the σ bonds connecting each oxygen to the central carbon, there are two π bond systems perpendicular to each other (Figure 10.20); interaction between these two systems produces bonds that are stronger than ordinary carbon to oxygen double bonds.

Plants convert carbon dioxide and water vapor, from air, into carbohydrates (compounds of general formula $(CH_2O)_n$). The energy for this process, called **photosynthesis,** is supplied by sunlight, and the process is catalyzed by the green-coloring matter of plants, **chlorophyll.**

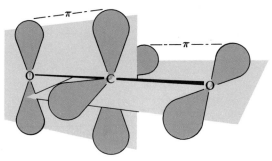

Figure 10.20   Representation of the formation of π bonds in CO_2.

Carbon dioxide is moderately soluble in water; it is the acid anhydride of carbonic acid, H_2CO_3. The acid, however, has never been obtained in the pure state, and solutions of CO_2 in water consist mainly of dissolved CO_2 molecules, less than 1% of the dissolved material being in the form of H_2CO_3 molecules. Carbonic acid is a weak, diprotic acid, and equations for the ionizations are best written

$$CO_2(aq) + H_2O \rightleftharpoons H^+(aq) + HCO_3^-(aq)$$

$$HCO_3^-(aq) \rightleftharpoons H^+(aq) + CO_3^{2-}(aq)$$

Two series of salts are formed: the normal carbonates (such as Na_2CO_3 and $CaCO_3$) and the bicarbonates (such as $NaHCO_3$ and $Ca(HCO_3)_2$. The structure of the carbonate ion may be represented as a resonance hybrid

In the carbonate ion, which is triangular planar, each atom has a p electron not involved in the formation of the σ bonds that join the atoms; these p electrons may be thought of as forming a multicenter π bonding system so that the net effect is a $1\frac{1}{3}$ bond between each atom as depicted by the resonance structures.

Sodium carbonate is an important industrial chemical, and over 90% of the compound is produced commercially by the **Solvay process.** Ammonia and carbon dioxide, under pressure, are passed into a saturated solution of sodium chloride. The ammonia and carbon dioxide react:

$$NH_3(g) + CO_2(g) + H_2O \rightleftharpoons NH_4^+(aq) + HCO_3^-(aq)$$

Sodium bicarbonate precipitates from the solution because of the high concentration of sodium ion, and ammonium chloride is left behind.

$$Na^+(aq) + HCO_3^-(aq) \rightarrow NaHCO_3(s)$$

The sodium bicarbonate is removed by filtration and washed; heating decomposes it into the normal carbonate.

$$2NaHCO_3(s) \rightarrow Na_2CO_3(s) + CO_2(g) + H_2O(g)$$

The ammonia is recovered, for reuse, from the mother liquor by heating this solution with quicklime, CaO.

$$2NH_4^+(aq) + CaO(s) \rightarrow 2NH_3(g) + Ca^{2+}(aq) + H_2O$$

The calcium oxide is obtained from limestone, $CaCO_3$, by heating; the CO_2 produced as a by-product of the preparation of CaO, as well as that produced by heating $NaHCO_3$, is used in the initial step of the process.

Although it is postulated that silicon monoxide exists in the vapor state, the only well-characterized oxide of silicon is SiO_2. In contrast to the oxides of carbon, which are volatile molecular species, held together by weak van der Waals forces in the solid state, SiO_2 forms very stable, nonvolatile, three-dimensional network crystals (melting point, $\sim 1700°C$). One of the three crystal modifications of SiO_2 has a lattice that may be considered to be derived from the diamond lattice with silicon atoms replacing carbon atoms and an oxygen atom midway between each pair of silicon atoms.

Of all the bonds that silicon forms, the Si—O bond has a larger bond energy than any other with the exception of the Si—F bond. It is not surprising that the chemistry of silicon is dominated by compounds containing the Si—O linkage, and that SiO_2 is a chemically stable substance. Silicon dioxide is the product of the reaction of the elements; it is produced by reaction of the spontaneously flammable silicon hydrides with air, and hydrous SiO_2 is the product of the hydrolysis of many silicon compounds. Silicon dioxide occurs in several forms in nature; among them are sand, flint, agate, jasper, onyx, and quartz.

Silicon dioxide is an acidic oxide; however, no acids of silicon have ever been isolated. The oxide does not react directly with water, and acidification of a water solution of a soluble silicate yields only hydrous SiO_2. Silicates may be made by heating metal oxides, or metal carbonates, with SiO_2. Certain silicates of the I A metals (with a molar ratio of silicon dioxide to metal oxide of not more than 2 to 1) are water soluble.

A large number of silicates, of various types, occur in nature. The basic structure of all silicates is a tetrahedral SiO_4 unit (Figure 10.21). The simple ion SiO_4^{4-} occurs in certain minerals, for example, zircon ($ZrSiO_4$). More complicated ions are known in which two or more SiO_4 tetrahedra are joined through common oxygen atoms. In the simple ion SiO_4^{4-}, each oxygen completes its octet by accepting an electron; when tetrahedra are joined, the bridge oxygens complete their octets exclusively through covalent bond formation with two silicon atoms. Thus the ion containing two tetrahedral units has the formula $Si_2O_7^{6-}$; the mineral thortveitite ($Sc_2Si_2O_7$) contains this ion. Cyclic silicate ions are known in which two oxygen atoms of each SiO_4 unit act as bridge atoms; bentonite ($BaTiSi_3O_9$) and beryl ($Be_3Al_2Si_6O_{18}$) contain such ions.

The sharing of two oxygen atoms per SiO_4 tetrahedron can lead to polymeric anion chains of the type $(SiO_3^{2-})_n$ found in the pyroxenes (e.g., spodumene, $LiAl(SiO_3)_2$) and the double-chain type $(Si_4O_{11}^{6-})_n$ found in the amphiboles (e.g., the asbestos minerals). These anion chains extend throughout the crystal, and consequently, minerals of these types have a fibrous nature.

If three oxygen atoms of each SiO_4 tetrahedron are used as bridge atoms, a sheetlike anion results. The anion $(Si_2O_5^{2-})_n$ occurs in talc

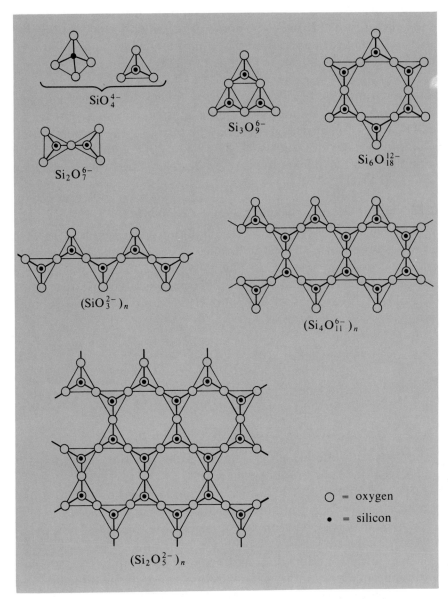

Figure 10.21 *Schematic representation of the arrangement of atoms in the silicate ions.*

$(Mg_3(Si_2O_5)(OH)_2)$, and the layer structure accounts for the slippery feel of this material. Occasionally, aluminum atoms take the places of some of the silicon atoms in certain anions. The hypothetical AlO_4 tetrahedra would have a 5− charge, however, since aluminum has one less proton in the nucleus than silicon; consequently, such substitutions increase the negative charge on the anion. Muscovite $(KAl_3Si_3O_{10}(OH)_2)$ contains a sheetlike aluminosilicate anion with one-fourth of the silicon atoms of the $(Si_2O_5^{2-})_n$ structure replaced by aluminum atoms.

If all four oxygen atoms of each SiO_4 tetrahedron are used as bridge atoms, SiO_2 results. However, if some of the silicon atoms of this three-dimensional network are replaced by aluminum atoms, an anion results. Framework aluminosilicates, such as the feldspars and the zeolites, are of this type.

Glass is a mixture of silicates made by fusing SiO_2 with metal oxides and carbonates. Common soda-lime glass is made from Na_2CO_3, $CaCO_3$, and SiO_2. Special glasses may be made by the addition of other acidic and basic oxides (such as Al_2O_3, B_2O_3, PbO, and K_2O). Cement is a complex aluminosilicate mixture made from limestone ($CaCO_3$) and clay ($H_4Al_2Si_2O_9$).

10.26   Sulfur Compounds and Halogen Compounds

Carbon disulfide, CS_2, is a volatile liquid prepared by heating carbon and sulfur together in an electric furnace. The electronic structure of the molecule is analogous to CO_2. Silicon disulfide, SiS_2, prepared by the reaction of the elements at high temperatures, is a colorless, crystalline material that hydrolyzes to SiO_2 and H_2S. Solid SiS_2 has a chainlike structure

Carbon tetrachloride is made by heating chlorine with carbon disulfide

$$CS_2(g) + 3Cl_2(g) \rightarrow CCl_4(g) + S_2Cl_2(g)$$

Carbon tetrachloride, which is a liquid under ordinary conditions, is a good solvent for many nonpolar materials.

Carbon tetrafluoride, CF_4, which may be obtained by the fluorination of almost any carbon-containing compound is a very stable gas. The mixed halide CCl_2F_2, "Freon," is a very stable, odorless, nontoxic gas used as a refrigerant.

Carbon tetrabromide, CBr_4, and carbon tetraiodide, CI_4, are solids; they are thermally unstable, presumably because of the difficulty of carbon in accommodating four large atoms around itself.

The silicon tetrahalides, SiX_4, are formed by the reactions of the elements; SiF_4 is a gas; $SiCl_4$ and $SiBr_4$ are liquids; and SiI_4 is a solid. Unlike the tetrahalides of carbon, the silicon tetrahalides readily hydrolyze

$$SiX_4 + (n + 2)H_2O \rightarrow SiO_2 \cdot nH_2O(s) + 4H^+(aq) + 4X^-(aq)$$

The difference in chemical reactivity of the tetrahalides of carbon and silicon is attributed to the availability of unoccupied d orbitals in silicon which make it possible for a water molecule to attach itself and thus facilitate hydrolysis.

With SiF_4, a secondary reaction follows the one previously given. The hydrofluoric acid formed in the initial reaction reacts with SiF_4 to form fluosilicic acid, a strong acid.

$$SiF_4(g) + 2HF(aq) \rightarrow 2H^+(aq) + SiF_6^{2-}(aq)$$

The SiF_6^{2-} ion is octahedral and uses sp^3d^2 hybrid bonding orbitals of silicon.

Catenated halides of carbon and silicon are known (e.g., C_2Cl_6 and Si_2Cl_6).

10.27 Carbon-Nitrogen Compounds

There are many compounds in which carbon is bonded to nitrogen. Sodium cyanide is commercially prepared by the reaction of sodium amide with carbon at red heat.

$$NaNH_2(l) + C(s) \rightarrow NaCN(l) + H_2(g)$$

The cyanide ion is isoelectronic with nitrogen and carbon monoxide (Section 10.15)

$$[:C:::N:]^-$$

and it has a strong tendency to form covalent complexes with metal cations (such as $Ag(CN)_2^-$, $Cd(CN)_4^{2-}$, $Ni(CN)_4^{2-}$, $Hg(CN)_4^{2-}$, $Fe(CN)_6^{4-}$, $Fe(CN)_6^{3-}$, and $Cr(CN)_6^{3-}$).

Treatment of a cyanide with dilute sulfuric acid produces hydrogen cyanide, HCN. The compound is a low-boiling liquid (boiling point, 26.5°C) and is readily soluble in water to produce solutions of hydrocyanic acid, a weak acid. Hydrogen cyanide and the cyanides are extremely poisonous.

The thermal decomposition of certain heavy metal cyanides (such as AgCN, $Hg(CN)_2$, and AuCN) yields the metal and cyanogen, C_2N_2, or $(CN)_2$. The molecule is linear,

$$:N:::C:C:::N:$$

This very poisonous, colorless gas is sometimes called a pseudohalogen because it resembles the halogens in its chemical reactions. For example,

$$Cl_2(g) + 2OH^-(aq) \rightarrow Cl^-(aq) + OCl^-(aq) + H_2O$$
$$(CN)_2(g) + 2OH^-(aq) \rightarrow CN^-(aq) + OCN^-(aq) + H_2O$$

Cyanides resemble chlorides in their water solubility.

The ion OCN^-, produced by the disproportionation reaction of cyanogen in alkaline solution, is the cyanate ion; the corresponding acid, cyanic acid (HOCN), is not stable. An analogous ion, the thiocyanate ion, SCN^-, is prepared by fusing I A cyanides with sulfur.

BORON

Of the group III A elements—boron, aluminum, gallium, indium, and thallium—boron alone is a nonmetal.

10.28   Group Properties

The electronic configurations of the elements are listed in Table 10.25, and properties of the elements appear in Table 10.26. Boron is a much smaller atom than the others of the group, which accounts for the sharp distinction in properties between the nonmetallic boron and the other, metallic, group members. The atomic sizes of Ga, In, and Tl are influenced by the electronic inner-building of elements immediately preceding them in the periodic classification (particularly in the case of Tl which follows the lanthanides); hence, atomic radius does not rapidly and regularly increase with increasing atomic number for these elements. The comparatively small sizes of the elements account for the relatively high ionization potentials which do not decline in the expected manner as the group is descended.

TABLE 10.25.
ELECTRONIC CONFIGURATIONS OF THE GROUP III A ELEMENTS.

Element	Z	1s	2s	2p	3s	3p	3d	4s	4p	4d	4f	5s	5p	5d	6s	6p
B	5	2	2	1												
Al	13	2	2	6	2	1										
Ga	31	2	2	6	2	6	10	2	1							
In	49	2	2	6	2	6	10	2	6	10		2	1			
Tl	81	2	2	6	2	6	10	2	6	10	14	2	6	10	2	1

TABLE 10.26.
SOME PROPERTIES OF THE GROUP III A ELEMENTS.

	Boron	Aluminum	Gallium	Indium	Thallium
melting point (°C)	2300	659	30	155	304
boiling point (°C)	2550	2500	2070	2100	1457
atomic radius (Å)	0.80	1.25	1.25	1.50	1.55
ionic radius, M^{+3} (Å)	0.20	0.52	0.62	0.81	0.95
ionization potential (ev)					
first	8.3	6.0	6.0	5.8	6.1
second	25.1	18.8	20.4	18.8	20.3
third	37.9	28.4	30.6	27.9	29.7
heat of hydration,					
M^{3+} (kcal/mole)	—	−1121	−1124	−994	−984
electrode potential, $E°$,					
(M^{3+}/M) (v)	—	−1.67	−0.52	−0.34	+0.72

None of the elements has the slightest tendency to form simple anions. Rather, as would seem reasonable from the electronic configurations of the elements, the most important oxidation state is 3+. This relatively high charge coupled with comparatively small ionic radii leads to species with significant polarizing abilities.

Hence, the compounds of the elements in the 3+ state are predominantly covalent, which also follows from the comparatively high values of the first three ionization potentials of the elements. With the exception of boron, which is exculsively nonmetallic in its chemistry, the III A elements exist as 3+ ions in water solution; these ions are strongly hydrated, however, and the heats of hydration are high.

The electrode potentials are indicative of a higher order of metallic reactivity than the ionization potentials of the gaseous ions might lead one to expect. This is because of the high heats of hydration that result from the high charge concentration of the small ions. The high charge density also accounts for the marked tendency of the elements to form complex ions.

The oxides and hydroxides (or hydrous oxides) exhibit the usual trend in decreasing acidic character with increasing atomic number. Thus B_2O_3 and $B(OH)_3$ (or H_3BO_3) are acidic; the compounds of aluminum and gallium are amphoteric; and In_2O_3 and Tl_2O_3 have no acidic character at all.

The $ns^2 np^1$ configuration of the valence level would lead one to anticipate the existence of 1+, inert-pair ions for the larger members of the group. This is indeed the case for thallium. The 1+ state of this element is considerably more stable than the 3+ state; TlOH is a strong electrolyte. Compounds of indium and gallium in which these elements are in a 1+ state are known, but this state is less important, and less stable, than the 3+ state.

Boron has a slight tendency for catenation (in, e.g., B_2Cl_4 the atoms of which are arranged Cl_2BBCl_2), but no other member of the family displays this characteristic.

In some instances, similarities exist between elements that are not members of the same group of the periodic table but adjoin each other diagonally. Such a diagonal relationship exists between boron and silicon.

B	C
Al	Si

Indeed, in some ways, boron resembles silicon more than it resembles aluminum. Boron and silicon form volatile, covalent hydrides that are spontaneously flammable in air; the halides of both elements are easily, and extensively, hydrolyzed. Both B_2O_3 and SiO_2 are acidic and are the precursors of complex, and in some instances structurally similar, anions; with metallic oxides, the oxides of boron and silicon form glasses. Neither boron nor silicon will liberate hydrogen from acids, but these elements react with alkalies to produce hydrogen gas and borates or silicates.

10.29   The Element

Boron ($3 \times 10^{-4}\%$ of the earth's crust) does not occur free in nature; the principal ores of boron are borates such as kernite ($Na_2B_4O_7 \cdot 4H_2O$), borax ($Na_2B_4O_7 \cdot 10H_2O$), colemanite ($Ca_2B_6O_{11} \cdot 5H_2O$), and ulexite ($NaCaB_5O_9 \cdot 8H_2O$).

A somewhat impure, dark-brown, amorphous form of the element is prepared by heating boric oxide, B_2O_3, with powdered magnesium. Pure, crystalline boron may be obtained by reducing BBr_3 by hydrogen on a hot tungsten filament (approximately 1500°C).

$$2BBr_3(g) + 3H_2(g) \rightarrow 2B(s) + 6HBr(g)$$

The crystals, which condense on the filament, are black with a metallic luster.

At least four types of boron crystals are believed to exist; in each, boron atoms are arranged in groups of 12 atoms in regular icosohedra (solid figures with 20, equivalent, triangular faces). These icosohedra (Figure 10.22) are linked together in different ways to form the various crystalline modifications. Each boron atom is bonded to five atoms of its icosohedron and to one atom from another B_{12} unit, thus making a total of six linkages per atom. Yet, boron has only three valence electrons and only four available orbitals in its valence level.

In metallic crystals, there are too few valence electrons to form covalent bonds between neighboring metal atoms of the crystal lattice; the electrons belong to the crystal as a whole and serve to bind many nuclei together. However, boron is a nonmetal, and the properties of crystalline boron (low electrical conductivity, extreme hardness, brittleness, and high melting point) are more typical of a covalent, giant-molecule type of crystal than a metallic crystal.

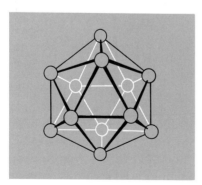

Figure 10.22   Arrangement of atoms in a B_{12} icosohedron.

The bonding in elementary boron has been described in terms of a valence-bond approach in which each boron atom forms three electron-pair bonds that resonate between six positions. Thus the fact that boron has three valence electrons is reconciled with the fact that each boron forms six linkages; the result is a structure that may be described as containing half bonds.

A more modern interpretation is based on multicenter molecular orbitals in which an electron pair bonds more atoms than the customary two. Three-center bonds between two boron atoms and a hydrogen atom in the boron hydrides (the boranes) are well established (Section 10.30). Each of the atoms of the bond supplies an orbital toward the formation of a three-center bond that holds all three atoms together. The bonding orbital, which is occupied by two electrons, may be represented as B---H---B or B $\overset{H}{\frown}$ B. In the higher boranes, two types of three-center bonds between boron atoms are postulated: an open bond, B $\overset{B}{\frown}$ B, or a closed bond, $_B\overset{B}{\triangle}_B$. Multicenter bonds of higher order are also postulated; for example, the boron framework of B_5H_9 (a pyramidal structure) is assumed to be held together by a five-center bond involving all of the boron atoms of the structure along with two three-center bonds of the open type that join the boron atom of the apex with diagonal boron atoms of the base.

It is assumed that in elementary boron, a B_{12} icosohedron is held together by multicenter bonding; in addition, each B_{12} unit has 12 radial bonding orbitals that are used in bonding neighboring icosohedra together. Multicenter bonding may be considered to be intermediate in character between the localized bonding of such substances as diamond and the completely delocalized bonding found in metals.

10.30 Compounds of Boron

At very high temperatures (about 2000°C) boron reacts with many metals to form borides. These substances are very hard, are chemically stable, and have metallic conductivity. In the crystals of some metallic borides, the boron atoms are interstitial; in others, chains, octahedra, or layers of boron atoms are present. Magnesium boride, MgB_2, unlike the other borides, is readily hydrolyzed to produce a mixture of boron hydrides.

Boron reacts with ammonia or nitrogen at elevated temperatures to produce boron nitride, BN. This material is isoelectronic with carbon and has a crystal structure similar to graphite but with alternating boron and nitrogen atoms. At very high temperatures and pressures, this modification of BN is converted to another form that has a diamond-type lattice and which is harder than diamond.

The halides of boron may be prepared by the reactions of the elements at elevated temperatures; BF_3 and BCl_3 are gases; BBr_3 is a liquid; and BI_3 is a solid. The molecules of the halides are triangular planar; presumably, sp^2 hybrid orbitals of boron are used for bonding.

$$:\overset{\displaystyle ..}{\underset{\displaystyle ..}{X}}:$$
$$:X:\overset{..}{B}:X:$$

Since the boron atom does not have an octet of electrons, these molecules react as electron acceptors (Lewis acids, Section 13.7).

$$[:\overset{..}{\underset{..}{F}}:]^- + \begin{matrix} :\overset{..}{F}\cdot \\ \overset{..}{B}:\overset{..}{F}: \\ :\overset{..}{F}\cdot \end{matrix} \rightarrow \left[\begin{matrix} :\overset{..}{F}:\\ :\overset{..}{F}:\overset{..}{B}:\overset{..}{F}: \\ :\overset{..}{F}: \end{matrix} \right]^-$$

$$NH_3 + BF_3 \rightarrow H_3N:BF_3$$
$$H_2O + BF_3 \rightarrow H_2O:BF_3$$

The fluoborate ion, BF_4^-, is tetrahedral, and is bonded by sp^3 hybrid bonds.

Many borates occur in nature; some may be prepared by fusion of metallic oxides with B_2O_3 or boric acid, and hydrated borates may be obtained by crystallization of the solution resulting from the neutralization of boric acid with aqueous alkali. The borate anions may be considered to be built up from triangular BO_3 units, with or without BO_4 tetrahedra, by the sharing of oxygen atoms between units in much the same way as the silicates are constructed. Examples are illustrated in Figure 10.23.

Two BO_3 triangles with an oxygen atom in common form the $B_2O_5^{4-}$ ion (found in $Co_2B_2O_5$). By sharing two oxygen atoms per BO_3 unit, a cyclic structure (in $K_3B_3O_6$) or a polymeric chain structure (in CaB_2O_4) results.

The anions exclusively formed from BO_3 triangles are not stable in water and are readily hydrated into forms containing one or more BO_4 tetrahedra. For example, the hydrated anion $B_4O_5(OH)_4^{2-}$ is composed of two tetrahedra and two triangles (Figure 10.23); it exists in borax, $Na_2B_4O_5(OH)_4 \cdot 8H_2O$ (commonly written as $Na_2B_4O_7 \cdot 10H_2O$) and results from the neutralization of boric acid by NaOH in aqueous solution.

The acidification of an aqueous solution of any borate precipitates orthoboric acid (or merely boric acid), $B(OH)_3$, as soft, white crystals. This acid, which may also be prepared by the complete hydration of B_2O_3, has a layer-type crystal lattice in which there is extensive hydrogen bonding between $B(OH)_3$ molecules (Figure 10.24). The crystal structure of the material accounts for its cleavage into sheets and its slippery feel.

Boric acid is a very weak, *monobasic* acid in solution. Its ionization

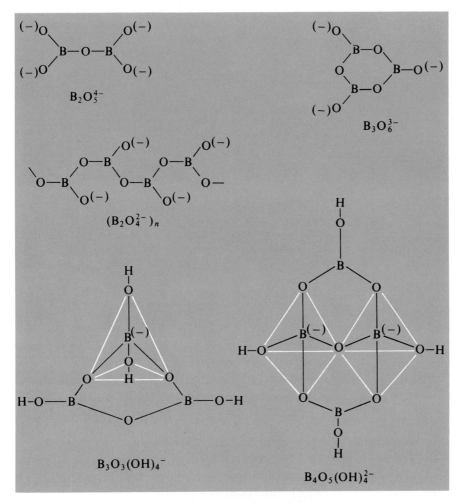

Figure 10.23   *Arrangement of atoms in borate ions.*

in fairly dilute solution may be represented as

$$B(OH)_3(aq) + H_2O \rightleftharpoons H^+(aq) + B(OH)_4^-(aq)$$

or

$$(H_2O)B(OH)_3(aq) \rightleftharpoons H^+(aq) + B(OH)_4^-(aq)$$

The $B(OH)_4^-$ ion is tetrahedral. In more concentrated solutions, polymeric anions, such as $B_3O_3(OH)_4^-$, exist (Figure 10.23).

When boric acid is heated to about 175°C, metaboric acid, HBO_2, results. The meta- acid reverts to the more highly hydrated ortho- form in water. Although salts of many hypothetical boric acids are known, these are the only two acids that exist in the pure condition.

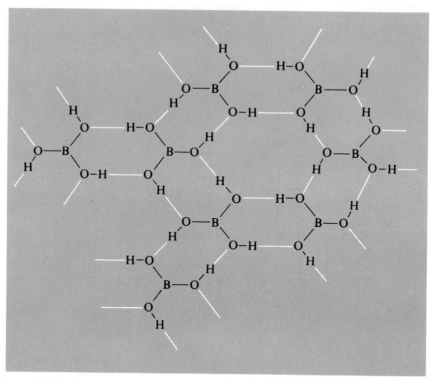

Figure 10.24   *Arrangement of atoms in a layer of H_3BO_3 crystal (white bonds represent hydrogen bonds).*

Metaboric acid may be dehydrated, by heating, into boric oxide, B_2O_3. The oxide may also be prepared by heating boron in air. Crystals of B_2O_3 consist of interconnected spiral chains of BO_4 tetrahedra. The material, however, is usually obtained as a glass.

Boron forms two series of hydrides: B_nH_{n+4}, where $n = 2, 5, 6$, and 10 and B_nH_{n+6}, where $n = 4, 5, 9$, and 10. Other compounds have been reported but are not well characterized. A boron hydride of formula BH_3 does not exist; instead the simplest hydride known is diborane, B_2H_6.

Diborane, which is a gas under ordinary conditions, may be prepared by the reaction of BF_3 and lithium hydride, in ether.

$$6LiH + 8BF_3 \rightarrow 6LiBF_4 + B_2H_6$$

A mixture of higher boranes is obtained by heating diborane.

The compounds of formula B_nH_{n+4} are thermally more stable (with regard to decomposition to the elements) than the second group, B_nH_{n+6}. The compounds B_2H_6, B_5H_9, and B_5H_{11} are spontaneously flammable in air, and all of the boranes hydrolyze, at various rates, to yield boric acid and hydrogen.

The boranes show promise as rocket and jet fuels. They have high heats of combustion (-482 kcal/mole for B_2H_6), and since they have low molecular weights, the energy obtainable per gram of fuel is very high.

The molecular structure of diborane is shown in Figure 10.25. In the illustration, two of the hydrogen atoms (bridge hydrogens) are apparently bonded to both boron atoms. Each of these bridge hydrogens par-

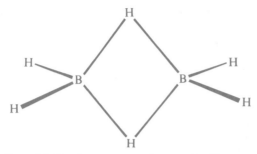

Figure 10.25   Arrangement of atoms in diborane, B_2H_6.

ticipates in a three-center B---H---B bond formed from a single electron pair. These two B---H---B bonds are coplanar and at right angles with the remainder of the molecule.

The electronic structure of diborane may be represented

$$\text{H}\, \overset{\cdot}{}\qquad \text{H}\, \overset{\cdot}{}\quad \overset{\cdot}{}\text{H}$$
$$\overset{\cdot}{}\,\text{B}\,\overset{\cdot}{}\qquad \overset{\cdot}{}\,\text{B}\,\overset{\cdot}{}$$
$$\text{H}\, \overset{\cdot}{}\qquad \text{H}\qquad \overset{\cdot}{}\text{H}$$

Two hydrogen atoms (terminal hydrogens) are bonded by ordinary electron-pair bonds to each boron atom, and each boron atom, therefore, has only one electron left. These two electrons and the two electrons contributed by the bridge hydrogens are used to form the two electron pairs of the three-center bridge bonds. The bond distance between a boron atom and a terminal hydrogen is shorter than the distance between a boron atom and a bridge hydrogen, indicating a stronger bond in the former case.

The structures of the higher boranes involve not only three-center hydrogen bonds but also multicenter bonds between boron atoms. Several of the higher boranes have skeletons of boron atoms that are fragments of the B_{12} icosohedron found in crystalline boron.

Boron forms a series of borohydride ions. The most important one is BH_4^-, a tetrahedral ion that may be prepared by the reaction of lithium hydride and B_2H_6 in ether.

$$2LiH + B_2H_6 \rightarrow 2LiBH_4$$

Lithium borohydride, and the alkali borohydrides in general, are ionic materials that are important reducing agents. Other borohydrides, such as $B_3H_8^-$, $B_{10}H_{13}^-$, and $B_{12}H_{12}^{2-}$ are known.

SOME SUGGESTED READINGS

Cooper, D. G., *The Periodic Table*, Washington, D.C., Butterworth, 1964 (paper).

Cotton, F. A., and Wilkinson, G., *Advanced Inorganic Chemistry*, 2nd ed., New York, Wiley, 1966.

Emeleus, H. J., and Anderson, J. S., *Modern Aspects of Inorganic Chemistry*, 3rd ed., Princeton, N.J., Van Nostrant, 1960.

Heslop, R. B., and Robinson, P. L., *Inorganic Chemistry*, New York, Elsevier, 1963.

Jolly, W. L., *The Chemistry of the Non Metals*, Englewood Cliffs, N.J., Prentice-Hall, 1966 (paper).

Kleinberg, J., Argersinger, W. J., Jr., and Griswold, E., *Inorganic Chemistry*, Boston, Heath, 1960.

Latimer, W., *Reference Book in Inorganic Chemistry*, 3rd ed., New York, Macmillan, 1964 (paper).

Mellor, J. W., and Parkes, G. D., *Modern Inorganic Chemistry*, 5th ed., New York, Wiley, 1961.

Moeller, T., *Inorganic Chemistry*, New York, Wiley, 1952.

Rich, R. L., *Periodic Correlations*, New York, Benjamin, 1965 (paper).

Sanderson, R. T., *Inorganic Chemistry*, New York, Reinhold, 1967.

Sherwin, E., and Weston, G. J., *Chemistry of the Non-Metallic Elements*, New York, Pergamon, 1966 (paper).

Weeks, M. E., and Leicester, H. M., *Discovery of the Elements*, 6th ed., Easton, Penna., Chemical Education Publishing Co., 1956.

PROBLEMS

10.1   List some properties that distinguish nonmetals from metals.

10.2   Write a chemical equation for the reaction of each of the following with water: (a) XeF_2 (Xe, O_2, and HF produced), (b) XeF_4 (XeO_3 and Xe produced), (c) XeF_6 ($XeOF_4$ produced), (d) XeF_6 (XeO_3 produced).

10.3   Use the ion-electron method to write equations for the following; (a) The oxidation of Cr^{3+} to $Cr_2O_7^{2-}$ by $XeO_3(s)$ in water solution. Xenon trioxide is a strong oxidizing agent and the product of its reduction is Xe(g). (b) The dissolution of $XeO_3(s)$ in NaOH solution. Xenon gas is evolved, and sodium perxenate, $Na_4XeO_6 \cdot 8H_2O$, precipitates. (c) The oxidation of Mn^{2+} to MnO_4^- by the perxenate ion, XeO_6^{4-}, in acid solution.

10.4   What is the difference between iodimetry and iodometry? What type of substance may be determined by each procedure?

10.5   A 1.20 g sample of a copper ore is dissolved in concentrated nitric acid. The resulting solution is diluted and treated to prevent the interference of iron, arsenic, and antimony ions. An excess of KI is added, and the following reaction occurs.

$$2Cu^{2+} + 4I^- \longrightarrow 2CuI + I_2$$

The liberated iodine is titrated with $0.120N$ $Na_2S_2O_3$; 32.5 ml of the thiosulfate solution is required. (a) What is the percentage of copper in the ore? (b) What weight of cuprous iodide is precipitated in the early part of the determination?

10.6 Show, by means of equations, how each of the following can be prepared: (a) F_2 from CaF_2, (b) Cl_2 from NaCl, (c) Br_2 from sea water, (d) HCl from NaCl, (e) HBr from NaBr.

10.7 Write equations for the electrolysis of (a) dry, molten NaCl, (b) cold NaCl solution, (c) cold NaCl solution with the electrolyte stirred, (d) hot, concentrated NaCl solution with the electrolyte stirred, (e) cold $NaClO_3$ solution.

10.8 Compare the disulfide ion, S_2^{2-}, to the peroxide ion, O_2^{2-}, with respect to structure and oxidizing power. What reasons can you give for the difference?

10.9 Write equations for the preparation of (a) H_2S, (b) H_2SO_3, (c) $Na_2S_2O_3$, (d) $NaHSO_4$, (e) Na_2TeO_3.

10.10 Discuss the uses of H_2SO_4 (a) as a strong acid, (b) as an oxidizing agent, (c) as a high-boiling, nonvolatile acid, and (d) as a dehydrating agent.

10.11 Draw sketches that show the geometry of (a) $H_2S_2O_7$, (b) $H_2S_2O_8$, (c) $S_2O_3^{2-}$, (d) $S_4O_6^{2-}$.

10.12 Describe the changes in sulfur that occur as the temperature is increased.

10.13 Discuss the comparative reactivities, solubilities, and electrical conductivities of the three allotropic forms of phosphorus in terms of molecular structure.

10.14 Discuss how the properties of the elements of group VA and their compounds change with increasing atomic number.

10.15 What are the meanings of the prefixes: pyro-, meta-, ortho-, hypo-, and per- when they are used in naming acids?

10.16 Write equations for the preparations of all of the acids that may be obtained by the hydrolysis of P_4O_{10}.

10.17 Write all of the equations that you can for the reactions of elementary nitrogen.

10.18 State the products of the thermal decomposition of each of the following: (a) NH_4NO_2, (b) NH_4NO_3, (c) $Pb(NO_3)_2$, (d) $NaNO_3$, (e) NaN_3.

10.19 Write redox equations for (a) the preparation of hydrazine from the reaction of ammonia with sodium hypochlorite, (b) the preparation of nitrogen trifluoride by the electrolysis of ammonium fluoride in anhydrous hydrogen fluoride.

10.20 Draw electronic structures for orthophosphoric, phosphorous, and hypophosphorous acids. Tell how these structures explain the number of H^+ (aq) dissociated per mole when each of these compounds is dissolved in water.

10.21 Write equations for the reactions of the following with water: (a) Cl_2,

(b) Ca_3P_2, (c) NO_2, (d) $H_2S_2O_7$, (e) AlN, (f) CaNCN, (g) PCl_5, (h) As_4O_6, (i) Al_4C_3, (j) CaC_2, (k) $SiCl_4$, (l) BF_3.

10.22 Explain the cause of the difference in reactivity toward water of CF_4 and SiF_4.

10.23 Describe the structures of diamond and graphite. What other substances have structures similar to these?

10.24 Explain why it is impossible to prepare $SiCl_6^{2-}$ from $SiCl_4$ whereas SiF_6^{2-} may be obtained from SiF_4.

10.25 Write an equation to illustrate a laboratory test for each of the following: (a) F^-, (b) Cl^-, (c) I^-, (d) IO_3^-, (e) S^{2-}, (f) SO_3^{2-}, (g) SO_4^{2-}, (h) $S_2O_3^{2-}$, (i) NH_4^+, (j) As, (k) CO_3^{2-}.

10.26 Write an equation for the reaction that occurs when each of the following is heated: (a) $NaHCO_3$, (b) Na_2CO_3, (c) SiO_2 and C, (d) SiO_2 and $CaCO_3$, (e) AgCN, (f) $NaNH_2$ and C, (g) $B(OH)_3$, (h) HBO_2.

10.27 Compare the chemistry of silicon and boron.

11

Elements of Chemical Thermodynamics

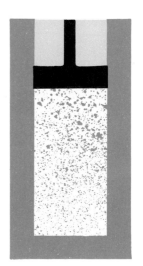

We have repeatedly referred to the energy effects accompanying chemical and physical changes. **Thermodynamics** is the study of these energy effects; in particular, it summarizes the relationship between heat, work, and other forms of energy that are involved in all types of change. The laws of thermodynamics, which are based on experience, enable predictions to be made as to whether particular chemical or physical transformations are possible.

11.1 Heat and Work

Thermodynamics, as a system of thought, had its origins in investigations of the equivalence of mechanical work and heat. The first quantitative experiments relating heat and work are ascribed to Count Rumford, originally Benjamin Thompson of Massachusetts, who was commissioned by the King of Bavaria to supervise the boring of cannon. In 1798, Rumford suggested that the large amount of heat evolved in the boring operation is a result of the work expended, and he estimated the amount of heat produced by a given quantity of work. Prior to this time, heat and work were regarded as separate and unrelated quantities.

Subsequently, further experiments on the equivalence of heat and work were reported by Humphry Davy, Nicholas Sadi Carnot and other scientists. The concept was reinforced by the realization of the connection between heat and the motion of bodies, particularly after the introduction and acceptance of the atomic-molecular theory. The careful and convincing work of James Joule, in the years from 1840 to 1849, firmly established the principle and provided a quantitative value for the mechanical equivalent of heat.

Joule studied the conversion of work into heat in many ways. He experimented by using the work done by a falling weight to turn a paddle wheel immersed in a container of water, and he determined the heat produced by measuring the increase in the temperature of the water. In a series of similar experiments, he used different weights and different quantities of water as well as mercury in place of the water. Joule also studied the heating effects of electric currents and the conversion of work into heat by the compression of gases. In all of his experiments, Joule found that a quantitative relationship exists between work done and heat produced. In modern terms, this is

$$4.1840 \text{ joules} = 1 \text{ cal}$$

One joule, the unit of work, is 10^7 ergs, and 1 erg is the work done by 1 dyne (or 1 g cm/sec^2) acting through 1 cm. The calorie, which was originally defined as the amount of heat required to raise the temperature of 1 g of water from 14.5° to 15.5°C, is now defined by its joule equivalent.*

It should be noted that the reverse process from that studied by Joule, the conversion of heat into work, poses special problems that are treated by the second law of thermodynamics (Section 11.7); nevertheless, for that quantity of heat converted into work, as well as for any quantity of work converted into heat, the preceding relationship holds. It is an important one since, in solving problems, the chemist is frequently required to convert measurements from one scale to the other.

11.2   First Law of Thermodynamics

The concept of the conservation of mechanical energy for changes in which appreciable heat effects do not arise was accepted long before the time of Joule. For example, it was understood that the increase in kinetic energy of a body falling in a vacuum is exactly equivalent to the decrease in potential energy at any given time. The recognition that both heat and work are manifestations of a larger classification called energy led to an extension of this principle. In 1847, Hermann von Helmholtz stated the law of conservation of energy: energy can be converted from one form into another, but it can neither be created nor destroyed; this may be regarded as a statement of the **first law of thermodynamics.**

In applying thermodynamic concepts, we frequently confine our attention to the changes that occur within definite boundaries. That portion of the universe included within these boundaries is called a **system;** the remainder of the universe is called the **surroundings.** If there is no ex-

---

*It is necessary to specify the temperature interval in the definition of the calorie because the density, and hence the specific heat, of water changes with changes in temperature. The 15° calorie is actually equal to approximately 4.1855 joules. However, since it is possible to make electrical measurements with greater precision than calorimetric measurements, the joule (which is a volt coulomb) is a better primary standard for heat measurements than is the calorie. Modern practice, therefore, defines the calorie in terms of the joule equivalent given above, and such a calorie is called a defined calorie.

change of mass between a system and its surroundings, the system is spoken of as a **closed system.** If, in addition, energy is not exchanged, the system is referred to as an **isolated system.** Work done on a system need not always result in an increase in the temperature of the system or the conversion of work into heat. For example, the charging of a storage battery by an automobile engine results in an increase of the "chemical energy" of the battery; doing work on (or adding heat to) a sample of ice at 0°C could result in melting a part of the ice with no increase in the temperature of the system. The first law introduces the concept of **internal energy,** E, of a system.

According to the first law of thermodynamics, the internal energy of an isolated system is constant. It is impossible to determine the exact internal energy of any system, nor is it particularly desirable to attempt such a hopeless task since we are concerned only with the effects brought about by *changes* in internal energy. We may say, however, that the internal energy of a system includes the kinetic and potential energies of all of its parts.

We include in potential energy such things as the attractions and repulsions between atoms, molecules, ions, and subatomic particles. For example, the lattice energies of crystalline materials, the ionization energies of atoms, the bond energies of molecules, and van der Waals attractions. It is the rearrangements of these atoms, molecules, ions, and subatomic particles that give rise to the energy effects observed in chemical reactions. If the first law is to hold for nuclear transformations (Section 18.5), the energy equivalent of the mass of the system must be included in our tally of the total internal energy of the system.

The internal energy of a system also includes the kinetic energies of its parts. Figure 11.1 illustrates the translational, rotational, and vibrational motions of gas molecules; the addition of energy to a gaseous system increases the kinetic energies of the gas molecules.

It is best, then, not to attempt to list all of the various contributions to the internal energy of a system but, rather, to leave the definition of internal energy open. If electromagnetic effects or the energy of a gravitational field are of interest, E may be said to include energy contributions from these.

The internal energy of a system depends only upon the physical state of the system and not upon how the system arrived at that state; internal energy, E, is therefore called a **state function.** Consider a closed system passing from state A to state B. From the first law, the internal energy of the system in state A, E_A, is a constant, as is the internal energy of the system in state B, E_B. It follows, then, that the difference in the internal energies of these two states, ΔE, is likewise a constant and is independent of the path taken between A and B.

$$\Delta E = E_B - E_A$$

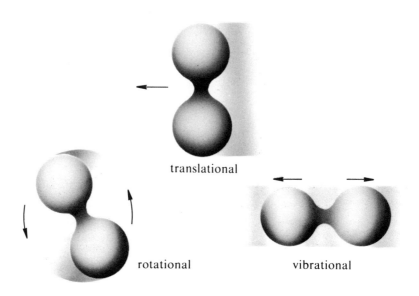

translational

rotational   vibrational

Figure 11.1   Types of molecular motion of diatomic gases.

If this were not true, it would be possible to obtain a net change in energy, in violation of the first law, by taking a system from A to B by one route and returning it to state A by a different route. Instead, in a cyclic process (in which a system is returned to its original state), the increase in E in one direction exactly equals the decrease in E in the opposite direction so that for the cycle there is no net gain or loss in energy. Since engines generally work by cyclic processes, the first law of thermodynamics is frequently stated in terms of the impossibility of constructing a perpetual motion machine—one that can do work without the expenditure of energy.

The change in internal energy of a system may be determined by measurement of the heat absorbed by the system from its surroundings, q, and the work done by the system on its surroundings, w. In these terms,

$$\Delta E = q - w$$

It is important to keep in mind the conventions regarding the signs of these quantities:

q, positive = heat *absorbed* by the system

q, negative = heat *evolved* by the system

w, positive = work done *by* the system

w, negative = work done *on* the system

The values of q and w involved in changing a system from state A to state B depend upon the way in which the change is carried out. However, the value of $(q - w)$ is a constant, equal to ΔE, for the change no matter how it is brought about. If a system undergoes a change in which the internal energy of the system remains constant, the work done by the system equals the heat absorbed by the system. If a system undergoes a change than reduces its internal energy, the energy released will be the sum of the heat evolved and the work done.

11.3 Enthalpy

Two types of change that give rise to work terms are of especial interest to chemists. For electrochemical systems, the work term results, in whole or in part, from the production or use of electrical energy. For ordinary chemical reactions, the work term generally arises as a consequence of pressure-volume changes—for example, the work done against the atmosphere if the system expands in the course of the reaction. The term PV has the dimensions of work. Pressure (force per unit area) may be expressed in dynes per square centimeter; multiplying pressure by volume (in cubic centimeters) gives a product in dyne centimeters (or ergs) which is a dimension of work (force times distance). In like manner, liter atmospheres are units of work. If the pressure is held constant, the work done in expansion from V_A to V_B is

$$w = P(V_B - V_A) = P\Delta V$$

No pressure-volume work can be done by a process carried out at constant volume. Since $w = 0$,

$$\Delta E = q_V$$

Processes carried out at constant pressure are far more common in chemistry than those conducted at constant volume. If we restrict our attention to pressure-volume work again, in the case of constant pressure processes, the work done is $P\Delta V$. Thus

$$\Delta E = q_p - P\Delta V$$

or

$$q_P = \Delta E + P\Delta V$$

This relationship may be written

$$q_P = (E_B - E_A) + P(V_B - V_A)$$

or by rearranging,

$$q_P = (E_B + PV_B) - (E_A + PV_A)$$

The thermodynamic function **enthalpy,** $H,$ is defined by the equation

$$H = E + PV$$

Therefore,

$$q_P = H_B - H_A = \Delta H$$

Thus the heat absorbed by a process conducted at constant pressure is equal to the change in enthalpy, and this is related to the change in the internal energy of the system by the expression

$$\Delta H = \Delta E + P\Delta V$$

Like internal energy (as well as pressure, volume, and temperature), enthalpy is a function of the state of the system alone and is independent of the manner in which that state was achieved.

When a bomb calorimeter is used to make a calorimetric determination, the heat effect measured is at constant volume; ordinarily, reactions are run at constant pressure. The relationship between change in enthalpy and change in internal energy is used to convert heats of reaction at constant volume ($q_V = \Delta E$) to heats of reaction at constant pressure ($q_P = \Delta H$). The appropriate conversion is made by considering the change in volume of the system—the total volume of the reactants subtracted from the total volume of the products. The changes in the volumes of liquids and solids are so small that they are neglected; if only liquids and solids are involved in the reaction, $q_V = q_P$.

For reactions involving gases, however, volume changes may be significant. Let us say that: V_A is the total volume of gaseous reactants; V_B is the total volume of gaseous products; n_A is the number of moles of gaseous reactants; n_B is the number of moles of gaseous products; and that the pressure and temperature are constant. (Calorimetric values are usually recorded at 25°C.) From the ideal gas law,

$$PV_A = n_A RT \qquad \text{and} \qquad PV_B = n_B RT$$

Thus

$$\begin{aligned} P\Delta V &= PV_B - PV_A \\ &= n_B RT - n_A RT \\ &= (\Delta n)RT \end{aligned}$$

Therefore,

$$\Delta H = \Delta E + (\Delta n)RT$$

where Δn is the number of moles of gaseous products minus the number of moles of gaseous reactants.

In order to solve problems using this equation, we must express the value of R in appropriate units. As noted previously in this section, liter atmospheres are the dimensions of energy; therefore the value of R in liter atm/°K mole may be converted to cal/°K mole or to joules/°K mole (see Table 11.1).

TABLE 11.1.
VALUE OF THE GAS CONSTANT, R, IN VARIOUS UNITS.

R	Units
0.082058	liter atm/$^\circ$K mole
8.3143	joules/$^\circ$K mole
1.9872	cal/$^\circ$K mole

Example 11.1 The heat of combustion at constant volume of $CH_4(g)$ is measured in a bomb calorimeter at 25°C as −211,613 cal/mole. What is the ΔH?

Solution For the reaction

$$CH_4(g) + 2O_2(g) \rightarrow CO_2(g) + 2H_2O(l) \qquad \Delta E = -211,613 \text{ cal}$$

$$\Delta n = 1 - (2 + 1) = -2$$

Therefore

$$\Delta H = \Delta E + (\Delta n)RT$$

$$\Delta H = -211,613 \text{ cal} + (-2 \text{ mole})(1.987 \text{ cal}/^\circ\text{K mole})(298.2^\circ\text{K})$$

$$= -211,613 \text{ cal} - 1185 \text{ cal}$$

$$= -212,798 \text{ cal} = -212.798 \text{ kcal}$$

It is convenient to note that a difference of 1 mole between the gaseous products and the gaseous reactants makes a change of 592.5 cal at 25°C.

11.4 Heat Capacities

The **heat capacity,** C, of a system is the amount of heat required to raise the temperature of the system by 1°C. Heat capacities of chemical substances are generally given in calories per degree mole. They may be determined at **constant volume** C_v, and at **constant pressure,** C_p.

Let us restrict our attention to systems capable of doing only pressure-volume work. At constant volume, $w = 0$. Upon an increase in temperature, ΔT, the heat absorbed goes to increase the internal energy of the system.

$$C_v = \frac{\Delta E}{\Delta T}$$

At constant pressure, $w = P\Delta V$. The heat absorbed by a system upon an increase in temperature, ΔT, goes to increase the internal energy of the system and do the work of expansion.

$$C_p = \frac{\Delta E + P\Delta V}{\Delta T}$$

$$C_p = \frac{\Delta H}{\Delta T}$$

In Section 5.6, the following expression was derived for 1 mole of an ideal gas.

$$PV = \tfrac{2}{3}(KE)$$

where (KE) is the average molecular kinetic energy. Therefore

$$(KE) = \tfrac{3}{2}PV$$

and since $PV = RT$ for 1 mole of an ideal gas,

$$(KE) = \tfrac{3}{2}RT$$

When an ideal gas is heated at constant volume, the added energy increases the translational kinetic energy of the gas molecules. Thus

$$\Delta E = \tfrac{3}{2}R\Delta T$$

and hence,

$$C_v = \frac{\Delta E}{\Delta T} = \frac{3}{2}R = 2.98 \text{ cal/}^{\circ}\text{ mole}$$

At constant pressure, a change in temperature causes an ideal gas to expand. For 1 mole, $P\Delta V = R\Delta T$. Therefore

$$\Delta H = \Delta E + P\Delta V$$

$$= \frac{3}{2}R\Delta T + R\Delta T = \frac{5}{2}R\Delta T$$

$$C_p = \frac{\Delta H}{\Delta T} = \frac{5}{2}R = 4.97 \text{ cal/}^{\circ}\text{ mole}$$

Certain monatomic gases, such as helium and argon, have molar heat capacities that correspond to these values derived for an ideal gas. Furthermore, the values of C_v and C_p for these gases show very little variation with temperature. More complicated molecules have larger molar heat capacities; in general, the more complex the molecule, the larger is the value of C_v or C_p. For monatomic gases, all of the molecular motion is translational; for polyatomic molecules, rotational and vibrational motions are possible (Figure 11.1).

Rotational motion adds approximately 1.99 cal/°mole (the ideal gas constant, R) to the values of C_v and C_p of diatomic gases. Thus for many diatomic gases (e.g., H_2, O_2, N_2, and CO) at 25°C, $C_v = 5/2(R) = 4.97$ cal/° mole and $C_p = 7/2\ (R) = 6.96$ cal/° mole. The vibrational motion of these diatomic molecules is negligible at room temperature. However, at higher temperatures, the vibrational motion of these molecules contributes to the molar heat capacities, and even at room temperature, vibrational motion significantly adds to the molar heat capacities of other gases. The heat capacities of solids, liquids, and gases are generally not constant over a wide range of temperatures. Much of this variation is due to different modes of vibrational motion. This topic is treated theoretically by statistical mechanics.

11.5 Adiabatic and Isothermal Changes

Two types of processes are frequently used to illustrate thermodynamic principles. An **adiabatic process** is one in which there is no heat flow between the system and the surroundings. Adiabatic conditions are approximated by well-insulated systems. Since $q = 0$, any work done is at the expense of the internal energy of the system

$$\Delta E = -w \quad \text{or} \quad w = -\Delta E$$

In the adiabatic expansion of a gas, therefore, the temperature of the gas falls as the gas does work on the surroundings in the expansion.

An **isothermal process** is one conducted at constant temperature. Isothermal conditions may be approximated by placing the reaction vessel in a constant temperature bath, or thermostat. In the isothermal expansion of an ideal gas, the internal energy of the gas is constant, $\Delta E = 0$, because the temperature is held constant. Thus

$$q = w$$

During the process, heat flows into the system to compensate for the loss in energy due to the work done by the expanding gas.

If 1 mole of an ideal gas expands isothermally at 273°K from 1 to 0.5 atm, the gas expands from 22.4 to 44.8 liters. On the other hand, in the adiabatic expansion of 1 mole of an ideal gas from 1 to 0.5 atm, the temperature of the gas falls from 273° to 207°K, and the volume increases from 22.4 to only 34.0 liters. The pressure-volume curves for these two expansions are plotted in Figure 11.2.

The way in which a change is carried out is of importance in the application of thermodynamic concepts. If a change is brought about in a reversible manner, it occurs in such a way that the process could at any moment be reversed by an infinitesimal change in one of the conditions. A reversible process proceeds infinitely slowly by a series of equilibrium states.

For example, consider the reversible expansion of a gas occurring in a cylinder with the expansion opposed by a pressure exerted by a piston. In order for the expansion to occur, the applied pressure must be lower than the pressure of the gas, but this difference is infinitesimally small in the reversible process. A maximum amount of work would have to be done by the gas to effect the expansion since the expansion is constantly opposed by the maximum pressure that will permit the gas to expand. If stored, the energy from the work of expansion would be enough to effect the compression of the gas.

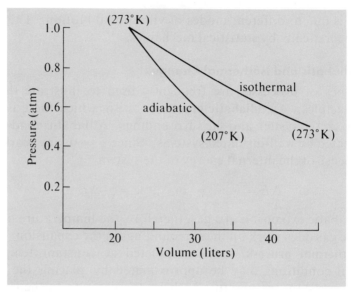

Figure 11.2   Isothermal and adiabatic expansions of 1 mole of an ideal
gas.

It is impossible to conduct an experimental change in a completely reversible manner although in certain instances (notably, the operation of electrochemical cells) reversibility may be approximated. Spontaneous processes are inherently irreversible. It is the lack of balance that provides the driving force for a spontaneous change. In the expansion of a gas into a vacuum, an example of an irreversible change, no work is done against a confining pressure, and no energy may be stored to bring about the compression.

11.6   The Carnot Cycle

The conversion of heat into work is of more practical importance than the reverse process. In its simplest terms, an engine withdraws heat from a hot reservoir, converts part of it into mechanical work, and returns the remainder to a cold reservoir. In the original steam engine of Thomas Newcomen (1705), heat is used to convert water into steam, and the steam is allowed to expand into a vertical cylinder. This expansion forces a piston upward and cools and condenses the steam into water which is withdrawn from the cylinder. A partial vacuum is therefore created inside the cylinder, and atmospheric pressure causes the piston to fall to its original position, thus completing a stroke or a cycle.

In the years from 1764 to 1800, James Watt substantially improved the steam engine of Newcomen (Watt obtained his first patent in 1769). During this period, and particularly at the beginning of the nineteenth century, the efforts of many "engineers" were directed toward developing more efficient engines. The efficiency of an engine is defined as the ratio of the work done by the engine divided by the heat supplied to the engine.

$$\text{efficiency} = \frac{w}{q_h}$$

Nicolas Sadi Carnot, in 1824, described and analyzed a hypothetical engine; his work not only provided a sound theoretical basis for the study of engines but also led to an important advance in thermodynamics. The engine of Carnot is an idealized, not a practical, device. The working substance is a gas which is confined in a cylinder equipped with a piston. There are two steps to the forward (or expansion) part of the stroke and two steps to the return (or compression) part of the stroke. The system is returned to its original state and the process is therefore cyclic.

Figure 11.3 shows the steps of the Carnot cycle diagrammatically; Figure 11.4 is a volume versus pressure plot for the cycle. All of the steps are carried out in a reversible manner so that the maximum amount of

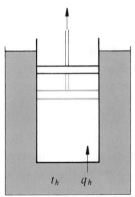

1. Isothermal expansion

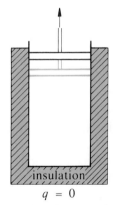

2. Adiabatic expansion

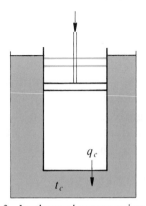

3. Isothermal compression

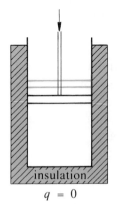

4. Adiabatic compression

Figure 11.3   Steps in the Carnot cycle.

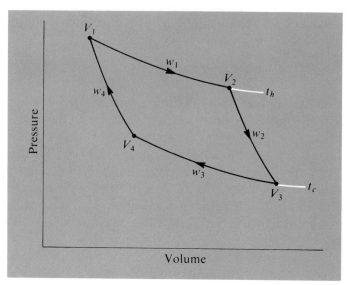

Figure 11.4   Volume–Pressure diagram for a Carnot cycle.

work is obtained from the expansion and the minimum amount of work is required for the compression. The steps are:

1. The isothermal reversible expansion of the gas from volume V_1 to volume V_2. A quantity of heat, q_h, flows into the system from the hot reservoir which is held at temperature t_h. The work done by the gas is w_1.

2. The adiabatic reversible expansion of the gas from volume V_2 to volume V_3. The system is insulated so that there is no heat transferred between it and the surroundings; $q = 0$. The temperature of the gas falls from t_h to t_c. The work done by the gas is w_2.

3. The isothermal reversible compression of the gas from volume V_3 to volume V_4. The system is held at the temperature of the cold reservoir, t_c, and a quantity of heat, q_c, flows from the gas into the cold reservoir. The work done on the gas is w_3. According to the conventions we employ, the numerical values of both q_c and w_3 are negative.

4. The adiabatic reversible compression of the gas from volume V_4 to volume V_1 which completes the cycle. The temperature of the gas increases from t_c to t_h, but $q = 0$. The work done on the gas is w_4, and the numerical value of w_4 is negative.

According to the first law of thermodynamics, $\Delta E = 0$ since the process is cyclic. The total heat absorbed by the system is

$$q = q_h + q_c$$

and the total work done by the system is

$$w = w_1 + w_2 + w_3 + w_4$$

From the first law,

$$\Delta E = q_h + q_c - w = 0$$

and therefore

$$w = q_h + q_c$$

The efficiency of the engine is

$$\text{efficiency} = \frac{w}{q_h} = \frac{q_h + q_c}{q_h}$$

The theoretical efficiency of the cycle is thus the quotient of the heat converted into work by the cycle divided by the total heat absorbed by the system; $q_h + q_c$ has a smaller numerical value than q_h.

Kelvin used the Carnot cycle to define a thermodynamic temperature scale. He made the assumption that, for a given system, the quantity of heat transferred is proportional to the absolute temperature. If the temperatures of the hot and cold reservoirs are used as fixed points,

$$\frac{q_h}{-q_c} = \frac{T_h}{T_c}$$

The negative sign on q_c is necessary because the numerical value of q_c is negative. It can be shown that this temperature scale is identical to that derived from the behavior of an ideal gas.

Solving this expression for q_c, we get

$$q_c = -\left(\frac{T_c}{T_h}\right) q_h$$

By substituting this value for q_c in the equation for the efficiency of an engine, we derive

$$\text{efficiency} = \frac{w}{q_h} = \frac{T_h - T_c}{T_h}$$

Therefore,

$$w = \left(\frac{T_h - T_c}{T_h}\right) q_h$$

Thus the maximum fraction of heat that can be converted into work in a given cycle is $(T_h - T_c)/T_h$; this represents an upper limit since the expression is derived from an idealized reversible process. Practical devices function in an irreversible manner and are subject to mechanical inefficiencies.

An engine working between a hot reservoir at 120°C (393°K) and 40°C (313°K) has a maximum thermal efficiency of 80/393 or 20%. If the temperature of the hot reservoir is increased to 220°C, the maximum thermal efficiency is increased to 180/493 or 36.5%. Internal combustion engines operate at much higher T_h's than steam engines and are therefore more efficient than steam engines.

Decreasing the temperature at which heat is discarded from the engine also leads to an increased maximum thermal efficiency. If it were possible to decrease the discharge temperature to absolute zero, the maximum thermal efficiency would become 100%.

In the event that $T_h = T_c$, the efficiency is zero. We thus derive one statement of the second law of thermodynamics: it is impossible to convert heat into work by means of an isothermal cyclic process.

11.7 Second Law of Thermodynamics

The **second law of thermodynamics** may be stated in several different, though equivalent, ways; it places limitations on the conversion of heat into work. On the basis of the Carnot cycle, we may state, as did Kelvin, that it is impossible by means of a cyclic process to remove heat from a reservoir and convert it into work without at the same time transferring heat from a hot to a cold reservoir. The equations for the maximum thermal efficiency of an engine, which may be summarized as follows,

$$\text{efficiency} = \frac{q_h + q_c}{q_h} = \frac{T_h - T_c}{T_h}$$

may be said to be mathematical statements of the second law. Like the first law of thermodynamics, the second law is based only on experience; no exceptions to the law have been observed.

Let us assume that an engine, B, exists that is more efficient than an ideal reversible engine, A, and that both engines operate between heat reservoirs at T_h and T_c. This means that the preceding equation for maximum thermal efficiency (which would apply to engine A) is not universally true, a statement contrary to the second law. If engine B does work, w', by extracting a quantity of heat, q_h', from the hot reservoir and rejecting a quantity of heat, q_c' (a negative value), to the cold reservoir, then

$$\frac{q_h' + q_c'}{q_h'} > \frac{T_h - T_c}{T_h}$$

There are two ways that engine B could be imagined to be more efficient than engine A. First, B could deliver more work than A ($w' > w$) from the same heat input ($q_h' = q_h$). It could do this only by discarding less heat to the cold reservoir ($-q_c' < -q_c$); otherwise, the operation of engine B would violate the first law of thermodynamics.

Now, let us imagine that engine B is coupled with engine A and that engine A functions in reverse—as a heat pump. This means that A absorbs heat from the cold reservoir and discards heat into the hot reservoir by having work done on it by B. In a single combined cycle, A would return to the hot reservoir exactly as much heat as B extracts from the hot reservoir since $q'_h = q_h$; therefore there would not be any change in the hot reservoir. The work done *by* B, however, would be more than the work done *on* A ($w' > w$) so that work would be obtained from the combination. The work would be obtained at the expense of the cold reservoir; A would extract more heat from the cold reservoir than B would supply to it.

The net effect of this combined operation is that heat, isothermally extracted from a single source, is converted into work without any other change in the system. Such a conversion of heat into work is called **perpetual motion of the second kind;** no one has ever devised a machine capable of doing useful work merely by extracting heat from its surroundings. The second law may be said to forbid perpetual motion of the second kind, and, on the basis of this analysis, we are forced to conclude that all engines operating between the same two temperatures have the same maximum thermal efficiency.

The second way that we may imagine that engine B could be more efficient than engine A is if B withdraws less heat from the hot reservoir than A but still does the same amount of work as A per cycle. Thus $w' = w$, and $q'_h < q_h$.

Again if B and A are coupled with A running in reverse, the work done by B would be exactly that needed by A to cause A to function as a heat pump. No net work would be obtained from the combination. However, B would extract less heat from the hot reservoir than A would return to it since $q'_h < q_h$. The additional heat must come from the cold reservoir, and B must discharge less heat to the cold reservoir than A removes. If the first law is not to be violated, q'_c cannot equal q_c. The only effect that would be observed in this combined operation is the transfer of heat from the cold reservoir to the hot reservoir.

This phenomenon, like perpetual motion of the second kind, has never been observed. In fact, the second law of thermodynamics was originally stated, by Rudolf Clausius, as: "heat does not flow spontaneously from a colder to a warmer body." Again we are forced to conclude that all engines operating between the same two temperatures have the same maximum thermal efficiency.

11.8 Entropy

An important thermodynamic function, **entropy,** S, is derived from the second law of thermodynamics and was introduced by Clausius in 1850. For an isothermal reversible process, the change in entropy may be defined as the heat absorbed divided by the absolute temperature at which it is absorbed

$$\Delta S = \frac{q_{rev}}{T}$$

Entropy thus has the units cal/$^\circ$K mole.

From the expressions for the thermodynamic efficiency of an engine,

$$\frac{q_h + q_c}{q_h} = \frac{T_h - T_c}{T_h}$$

This equation may be transformed, by cross multiplication, into

$$T_h q_h + T_h q_c = T_h q_h - T_c q_h$$

which reduces to

$$\frac{q_h}{T_h} + \frac{q_c}{T_c} = 0$$

Steps 2 and 4 of the Carnot cycle are adiabatic processes, $q = 0$, and for these steps, $\Delta S_2 = 0$ and $\Delta S_4 = 0$. Thus by comparing the preceding equation with the Carnot cycle, from which it was derived, we see

$$\Delta S_1 + \Delta S_3 = 0$$

The numerical value of q_c is negative since heat is evolved in this step; ΔS_3 likewise has a negative value.

Thus the total change in entropy for a reversible cyclic process is zero, and entropy, like internal energy and enthalpy, is a state function. The entropy of a closed system in a given state is a definite value, and the change in entropy as that system is taken from state A to state B is a constant amount. The amount of heat absorbed, or evolved, in taking a system from state A to state B varies with the path taken between the initial and final states. The change in entropy, however, is defined in terms of heat and temperature measurements along a *reversible* path. Hence, it is necessary to devise, in principle, a reversible path between A and B in order to calculate the change in entropy between state A and state B.

A reversible process is one that occurs infinitely slowly and produces the maximum amount of work. In the isothermal expansion of a gas, each step of the expansion is opposed by a pressure infinitesimally smaller than that of the expanding gas. The process may be reversed at any time by the application of a pressure infinitesimally greater than that of the gas. Spontaneous processes do not occur in this way—a gas expands in a finite time and in an irreversible manner, and the maximum amount of work is not obtained.

We may say, then, that the work obtained from a given change is always less than or equal to the work derived from the same change brought about in a reversible manner.

$$w_{rev} \geq w$$

According to the first law, ΔE for a given change in state is the same whether the change is brought about reversibly or irreversibly.

$$\Delta E = q_{rev} - w_{rev} = q - w$$

Therefore

$$q_{rev} \geq q$$

or

$$\frac{q_{rev}}{T} \geq \frac{q}{T}$$

and therefore

$$\Delta S \geq \frac{q}{T}$$

An isolated system does not exchange heat with its surroundings; $q = 0$. Therefore for an *isolated system,*

$$\Delta S \geq 0$$

When a reversible change occurs in an isolated system, the total entropy of the system does not change; $\Delta S = 0$. When an irreversible, spontaneous change occurs in an isolated system, the total entropy of the system increases; $\Delta S > 0$. If the universe is viewed as an isolated system, the entropy of the universe steadily increases as spontaneous processes occur. Clausius summarized the first and second laws of thermodynamics as: "The energy of the universe is constant; the entropy of the universe strives towards a maximum." Thus the ΔS of a hypothetical change may be used as a criterion for whether the change will occur spontaneously.

To apply this concept to a specific change, one must consider that the isolated system (one that does not exchange mass or energy with its surroundings) includes all parts that interact to produce the change. An isolated system, therefore, may incorporate parts (such as the heat reservoirs of a Carnot cycle) that in other situations are considered as a portion of the surroundings.

Thus a zero change in entropy is calculated not only for a closed system taken around a reversible Carnot cycle but also for *each step* of the cycle *if the heat reservoirs are taken into account.* In the latter instance, we are considering an isolated system, and since each step is conducted reversibly, $\Delta S = 0$ for each step. The increase in entropy of the gas in step 1 (gain of q_h at T_h) exactly equals the decrease in entropy of the hot reservoir (loss of q_c at T_h). The loss of entropy by the gas in step 3 (loss of q_c at T_c) is exactly counterbalanced by the gain in entropy of the cold reservoir (gain of q_c at T_c).

Let us consider, as an example of a spontaneous process, the adiabatic expansion of an ideal gas into a vacuum. A flask of gas under pressure is

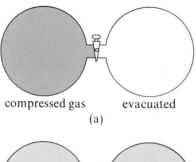

compressed gas   evacuated

(a)

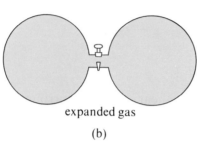

Figure 11.5   Spontaneous expansion of a gas.

expanded gas

(b)

connected, by means of a stopcock, to an evacuated flask (Figure 11.5). When the stopcock is opened, the gas spontaneously expands into the second flask until the pressure is the same in both flasks. The gas expands from volume V_A to V_B. Since the gas is ideal, no work is done in separating the gas molecules (an ideal gas has no intermolecular forces of attraction); neither is work done against a confining pressure. For the total process, $q = 0$, $w = 0$, and $\Delta E = 0$; the temperature of the gas as a whole is the same after the expansion as before.

In order to determine ΔS for the process, we must visualize the change carried out reversibly. In the reversible expansion of an ideal gas, the gas expands infinitely slowly against a pressure infinitesimally smaller than that of the gas; work is done and heat must be supplied (from a heat reservoir) to do the work. Since the temperature is constant, this is, in fact, an isothermal expansion of an ideal gas similar to step 1 of a Carnot cycle. The gas gains in entropy, q_{rev}/T, and the heat reservoir loses an exactly equivalent amount. For everything involved in the *reversible* process, $\Delta S = 0$.

In the spontaneous process, however, no work is done and no heat flows into the gas; a heat reservoir does not constitute a part of the isolated system. The change in entropy of the gas is nevertheless q_{rev}/T since entropy changes are defined on the bases of reversible processes. In this spontaneous process there had been an increase in entropy.

In the adiabatic expansion of a *real* gas into a vacuum, the temperature of the gas falls from T_h to T_c since work is done against the intermolecular forces of attraction to separate the gas molecules (Section 5.14). A reversible path from V_A to V_B could be imagined to include a reversible isothermal expansion to a volume intermediate between V_A

and V_B at T_h followed by an adiabatic expansion that takes the gas the rest of the way to V_B and lowers its temperature to T_c. These are, in fact, the first two steps of a reversible Carnot cycle. For the spontaneous process (gas alone), the increase in entropy would be q_{rev}/T_h from the isothermal expansion; the adiabatic expansion would contribute nothing to the change in entropy. The ΔS for the expansion of a real gas would not have the same numerical value as that for the ideal gas, however, since the value of q_{rev} would not be the same for both processes.

In step 3 of a Carnot cycle, the gas suffers a loss of entropy since it discharges heat to a reservoir. This is a sufficient criterion to tell us that no spontaneous process exists in which a gas alone, in an isolated system, compresses itself isothermally so that it occupies a volume smaller than its initial volume. Obviously, the ideal gas in Figure 11.5(b) is not going to concentrate spontaneously in one of the flasks.

No molecular model is necessary for the application of thermodynamic concepts; however, it is convenient to visualize entropy in such terms. A molecular interpretation of entropy was introduced by Ludwig Boltzmann in 1896. In this concept, entropy is a measure of the randomness, or disorder, of a system. Since a disordered state is more statistically probable than an ordered one, entropy may also be viewed as a probability function. For example, the probability that a bridge hand dealt from a well-shuffled deck of cards will contain a random mixture of suits is higher than the probability that it will contain thirteen cards of the same suit.

The random distribution of a gas in the apparatus shown in Figure 11.5(b) would result in as many gas molecules occupying the left-hand flask as the right-hand flask. Thus the change represented by the diagram represents an increase in randomness—an increase in entropy. If both flasks are of equal volume, the chance of finding a certain molecule in the left-hand flask is $\frac{1}{2}$; the chance of finding the molecule in the whole apparatus is 1. If 1 mole of gas is used, the probability that it will occupy only the left-hand flask is 1 out of $10^{1.8 \times 10^{23}}$. This is 1 chance out of a number so large that there is no name for it—1 followed by 180 sextillion zeros. Thus with the stopcock open, the probability that the gas will occupy the entire apparatus is much higher than the probability that it will occupy only half of the apparatus, and the expansion of the gas represents an increase in entropy.

In Section 6.5, Trouton's rule was discussed. For many liquids, the molar heat of vaporization (heat absorbed) at the boiling point, divided by the boiling point (in °K) is a constant (approximately 21 cal/°K mole); this is actually the molar entropy of vaporization at the boiling point. The molecules of a liquid are more ordered than the molecules of a gas, and it is easy to see that the change from liquid to vapor represents an increase in randomness and hence an increase in entropy. A liquid, such as water, with exceptionally strong intermolecular attractive forces is more ordered than a liquid with weaker intermolecular forces of attraction; hence the increase in entropy upon vaporization for water (ca., 26 cal/°K mole) is higher than the average.

In like manner, the molar entropy of a liquid is greater than the molar entropy of the solid at the melting point. Thus the molecules of a gas are more disordered than the molecules of a liquid, and the molecules of a liquid are more disordered than the molecules of a solid. This applies to pure materials, the degree of disorder in solution is a more complicated topic and will be touched on later.

When entropy is described in terms of randomness or probability, usually only the chemical system is considered. It must be remembered, however, that the total entropy change of the chemical system and its immediate surroundings (an isolated system) must be considered if ΔS is to be used as a criterion of spontaneity.

Thus for the vaporization of a liquid at its boiling point, the entropy of the system increases (increase in randomness, heat absorbed); however, the entropy of the surroundings decreases by an equivalent amount (heat lost). For the system plus its immediate surroundings, $\Delta S = 0$, which indicates an equilibrium condition. At the boiling point, no *net* spontaneous change occurs.

Below the boiling point, a vapor spontaneously condenses into a liquid. The chemical system goes to a less random, and less probable, state (heat evolved, decrease in entropy), but the entropy gained by the immediate surroundings is larger than the entropy lost by the chemical system. The total entropy increases—as it must for a spontaneous process. The ΔS for the system must be calculated on the basis of a reversible process: ΔS for heating the vapor to the boiling point plus ΔS for liquefaction of the vapor at the boiling point plus ΔS for cooling the liquid to the initial temperature; the resulting ΔS for the change is less than the actual heat absorbed by the immediate surroundings from the irreversible change divided by the temperature at which it is absorbed. Notice that the isothermal absorption of heat by the immediate surroundings is a reversible process so that the ΔS for the surroundings may be determined from the actual heat absorbed by the surroundings.

In general, the entropy of an isolated system increases when a spontaneous process occurs within it. The increase continues until equilibrium is attained at which point the entropy of the isolated system is a maximum, $\Delta S = 0$, and no further net spontaneous change occurs.

11.9 Gibbs Free Energy

We can see that the change in entropy of the immediate surroundings (which must be counted as a part of an isolated system) often plays a dominant role in determining whether the total entropy change of the experimental process is positive and the process, therefore, spontaneous. It is convenient to develop a thermodynamic function that can serve as a criterion for spontaneity by centering only on the system—a function that automatically takes into account the entropy change of the immediate surroundings. Such a function was introduced by J. Willard Gibbs in 1876 and is called the **Gibbs free energy**, G.

The chemist is primarily concerned with chemical reactions that are conducted at constant temperature and pressure. Let us direct our attention to a chemical reaction that *evolves* heat at constant temperature and pressure; $\Delta H = -q$. This heat is isothermally, and hence reversibly, *absorbed* by the immediate surroundings. Therefore, $q_{rev} = -\Delta H$ for the surroundings, and the entropy change for the immediate surroundings ($\Delta S_{i.s.}$) is

$$\Delta S_{i.s.} = \frac{-\Delta H}{T}$$

Notice that the same equation would have been secured if the reaction had absorbed heat and surroundings evolved heat.

If the system in which the chemical reaction occurs has a change in entropy of ΔS, then the total change in entropy of the hypothetical isolated system is

$$-\frac{\Delta H}{T} + \Delta S$$

This total must be larger than, or equal to, zero. Thus

$$-\frac{\Delta H}{T} + \Delta S \geq 0$$

or

$$-\Delta H + T\Delta S \geq 0$$

By changing signs, we get

$$\Delta H - T\Delta S \leq 0$$

The Gibbs free energy function is defined by the equation

$$G = H - TS$$

For a change at constant temperature,

$$\Delta G = \Delta H - T\Delta S$$

Therefore, we can say that

$$\Delta G \leq 0$$

For a spontaneous process conducted at constant temperature and pressure, in which pressure-volume work is the only type of work done, the

Gibbs free energy decreases; it becomes a minimum at equilibrium, where $\Delta G = 0$. Since ΔH is defined as the heat effect at constant pressure when *no work other than pressure-volume work* is done, this restriction must be included in the preceding statement. However, chemical reactions are usually carried out in such a manner that only pressure-volume work is involved.

Free energy is a state function just as the functions that define it— enthalpy, temperature, and entropy. Some insight into the meaning of free energy can be gained by recalling that, at constant pressure,

$$\Delta H = \Delta E + P\Delta V$$

Substituting this expression into

$$\Delta G = \Delta H - T\Delta S$$

we arrive at

$$\Delta G = \Delta E + P\Delta V - T\Delta S$$

If the process is carried out reversibly,

$$\Delta E = q_{rev} - w_{max}$$

and therefore

$$\Delta G = q_{rev} - w_{max} + P\Delta V - T\Delta S$$

For an isothermal reversible process,

$$\Delta S = \frac{q_{rev}}{T} \qquad \text{or} \qquad q_{rev} = T\Delta S$$

Thus

$$\Delta G = T\Delta S - w_{max} + P\Delta V - T\Delta S$$

or

$$-\Delta G = w_{max} - P\Delta V$$

At constant temperature and pressure, the *decrease* (note minus sign) in Gibbs free energy is equal to the maximum work that a system can do in a reversible process minus the work of expansion.

If the work is restricted to pressure-volume work, $w_{max} = P\Delta V$, and therefore

$$-\Delta G = 0 \quad \text{(reversible process)}$$

(A prime exception to this is the operation of a voltaic cell in which electrical work is done.) Notice that the definition is based on a reversible process. The work done by a spontaneous, irreversible, process is not maximum work.

$$- \Delta G > w - P\Delta V$$

The decrease in Gibbs free energy for irreversible processes is greater than the work done in excess of the pressure-volume work (net work).

Gibbs free energy is an important thermodynamic function for the chemist. Why some chemical reactions are possible and others are not is of fundamental importance. The earliest answer to the question was that reactions proceed because the reactants have a chemical affinity for each other; this "explanation" is still valid but, unfortunately, not very illuminating. In an effort to relate chemical affinity to some measurable quantity, Julius Thomsen and Marcellin Berthelot (1878) proposed that chemical reactions proceed spontaneously only if they evolve heat; presumably the heat evolved measures the chemical affinity of the reactants in going from a more energetic to a lesser energetic (more stable) state. Most chemical reactions are exothermic; however, the hypothesis of Thomsen and Berthelot is not tenable because spontaneous endothermic reactions are known and many spontaneous physical processes absorb heat (e.g., the melting of ice at room temperature).

The flaw of the hypothesis of Thomsen and Berthelot is that it ignores the role of entropy. The materials of a chemical reaction do indeed seek a minimum in energy, but they also seek a maximum in randomness (entropy). At times, these two factors work together; at other times, they oppose one another. The change in free energy takes into account both factors

$$\Delta G = \Delta H - T\Delta S$$

A system is more ordered at low temperatures than high temperatures; as the temperature increases, the randomness increases. The probability factor, $T\Delta S$, includes both temperature and change in entropy. Gibbs free energy and enthalpy are usually measured in calories or kilocalories; the factor $T\Delta S$ has the same dimensions.

It must be emphasized that whereas thermodynamic concepts can be used to determine what changes are possible, thermodynamics has nothing to say about the rapidity of change. Some thermodynamically favored changes occur very slowly. Although reactions between carbon and oxygen, as well as between hydrogen and oxygen, at 25°C and 1 atm pressure are definitely predicted by theory, mixtures of carbon and oxygen and mixtures of hydrogen and oxygen can be kept for prolonged periods without significant reaction; such reactions are generally initiated by suitable means. Thermodynamics can authoritatively indicate postulated changes that will *not* occur and need not be attempted, and it can tell us how to alter the conditions of a presumably unfavored reaction in such a manner that the reaction will then be thermodynamically possible.

Example 11.2   The heat of the reaction

$$Zn(s) + 2H^+(aq) \rightarrow Zn^{2+}(aq) + H_2(g)$$

is -37.02 kcal when 1 gram atom of zinc is added to excess dilute hydrochloric acid in a bomb calorimeter at 25°C. For the same reaction run in a voltaic cell,

$$Zn(s) \mid Zn^{2+}(aq) \parallel H^+(aq) \mid H_2(g) \mid Pt$$

$E° = +0.763$ v. For this reaction, what are the values of $\Delta E°$, $\Delta H°$, $\Delta G°$, and $\Delta S°$? (The superscript is used to indicate changes for reactants in their standard states to products in their standard states at 25°C—Section 11.10).

Solution   (a) The change in internal energy is measured in a bomb calorimeter; therefore $\Delta E° = -37.02$ kcal. (b) The change in enthalpy, $\Delta H°$, may be obtained by correcting the value of $\Delta E°$ to constant pressure. The reaction shows that $\Delta n = +1$. Therefore

$$\Delta H° = \Delta E° + (\Delta n) RT$$
$$= -37.02 \text{ kcal} + (+1)(1.987)(298.2) \text{ cal}$$
$$= -37.02 \text{ kcal} + 590 \text{ cal}$$
$$= -36.43 \text{ kcal}$$

(c) The change in free energy, $\Delta G°$, may be calculated from the reversible emf of a standard cell, $E°$ (Section 9.7). The number of faradays involved in the reaction, *n,* is 2.

$$\Delta G° = -nFE°$$
$$= -2 (23.06)(0.763) \text{ kcal}$$
$$= -35.19 \text{ kcal}$$

(d) The change in entropy, $\Delta S°$, may be calculated from $\Delta H°$ and $\Delta G°$. Thus

$$\Delta G° = \Delta H° - T\Delta S°$$
$$T\Delta S° = \Delta H° - \Delta G°$$
$$= -36.43 \text{ kcal} - (-35.19) \text{ kcal}$$
$$= -1.24 \text{ kcal}$$
$$\Delta S° = -1,240 \text{ cal}/298.2°K$$
$$= -416 \text{ cal}/°K$$

For the preparation of the products in their standard states from the reactants in their standard states at 25°C, an unfavorable entropy change is overshadowed by a favorable energy change. The reaction is spontaneous because the change in Gibbs free energy is negative. Superficially, it might appear that the products represent a more disordered state than the reactants; on this basis a positive $\Delta S°$ for the system would be predicted— not the negative $\Delta S°$ observed. The production of hydrogen gas does represent an increase in randomness; however, this increase is more than balanced by the production of a solution of zinc chloride which is highly ordered. Theoretically, solutions containing highly charged ions are very ordered because of electrostatic attractions.   At the present time, statistical thermodynamics is not developed to the point that all states are thoroughly understood.   Caution must be exercized in the qualitative assignment of entropy changes based on presumed increases in randomness.

11.10 Standard Free Energies

It is convenient to tabulate changes in Gibbs free energy based on standard states; such values are given the symbol $\Delta G°$ and are generally determined at 25°C. The standard state of a substance is its stable form at 1 atm pressure; for materials in solution, the standard state is unit activity.   Similar conventions are used for standard changes in enthalpy (Section 4.9) and standard electrode potentials (Section 9.7).

The **standard free energy of formation,** $\Delta G_f°$, is defined as the change in standard free energies when 1 mole of a substance is prepared from its constituent elements.   In this system, the most stable form of an element at 25°C is assigned a standard free energy of zero.   Chemical equations for which standard free energy changes are known may be added or subtracted in the same way as thermochemical equations are (Law of Hess, Section 4.9).

In this manner, $\Delta G_f°$ values may be used to calculate standard free energy changes for many reactions.   The $\Delta G°$ for a reaction is equal to the sum of the standard free energies of formation of the products minus the sum of the standard free energies of the reactants.   Remember that the $\Delta G_f°$ of a compound is recorded for 1 mole; if 2 moles of a compound appear in the equation, the $\Delta G_f°$ for that compound must be multiplied by 2.

Example 11.3   (a) What is $\Delta G°$ for the reaction

$$Cl_2(1 \text{ atm}) + 2I^-(1m) \rightarrow 2Cl^-(1m) + I_2(s)$$

For I^-, $\Delta G_f° = -12.35$ kcal/mole; for Cl^-, $\Delta G_f° = -31.35$ kcal/mole. (b) On the basis of the $\Delta G°$ calculated, determine the $E°$ for the cell

$$Pt \mid I_2(s) \mid I^-(1m) \parallel Cl^-(1m) \mid Cl_2(1 \text{ atm}) \mid Pt$$

Solution   (a)

$$\Delta G° = 2[\Delta G_f°(Cl^-)] - 2[\Delta G_f°(I^-)]$$
$$= 2(-31.35 \text{ kcal}) - 2(-12.35 \text{ kcal})$$
$$= -38.00 \text{ kcal}$$

(b)
$$\Delta G^\circ = -nFE^\circ$$

$$E^\circ = \frac{-37.0 \text{ kcal}}{-(2)(23.1 \text{ kcal/v})}$$

$$E^\circ = +0.822 \text{ v}$$

The value of E° derived from standard electrode potentials is $+0.82$ v.

11.11   Third Law of Thermodynamics

The entropy of a substance increases as the temperature is increased; this fact is readily understood on the basis of the concept that entropy is a measure of disorder. Conversely, cooling a substance makes a substance more ordered and decreases its entropy. At absolute zero, the entropy of a perfect crystalline substance may be taken as zero. This is a statement of the **third law of thermodynamics** which was first formulated by Walther Nernst in 1906. The entropy of an imperfect crystal. a glass, or a solid solution is not zero at 0°K.

On the basis of the third law, absolute entropies can be calculated from heat capacity data by extrapolating to absolute zero. Standard third-law entropies are recorded for substances in their standard states at 25°C and may be used to calculate ΔS° values for reactions. The ΔS° for a reaction is equal to the sum of the entropies of the products minus the sum of the entropies of the reactants.

Example 11.4   For the reaction

$$2\text{Hg}(l) + O_2(g) \rightarrow 2\text{HgO}(s)$$

the third law entropies are

$$S^\circ(\text{Hg}) = 18.5 \text{ cal/mole}$$
$$S^\circ(O_2) = 49.0 \text{ cal/mole}$$
$$S^\circ(\text{HgO}) = 17.2 \text{ cal/mole.}$$

The heat of formation, ΔH_f°, of HgO is -21.68 kcal/mole. What is the standard free energy of formation of HgO(s)? Is the reaction, at 25°C, for the production of HgO in its standard state from Hg and O_2 in their standard states spontaneous?

Solution
$$\Delta S^\circ = 2S^\circ(\text{HgO}) - [2S^\circ(\text{Hg}) + S^\circ(O_2)]$$
$$= 2(17.2) - [2(18.5) + 49.0]$$
$$= -51.6 \text{ cal}$$

For the reaction as written
$$\Delta H^\circ = 2\Delta H_f^\circ = -43,400 \text{ cal}$$
$$\Delta G^\circ = \Delta H^\circ - T\Delta S^\circ$$
$$= -43,400 - (298)(51.6)$$
$$= -28,000 \text{ cal}$$

the equation shows the formation of 2 moles of HgO; for 1 mole, $\Delta G_f^\circ =$ -14.0 kcal/mole.

The reaction is spontaneous; the change in enthalpy compensates for the unfavorable change in entropy so that the free energy change is negative.

SOME SUGGESTED READINGS

Allen, J. A., *Energy Changes in Chemistry*, Rockleigh, N.J., Allyn & Bacon, 1966 (paper).

Buckingham, A. D., *Laws and Applications of Chemical Thermodynamics*, New York, Pergamon, 1963 (paper).

Campbell, A. J., *Why Do Chemical Reactions Occur?*, Englewood Cliffs, N.J., Prentice-Hall, 1965 (paper).

Hargreaves, G., *Elementary Chemical Thermodynamics*, 2nd ed., Washington, D.C., Butterworth, 1963 (paper).

Klotz, I. M., *Introduction to Chemical Thermodynamics*, New York, Benjamin, 1964 (paper).

Mahan, B. H., *Elementary Chemical Thermodynamics*, New York, Benjamin, 1963 (paper).

Nash, L., *Elements of Chemical Thermodynamics*, Reading, Mass., Addison-Wesley, 1962 (paper).

Reid, C. E., *Principles of Chemical Thermodynamics*, New York, Reinhold, 1960.

Strong, L. E., and Stratton, W. J., *Chemical Energy*, New York, Reinhold, 1965 (paper).

Waser, J., *Basic Chemical Thermodynamics*, New York, Benjamin, 1966 (paper).

PROBLEMS

11.1 Oxidation of a 5.400 g sample of oxalic acid, $H_2C_2O_4(s)$, in a bomb calorimeter caused a temperature rise of 2.238°C; the calorimeter had a water equivalent of 600 g, and 1000 g of water were employed. (a) What is the heat of combustion of oxalic acid at constant volume, ΔE? (b) What is the enthalpy of combustion of oxalic acid at constant pressure, ΔH?

11.2 For pentane, $C_5H_{12}(g)$, the standard enthalpy of combustion at 25°C is -845.16 kcal/mole. What is ΔE° for this reaction at 25°C?

11.3 What is the maximum thermal efficiency of an engine working between 300°C and 30°C?

11.4 What minimum quantity of heat (in calories) must be absorbed by an engine that operates between 160°C and 30°C in order to secure 100 joules of work?

11.5 The heat of vaporization of carbon disulfide is 84.1 cal/g at 46.3°C, which is the normal boiling point of CS_2. For the vaporization of 1 mole of liquid CS_2 at the normal boiling point, calculate (a) ΔH, (b) ΔE, (c) ΔS, and (d) ΔG.

11.6 A hydrocarbon has the empirical formula CH_3. The compound boils at -88°C (185°K) and has a heat of vaporization of 127 cal/g at the boiling point. Determine the molecular formula of the compound from these data by means of Trouton's rule.

11.7 The $\Delta E°$ of the reaction

$$Cl_2(g) + 2Fe^{2+}(aq) \rightarrow 2Fe^{3+}(aq) + 2Cl^-(aq)$$

is -60.26 kcal. For the standard cell

$$Pt \mid Fe^{2+}, Fe^{3+} \parallel Cl^- \mid Cl_2 \mid Pt$$

the standard cell potential, $E°$, may be derived from the data of Table 9.3. Calculate for this reaction: (a) $\Delta H°$, (b) $\Delta G°$, and (c) $\Delta S°$.

11.8 For the reaction

$$2AgCl(s) + H_2(g) \rightarrow 2Ag(s) + 2H^+(aq) + 2Cl^-(aq)$$

$\Delta H°$ is -19.32 kcal and $\Delta S°$ is -30.5 cal/°K. Calculate the standard cell potential, $E°$, for the cell

$$Pt \mid H_2 \mid H^+, Cl^- \mid AgCl \mid Ag$$

11.9 Calculate $E°$ for the half reaction

$$ReO_4^- + 8H^+ + 7e^- \rightarrow Re + 4H_2O$$

For ReO_4^-, $\Delta G_f° = -168.3$ kcal/mole; for H_2O, $\Delta G_f° = -56.69$ kcal/mole; for H^+, $\Delta G_f° = 0$.

11.10 Calculate the standard free energy of formation, $\Delta G_f°$, of ReO_2 from the $\Delta G_f°$ values given in Problem 11.9, and the following standard electrode potential.

$$ReO_4^- + 4H^+ + 3e^- \rightarrow ReO_2 + 2H_2O \qquad E° = +0.51 \text{ v}$$

11.11 (a) Calculate the entropy change, $\Delta S°$, for the formation of methane, CH_4, at 25°C.

$$C(graphite) + 2H_2(g) \rightarrow CH_4(g)$$

The third law entropies at 25°C are: for C(graphite), 1.36 cal/°K mole; for $H_2(g)$, 31.21 cal/°K mole; and for $CH_4(g)$, 44.50 cal/°K mole. (b) The standard enthalpy of formation, $\Delta H_f°$, of $CH_4(g)$ is -17.889 kcal/mole. What is $\Delta G°$ for the reaction of part (a)?

11.12 Given the following Gibbs free energy of formation values and standard third law entropies at 25°C.

	CO(g)	H₂O(g)	CO₂(g)	H₂(g)
$S°$ (cal/°K mole)	47.301	45.106	51.061	31.211
$\Delta G_f°$ (kcal/mole)	-32.8079	-54.6357	-94.2598	0

Calculate the $\Delta H°$ for the reaction

$$CO(g) + H_2O(g) \rightarrow CO_2(g) + H_2(g)$$

11.13 (a) From the following data, calculate the entropy change at 25°C, $\Delta S°$, for the preparation of each of the hydrogen halides from the elements.

	HF	HCl	HBr	HI
ΔH_f° (kcal/mole)	-64.2	-22.063	-8.66	$+6.20$
ΔG_f° (kcal/mole)	-64.7	-22.769	-12.72	$+0.31$

(b) Discuss the practicality of preparing each hydrogen halide in essentially pure form by reaction of the elements. Use both ΔG° and ΔS° as the basis of your discussion. For each reaction, how can the change in entropy of the immediate surroundings be calculated?

12

Chemical Kinetics and Chemical Equilibrium

Chemical kinetics is the study of the rates of chemical reactions, the means by which reaction rates may be controlled, and the ways in which reactions proceed on the atomic-molecular level.

Reactions are frequently classed as **homogeneous** or **heterogeneous.** A homogeneous reaction occurs in a single phase; for example,

$$H^+(aq) + OH^-(aq) \rightarrow H_2O(l)$$

$$2NO(g) + O_2(g) \rightarrow 2NO_2(g)$$

Heterogeneous reactions take place on a phase boundary; for example,

$$Zn(s) + 2H^+(aq) \rightarrow Zn^{2+}(aq) + H_2(g)$$

$$2Mg(s) + O_2(g) \rightarrow 2MgO(s)$$

Many chemical reactions are reversible. For example, the reaction

$$N_2(g) + 3H_2(g) \rightleftharpoons 2NH_3(g)$$

may be made to give a good yield of ammonia through a judicious choice of conditions; under other reaction conditions, virtually complete dissociation of ammonia is observed.

12.1 Molecular Collisions and Reaction Rates

Consider a hypothetical homogeneous gas phase reaction between two diatomic molecules A_2 and B_2.

$$A_2(g) + B_2(g) \rightleftharpoons 2AB(g)$$

The reaction is reversible, but for the moment, let us consider only the forward reaction.

Not every reaction proceeds in a manner described by the net chemical equation; many reactions occur through a series of steps (called the **re-**

action mechanism), and the net equation represents the sum of the equations for the steps. In the case of the reaction between A_2 and B_2, however, let us assume that the reaction proceeds, as depicted by the equation, through the collisions of A_2 and B_2 molecules (Figure 12.1).*

Not every collision between molecules results in a reaction. Comparison of the calculated total number of collisions per unit time with the observed rate of a reaction shows that generally only a small fraction of the total number of collisions are effective.

There are two reasons why a given collision may not be effective. First, the molecules may be improperly alligned (Figure 12.2). Second, the impact of the collision may be so gentle that the molecules rebound unchanged. The negatively charged electron clouds surrounding molecules produce a force of repulsion that acts between molecules; this repulsion causes molecules with low energies to rebound when they collide. In a collision between high-energy molecules, however, the molecules possess sufficient energy to overcome the forces of repulsion, and the rearrangement typical of the chemical reaction may then follow. For an effective collision, the sum of the energies of the colliding molecules must equal or exceed some minimum value.

*Until recently, the formation of hydrogen iodide from hydrogen and iodine was thought to proceed by such a mechanism; however, studies have shown the mechanism of this reaction to be more complicated.

Figure 12.1   Collision between an A_2 molecule and a B_2 molecule resulting in a reaction.

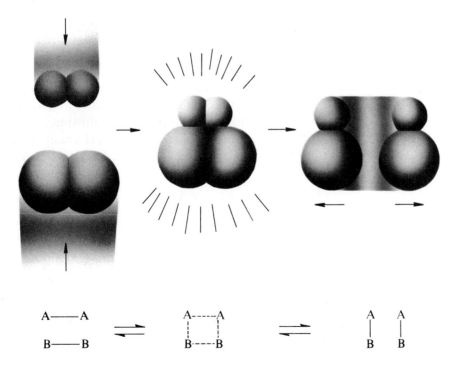

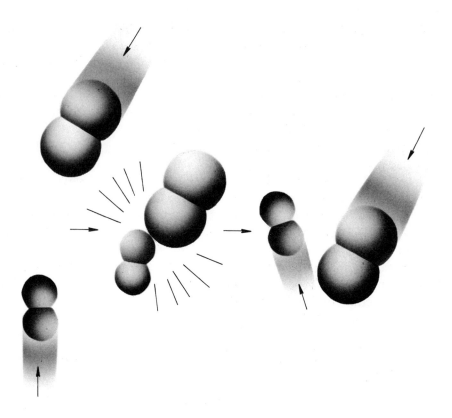

Figure 12.2   Collison between an A₂ molecule and a B₂ molecule producing no reaction.

Therefore, when the rate of a given reaction is increased through an alteration in an experimental condition, this increase is brought about by either an increase in the total number of collisions per unit time, an increase in the fraction of the total number of collisions that are effective, or a combination of both factors. The data of Table 12.1 for a hypothetical reaction

$$A_2(g) + B_2(g) \rightarrow 2AB(g)$$

show that the reaction rate may be doubled by doubling either the number of collisions per second *or* the fraction effective. If it were possible to double both the total number of collisions per second *and* the fraction effective, the reaction rate would be quadrupled.

12.2   Temperature and Reaction Rate

The rate of any chemical reaction is increased when the temperature is raised; this effect is observed for endothermic as well as exothermic re-

TABLE 12.1
ANALYSIS OF THE HYPOTHETICAL REACTION $A_2(g) + B_2(g) \rightarrow 2AB(g)$
(1 LITER OF REACTING MOLECULES AT 25°C AND 1 ATM).

No. Collisions (per sec)	Fraction Effective	No. Collisions Resulting in Reaction (per sec)	Rate of Production of AB (moles/liter sec)
1.0×10^{31}	1.0×10^{-14}	1.0×10^{17}	3.2×10^{-7}
2.0×10^{31}	1.0×10^{-14}	2.0×10^{17}	6.4×10^{-7}
1.0×10^{31}	2.0×10^{-14}	2.0×10^{17}	6.4×10^{-7}
2.0×10^{31}	2.0×10^{-14}	4.0×10^{17}	1.3×10^{-6}

actions. The more rapid molecular motion resulting from an increase in temperature brings about a larger number of molecular collisions per unit time. However, raising the temperature from 25° to 35°C causes the average speed of the molecules to increase by only 2 to 3%, whereas the same temperature rise brings about an increase in the reaction rate of approximately 200 to 300%. Obviously, increasing the temperature must increase the fraction of molecular collisions that are effective, and this factor must far outweigh the concomitant increase in the total number of collisions per unit time.

By an examination of Figure 12.3, we can understand why proportionately more molecular collisions result in reactions at a higher temperature than at a lower temperature. Two molecular energy distribu-

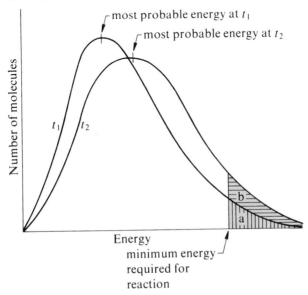

Figure 12.3 *Molecular energy distributions at temperatures t_1 and t_2.*

tion curves are shown—one for a temperature, t_1, and another for a higher temperature, t_2 (see Section 5.12). The minimum energy required for reaction is indicated on the diagram; the number of molecules at t_1 with energies equal to or greater than this minimum energy is proportional to the area, a, under the curve for t_1. The curve for temperature t_2 is shifted only slightly in the direction of higher energy; however, at t_2 the number of molecules possessing sufficient energy to react successfully upon collision is greatly increased and is proportional to the area $a + b$. Thus a temperature rise produces an increase in reaction rate principally because the fraction of the collisions that are effective is increased; the increase in the total number of collisions per unit time is only a minor factor.

In a successful collision between reacting molecules, the molecules form a transitory intermediate called an **activated complex.** Let us again consider the reaction between A_2 and B_2. In a gentle collision, the A_2 and B_2 molecules are repelled by the molecular electron clouds and never get close enough for A—B bonds to form. However, a collision between high-energy molecules results in the formation of a short-lived molecule, A_2B_2, which is the activated complex for the reaction; the atoms of the complex assume the square configuration diagrammed in Figure 12.1. The H_2I_2 complex may split to form two AB molecules or may decompose to re-form A_2 and B_2 molecules. In fact, this same activated complex is produced by the collison of two high-energy AB molecules and is the intermediate in the reverse reaction—the formation of A_2 and B_2 from AB.

$$A_2 + B_2 \rightleftharpoons \begin{matrix} A \text{---} A \\ \vdots \quad \vdots \\ B \text{---} B \end{matrix} \rightleftharpoons 2AB$$

The bonding arrangement of the acticated complex is not so stable as that of either the reactants or the products; the activated complex represents a state of relatively high potential energy. A potential energy diagram for the hypothetical reaction

$$A_2 + B_2 \rightleftharpoons A_2B_2 \rightleftharpoons 2AB$$

is shown in Figure 12.4; potential energy is plotted against a reaction coordinate that may be interpreted as showing the progress of the reaction. The difference between the potential energy of the reactants, $A_2 + B_2$, and the potential energy of the activated complex is called the **energy of activation** and is given the symbol E_a; typical values of E_a range from 15 to 60 kcal/mole.

The energy of activation constitutes a potential energy barrier between the reactants and products. Even though the energy of the reactants, $A_2 + B_2$, is higher than that of the products and the overall reaction is

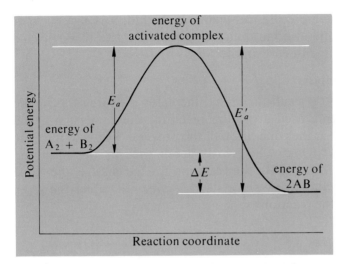

Figure 12.4 *Potential energy diagram for the hypothetical reaction* $A_2 + B_2 \rightleftharpoons A_2B_2 \rightleftharpoons 2AB$.

exothermic, the system must climb a potential energy hill before it can coast down to a state of lower potential energy. In a successful collision, part of the kinetic energy of the fast-moving A_2 and B_2 molecules is used to provide the energy of activation and thus produce the high-energy molecular arrangement of the activated complex. If the activated complex re-forms A_2 and B_2 molecules, the energy of activation is released in the form of the kinetic energy of the molecules. If the activated complex splits into the product, two molecules of AB, the energy indicated as E_a' on the diagram is released as kinetic energy. The overall difference between the energy released and the energy absorbed is the ΔE (or ΔH, depending on conditions) for the reaction.

$$\Delta E = E_a - E_a'$$

As shown on the diagram, $E_a' > E_a$; therefore ΔE is negative, and the forward reaction is exothermic.

The reaction diagrammed in Figure 12.4 is reversible; E_a' is the energy of activation of the reverse reaction. If the diagram is read from right to left, then E_a' is absorbed and E_a evolved.

$$\Delta E = E_a' - E_a$$

The reverse reaction is endothermic; ΔE is positive, since $E_a' > E_a$.

If molecules of A_2 and B_2 with relatively low kinetic energies approach each other, sufficient energy is lacking to produce the arrangement of the activated complex by forcing the molecules together in opposition to the repulsive forces. In this instance, the molecules possess only enough energy between them to get part way up the hill; then, repelling each other, they coast back down the hill and fly apart unchanged. Since only high-energy molecules can get over the hill, it is easy to understand the role of temperature in influencing reaction rate through changes in the fraction of high-energy molecules.

12.3 Catalysts

A **catalyst** is a substance that increases the rate of a chemical reaction without being used up in the reaction; the catalyst may be recovered unchanged at the conclusion of the process. For example, the decomposition of $KClO_3$ can be greatly accelerated by the addition of a small quantity of MnO_2. In the equation for the change, the catalyst is indicated over the arrow since its use does not affect the overall stoichiometry of the reaction.

$$2KClO_3 \xrightarrow{\text{MnO}_2} 2KCl + 3O_2$$

Catalysts cannot cause thermodynamically impossible reactions to occur. Furthermore, it is not the mere *presence* of a catalyst (presumably acting as a cheering section) that causes the effect on the reaction rate. In a catalyzed reaction, the catalyst is actually consumed in one step and regenerated in a subsequent step; thus it is used over and over again without undergoing any permanent change.

A catalyst, then, functions by opening an alternative path by which a reaction can proceed, and the mechanism of the catalyzed reaction is different from that of the uncatalyzed reaction. The catalyzed path has a lower energy of activation than the uncatalyzed path (Figure 12.5) which

Figure 12.5   *Potential energy diagrams for catalyzed and uncatalyzed reactions.*

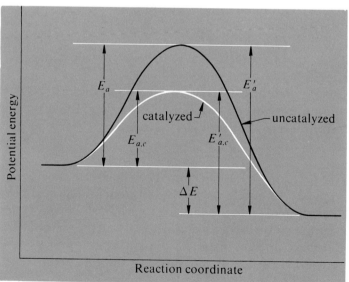

accounts for the more rapid reaction rate. When a catalyst is used, pro-portionately more molecules possess the energy required for a successful collision (Figure 12.6); thus of the total number of collisions per unit time, the fraction that results in reaction is increased.

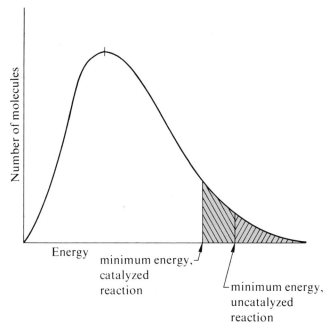

Figure 12.6 Molecular energy distribution showing the effect of a catalyst on the number of molecules possessing sufficient energy to react.

Two additional observations may be derived from an examination of Figure 12.5. First, ΔE for the catalyzed reaction is the same as ΔE for the uncatalyzed reaction. Second, the energy of activation for the reverse reaction, E_a', is lowered by the use of the catalyst to the same extent that the energy of activation of the forward reaction, E_a, is lowered. This means that a catalyst has the same effect on the reverse reaction that it has on the forward reaction. If a catalyst doubles the speed of a forward reaction, the same catalyst will double the speed of the reverse reaction.

Many industrial processes depend upon catalytic procedures, but even more important to man are the natural catalysts known as **enzymes.** These extremely complicated substances catalyze life processes such as digestion and cell synthesis. The large number of complex chemical reactions that occur in the body, and are necessary for life, can occur at the relatively low temperature of the body because of the action of enzymes. Thousands of enzymes are known to exist, each serving a specific function. Research into the structure and action of enzymes offers great promise for the advancement of knowledge of the causes of disease and the mechanism of growth.

In **homogeneous** catalysis, the substance serving as a catalyst is present in the same phase as the reactants; in **heterogeneous,** or **surface,** catalysis, the reactants and catalyst comprise two separate phases, and the reaction occurs on a catalytic surface. An example of homogeneous catalysis in the gas phase is the effect of chlorine on the decomposition of dinitrogen oxide.

Gaseous N_2O is a relatively inert substance at room temperature; however, at temperatures in the neighborhood of 1000°K it decomposes according to the equation

$$2N_2O(g) \rightarrow 2N_2(g) + O_2(g)$$

Kinetic studies show that the reaction proceeds by means of collisions between two molecules of N_2O. The reaction is catalyzed by traces of chlorine gas.

A proposed mechanism for the catalyzed path follows. At the temperature of the experiment, and particularly in the presence of light, some chlorine molecules are dissociated into chlorine atoms.

$$Cl_2(g) \rightarrow 2Cl(g)$$

These chlorine atoms readily react with N_2O

$$N_2O(g) + Cl(g) \rightarrow N_2(g) + ClO(g)$$

and the decomposition of ClO is rapid

$$2ClO(g) \rightarrow Cl_2(g) + O_2(g)$$

In this last step, the catalyst is returned to its original form; the final products of the catalyzed reaction are the same as those of the uncatalyzed reaction.

Another example of homogeneous catalysis is the decomposition of ozone in the presence of N_2O_5. Dinitrogen pentoxide decomposes readily into oxygen and lower oxides of nitrogen. For example,

$$2N_2O_5(g) \rightarrow 2N_2O_4(g) + O_2(g)$$

Ozone reacts rapidly with N_2O_4 producing oxygen and regenerating the catalyst, N_2O_5.

$$O_3(g) + N_2O_4(g) \rightarrow O_2(g) + N_2O_5(g)$$

The proper addition of these two equations gives the net change

$$2O_3(g) \xrightarrow{\ N_2O_5\ } 3O_2(g)$$

It must be emphasized that these mechanisms are merely plausible hypotheses. Undoubtedly, the actual mechanism of the N_2O_5-catalyzed decomposition of ozone is much more complicated and may involve steps such as

$$N_2O_4(g) \rightarrow 2NO_2(g)$$
$$NO_2(g) + O_3(g) \rightarrow NO_3(g) + O_2(g)$$
$$NO_2(g) + NO_3(g) \rightarrow N_2O_5(g)$$

Homogeneous catalysis also occurs in aqueous solution; many reactions are catalyzed by acids and bases. The decomposition of hydrogen peroxide

$$2H_2O_2(aq) \rightarrow 2H_2O(l) + O_2(g)$$

is catalyzed by the presence of iodide ion. A postulated mechanism for the catalyzed reaction is

$$H_2O_2(aq) + I^-(aq) \rightarrow H_2O(l) + IO^-(aq)$$
$$H_2O_2(aq) + IO^-(aq) \rightarrow H_2O(l) + O_2(g) + I^-(aq)$$

Heterogeneous catalysis generally proceeds through **chemical adsorption** (or **chemisorption**) of the reactants on the surface of the catalyst. Adsorption is a process in which molecules adhere to the surface of a solid; charcoal is used in gas masks as an adsorbent for noxious gases. In ordinary **physical adsorption,** the molecules are held to the surface of the adsorbent by van der Waals forces; thus the adsorbed gas molecules are affected to about the same extent that they would be if the gas were liquefied.

In chemisorption, the adsorbed molecules are held to the catalytic surface by bonds comparable to those of chemical compounds. In the process of forming bonds with the adsorbent, chemisorbed molecules undergo internal electron rearrangements. The bonding within certain molecules is stretched and weakened, and the bonds of some molecules are even broken. For example, hydrogen is adsorbed in atomic form on the surface of platinum. Thus the chemisorbed layer of molecules functions as an activated complex in a surface-catalyzed reaction.

At the present time, chemisorption and surface catalysis are far from completely understood; we can only make reasonable postulates for the mechanisms of specific reactions. A suggested mechanism for the decomposition of N_2O on gold is diagrammed in Figure 12.7. Molecules of N_2O are chemisorbed on the surface of the gold, and the following reactions take place on this surface.

$$N_2O \rightarrow N_2(g) + O$$
$$O + O \rightarrow O_2(g)$$

The release of the gaseous products from the surface is called **desorption.**

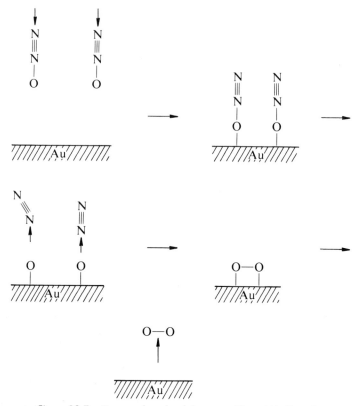

Figure 12.7   Proposed mode of decomposition of N_2O on Au.

Some empirical observations have great utility in the selection of suitable catalysts for particular reactions; for example, most reactions of gaseous hydrogen are catalyzed by platinum. However, the fundamental theory of catalytic processes has not been developed to the point where it can be used to select or design a catalyst for a specific use. It appears that the electronic structure of the solid as well as the geometric arrangement and spacing of the atoms on the surface of the solid are critical considerations.

It has been proposed that lattice defects or irregularities in the surface of the catalyst are active sites for catalysis; this hypothesis has been used to explain the action of **promoters,** which are materials that enhance the activity of catalysts. For example, in the synthesis of ammonia,

$$2N_2(g) + 3H_2(g) \xrightarrow{\text{Fe}} 2NH_3(g)$$

an iron catalyst is made more effective by incorporating traces of potassium or vanadium.

Catalytic **poisons** are substances that inhibit the activity of catalysts. For example, small amounts of arsenic destroy the power of platinum to catalyze the preparation of sulfur trioxide from sulfur dioxide.

$$2SO_2(g) + O_2(g) \xrightarrow{\text{Pt}} 2SO_3(g)$$

Presumably, platinum arsenide forms on the surface of the platinum and destroys its catalytic activity.

Catalysts are generally highly specific in their activity. In some cases, a given substance will catalyze the synthesis of one set of products from certain reagents, whereas another substance will catalyze the synthesis of completely different products from the same reactants. In these instances, of course, both reactions are thermodynamically sound. Carbon monoxide and hydrogen can be made to yield a wide variety of products depending upon the catalyst employed and the conditions of the reaction.

If a cobalt or nickel catalyst is used, CO and H_2 produce mixtures of hydrocarbons. For example,

$$CO(g) + 3H_2(g) \xrightarrow{\text{Ni}} CH_4(g) + H_2O(g)$$

On the other hand, methanol is the product of the reaction of CO and H_2 when a mixture of zinc and chromic oxides is employed as a catalyst.

$$CO(g) + 2H_2(g) \xrightarrow{\text{ZnO/Cr}_2\text{O}_3} CH_3OH(g)$$

12.4 Heterogeneous Reactions

Heterogeneous reactions occur on a surface or phase boundary; hence, the rate of such a reaction can be greatly increased if the surface is increased. In a reaction between a solid and a gas, or a solid and a liquid, the total number of collisions per unit time can be increased by pulverizing the solid. A finely divided combustible material may burn with such rapidity as to produce an explosion. The rate of a heterogeneous process may be increased by agitation of the reacting mixture since agitation keeps the reactive surface continuously exposed. Thus sugar dissolves more quickly in coffee if the mixture is stirred.

For this same reason, surface catalysts are usually prepared in a way that will produce a large surface area for a given amount of solid. Solids used as catalysts are generally porous and extremely finely divided.

12.5 Concentrations and Reaction Rates

Reaction rate is generally dependent upon the concentrations of the reacting substances. When the concentration of a reactant is increased, more molecules are crowded into a given volume, and the total number of molecular collisions per unit time is increased; this results in an increase in the rate of the reaction. If all other conditions are held constant, there is no change in the proportion of collisions that are effective.

Many different techniques are employed to study reaction rates—the appropriate one depending upon the reaction under consideration. In addition to chemical analysis, physical methods are sometimes used to follow the progress of chemical reactions. These physical methods are applicable only when some measurable change takes place in the course of the reaction; for example, physical methods have been devised to study reactions in which there is a change in one of the following: total pressure, color (appearance or disappearance of a colored substance), acidity or alkalinity, conductivity, volume, or viscosity.

Since the concentrations of the reactants decrease as the reaction proceeds, the rate of a chemical reaction decreases with time as well. In Figure 12.8 concentrations are plotted against time for the hypothetical reaction

$$A_2 + B_2 \longrightarrow 2AB$$

The rate of the reaction, in terms of the change in concentration of A_2, B_2, or AB per unit time is given by the slope of the appropriate curve. The rate of this reaction may be expressed in terms of the rate of disappearance of A_2 and B_2 or the rate of appearance of AB; because of the stoichiometry of the reaction, these rates are not equal. The rate of appearance of AB is twice that of the rate of disappearance of A_2 and B_2.

Concentrations are generally expressed in moles per liter (molarity for substances in solution); in mathematical expressions, the concentration of a substance is usually represented by its formula enclosed in brackets. Since the pressure of a gas is a measure of its concentration, expressions are frequently derived on the basis of the partial pressures of reacting gases (in millimeters of mercury or atmospheres); the partial pressure of nitrogen is given the symbol p_{N_2}.

For a chemical reaction, a mathematical expression (a **rate equation**) relating the concentrations of reactants to the reaction rate may usually

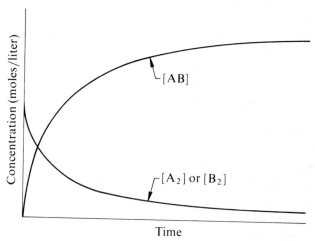

Figure 12.8 Curves showing changes in concentrations of materials with time for the reaction $A_2 + B_2 \longrightarrow 2AB$.

be determined experimentally. The chemical equation for a reaction stoichiometrically describes only the initial reactants and final products; frequently, the chemical change itself occurs by way of a mechanism consisting of several steps. Each of these steps proceeds at its own rate— some rapid, some slow—and each is dependent upon the concentrations of the initial reactants and/or the reaction intermediates. Therefore the rate expression for the chemical reaction may not generally be derived from an inspection of the balanced chemical equation for the overall chemical change but must be determined experimentally.

For reactions that are known to be simple one-step processes (which itself must be determined experimentally), a rate expression can be derived from the chemical equation; such reactions are not numerous. For example, we have assumed the reaction

$$A_2(g) + B_2(g) \rightarrow 2AB(g)$$

proceeds in one step through collisions between A_2 molecules and B_2 molecules. If the concentration of A_2 is doubled in a given system, the number of A_2 molecules is doubled. In this instance, the number of A_2—B_2 collisions per second is doubled, and the reaction rate is doubled. If the conecentration of B_2 is doubled and the concentration of A_2 is constant, the same effect on the rate is observed. Doubling both the A_2 and B_2 concentrations increases the reaction rate by a factor of four. The rate of the reaction, then, is proportional to the product of the concentrations of A_2 and B_2, or

$$\text{rate} = k[A_2][B_2]$$

The proportionality constant, k, is called the **rate constant;** its numerical value is dependent upon temperature, catalysis, and the terms in which the reaction rate is expressed.

The rate equation may also be expressed in terms of pressures,

$$\text{rate} = k p_{A_2} p_{B_2}$$

The value of k in this equation is not the same as that of the previous rate equation.

The reaction

$$2N_2O(g) \rightarrow 2N_2(g) + O_2(g)$$

proceeds by means of collisions between two N_2O molecules. For a given system of definite volume, the number of collisions per second for a *single* N_2O molecule is proportional to the total number of molecules present less one $(n - 1)$. This is true of all n of the molecules present so that the total number of collisions per second is proportional to $\frac{1}{2} n$ $(n - 1)$. The factor $\frac{1}{2}$ must be included so that a given collision is not counted twice—once for each molecule in the collision. The number of molecules in a sample is so large that $(n - 1)$ is approximately equal to n; thus the total number of collisions per second is proportional to $\frac{1}{2} n^2$ to a good approximation. The constant $\frac{1}{2}$ may be incorporated into the rate constant and the number of molecules of N_2O in the system is proportional to the concentration of N_2O. Thus

$$\text{rate} = k\,[N_2O]^2$$

In general, for any single step reaction (or for one step of a multistep mechanism) such as

$$w\,W + x\,X + \cdots \longrightarrow \text{products}$$

the rate equation is

$$\text{rate} = k\,[W]^w[X]^x\cdots$$

This is a statement of the **law of mass action** which was first expressed in general form by Cato Guldberg and Peter Waage in 1864. If the reactants are gases, similar expressions using partial pressures may be derived.

The **order** of a rate equation is given by the sum of the exponents of the concentrations appearing in the equation. Thus for the reaction between NO and O_2 listed in Table 12.2, the rate expression is said to be

TABLE 12.2.
RATE EQUATIONS FOR SOME GAS PHASE REACTIONS.

First Order	
$2N_2O_5 \longrightarrow 4NO_2 + O_2$	$\text{rate} = k\,[N_2O_5]$
$2N_2O \xrightarrow{\text{Au}} 2N_2 + O_2$	$\text{rate} = k\,[N_2O]$
$SO_2Cl_2 \longrightarrow SO_2 + Cl_2$	$\text{rate} = k\,[SO_2Cl_2]$
$2NO_2Cl \longrightarrow 2NO_2 + Cl_2$	$\text{rate} = k\,[NO_2Cl]$
$N_2O_4 \longrightarrow 2NO_2$	$\text{rate} = k\,[N_2O_4]$

Second Order	
$2N_2O \rightarrow 2N_2 + O_2$	$\text{rate} = k\,[N_2O]^2$
$2NOCl \rightarrow 2NO + Cl_2$	$\text{rate} = k\,[NOCl]^2$
$2NO_2 \rightarrow 2NO + O_2$	$\text{rate} = k\,[NO_2]^2$

Third Order	
$2NO + O_2 \rightarrow 2NO_2$	$\text{rate} = k\,[NO]^2[O_2]$
$2NO + Cl_2 \rightarrow 2NOCl$	$\text{rate} = k\,[NO]^2[Cl_2]$
$2NO + Br_2 \rightarrow 2NOBr$	$\text{rate} = k\,[NO]^2[Br_2]$

second order in NO, first order in O_2, and third order overall. Since experimentally determined rate expressions may represent a mathematical summary of several rate equations (one for each step of a multistep mechanism), equations of fractional order are sometimes obtained.

Example 12.1   The data of Table 12.3 were obtained at 25°C for the reaction

$$S_2O_8^{2-}(aq) + 2I^-(aq) \rightarrow 2SO_4^{2-}(aq) + I_2(aq)$$

What is the rate equation for the reaction and the value of k?

TABLE 12.3

Experiment	Initial Conc. $S_2O_8^{2-}$ (M)	Initial Conc. I^- (M)	Initial Rate— Increase in Conc. of I_2 (M/min.)
A	1.0×10^{-4}	1.0×10^{-2}	0.65×10^{-6}
B	2.0×10^{-4}	1.0×10^{-2}	1.30×10^{-6}
C	2.0×10^{-4}	0.5×10^{-2}	0.65×10^{-6}

Solution   Comparison of the data from experiment A with that from experiment B shows that the rate is doubled when the concentration of $S_2O_8^{2-}$ is doubled. According to the data from experiments B and C, doubling the concentration of I^- has the same effect on the reaction rate. The reaction, therefore, is first order in $S_2O_8^{2-}$, first order in I^-, and second order overall.

$$\text{rate} = k\,[S_2O_8^{2-}][I^-]$$

Note that the chemical equation for the reaction might lead one to expect a rate expression of third order.

The data from any of the experiments may be used to derive the value for the rate constant; $k = 0.65/M$ min.

12.6   Reaction Mechanisms and Rate Equations

Mechanisms of chemical reactions are generally proposed on the basis of experimentally derived rate equations and other experimental evidence (e.g., the detection of short-lived reaction intermediates). It is practically impossible to be completely certain of the mechanism of any reaction; mechanisms are only plausible hypotheses consistent with all known facts.

Table 12.2 lists the uncatalyzed decomposition of N_2O as a second-order reaction, whereas the gold catalyzed decomposition of the same compound is listed as a first-order reaction. The uncatalyzed reaction is thought to be a simple one-step process involving bimolecular collisions (Section 12.5); such a mechanism would call for a second-order rate expression.

On the other hand, the gold catalyzed reaction (Section 12.3, Figure 12.7) is thought to occur by chemisorption of N_2O molecules on gold followed by

$$N_2O \rightarrow N_2(g) + O \qquad \text{(slow)}$$

$$O + O \rightarrow O_2(g) \qquad \qquad \text{(rapid)}$$

The rate expression for either the chemisorption or the first reaction is first order since the rate of either is determined by the concentration of N_2O. However, there is evidence that the first reaction is the slower process and as such is the **rate-determining step.** The second reaction occurs much more rapidly than the first; as fast as the first reaction produces oxygen atoms, the second reaction uses them up. The first reaction, therefore, is the bottleneck and determines the overall rate of the entire process.

The decomposition of NO_2 is second order.

$$2NO_2(g) \rightarrow 2NO(g) + O_2(g)$$

$$\text{rate} = k\,[NO_2]^2$$

Even though the chemical equation for the uncatalyzed decomposition of N_2O_5 is very similar,

$$2N_2O_5(g) \rightarrow 4NO_2(g) + O_2(g)$$

this reaction has been found to be first order.

$$\text{rate} = k\,[N_2O_5]$$

We could account for the observed rate expression by visualizing a simple one-step unimolecular decomposition or a rate-determining unimolecular decomposition followed by one or more rapid steps.

However, there is evidence that the following is the mechanism for the decomposition of N_2O_5, with the third step being the slowest one.

$$N_2O_5 \xrightarrow{k_1} NO_2 + NO_3$$

$$NO_2 + NO_3 \xrightarrow{k_2} N_2O_5$$

$$NO_2 + NO_3 \xrightarrow{k_3} NO + O_2 + NO_2$$

$$NO + NO_3 \xrightarrow{k_4} 2\,NO_2$$

The second step listed is the reverse of the first.

We can reconcile this mechanism with the experimentally determined rate expression by the use of a **steady state approximation.** It is assumed that, after the reaction has proceeded for a while, the concentrations of the intermediates NO and NO_3 (which do not appear as final products) obtain constant values; the rate of change in the concentration of these intermediates is, therefore, set equal to zero. In any event, the concentrations of these substances are extremely small so that the rates of change may be set equal to zero without significant error. The third reaction (the slowest one) produces NO at a much slower rate than it is used in the fourth reaction. The intermediate NO_3 is produced only by the first reaction, whereas it is consumed by the second, third, and fourth reactions.

Applying the law of mass action to the appropriate steps, we derive an expression for the rate of increase in the concentration of NO which, according to the steady state approximation, is equal to zero. Nitrogen oxide is *produced* in the third reaction at a rate equal to $k_3[NO_2][NO_3]$; it is *used* in the fourth reaction at a rate equal to $k_4[NO][NO_3]$. Therefore the rate of *production* of NO is

$$+k_3[NO_2][NO_3] - k_4[NO][NO_3] = 0$$

From this, we derive

$$[NO] = \frac{k_3}{k_4}[NO_2] \qquad (1)$$

In like manner, we can derive an expression for the rate of *production* of NO_3

$$+k_1[N_2O_5] - k_2[NO_2][NO_3] - k_3[NO_2][NO_3] - k_4[NO][NO_3] = 0$$

Solving for $[NO_3]$, we get

$$[NO_3] = \frac{k_1[N_2O_5]}{(k_2 + k_3)[NO_2] + k_4[NO]}$$

If we substitute equation (1) into this expression, we derive

$$[NO_3] = \frac{k_1[N_2O_5]}{(k_2 + 2k_3)[NO_2]} \qquad (2)$$

We are now ready to find a single rate equation for the overall reaction in terms of the concentration of the starting material, N_2O_5. From the chemical equations for the first two steps of the mechanism,

$$\text{rate of } \textit{decrease} \text{ in } [N_2O_5] = +k_1[N_2O_5] - k_2[NO_2][NO_3]$$

Substitution of (2) yields

$$= k_1[N_2O_5] - k_2[NO_2]\left(\frac{k_1[N_2O_5]}{(k_2 + 2k_3)[NO_2]}\right)$$

$$= \frac{2k_1k_3}{k_2 + 2k_3}[N_2O_5]$$

If we combine all of the rate constants into a single constant, we get

$$\text{rate of decrease in } [N_2O_5] = k\,[N_2O_5]$$

which is the experimentally determined rate equation.

The mathematical treatment of mechanisms of other chemical reactions may be much more involved; it is not surprising that complicated rate equations, which may be of fractional order, are often derived from the data obtained from experimental studies of chemical reactions.

The study of reactions that are initiated by means of light is called **photochemistry.** The most famous example of a photochemical reaction is photosynthesis which occurs in plants and converts carbon dioxide and water into plant carbohydrates. The green coloring-matter in plants, chlorophyll, acts as a catalyst for photosynthesis.

Light also initiates the reaction between hydrogen and chlorine. The primary, light-induced, step of the reaction is the dissociation of chlorine molecules into chlorine atoms.

$$Cl_2 \rightarrow 2Cl$$

These chlorine atoms initiate a **chain reaction** in which the cycle

$$Cl + H_2 \rightarrow HCl + H$$
$$H + Cl_2 \rightarrow HCl + Cl$$

is repeated again and again. A chain may be terminated by such reactions as

$$2H \rightarrow H_2$$
$$2Cl \rightarrow Cl_2$$

or

$$H + Cl \rightarrow HCl$$

Chain reactions usually proceed very rapidly. Many explosive reactions occur by a chain mechanism; atomic fission and atomic fusion are of this type. In the reaction of hydrogen and chlorine, the chain is sustained by the chlorine atoms and the hydrogen atoms; these extremely reactive intermediates are called chain propagators.

A branched chain reaction, such as that between hydrogen and oxygen is a reaction in which one or more of the steps produce more than one chain propagator. Following are some of the steps that have been postulated for the H_2–O_2 reaction.

(1) $$H_2 + O_2 \rightarrow 2OH$$

(2) $$OH + H_2 \rightarrow H_2O + H$$

(3) $$H + O_2 \rightarrow OH + O$$

(4) $$O + H_2 \rightarrow OH + H$$

Reaction (1) is a chain-initiating step, and reaction (2) merely sustains the chain. The chain propagators are OH, H, and O, and steps (3) and (4) are chain-branching steps. Each of these steps produces two chain propagators so that two reactions follow from either reaction (3) or reaction (4); this increases the overall rate of the reaction. Chains terminate upon collisions of the chain propagators—usually at the walls of the container. Generally, a third body is necessary in these collisions to absorb the energy evolved by the highly exothermic recombination.

12.7   Reversible Reactions and Chemical Equilibrium

In Sections 12.1 and 12.2 we discussed the reversible reaction

$$A_2(g) + B_2(g) \rightleftharpoons 2AB(g)$$

This equation may be read either forward or backward. If A_2 and B_2 are mixed, they react to produce AB. The rate of this forward reaction declines as the reaction proceeds since A_2 and B_2 are used up and their concentrations decrease. If no AB is present at the start, the backward reaction is initially impossible. However, the forward reaction produces AB, so that the backward reaction begins soon after the A_2 and B_2 are mixed. This reaction starts slowly (the concentration of AB is low) but picks up speed as the concentration of AB is built up by the more rapid forward reaction.

With time, the forward reaction rate decreases and the backward reaction rate increases until eventually a condition is reached in which the two rates are equal. At this point, chemical equilibrium is established, and the concentrations of all chemical species are constant. The rate at which AB is produced by the forward reactions equals the rate at which AB is consumed by the backward reaction. In like manner, A_2 and B_2 are produced at rates exactly equal to the rates at which they are used.

It is important to note that equilibrium is a dynamic condition; equilibrium concentrations are constant because the rates of the opposing reactions are equal and not because all activity has ceased. Typical data for this reaction are plotted in Figure 12.9; equilibrium is attained at t_e.

The rate of the forward reaction is given by

$$\text{rate}_f = k[A_2][B_2]$$

and the rate of the backward reaction is

$$\text{rate}_b = k'[AB]^2$$

At equilibrium these rates are equal, and therefore,

$$k[A_2][B_2] = k'[AB]^2$$

or

$$\frac{k}{k'} = \frac{[AB]^2}{[A_2][B_2]}$$

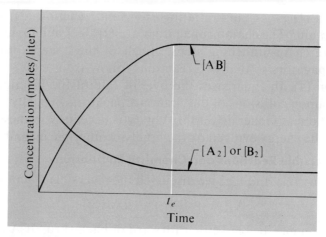

Figure 12.9 *Curves showing changes in concentrations of materials with time for the reaction* $A_2 + B_2 \rightleftharpoons 2AB$; *equilibrium is attained at time* t_e.

The rate constant of the forward reaction, k, divided by the rate constant of the backward reaction, k', is equal to a third constant—the **equilibrium constant**, K.

$$K = \frac{[AB]^2}{[A_2][B_2]}$$

The numerical value of K varies with temperature. There are an infinite number of possible equilibrium systems for this reaction. However, the concentrations of A_2, B_2, and AB for any system in equilibrium will, when expressed in the preceding manner, equal K for the particular temperature under consideration.

In general, for any reversible reaction,

$$w\,W + x\,X + \cdots \rightleftharpoons y\,Y + z\,Z + \cdots$$

at equilibrium,

$$K = \frac{[Y]^y\,[Z]^z \cdots}{[W]^w[X]^x \cdots}$$

By convention, the concentration terms for the materials on the right of the chemical equation are written in the numerator of the expression for the equilibrium constant. If the equation is written in reverse form, the equilibrium constant becomes the reciprocal of that for the original equation. The preceding equation constitutes a statement of the **law of chemical equilibrium** which Guldberg and Waage derived from their law of mass action (Section 12.5).

In the rate equation for the reaction of A_2 and B_2 and the rate equation for the decomposition of AB, the exponents of the concentrations correspond to the coefficients of the balanced chemical equation. In this instance, both the forward and backward reactions occur through single-step bimolecular collisions, and the rate expressions may be derived from the chemical equation. It is not immediately apparent that the law of chemical equilibrium holds for a reaction that occurs by means of a mechanism of more than one step. However, an equilibrium constant may be derived for any reversible chemical change on the basis of the overall equation for the change.

For example, the forward reaction

$$2NO_2Cl \rightleftharpoons 2NO_2 + Cl_2$$

is first order; $rate_f = k[NO_2Cl]$. The reaction is assumed to follow the mechanism

$$NO_2Cl \overset{k_1}{\rightleftharpoons} NO_2 + Cl$$

$$NO_2Cl + Cl \overset{k_2}{\rightleftharpoons} NO_2 + Cl_2$$

Both steps of the mechanism must be reversible, and when equilibrium is established for the overall change, each step of the mechanism must exist in equilibrium. Thus

$$K_a = \frac{k_1}{k_1'} = \frac{[NO_2][Cl]}{[NO_2Cl]}$$

and

$$K_b = \frac{k_2}{k_2'} = \frac{[NO_2][Cl_2]}{[NO_2Cl][Cl]}$$

By combining these expressions, we get

$$K_a K_b = \frac{k_1 k_2}{k_1' k_2'} = \frac{[NO_2]^2[Cl_2]}{[NO_2Cl]^2}$$

which is the same as the expression for the equilibrium constant that would have been derived directly from the equation for the overall change. In this case, the equilibrium constant for the overall change is the product of the equilibrium constants of each of the steps.

12.8 Equilibrium Constants

For the reaction

$$H_2(g) + I_2(g) \rightleftharpoons 2HI(g)$$

the equilibrium constant at 425°C is

$$K = \frac{[HI]^2}{[H_2][I_2]} = 54.8$$

The numerical value of K must be determined experimentally. At 425°C, the concentrations of the materials present in any equilibrium mixture when expressed in the manner prescribed by the equilibrium constant will equal 54.8; if this is not the case, the mixture is not in equilibrium.

The equilibrium condition may be approached from either direction. That is, an equilibrium mixture can be obtained by mixing hydrogen and iodine, by allowing pure hydrogen iodide to dissociate, or by mixing all three materials.

The magnitude of the value of the equilibrium constant gives an indication of the position of equilibrium. Recall that the concentration terms of materials on the right of the equation are written in the numerator of the expression for the equilibrium constant. For the reaction

$$CO(g) + Cl_2(g) \rightleftharpoons COCl_2(g)$$

at 100°C,

$$K = \frac{[COCl_2]}{[CO][Cl_2]} = 4.57 \times 10^9$$

From this relatively large value of K, we conclude that equilibrium concentrations of CO and Cl_2 are small and that the synthesis of $COCl_2$ is virtually complete. In other words, the reaction to the right is fairly complete at equilibrium

For the reaction

$$N_2(g) + O_2(g) \rightleftharpoons 2NO(g)$$

at 2000°C,

$$K = \frac{[NO]^2}{[N_2][O_2]} = 4.08 \times 10^{-4}$$

We conclude from this small value of K that NO is largely dissociated into N_2 and O_2 at equilibrium; the reaction to the left is fairly complete.

Equilibria between substances in two or more phases are called **heterogeneous equilibria.** The concentrations of pure solids or pure liquids are proportional to their densities and are constant at constant temperature. Hence, for any heterogeneous equilibrium, the values of the concentrations of solids or liquids involved are included in the value of K, and concentration terms for these substances do not appear in the expression for the equilibrium constant.

For example, for the reaction

$$CaCO_3(s) \rightleftharpoons CaO(s) + CO_2(g)$$

the values for the concentrations of CaO and $CaCO_3$ are included in the value of K, and the expression for the equilibrium constant is

$$K = [CO_2]$$

Hence at any temperature, the equilibrium concentration of CO_2 over a mixture of the solids is a definite value. The equilibrium constant for the reaction

$$3Fe(s) + 4H_2O(g) \rightleftharpoons Fe_3O_4(s) + 4H_2(g)$$

is expressed in the following terms

$$K = \frac{[H_2]^4}{[H_2O]^4}$$

Since the partial pressure of a gas is a measure of its concentration, equilibrium constants for reactions involving gases may be given in terms of the partial pressures of the reacting gases; such an equilibrium constant is given the designation K_p. For the calcium carbonate equilibrium, the constant in terms of partial pressures is

$$K_p = p_{CO_2}$$

For the equilibrium

$$N_2(g) + 3H_2(g) \rightleftharpoons 2NH_3(g)$$

the K_p is

$$K_p = \frac{(p_{NH_3})^2}{(p_{N_2})(p_{H_2})^3}$$

There is a simple relation between the K_p for a reaction and the equilibrium constant derived from concentrations. Consider the reaction

$$wW + xX \rightleftharpoons yY + zZ$$

If all of these materials are gases,

$$K_p = \frac{(p_Y)^y(p_Z)^z}{(p_W)^w(p_X)^x}$$

If we assume that these gases follow the ideal gas law, the partial pressure of any gas is

$$p = \frac{n}{V} RT$$

The concentration of a gas in moles per liter is equal to n/V. Hence, for W,

$$p_W = [W]RT$$

If we substitute terms such as this for the partial pressures in the expression for K_p, we get

$$K_p = \frac{[Y]^y(RT)^y[Z]^z(RT)^z}{[W]_w(RT)^w[X]^x(RT)^x} = K(RT)^{+y+z-w-x}$$

We shall designate the quantity $(+y+z-w-x)$, which is equal to the number of moles of products minus the number of moles of reactants, as Δn. Therefore

$$K_p = K(RT)^{\Delta n}$$

Generally, partial pressures are expressed in atmospheres; concentrations are expressed in moles per liter; R is 0.08206 liter atm/°K mole; and T is the absolute temperature.

It is obvious that when $\Delta n = 0$, as in the reaction

$$H_2(g) + I_2(g) \rightleftharpoons 2HI(g)$$

$K = K_p$.

To be strictly accurate, equations for equilibrium constants should be given in terms of activities rather than concentrations or partial pressures. The activity of a substance may be regarded as its effective concentration and may be obtained by multiplying the actual concentration by an activity coefficient (Section 8.12). By this means, deviations, due principally to the existence of intermolecular forces of attraction, may be minimized. However, at low concentrations and pressures up to a few atmospheres, ideality may be assumed, and concentrations may be used with reasonable accuracy.

Example 12.2   For the reaction

$$N_2O_4(g) \rightleftharpoons 2NO_2(g)$$

the concentrations of an equilibrium mixture at 25°C are $[N_2O_4] = 4.50 \times 10^{-2}$ moles/liter and $[NO_2] = 1.61 \times 10^{-2}$ moles/liter. What is K?

Solution

$$K = \frac{[NO_2]^2}{[N_2O_4]}$$

$$= \frac{(1.61 \times 10^{-2}\,\text{moles/liter})^2}{(4.50 \times 10^{-2}\,\text{moles/liter})}$$

$$= 5.76 \times 10^{-3}\,\text{moles/liter}$$

Example 12.3   What is K for the reaction

$$N_2(g) + 3H_2(g) \rightleftharpoons 2NH_3(g)$$

at 500°C if $K_p = 1.50 \times 10^{-5}/\text{atm}^2$ at this temperature?

Solution   For the reaction, $\Delta n = -2$

$$K = K_p(RT)^{-\Delta n}$$

$$= (1.50 \times 10^{-5}/\text{atm}^2)\,[(0.08206\ \text{liter atm/°K mole})(773°K)]^2$$

$$= 6.04 \times 10^{-2}\ \text{liter}^2/\text{mole}^2$$

Example 12.4 K for the reaction

$$H_2(g) + CO_2(g) \rightleftharpoons H_2O(g) + CO(g)$$

at 750°C is 0.771. If 1 mole of H_2 and 1 mole of CO_2 are mixed in a 1 liter container at 750°C, what are the concentrations of all substances at equilibrium?

Solution   If x moles of H_2 react with x moles of CO_2, then x moles of H_2O and x moles of CO will be produced. Since the container has a volume of 1 liter, at equilibrium the concentrations are (in moles/liter):

$$H_2(g) + CO_2(g) \rightleftharpoons H_2O(g) + CO(g)$$
$$(1 - x) \quad (1 - x) \qquad x \qquad x$$

$$K = \frac{[H_2O][CO]}{[H_2][CO_2]} = 0.771$$

$$= \frac{x^2}{(1 - x)(1 - x)} = 0.771$$

If we extract the square root of both sides of this equation, we get

$$\frac{x}{(1 - x)} = 0.878$$

$$x = 0.468$$

Therefore, at equilibrium,

$$[H_2] = [CO_2] = (1 - x) = 0.532 \text{ moles/liter}$$
$$[H_2O] = [CO] = x = 0.468 \text{ moles/liter}$$

12.9   Free Energy and Chemical Equilibrium

The law of chemical equilibrium can be derived from thermodynamics as well as from kinetics. At constant temperature and pressure, any spontaneous chemical change results in a decrease in the Gibbs free energy of a system (Section 11.9). If the ΔG for a proposed reaction is positive, net work must be done on the system to bring about the change; the reaction is not spontaneous. If ΔG is negative, the reaction is spontaneous and, in theory, can be used to accomplish net work. At equilibrium, $\Delta G = 0$ since there is no *net* change in the system that requires work or that can be harnessed to do work. The macroscopic properties of a system in equilibrium do not change with time (the concentrations of all substances present are constant) even though the reversible reaction is proceeding in both directions.

Equation (7) in Section 9.9,

$$\Delta G = \Delta G° + RT \ln \left(\frac{(a_Y)^y (a_Z)^z}{(a_W)^w (a_X)^x} \right)$$

was derived for the reaction

$$w W + x X \rightleftharpoons y Y + z Z$$

In this equation, $\Delta G°$ is the change in free energy for the preparation of the products in their standard states from the reactants in their standard states; the logarithmic term corrects the standard free-energy change to the free-energy change for a more general condition in which the activities of the substances are not unity. We shall use the approximations that the activity of gases are given by their partial pressures and the activities of substances in solution equal their concentrations.

At equilibrium, $\Delta G = 0$, and if we assume that the preceding reaction takes place in the gas phase,

$$0 = \Delta G° + RT \ln\left(\frac{(p_Y)^y(p_Z)^z}{(p_W)^w(p_X)^x}\right)$$

But, this fraction is simply an equilibrium constant in terms of partial pressures. Therefore,

$$\Delta G° = -RT \ln K_p$$

If $\Delta G°$ is expressed in terms of kilocalories and the natural logarithm is converted to a base 10 logarithm, at 25°C,

$$\Delta G° = -1.364 \log K_p$$

The partial pressures used in K_p are expressed in atmospheres. A similar expression can be derived for equilibrium constants that are based on concentrations (in moles per liter).

This relationship between $\Delta G°$ and K is an important one since it may be used to calculate equilibrium constants from thermochemical data. Furthermore, since

$$\Delta G° = -nFE°$$

(Section 9.7), electrochemical data can be used to calculate equilibrium constants for reactions that can be studied in voltaic cells.

The change in free energy of a system in which the reaction

$$N_2O_4(g) \rightleftharpoons 2NO_2(g)$$

occurs is plotted in Figure 12.10. The curve is plotted for the reaction at 25°C and a total pressure of 1 atm, and for a system containing the equivalent of 1 mole of N_2O_4. Point A, therefore, represents the free energy of 1 mole of N_2O_4; point B represents the free energy of 2 moles of NO_2; and the intervening points on the curve represent mixtures of N_2O_4 and NO_2 such that a material balance exists. The absolute values of free energies are not known, and no scale is indicated on the vertical axis of the diagram; however, differences in free energies may be calculated so that the shape of the curve is accurately represented.

The free energy of the system exhibits a minimum at the equilibrium

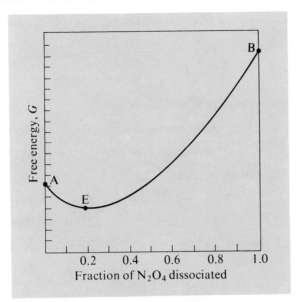

Figure 12.10 *Free energy of a system that contains the equivalent of 1 mole of N_2O_4 as the reaction $N_2O_4(g) \rightleftharpoons 2NO_2(g)$ occurs (25°C and 1 atm pressure).*

point, E, where 18.5% of the N_2O_4 is dissociated; $K_p = 0.141$. Since standard free energies are defined in terms of a total pressure of 1 atm, the difference between the free energy at point B and the free energy at point A (+1.15 kcal) is the $\Delta G°$ of the reaction. On this basis alone, one might predict that the formation of NO_2 from N_2O_4 is impossible. However, the difference between the free energy of pure N_2O_4 (point A) and the free energy of the equilibrium mixture (point E), which is -0.22 kcal, shows that N_2O_4 will dissociate into NO_2 until equilibrium is reached.

The graph shows that equilibrium may be approached from either direction, and experiment bears this out. Thus $\Delta G = -1.37$ kcal for the preparation of the equilibrium mixture (point E) from pure NO_2 (point B). The negative values of ΔG for both changes (from A to E and from B to E) indicate that both changes are spontaneous.

Example 12.5 Calculate K_p for the following reaction at 25°C.

$$2SO_2(g) + O_2(g) \rightleftharpoons 2SO_3(g)$$

$\Delta G°_f(SO_2) = -71.79$ kcal/mole; $\Delta G°_f(SO_3) = -88.52$ kcal/mole.

Solution The standard free energy change for the reaction is

$\Delta G° = 2 \text{ mole } (-88.52 \text{ kcal/mole}) - 2 \text{ mole } (-71.79 \text{ kcal/mole})$

$\Delta G° = -33.46$ kcal

K_p may be calculated from this value.

$$\Delta G^\circ = -1.364 \log K_p$$

$$\log K_p = \frac{-33.46 \text{ kcal}}{-1.364 \text{ kcal}} = 22.09$$

$$K_p = 1.2 \times 10^{22}$$

The reaction to the right is virtually complete.

Example 12.6   Using electrochemical data, calculate K for the reaction

$$Fe^{2+} + Ag^+(aq) \rightleftharpoons Fe^{3+}(aq) + Ag(s)$$

Solution   The half reactions are

$$Fe^{2+} \rightarrow Fe^{3+} + e^- \qquad E^\circ_{ox} = -0.771 \text{ v}$$
$$e^- + Ag^+ \rightarrow Ag(s) \qquad E^\circ = +0.799 \text{ v}$$

Therefore, $E^\circ = +0.028$ v and 1 F of electricity is involved. The standard change in free energy is

$$\Delta G^\circ = -nFE^\circ$$
$$= -1 \, (23.1 \text{ kcal/v})(0.028 \text{ v})$$
$$= -0.65 \text{ kcal}$$

The equilibrium constant may be calculated from:

$$\Delta G^\circ = -1.36 \log K$$

$$\log K = \frac{-0.65 \text{ kcal}}{-1.36 \text{ kcal}} = 0.48$$

$$K = 3.0$$

12.10   Le Chatelier's Principle

The effect of an alteration in a reaction condition on a system in equilibrium was summarized in 1884 by Henri Le Chatelier. **Le Chatelier's principle** may be stated as: an alteration in any condition that determines the state of a system in equilibrium will cause the position of equilibrium to shift in a manner that tends to counteract the alteration. This important and powerful generalization is very simple to apply.

Alterations in three conditions cause changes in the position of equilibrium: concentration, pressure, and temperature.   Of these three, only a change in temperature will affect the value of the equilibrium constant. The presence or absence of a catalyst has no effect on the position of equilibrium since a catalyst will affect the rate of the forward and backward reaction to an equal extent (Section 12.3).   However, the introduction of a catalyst into a system not in equilibrium will cause the system to attain equilibrium more rapidly than it otherwise would.

If we have a system in equilibrium,

$$H_2(g) + I_2(g) \rightleftharpoons 2HI(g)$$

and we increase the concentration of H_2, the equilibrium will be upset and the system will react to establish a new equilibrium condition. When equilibrium is again attained, the concentration of HI will be increased over its initial value; the concentration of I_2 will be decreased in comparison to its initial value; and the concentration of H_2 will be lower than its value after the addition. In summary, the reaction will proceed to the right, thereby partially counteracting the alteration and decreasing the concentration of H_2.

If additional HI is added to a system in equilibrium, the reaction will proceed to the left, thus increasing the concentrations of H_2 and I_2 and using up HI. Removal of one of the substances from an equilibrium system also cause the position of equilibrium to shift. For example, removal of HI would cause the reaction to proceed to the right, thus producing more HI and decreasing the concentrations of H_2 and I_2.

Example 12.7 K for the HI equilibrium

$$H_2(g) + I_2(g) \rightleftharpoons 2HI(g)$$

is 54.8 at 425°C, and for a particular equilibrium system the concentrations are: $[H_2] = [I_2] = 0.010$ moles/liter and $[HI] = 0.074$ moles/liter. If the concentration of HI is momentarily increased to 0.100 moles/liter, what will be the concentrations of all substances when a new equilibrium is established?

Solution If we consider 1 liter of the reaction mixture and let $2x$ be the number of additional moles of HI dissociated at equilibrium, then x additional moles of H_2 and x additional moles of I_2 will be formed at equilibrium. The new equilibrium concentrations will be (in moles/liter):

$$H_2(g) \quad + \quad I_2(g) \quad \rightleftharpoons \quad 2HI(g)$$
$$(0.010 + x) \quad (0.010 + x) \quad (0.100 - 2x)$$

$$K = \frac{[HI]^2}{[H_2][I_2]} = 54.8$$

$$= \frac{(0.100 - 2x)^2}{(0.010 + x)^2} = 54.8$$

$$= \frac{(0.100 - 2x)}{(0.010 + x)} = 7.4$$

$$x = 0.0028$$

The new equilibrium concentrations are

$$[H_2] = [I_2] = 0.010 + x = 0.013 \text{ moles/liter}$$
$$[HI] = 0.100 - 2x = 0.094 \text{ moles/liter}$$

Le Chatelier's principle predicts that the position of equilibrium will shift to the left for a change of this type; this prediction is borne out by the calculation.

Le Chatelier's principle may also be used to make qualitative predictions of the effect of pressure changes on systems in equilibrium. Consider the effect of a pressure increase on an equilibrium mixture of SO_2, O_2, and SO_3.

$$2SO_2(g) + O_2(g) \rightleftharpoons 2SO_3(g)$$

In the forward reaction, two gas molecules ($2SO_3$) are produced by the disappearance of three gas molecules ($2SO_2 + O_2$); two gas molecules do not exert as high a pressure as three gas molecules. Hence, when the pressure on an equilibrium mixture is increased (or the volume of the system decreased), the position of equilibrium shifts to the right and thus counteracts the change. Alternatively, decreasing the pressure (or increasing the volume) would cause the position of this equilibrium to shift to the left.

For certain reactions, in which $\Delta n = 0$, pressure changes have no effect on the equilibria. For example, equilibria involving the systems

$$H_2(g) + I_2(g) \rightleftharpoons 2HI(g)$$
$$N_2(g) + O_2(g) \rightleftharpoons 2NO(g)$$
$$H_2(g) + CO_2(g) \rightleftharpoons H_2O(g) + CO(g)$$

are not influenced by changing the pressure since there is no difference in the total volume in either the forward or backward direction for any one of these reactions.

For a system that involves only liquids and solids, the effect of pressure on the position of equilibrium is slight and may usually be ignored for ordinary changes in pressure. However, large pressure changes can significantly alter such equilibria, and, at times, even slight changes in such equilibria are of interest. For example, the equilibrium

$$H_2O(s) \rightleftharpoons H_2O(l)$$

is forced to the right by an increase in pressure because a given quantity of water occupies a smaller volume in the liquid state than in the solid state (its density is higher).

Pressure changes affect equilibria involving gases to a much greater degree and are much more important. For example, a high pressure would favor the production of a high yield of ammonia from the equilibrium

$$N_2(g) + 3H_2(g) \rightleftharpoons 2NH_3(g)$$

Hence, Le Chatelier's principle is of practical importance as an aid in determining favorable reaction conditions for the production of a desired substance.

For heterogeneous equilibria, the effect of pressure is predicted by counting the number of *gas* molecules on each side of the equation. For example, the equilibrium

$$3Fe(s) + 4H_2O(g) \rightleftharpoons Fe_3O_4(s) + 4H_2(g)$$

is virtually unaffected by pressure because there are four gas molecules on each side of the equation.

Example 12.8 For the equilibrium

$$PCl_5(g) \rightleftharpoons PCl_3(g) + Cl_2(g)$$

$K = 4.16 \times 10^{-2}$ moles/liter at 250°C. In a given system at 250°C, the equilibrium concentrations are $[PCl_5] = 1$ mole/liter and $[PCl_3] = [Cl_2] = 0.204$ mole/liter. If the pressure is reduced by half (volume doubled), what are the new equilibrium concentrations?

Solution One would predict, by Le Chatelier's principle, that a decrease in pressure would favor the forward reaction since there are two gas molecules on the right and only one gas molecule on the left. Immediately after the initial change, the concentrations are each cut in half. For example, the concentration of PCl_5, instead of being 1 mole/liter, is now 1 mole/ 2 liters, or 0.5 mole/liter.

If when equilibrium is reestablished, x additional moles/liter of PCl_5 have dissociated, then x moles/liter of PCl_3 and x moles/liter of Cl_2 have been formed. The new equilibrium concentrations are (in moles/liter):

$$PCl_5(g) \quad \rightleftharpoons \quad PCl_3(g) \quad + \quad Cl_2(g)$$
$$(0.500 - x) \qquad (0.102 + x) \qquad (0.102 + x)$$

$$K = \frac{[PCl_3][Cl_2]}{[PCl_5]} = 4.16 \times 10^{-2} \text{ moles/liter}$$

$$\frac{(0.102 + x)^2}{(0.500 - x)} = 4.16 \times 10^{-2} \text{ moles/liter}$$

Expanding,

$$x^2 + 0.246x - 0.0104 = 0$$

By use of the quadratic formula,*

$$x = 0.0365$$

Therefore the new equilibrium concentrations are

$$[PCl_5] = 0.464 \text{ moles/liter}$$
$$[PCl_3] = [Cl_2] = 0.138 \text{ moles/liter}$$

In order to predict the effect of a temperature change on a system in equilibrium, the thermochemical nature of the chemical reaction must be known. At 25°C, the thermochemical equation for the synthesis of ammonia is

$$N_2(g) + 3H_2(g) \rightleftharpoons 2NH_3(g) + 22.1 \text{ kcal}$$

---

*For an equation in the form $ax^2 + bx + c = 0$, $x = \dfrac{-b \pm \sqrt{b^2 - 4ac}}{2a}$

The forward reaction is exothermic, and the backward reaction is endothermic. If the temperature of an equilibrium mixture is raised, the equilibrium will shift to the left—the direction that absorbs heat. Lowering the temperature favors the reaction to the right in which heat is produced. We conclude that the highest yields of ammonia are obtained at the lowest temperatures.

Thermochemical equations for reversible reactions may be written with the heat term on either the left or the right side of the equation. In each case, increasing the temperature favors the endothermic change, and decreasing the temperature favors the exothermic change. The reaction (ΔH measured at 25°C)

$$9.83 \text{ kcal} + CO_2(g) + H_2(g) \rightleftharpoons CO(g) + H_2O(g)$$

is forced to the right by an increase in temperature.

The numerical value of the equilibrium constant changes with a change in temperature. For the preceding reaction, the position of equilibrium is displaced to the right by an increase in temperature. Thus the concentrations of the materials on the right are increased; concentration terms for these materials appear in the numerator of the expression for K. Hence, as the temperature is increased, the value of K for this reaction increases; at 700°C, $K = 0.63$, and at 1000°C, $K = 1.66$.

SOME SUGGESTED READINGS

Bak, T. A., *Theory of Chemical Kinetics,* New York, Benjamin, 1963 (paper).

Basolo, F., and Pearson, R. G., *Mechanisms of Inorganic Reactions,* New York, Wiley, 1958.

Campbell, A. J., *Why Do Chemical Reactions Occur?*, Englewood Cliffs, N.J., Prentice-Hall, 1965 (paper).

Denbigh, K., *Principles of Chemical Equilibrium,* New York, Oxford, 1955 (paper).

Edwards, J. O., *Inorganic Reaction Mechanisms: An Introduction,* New York, Benjamin, 1964 (paper).

Eyring, H., and Eyring, E. M., *Modern Chemical Kinetics,* New York, Reinhold, 1963 (paper).

King, E. L., *How Chemical Reactions Occur,* New York, Benjamin, 1963 (paper).

Laidler, K. J., *Reaction Kinetics,* (2 vols.), New York, Pergamon, 1963 (paper).

Latham, J. L., *Elementary Reaction Kinetics,* Washington, D.C., Butterworth, 1962 (paper).

Prettre, M., *Catalysis and Catalysts,* New York, Dover, 1963 (paper).

Sykes, A. G., *Kinetics of Inorganic Reactions,* New York, Pergamon, 1966 (paper).

PROBLEMS

12.1 For a reaction of A and B to form C the following data were obtained from three experiments.

Experiment	[A]	[B]	Rate (formation of C)
1	$0.20\,M$	$0.20\,M$	$3.0 \times 10^{-4}\,M/\text{min}$
2	$0.60\,M$	$0.60\,M$	$81.0 \times 10^{-4}\,M/\text{min}$
3	$0.60\,M$	$0.20\,M$	$9.0 \times 10^{-4}\,M/\text{min}$

(a) What is the rate expression for the reaction? (b) What is the numerical value of the rate constant, k? (c) Give a plausible equation for the rate-determining step.

12.2 Assume that the rate-determining step of a reaction is

$$2A(g) + B(g) \rightarrow C(g)$$

and that 2 moles of $A(g)$ and 1 mole of $B(g)$ are mixed in a 1 liter container. Compare the following to the initial reaction rate of this mixture: (a) rate when half of both $A(g)$ and $B(g)$ have been consumed, (b) rate when two-thirds of both $A(g)$ and $B(g)$ have been consumed, (c) initial reaction rate of a mixture of 2 moles of $A(g)$ and 2 moles of $B(g)$ in a 1 liter container, (d) initial reaction rate of a mixture of 4 moles of $A(g)$ and 2 moles of $B(g)$ in a 1 liter container.

12.3 The rate expression for the reaction

$$2O_3 \rightarrow 3O_2$$

has been determined experimentally as

$$\text{rate of decrease of } [O_3] = k\,\frac{[O_3]^2}{[O_2]}$$

The following mechanism has been postulated for the decomposition of ozone.

(1) $$O_3 \underset{k_2}{\overset{k_1}{\rightleftharpoons}} O_2 + O$$

(2) $$O + O_3 \xrightarrow{k_3} 2O_2$$

The first step is a rapidly established equilibrium (for which an equilibrium constant may be derived), and the slower second step is rate determining. Show how the suggested mechanism leads to the observed rate expression.

12.4 A mixture of 0.81 mole of $N_2(g)$ and 0.53 mole of $H_2(g)$ is allowed to come to equilibrium in a 1.00 liter container.

$$N_2(g) + 3H_2(g) \rightleftharpoons 2NH_3(g)$$

At equilibrium, the concentration of ammonia is 0.020 mole/liter. (a) What are the equilibrium concentrations of $N_2(g)$ and $H_2(g)$? (b) What is the equilibrium constant, K, for the reaction at the temperature of the experiment?

12.5 For the equilibrium $A(g) + B(g) \rightleftharpoons C(g)$, K is 10^{-3} liter/mole at 100°C and 10^{-7} liter/mole at 200°C. (a) Is the reaction, as written, exothermic or endothermic? (b) What effect would an increase in total pressure have on the numerical value of K_p? K?

12.6 At a given temperature and a total pressure of 1.00 atm, N_2O_4 is 20.0% dissociated.

$$N_2O_4(g) \rightleftharpoons 2NO_2(g)$$

Assume that 1.00 mole of N_2O_4 is present initially. (a) How many moles of $N_2O_4(g)$ and $NO_2(g)$ are present at equilibrium? (b) What is the total number of moles of gas present at equilibrium? (c) What are the equilibrium partial pressures of $N_2O_4(g)$ and $NO_2(g)$? (d) What is the numerical value of K_p at this temperature?

12.7 At a given temperature and a total pressure of 2.00 atm, $PCl_5(g)$ is 75.0% dissociated.

$$PCl_5(g) \rightleftharpoons PCl_3(g) + Cl_2(g)$$

What is K_p for the equilibrium at the reference temperature?

12.8 At a given temperature and a total pressure of 1.00 atm, the partial pressures of an equilibrium mixture

$$N_2O_4(g) \rightleftharpoons 2NO_2(g)$$

are $p_{N_2O_4} = 0.50$ atm and $p_{NO_2} = 0.50$ atm. (a) What is K_p at this temperature? (b) If the total pressure is increased to 2.00 atm, temperature constant, what are the partial pressures of the components of an equilibrium mixture?

12.9 At 100°C, the equilibrium constant, K, for the reaction

$$CO(g) + Cl_2(g) \rightleftharpoons COCl_2(g)$$

is 4.57×10^9 liters/mole. If 1.00 mole of $COCl_2$ is confined in a 1.00 liter container, what is the concentration of CO after equilibrium has been established? Note that the subtraction of a very small number from a large number may be neglected.

12.10 Carbon monoxide and hydrogen react in several different ways depending upon the catalyst employed (Section 12.3). Calculate $\Delta G°$ and K_p for each of the following at 25°C.
(a) $CO(g) + H_2(g) \rightleftharpoons CH_4(g) + H_2O(l)$
(b) $CO(g) + H_2(g) \rightleftharpoons CH_3OH(l)$
The values of $\Delta G_f°$ are: -32.81 kcal/mole for $CO(g)$, -12.14 kcal/mole for $CH_4(g)$, -56.69 kcal/mole for $H_2O(l)$, and -39.73 kcal/mole for $CH_3OH(l)$.

12.11 The equilibrium constant for the reaction

$$H_2(g) + CO_2(g) \rightleftharpoons H_2O(g) + CO(g)$$

at 750°C is 0.771. What is $\Delta G°$ for this reaction at 750°C?

12.12 Calculate K_p for the following equilibrium at 25°C.

$$2NOCl(g) \rightleftharpoons 2NO(g) + Cl_2(g)$$

The values of ΔG_f° at 25°C are: +15.86 kcal/mole for NOCl(g) and +20.719 kcal/mole for NO(g).

12.13   What is the value of K corresponding to the K_p of Problem 12.12?

12.14   What is K_p at 25°C for the reaction

$$4NH_3(g) + 5O_2(g) \rightleftharpoons 4NO(g) + 6H_2O(g)$$

The values of ΔG_f° at 25°C are: NH$_3$(g), -3.976 kcal/mole; NO(g), +20.719 kcal/mole; H$_2$O(g), -54.636 kcal/mole.

12.15   At 250°C, K is 4.16×10^{-2} mole/liter for the equilibrium

$$PCl_5(g) \rightleftharpoons PCl_3(g) + Cl_2(g)$$

What is (a) K and (b) K_p for the reaction

$$PCl_3(g) + Cl_2(g) \rightleftharpoons PCl_5(g)$$

at this temperature?

12.16   (a) Calculate the equilibrium constant for

$$16H^+(aq) + 2MnO_4^-(aq) + 10Cl^-(aq) \rightleftharpoons$$
$$2Mn^{2+}(aq) + 5Cl_2(g) + 8H_2O$$

from E° values listed in Table 9.3.

(b) What is ΔG° for the reaction?

12.17   Calculate the equilibrium constant for the reaction

$$In(s) + 3Tl^+(aq) \rightleftharpoons In^{3+}(aq) + 3Tl(s)$$

from the electrode potentials

$$In^{3+} + 3e^- \rightleftharpoons In \qquad E^{\circ} = -0.342 \text{ v}$$
$$Tl^+ + e^- \rightleftharpoons Tl \qquad E^{\circ} = -0.336 \text{ v}$$

12.18   From the electrode potentials

$$2H_2O + 2e^- \rightleftharpoons H_2 + 2OH^- \qquad E^{\circ} = -0.828 \text{ v}$$
$$2H^+ + 2e^- \rightleftharpoons H_2 \qquad E^{\circ} = 0$$

calculate the equilibrium constant for

$$H_2O \rightleftharpoons H^+(aq) + OH^-(aq)$$

12.19   For the hypothetical reaction

$$H_2 + X \rightleftharpoons 2H^+ + X^{2-}$$

assume that the equilibrium constant is 1.0×10^{30}. (a) What is the value of the electrode potential for the half reaction.

$$2e^- + X \rightarrow X^{2-}$$

(b) What is ΔG° for the reaction?

12.20   State the direction that each of the following equilibrium systems would be shifted upon the application of the stress listed beside the equation.

(a) $2SO_2(g) + O_2(g) \rightleftharpoons$
        $2SO_3(g)$ (exothermic)   increase temperature

(b) $CO_2(g) + C(s) \rightleftharpoons$
        $2CO(g)$ (endothermic)   decrease temperature

(c) $N_2(g) + O_2(g) \rightleftharpoons$
     $2NO(g)$ (endothermic)   increase total pressure

(d) $CO_2(g) + C(s) \rightleftharpoons$
     $2CO(g)$ (endothermic)   decrease total pressure

(e) $N_2(g) + 3H_2(g) \rightleftharpoons$
     $2NH_3(g)$ (exothermic)   remove $NH_3(g)$

(f) $CaCO_3(s) \rightleftharpoons$
     $CaO(s) + CO_2(g)$ (endothermic)   add $CaO(s)$

(g) $2NOBr(g) \rightleftharpoons$
     $2NO(g) + Br_2(g)$ (endothermic)   add a catalyst

(h) $PCl_3(g) + Cl_2(g) \rightleftharpoons$
     $PCl_5(g)$ (exothermic)   increase $[PCl_5]$

13

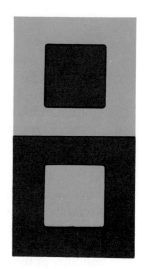

Acids and Bases

Throughout the history of chemistry, various acid-base concepts have been proposed and used. In this chapter, four concepts in current use are reviewed. Each of the definitions can be applied with advantage in appropriate circumstances; in a given situation, the chemist uses the concept that best suits his purpose.

13.1 The Arrhenius Concept

The earliest criteria for the characterization of acids and bases were the experimentally observed properties of aqueous solutions of these substances (taste, effect on indicators, neutralization of one by the other, etc.). Concurrent with the development of generalizations concerning the structure of matter, scientists searched for a correlation between acidic and basic properties and the structure of the compounds exhibiting these properties.

Acids, bases, and salts were classified as electrolytes by Faraday in 1834. Justus von Liebig proposed (1838) that acids are compounds containing hydrogen that can be replaced by metals. The role of water as an ionizing solvent was emphasized by Svante Arrhenius in his theory of electrolytic dissociation (1884), which led to the definition of acids and bases in terms of the ions of water; Arrhenius' views were vigorously championed and developed by Wilhelm Ostwald.

At the time of Arrhenius, the distinction between ionic and covalent compounds was not clear (Section 3.10), and the nature of $H^+(aq)$ was not understood (Section 3.17). Consequently, the **water system** (or **Arrhenius concept**) has been modified throughout its history. In present day terms, an **acid** is a substance that ionizes in water solution to produce $H^+(aq)$, or the hydronium ion; a **base** is a substance that dissolves in water to produce hydroxide ion, $OH^-(aq)$. The strength of an acid is defined in terms of the concentration of $H^+(aq)$ that is present in a water solution of given concentration of acid, and the strength of a base depends upon the relative concentration of $OH^-(aq)$ in an aqueous solution of base (Section 14.2).

Neutralization, then, may be represented by the equation

$$H^+(aq) + OH^-(aq) \rightarrow H_2O + 13.7\,kcal$$

As indicated in the preceding equation, the enthalpy for the neutralization of a dilute solution of any strong acid by a dilute solution of any strong base is a constant value. If a weak acid or a weak base is involved in the neutralization, or if a slightly soluble salt is formed from the cation derived from the base and the anion derived from the acid, the enthalpy of the reaction is different; in such cases, the total enthalpy includes heat effects due to the ionization of the weak acid or base or due to the precipitation of a salt as well as the enthalpy of neutralization.

The properties that all acids have in common are those of $H^+(aq)$; chemical properties include such reactions as those of acids with reactive metals and with the bicarbonate ion.

$$2H^+(aq) + Zn(s) \rightarrow H_2(g) + Zn^{2+}(aq)$$
$$H^+(aq) + HCO_3^-(aq) \rightarrow H_2O + CO_2(g)$$

The properties that are characteristic of bases are due to the $OH^-(aq)$ ion; among the reactions of strong bases are

$$2OH^-(aq) + H_2O + Si(s) \rightarrow SiO_3^{2-}(aq) + 2H_2(g)$$
$$OH^-(aq) + NH_4^+(aq) \rightarrow H_2O + NH_3(g)$$

The oxides of many nonmetals react with water to form acids and are called acidic oxides, or acid anhydrides.

$$N_2O_5(s) + H_2O \rightarrow 2H^+(aq) + 2NO_3^-(aq)$$

Many oxides of metals dissolve in water to form hydroxides; such compounds are called basic oxides.

$$Na_2O(s) + H_2O \rightarrow 2Na^+(aq) + 2OH^-(aq)$$

Acidic oxides and basic oxides react to produce salts in the absence of water. It must be noted, however, that not all acids and bases may be derived from oxides (e.g., HCl and NH_3).

The Arrhenius concept is severely limited by its emphasis on water and reactions in aqueous solution. Later definitions are more general, serve to correlate more reactions, and are applicable to reactions in nonaqueous media.

13.2   The Solvent System Concept

The principles of the Arrhenius-water concept can be used to devise acid-base schemes for many solvents. In a solvent system, an acid is a substance that gives the cation characteristic of the solvent, and a **base** is a substance that yields the anion characteristic of the solvent. Thus the reaction of an acid and a base, a **neutralization**, yields the solvent as one of its products. Many solvent systems of acids and bases have been developed (Table 13.1); the water concept is but a single example of a solvent system.

The ammonia system has been investigated more extensively than any other with the exception of the water system. The properties of liquid ammonia (boiling point, $-33.4°C$) are strikingly similar to those of water. Liquid ammonia is associated through hydrogen bonding (Section 7.11), and the NH_3 molecule is polar (Section 3.13). Hence, liquid ammonia is an excellent solvent for ionic and polar compounds, and it functions as an ionizing solvent for electrolytes. Many compounds form ammoniates, which are analogous to hydrates (e.g., $BaBr_2 \cdot 8NH_3$ and $CaCl_2 \cdot 6NH_3$), and ions are solvated in liquid ammonia solutions (e.g., $Ag(NH_3)_2{}^+$ and $Cr(NH_3)_6^{3+}$). Whereas solutions of electrolytes in ammonia are good conductors of electricity, pure liquid ammonia, like water, has a relatively low conductance.

The autoionization of ammonia

$$2NH_3 \rightleftharpoons NH_4{}^+ + NH_2{}^-$$

which occurs only to a low degree, is responsible for the electrical conductivity of the pure solvent, just as the autoionization of water

$$2H_2O \rightleftharpoons H_3O^+ + OH^-$$

is responsible for the electrical properties of this compound.

TABLE 13.1.
SOME SOLVENT SYSTEMS

Solvent	Acid Ion	Base Ion	Typical Acid	Typical Base
H_2O	H_3O^+ $(H^+ \cdot H_2O)$	OH^-	HCl	$NaOH$
NH_3	$NH_4{}^+$ $(H^+ \cdot NH_3)$	$NH_2{}^-$	NH_4Cl	$NaNH_2$
NH_2OH	NH_3OH^+ $(H^+ \cdot NH_2OH)$	$NHOH^-$	$NH_2OH \cdot HCl$ (NH_3OH^+, Cl^-)	$K(NHOH)$
$HC_2H_3O_2$	$H_2C_2H_3O_2{}^+$ $(H^+ \cdot HC_2H_3O_2)$	$C_2H_3O_2{}^-$	HCl	$NaC_2H_3O_2$
SO_2	SO^{2+}	SO_3^{2-}	$SOCl_2$	Cs_2SO_3
N_2O_4	NO^+	$NO_3{}^-$	$NOCl$	$AgNO_3$
$COCl_2$	$COCl^+$	Cl^-	$(COCl)AlCl_4$	$CaCl_2$
$SeOCl_2$	$SeOCl^+$	Cl^-	$(SeOCl)_2SnCl_6$	KCl
BrF_3	$BrF_2{}^+$	$BrF_4{}^-$	$(BrF_2)SbF_6$	$Ag(BrF_4)$

Any compound that produces ammonium ion, NH_4^+, in liquid ammonia solution is an acid, and any compound that yields amide ion, NH_2^-, is a base. Thus the neutralization reaction is the reverse of the autoionization reaction.

$$NH_4^+ + NH_2^- \rightarrow 2NH_3$$

Indicators may be used to follow an acid-base reaction in liquid ammonia. For example, phenolphthalein is red in a liquid ammonia solution of potassium amide, KNH_2, and the indicator becomes colorless after a stoichiometrically equivalent amount of ammonium chloride has been added.

In addition to the neutralization reaction, the ammonium ion in liquid ammonia undergoes other reactions analogous to the reactions of the hydronium ion in water. For example, metals such as sodium react with the ammonium ion to liberate hydrogen.

$$2Na(s) + 2NH_4^+ \rightarrow 2Na^+ + H_2(g) + 2NH_3(l)$$

The reactions of the amide ion are analogous to those of the hydroxide ion.

$$Zn(OH)_2(s) + 2OH^- \rightarrow Zn(OH)_4^{2-}$$
$$Zn(NH_2)_2(s) + 2NH_2^- \rightarrow Zn(NH_2)_4^{2-}$$
$$Hg^{2+} + 2OH^- \rightarrow HgO(s) + H_2O$$
$$3Hg^{2+} + 6NH_2^- \rightarrow Hg_3N_2(s) + 4NH_3$$

The analogy can be extended to derive a nitrogen system of compounds comparable to the oxygen system (Table 13.2). The comparison is somewhat complicated by the fact that nitrogen is customarily trivalent, whereas oxygen is divalent; thus the analog of the hydroxide ion, OH^-, or —OH group is the amide ion, NH_2^-, or —NH_2 group, whereas the oxide ion, O^{2-}, or =O group must be compared to both the imide ion, NH^{2-}, or =NH group and the nitride ion, N^{3-}, or ≡N group. Nevertheless, the analogy is a good one; ammonium ion will neutralize the imide and nitride ions as well as the amide ion.

$$2NH_4^+ + NH^{2-} \rightarrow 3NH_3$$
$$3NH_4^+ + N^{3-} \rightarrow 4NH_3$$

Therefore metal nitrides and imides are basic compounds in the nitrogen system in the same way that metal oxides are classified as basic oxides in the oxygen system. In addition, the nitrides of the nonmetals have acidic properties similar to the acidic characteristics of the nonmetal oxides of the oxygen system.

Many properties and reactions of compounds belonging to the nitrogen-ammonia system have been predicted and correlated by com-

TABLE 13.2.
COMPARABLE COMPOUNDS OF THE NITROGEN SYSTEM
AND THE OXYGEN SYSTEM.

Nitrogen System		Oxygen System	
KNH_2	potassium amide	KOH	potassium hydroxide
$Ca(NH_2)_2$	calcium amide	$Ca(OH)_2$	calcium hydroxide
PbNH	lead(II) imide	PbO	lead(II) oxide
$Hg(NH_2)Cl$	mercury(II) amido-chloride	$Hg(OH)Cl$	mercury(II) hydroxo-chloride
Ca_3N_2	calcium nitride	CaO	calcium oxide
H_2NCl	chloramine	HOCl	hypochlorous acid
HNNN	hydrazoic acid	$HONO_2$	nitric acid
$(HNPN)_n$	phospham	$(HOPO_2)_n$	metaphosphoric acid
P_3N_5	phosphorus(V) nitride	P_4O_{10}	phosphorus(V) oxide
CaNCN	calcium cyanamide	$CaCO_3$	calcium carbonate
H_2NNH_2	hydrazine	HOOH	hydrogen peroxide
CH_3NH_2	methyl amine	CH_3OH	methyl alcohol

parison to the better known chemistry of the compounds of the oxygen-water system. In fact, the study of various solvent systems has been responsible for greatly increasing our knowledge of the reactions that occur in solvents other than water. The solvent system approach, however, is compartmentalized and does not offer extensive correlation or generalization.

A unique aspect of liquid-ammonia chemistry deserves special mention although it is not related to acid-base phenomena. Liquid ammonia dissolves the group IA metals thereby producing unusual solutions. In the presence of catalysts (such as iron) a reaction occurs

$$2Na(s) + 2NH_3 \rightarrow 2Na^+ + 2NH_2^- + H_2(g)$$

(Compare the reaction of sodium with water.) In the absence of catalysts however, the solutions are stable for some time.

Dilute solutions of the metals are blue, and concentrated solutions have a bronze color. Evaporation of a solution yields the original metal. The conductance of a solution is higher than that of any known electrolytic solution and, for a concentrated solution, approaches metallic conductance. Conductance studies also show that the negative species is the same no matter what metal is dissolved. Dilute solutions are strongly paramagnetic. All solutions of the same concentration have identical absorption spectra, indicating that the same species causes the blue color in each case; since the IA metal cations are colorless, the blue color is due to the negative species.

On the basis of the preceding studies, and many more, it has been postulated that metal atoms in the solutions exist in equilibrium with metal cations and electrons, both of which are solvated. The essentially free electrons are responsible for the strong reducing properties of the solutions that are experimentally observed.

13.3 The Brønsted-Lowry Concept

In 1923, Johannes Brønsted and Thomas Lowry independently proposed a broader concept of acids and bases. According to the Brønsted-Lowry definitions, an **acid** is a substance that can donate protons, and a **base** is a substance that can accept protons. In these terms, the reaction of an acid with a base constitutes a transfer of a proton from the acid to the base, and this is the only characteristic reaction of these substances treated by the Brønsted-Lowry concept. We shall see, however, that many reactions are included in this classification.

The dissolution of ammonia in water may be represented by the equation

$$H_2O + NH_3 \rightleftharpoons NH_4^+ + OH^-$$

In the reaction as written, H_2O is serving as an acid and is releasing a proton to the base, NH_3. Whereas the solution resulting from the addition of NH_3 to H_2O is alkaline, conductivity and i factor measurements show that the ionization is incomplete. Furthermore, if a solution of an ammonium salt is made strongly alkaline, ammonia gas is released. The reaction, therefore, is reversible, and the system exists in equilibrium.

According to the Brønsted-Lowry concept, acids and bases may be molecules or ions. In the reverse reaction, NH_4^+ is serving as an acid and OH^- is a base since the equation, from right to left, shows NH_4^+ releasing a proton to OH^-. It follows, then, that in this Brønsted acid-base reaction, two acids (H_2O and NH_4^+) and two bases (OH^- and NH_3) are involved; the reaction is actually a competition between the two bases for a proton.

The base NH_3 gains a proton and thereby forms the acid NH_4^+, and the acid NH_4^+ upon the loss of a proton forms the base NH_3. Such an acid-base pair, related through the loss or gain of a proton, is called a **conjugate pair**; NH_4^+ is the conjugate acid of the base NH_3, and NH_3 is the conjugate base of the acid NH_4^+. In like manner, the acid H_2O and the base OH^- constitute a second conjugate pair in the preceding reaction. We may indicate conjugate relationships by the use of subscripts in the following manner:

$$\underset{\text{Acid}_1}{H_2O} + \underset{\text{Base}_2}{NH_3} \rightleftharpoons \underset{\text{Acid}_2}{NH_4^+} + \underset{\text{Base}_1}{OH^-}$$

There are many molecules and ions that can function as acids in certain reactions and as bases in other reactions; such species are called **amphiprotic**. For example, in the reaction with ammonia, water acts as an acid (conjugate base, OH^-); in the reaction with acetic acid, water is a base (conjugate acid, H_3O^+).

$$\overset{\text{Acid}_1}{HC_2H_3O_2} + \overset{\text{Base}_2}{H_2O} \rightleftharpoons \overset{\text{Acid}_2}{H_3O^+} + \overset{\text{Base}_1}{C_2H_3O_2^-}$$

In like manner, NH_3 is seen as a base (conjugate acid, NH_4^+) in its reaction with water. In the reaction of the hydride ion, H^-, with liquid ammonia, NH_3 acts as an acid (conjugate base, NH_2^-).

$$\overset{\text{Acid}_1}{NH_3} + \overset{\text{Base}_2}{H^-} \rightarrow \overset{\text{Acid}_2}{H_2} + \overset{\text{Base}_1}{NH_2^-}$$

Several amphiprotic substances are listed in Table 13.3.

The neutralization reactions of the Arrhenius system and certain solvent systems may, therefore, be interpreted in terms of the Brønsted definitions. Such neutralizations are merely acid-base reactions between the conjugate acid and the conjugate base of an amphiprotic solvent. Thus

$$\overset{\text{Acid}_1}{H_3O^+} + \overset{\text{Base}_2}{OH^-} \rightleftharpoons \overset{\text{Acid}_2}{H_2O} + \overset{\text{Base}_1}{H_2O}$$

$$\overset{}{NH_4^+} + \overset{}{NH_2^-} \rightleftharpoons NH_3 + NH_3$$

13.4 Strengths of Brønsted Acids and Bases

In Brønsted terms, the strength of an acid is determined by its tendency to donate protons, and the strength of a base is dependent upon its tendency to receive protons. The reaction

$$\overset{\text{Acid}_1}{HCl} + \overset{\text{Base}_2}{H_2O} \rightleftharpoons \overset{\text{Acid}_2}{H_3O^+} + \overset{\text{Base}_1}{Cl^-}$$

proceeds virtually to completion (from left to right). We must conclude, therefore, that HCl is a stronger acid than H_3O^+ since it has the stronger tendency to lose protons and the equilibrium is displaced far to the right. In addition, it is apparent that H_2O is a stronger base than Cl^- since in the competition for protons, water molecules succeed in holding practically all of them. The strong acid, HCl, has a weak conjugate base, Cl^-.

A strong acid, with a great tendency to lose protons, is necessarily conjugate to a weak base, with a small tendency to gain, and hold, protons. Hence, the stronger the acid, the weaker is its conjugate base. In like manner, a strong base attracts protons strongly and is necessarily conjugate to a weak acid, one that does not readily lose protons. The stronger the base, the weaker is its conjugate acid.

Acetic acid, in $1.0M$ solution, is 0.42% ionized at $25°C$ (Section 14.1). The equilibrium

$$\overset{\text{Acid}_1}{HC_2H_3O_2} + \overset{\text{Base}_2}{H_2O} \rightleftharpoons \overset{\text{Acid}_2}{H_3O^+} + \overset{\text{Base}_1}{C_2H_3O_2^-}$$

TABLE 13.3.
SOME AMPHIPROTIC SUBSTANCES.

Amphiprotic Substance	Conjugate Acid	Conjugate Base	Typical Reaction			
			$Acid_1$	$Base_2$	$Acid_2$	$Base_1$
H_2O	H_2O H_3O^+	OH^- H_2O	H_2O HCN	$+\ H^-$ $+\ H_2O$	$\rightleftharpoons H_2$ $\rightleftharpoons H_3O^+$	$+\ OH^-$ $+\ CN^-$
NH_3	NH_3 NH_4^+	NH_2^- NH_3	H_2O HCl	$+\ NH_2^-$ $+\ NH_3$	$\rightleftharpoons NH_3$ $\rightleftharpoons NH_4^+$	$+\ OH^-$ $+\ Cl^-$
H_2SO_4	H_2SO_4 $H_3SO_4^+$	HSO_4^- H_2SO_4	H_2SO_4 $HClO_4$	$+\ H_2O$ $+\ H_2SO_4$	$\rightleftharpoons H_3O^+$ $\rightleftharpoons H_3SO_4^+$	$+\ HSO_4^-$ $+\ ClO_4^-$
HSO_4^-	H_2SO_4 HSO_4^-	HSO_4^- SO_4^{2-}	H_2SO_4 HSO_4^-	$+\ H_2O$ $+\ H_2O$	$\rightleftharpoons H_3O^+$ $\rightleftharpoons H_3O^+$	$+\ HSO_4^-$ $+\ SO_4^{2-}$
$Al(H_2O)_5(OH)^{2+}$	$Al(H_2O)_6^{3+}$ $Al(H_2O)_5(OH)^{2+}$	$Al(H_2O)_5(OH)^{2+}$ $Al(H_2O)_4(OH)_2^+$	$Al(H_2O)_6^{3+}$ $Al(H_2O)_5(OH)^{2+}$	$+\ OH^-$ $+\ OH^-$	$\rightleftharpoons H_2O$ $\rightleftharpoons H_2O$	$+\ Al(H_2O)_5(OH)^{2+}$ $+\ Al(H_2O)_4(OH)_2^+$

is displaced to the left. This equation may be said to represent a competition between bases, acetate ions and water molecules, for protons. The position of the equilibrium shows that the $C_2H_3O_2^-$ ion is a stronger base than H_2O; at equilibrium, more protons form $HC_2H_3O_2$ molecules than form H_3O^+ ions. We may also conclude that H_3O^+ is a stronger acid than $HC_2H_3O_2$; at equilibrium, more H_3O^+ ions than $HC_2H_3O_2$ molecules have lost protons. In the preceding example, we note again that the stronger acid, H_3O^+, is conjugate to the weaker base, H_2O, and the stronger base, $C_2H_3O_2^-$, is conjugate to the weaker acid, $HC_2H_3O_2$.

One further conclusion should be stated. In a given reaction, the position of equilibrium favors the formation of the weaker acid and the weaker base. Thus in the reaction of HCl and H_2O, the equilibrium concentrations of H_3O^+ and Cl^- (the *weaker* acid and base, respectively) are *high*, whereas in the solution of acetic acid, the equilibrium concentrations of H_3O^+ and $C_2H_3O_2^-$ (the *stronger* acid and base, respectively) are *low*.

Notice that the Brønsted concept is an extension of the Arrhenius concept. According to the Arrhenius scheme, strong acids, such as HCl, are strong electrolytes, virtually 100% ionized in water solution to produce solutions with relatively high concentrations of H_3O^+. According to the Arrhenius concept, weak acids, such as acetic acid, are weak electrolytes, incompletely ionized in water solution to produce solutions with relatively low concentrations of H_3O^+. Although the Brønsted system classifies many more substances as acids, compounds that qualify as acids according to the Arrhenius definition are also acids in the Brønsted concept; that is, they are proton donors.

In the Brønsted system, acids are classified according to their ability to donate protons to the specific base under consideration. If water is used as a reference base, the acid strengths of the Arrhenius-water concept may be explained in terms of the Brønsted concept. Thus strong Arrhenius acids are those compounds that are stronger acids than H_3O^+. and weak Arrhenius acids are those compounds that are weaker acids than H_3O^+.

It is apparent that acid strengths are influenced by the solvent water. Acids that are stronger than H_3O^+ are essentially completely ionized in water solution.

$$HClO_4 + H_2O \rightleftharpoons H_3O^+ + ClO_4^-$$

$$HCl + H_2O \rightleftharpoons H_3O^+ + Cl^-$$

$$HNO_3 + H_2O \rightleftharpoons H_3O^+ + NO_3^-$$

Aqueous solutions of $HClO_4$, HCl, and HNO_3 of the same concentration appear to be of the same acid strength; the acid properties of the solutions are due to the H_3O^+ ion which the compounds produce to an

equivalent extent in their reactions with water. Water is said to have a
leveling effect on acids stronger than H_3O^+. The strongest acid that can
exist in water solution is the conjugate acid of water, H_3O^+. Acids that
are weaker than H_3O^+ are not leveled by water. Thus $HC_2H_3O_2$,
H_3PO_4, HNO_2, H_2S, and other weak acids show a wide variation in their
degree of ionization—the extent to which they form H_3O^+ in their reactions with water (Section 14.1).

The leveling effect is also observed for solvents other than water. The
strongest acid in liquid ammonia solutions is the conjugate acid of
ammonia, NH_4^+. Acetic acid, in liquid ammonia solution, is essentially
completely ionized since $HC_2H_3O_2$ is a stronger acid than NH_4^+.

$$HC_2H_3O_2 + NH_3 \rightleftharpoons NH_4^+ + C_2H_3O_2^-$$

Nitric acid, in methanol (CH_3OH) solution, is incompletely dissociated
since HNO_3 is a weaker acid than the conjugate acid of methanol,
$CH_3OH_2^+$.

$$HNO_3 + CH_3OH \rightleftharpoons CH_3OH_2^+ + NO_3^-$$

Solvents that can function as acids exert a leveling effect on bases.
The strongest base capable of existing in water solution is the conjugate
base of water, OH^-. Many substances, such as NH_2^- and H^-, are
stronger bases than OH^-. However, in water solution, these strongly
basic substances accept protons from water to form OH^- ions; these
reactions are essentially complete. The apparent basicity of strongly
basic materials in water solution is reduced to the level of the OH^- ion.

$$H_2O + NH_2^- \rightleftharpoons NH_3 + OH^-$$

$$H_2O + H^- \rightleftharpoons H_2 + OH^-$$

Materials, such as ammonia, that are less basic than OH^- are not leveled
by water and show varying degrees of ionization in aqueous solution
(Section 14.1).

Other solvents, in addition to water, level bases. Since H^- and NH_2^-
appear equally strong in water solution, we must examine their reactions
in other solvents to compare their relative basicities. It would be surprising if both ions had exactly the same basic character. In liquid ammonia, the hydride ion reacts rapidly and essentially completely to form
hydrogen and the amide ion.

$$NH_3 + H^- \rightleftharpoons H_2 + NH_2^-$$

We conclude that the hydride ion is a stronger base than the amide ion;
liquid ammonia reduces H^- to the level of the conjugate base of ammonia, NH_2^-—the strongest base possible in liquid ammonia solution.

The Brønsted definition enlarges the Arrhenius concept even more for
bases than it does for acids. In essence, the Arrhenius concept treats

only one Brønsted base—the hydroxide ion. According to the Arrhenius concept, strong bases are completely ionic in water solution and form solutions with high concentrations of OH^- ion. In fact, a compound such as NaOH is ionic when pure; molecules of NaOH do not exist (Section 3.4). Solutions of weak bases, according to the Arrhenius concept, are prepared from compounds that produce low concentrations of OH^- ion in water (such as NH_3).

The Brønsted system classifies many more substances as bases, and in this system, it is the OH^- ion of NaOH that is the base, not the compound itself. From the Arrhenius view, solutions resulting from the addition of such compounds as NaH or Na_2O to water owe their basic character to the fact that they are merely solutions of NaOH after the reaction of H^- or O^{2-} with water.

$$H_2O + H^- \rightarrow H_2 + OH^-$$
$$H_2O + O^{2-} \rightarrow OH^- + OH^-$$

13.5 Hydrolysis

A reaction of a substance with water in which the water molecule is split is called a *hydrolysis*. Some hydrolysis reactions involving covalent molecules such as

$$PBr_3(l) + 3H_2O \rightarrow 3HBr(g) + H_3PO_3(aq)$$
$$SOCl_2(l) + H_2O \rightarrow 2HCl(g) + SO_2(g)$$

bear no direct relation to Brønsted acid-base reactions. However, the hydrolysis of salts, or more accurately the hydrolysis of ions, are Brønsted acid-base reactions.

Anions that function as bases in water solution (B^- in the equation that follows) are hydrolyzed.

$$\underset{\text{Acid}_1}{H_2O} + \underset{\text{Base}_2}{B^-} \rightleftharpoons \underset{\text{Acid}_2}{HB} + \underset{\text{Base}_1}{OH^-}$$

In the reaction, water acts as an acid, and a proton is transferred to the anion. The extent of hydrolysis of a given anion depends upon the base strength of the anion, and an indication of the degree of hydrolysis is given by the concentration of OH^- relative to the concentration of anion present in the solution. Anions that are extensively hydrolyzed are strong bases with weak conjugate acids.

Hydrolysis is complete in the reaction

$$H_2O + H^- \rightarrow H_2 + OH^-$$

The anion undergoing hydrolysis, H^-, is a stronger base than OH^-, and the conjugate acid of the anion, H_2, is a much weaker acid than H_2O; complete hydrolysis is characteristic of such anions. This equation, in fact, illustrates the leveling effect of water on bases stronger than OH^-.

At the other extreme, some anions, such as Cl^-, do not hydrolyze at all.

$$H_2O + Cl^- \leftarrow HCl + OH^-$$

The Cl^- ion is a very weak base, and its conjugate acid, HCl, is not only stronger than H_2O but is also stronger than H_3O^+. In fact, HCl is leveled in water solution to H_3O^+, and therefore HCl molecules do not exist in measurable quantities in aqueous solutions of moderate concentrations. The chloride ion is simply too weak a base to accept a proton from water to a significant extent. Anions that have conjugate acids stronger than H_3O^+ do not hydrolyze.

The behavior of many anions in water solution is intermediate between the two extremes represented by H^- and Cl^-. For example,

$$H_2O + C_2H_3O_2^- \rightleftharpoons HC_2H_3O_2 + OH^-$$

The $C_2H_3O_2^-$ ion is a weaker base than OH^- but not so weak as Cl^-. Even though $HC_2H_3O_2$, the conjugate acid of $C_2H_3O_2^-$, is a stronger acid than water, it is a weaker acid than HCl or H_3O^+. Acetic acid is not leveled by water; molecules of the weak acid $HC_2H_3O_2$ can exist in aqueous solution. The hydrolysis represented by the equation occurs only to a slight extent; the equilibrium, as written, is displaced to the left because the substances written on the left are the weaker acid and the weaker base of the reaction. Nevertheless, in a solution of sodium acetate, there is a measurable concentration of OH^- from the hydrolysis of the acetate ion—enough to cause red litmus to turn blue. Anions, such as $C_2H_3O_2^-$, CN^-, NO_2^-, and S^{2-}, that have conjugate acids stronger than water but weaker than H_3O^+ are measurably, but not completely, hydrolyzed in water solution.

The equation for the hydrolysis of the acetate ion written in reverse order

$$HC_2H_3O_2 + OH^- \rightleftharpoons H_2O + C_2H_3O_2^- \tag{1}$$

may be said to represent an Arrhenius neutralization of a weak acid by an alkali. One may consider the neutralization of a weak acid in terms of the ionization of the acid

$$HC_2H_3O_2 + H_2O \rightleftharpoons H_3O^+ + C_2H_3O_2^- \tag{2}$$

followed by the reaction of the hydronium ion with the hydroxide ion.

$$H_3O^+ + OH^- \rightleftharpoons H_2O + H_2O \tag{3}$$

According to this interpretation, reaction (3) removes H_3O^+ from the solution and forces the equilibrium represented in (2) to the right.

Equation (1) probably is a better representation of the process. First, equation (1) shows OH^- ion reacting directly with the principal acidic species of the solution—$HC_2H_3O_2$. Second, equation (1) directly explains why such a neutralization reaction produces a solution that is not neutral (in terms of equal numbers of H_3O^+ and OH^- ions); the reaction is reversible to a significant extent—the $C_2H_3O_2^-$ produced by the forward reaction hydrolyzes.

There are some hydrogen-containing cations, of which the ammonium ion is the principal example, that hydrolyze to produce H_3O^+.

$$NH_4^+ + H_2O \rightleftharpoons H_3O^+ + NH_3$$

Ammonia is a stronger base than water, and therefore the position of equilibrium is to the left. However, water is a sufficiently strong base to gain some of the protons in the competition; although the hydrolysis is far from complete, a solution of NH_4Cl gives an acid reaction toward litmus because of the hydrolysis of the NH_4^+ ion.

There are a few relatively unimportant cations that hydrolyze completely. For example, the phosphonium ion, PH_4^+, is a stronger acid than the hydronium ion; in water solution, the phosphonium ion is leveled.

$$PH_4^+ + H_2O \rightarrow H_3O^+ + PH_3$$

Metal cations are hydrated in water solution, and some of these hydrated cations hydrolyze. Solutions of aluminum chloride, zinc chloride, and iron(III) chloride show acidic characteristics because of the hydrolysis of the cations. The hydrolysis of the aluminum ion (which we shall indicate as $Al(H_2O)_6^{3+}$) may be represented as follows:

$$Al(H_2O)_6^{3+} + H_2O \rightleftharpoons H_3O^+ + Al(H_2O)_5(OH)^{2+}$$

In the hydrolysis, $Al(H_2O)_6^{3+}$ functions as an acid and donates a proton to H_2O which acts as a base. A water molecule coordinated to the Al^{3+} ion has an enhanced acidic character because the O—H bonds of

$$Al\text{---}O\begin{matrix} \diagup H \\ \diagdown H \end{matrix}$$

are weakened by the displacement of electrons toward the positively charged central ion. Thus the coordinated water molecules release protons and act as Brønsted acids.

In general, small ions with high positive charges form hydrated species that act as Brønsted acids in hydrolysis reactions. The cations of the group IA and group IIA metals have comparatively low charges for their relatively large sizes; the hydrated species of these ions have no significant acid character and consequently do not hydrolyze appreciably. Amphoterate ions such as $Al(H_2O)_2(OH)_4^-$ and $Zn(OH)_4^{2-}$ may be considered as being formed in Brønsted acid-base reactions in which the hydrated ions $Al(H_2O)_6^{3+}$ and $Zn(H_2O)_4^{2+}$ act as Brønsted acids and transfer protons to the hydroxide ion (Section 14.13).

13.6 Acid and Base Strengths and Structure

The correlation between molecular structure and acid or base strength is complex and involves many factors. Polar molecules with a hydrogen atom situated at the positive end of the dipole are acids; in such molecules, electrons are withdrawn from the hydrogen atom, thereby facilitating its release as a proton. For the hydrogen compounds of the elements of a given period, increasing acid strength parallels increasing electronegativity of the atom combined with hydrogen. For the elements of the second period, the order of increasing acid strength of the hydrogen compounds of the last three elements is $NH_3 < H_2O < HF$.

However, increasing acid strength does not always parallel increasing electronegativity of the atom bonded to hydrogen; evidently other factors are also involved. There is an increase in acid strength of the hydro acids of the elements in any group of the periodic classification with increasing atomic size of the electronegative element. For example, the hydrogen compounds of the group VI A and group VII A elements arranged according to increasing acid strength are

$$H_2O < H_2S < H_2Se < H_2Te$$
$$HF < HCl < HBr < HI$$

In each series, the last compound is the strongest acid and is formed by the element of lowest electronegativity.

When the hydrogen compounds of a period are compared, the small differences in the atomic radius of the electronegative elements are unimportant. However, in the hydrogen halide series, the bond distance increases from 1.0 Å for HF to 1.7 Å for HI, and with it the bond energy decreases from 135 kcal/mole for HF to 71 kcal/mole for HI (Section 10.5). The bond energy pertains to a process in which the molecule is broken into atoms, not ions. However, the energy required for the removal of a proton from each hydrogen halide may be calculated by adding the bond energy, the ionization energy of hydrogen, and the electron affinity of the halogen; the values for the hydrogen halides fall in the same order as do the bond energies themselves. If the reaction of HX with water is of interest, the heats of hydration of the ions may be added without altering the observed order. The actual process

$$HX + H_2O \rightleftharpoons H_3O^+ + X^-$$

does not, of course, occur by the mechanism used for the analysis of the energy effect.

A base must have an unshared electron pair in order to attract and hold a proton; a polar molecule that has an electron pair situated at the negative end of the dipole is a base. Trends in the base strength of anions are readily derived from conjugate relationships. Thus since H_2S is a stronger acid than H_2O, S^{2-} is a weaker base than O^{2-}; for monatomic anions of similar charge, base strength decreases with increasing size.

The base strength of the uninegative ions of elements of the second period

$$NH_2^- > OH^- > F^-$$

parallels a decrease in the electronegativity for the element of the second period; a similar trend is observed for the hydrogen-containing molecules of these elements

$$NH_3 > H_2O > HF$$

In these series, size differences are small and unimportant; the trend is set by the decreasing electronegativity of the central element. Both small size and low electronegativity are found in the hydride ion, H^-, which is a powerful base.

A third factor that influences the base strength of anions is the charge on the ion. Thus the base strength of the monatomic anions of the elements of the second period

$$N^{3-} > O^{2-} > F^-$$

decreases with increasing electronegativity and with decreasing negative charge on the ion.

The oxy acids have been studied more extensively than any other type of acids. For acids with the structure

$$H-O-Z$$

the acid strength increases with increasing electronegativity of Z. The higher the electronegativity of Z, the more the electrons of the molecule are displaced toward Z, and the more readily the proton is removed. For example,

$$HOCl > HOBr > HOI$$

is the order of decreasing acidity of the hypohalous acids.

In compounds in which additional oxygen atoms are bonded to Z, the electron-withdrawing power of the group bonded to hydrogen is increased; thus the proton is more readily removed. This effect is illustrated by the series

$$HOCl < \underset{(HClO_2)}{HOClO} < \underset{(HClO_3)}{HOClO_2} < \underset{(HClO_4)}{HOClO_3}$$

in which acidity increases with increasing oxidation state of chlorine.

A qualitative indication of the strength of acids of general formula $(HO)_m ZO_n$ is provided by the value of n in the formula. In general, acids are very strong when $n = 3$ ($HOClO_3$, $HOIO_3$), strong when $n = 2$ ($HOClO_2$, $(HO)_2SO_2$, $HONO_2$), weak when $n = 1$ ($HOClO$, $(HO)_3PO$,

HONO), and very weak when $n = 0$ (HOCl, $(HO)_3B$). There are, of course, variations within any of the groups, and the electronegativity of the central atom provides the key to these variations. Thus for the halic acids, the oxidation state of each halogen atom is 5+, and $n = 2$; the acidity of the compounds in the series increases with increasing electronegativity of the halogen atom.

$$HOClO_2 > HOBrO_2 > HOIO_2$$

Increasing acid strength parallels decreasing base strength of the conjugate base. Thus for the series

$$HOCl < HOClO < HOClO_2 < HOClO_3$$

the order of base strengths of the anions is

$$OCl^- > ClO_2^- > ClO_3^- > ClO_4^-$$

The addition of oxygen atoms provides a larger volume to accommodate the charge of the ion. A large uninegative ion attracts and holds a proton less strongly than a small uninegative ion; the ClO_4^- ion is more stable than the ClO^- ion.

13.7   The Lewis Concept

In reality, the Brønsted concept enlarges the definition of a base much more than it does that of an acid. In the Brønsted system, a base is a molecule or ion that has an unshared electron pair with which it can attract and hold a proton, and an acid is a substance that can supply a proton to a base. If a molecule or ion can share an electron pair with a proton, it can do the same thing with other substances as well.

Gilbert N. Lewis proposed a broader concept of acids and bases that liberated acid-base phenomena from the proton; although Lewis first proposed his system in 1923, he did little to develop it until 1938. Lewis defined a **base** as a substance that has an unshared electron pair with which it can form a covalent bond with an atom, molecule, or ion. An **acid** is a substance that can form a covalent bond by accepting an electron pair from a base. The emphasis has been shifted, by the Lewis concept, from the proton to the electron pair and covalent-bond formation.

An example of a Lewis acid-base reaction that is not treated as such by any other acid-base concept is

$$
\begin{array}{ccccccc}
& :\!\overset{\cdot\cdot}{F}\!: & H & & :\!\overset{\cdot\cdot}{F}\!: & H \\
:\!F\!:\!B & + & :\!N\!:\!H & \rightarrow & :\!F\!:\!B & :\ :\!N\!:\!H \\
& :\!\underset{\cdot\cdot}{F}\!: & H & & :\!\underset{\cdot\cdot}{F}\!: & H \\
& \text{(acid)} & \text{(base)} & & &
\end{array}
$$

Many Lewis acids and bases of this type can be titrated against one another by the use of suitable indicators in the same way that traditional acids and bases can be titrated.

Substances that are bases in the Brønsted system are also bases according to the Lewis concept. However, the Lewis definition of an acid considerably expands the number of substances that are classified as acids. A Lewis acid must have an empty orbital capable of receiving the electron pair of the base; the proton is but a single example of a Lewis acid.

Lewis acids include molecules or atoms that have incomplete octets.

$$:\ddot{F}:B + :\ddot{F}:^- \longrightarrow \left[:\ddot{F}:B:\ddot{F}:\right]$$

$$:\ddot{S} + \left[:\ddot{S}:\ddot{O}:\right]^{2-} \rightleftharpoons \left[:\ddot{S}:\ddot{S}:\ddot{O}:\right]^{2-}$$

$$:\ddot{Cl}:Al + :\ddot{Cl}:^- \longrightarrow \left[:\ddot{Cl}:Al:\ddot{Cl}:\right]^-$$

Aluminum chloride, although it reacts as $AlCl_3$, is actually a dimer— Al_2Cl_6 (Figure 13.1). The formation of the dimer from the monomer may be regarded as a Lewis acid-base reaction in itself since a chlorine atom in each $AlCl_3$ unit supplies an electron pair to the aluminum atom of the other $AlCl_3$ unit to complete the octet of the aluminum atom; these bonds are indicated by··· in the diagram

$$\begin{array}{c} Cl \diagdown \quad Cl \cdot \cdot \quad Cl \\ \quad Al \quad \cdot Al \\ Cl \diagup \quad \cdot \cdot Cl \diagup \diagdown Cl \end{array}$$

Most simple cations can function as Lewis acids; for example,

$$Cu^{2+} + 4:NH_3 \longrightarrow Cu(:NH_3)_4^{2+}$$

$$Fe^{3+} + 6:C:::N:^- \longrightarrow Fe(:C:::N:)_6^{3-}$$

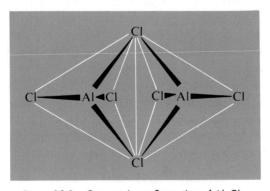

Figure 13.1   Geometric configuration of Al_2Cl_6.

Some metals atoms can function as acids in the formation of compounds such as the carbonyls which are produced by the reaction of the metal with carbon monoxide.

$$Ni + 4 :C:::O: \longrightarrow Ni(:C:::O:)_4$$

Compounds that have a central atom capable of expanding its valence shell are Lewis acids in reactions in which this expansion occurs. For example,

$$SiF_4 + 2F^- \longrightarrow SiF_6^{2-}$$

In the reaction of phosphorus pentafluoride or arsenic pentafluoride with the fluoride ion, the valence shell of the phosphorus or arsenic atom is expanded from 10 electrons to 12 electrons.

$$PF_5 + F^- \longrightarrow PF_6^-$$

In addition, some compounds have an acidic site because of one or more multiple bonds in the molecule. Examples are

The reactions of silica, SiO_2, with metal oxides are analogous to the reaction of carbon dioxide with the oxide ion although both silica and the silicate products (compounds of SiO_3^{2-}) are polymeric. This reaction is important in high-temperature metallurgical processes where a basic oxide is added to an ore to remove silica in the form of silicates (slag). Many of the processes used in the manufacture of glass, cement, and ceramics involve the reaction of the base O^{2-} (from metal oxides, carbonates, etc.) with acid oxides (such as SiO_2, Al_2O_3, and B_2O_3).

Arrhenius and Brønsted acid-base reactions may be interpreted in Lewis terms by focusing attention on the proton, as a Lewis acid

$$H^+(aq) + OH^-(aq) \longrightarrow H_2O$$

in which case the Brønsted acid is termed a **secondary** Lewis acid since it serves to provide the **primary** Lewis acid, the proton. Probably a better interpretation is that which classifies Brønsted acid-base reactions as Lewis base displacements. The Brønsted acid is interpreted as a complex in which the Lewis acid (proton) is already combined with a base; the reaction is viewed as a displacement of this base by another, stronger, base.

$$H_3O^+ + OH^- \rightarrow H_2O + H_2O$$

In this reaction, the base OH^- displaces the weaker base H_2O from its combination with the acid, the proton.

All Brønsted acid-base reactions are Lewis base displacements. In the reaction

$$HCl + H_2O \rightarrow H_3O^+ + Cl^-$$

the base H_2O displaces the weaker base, Cl^-. A base supplies an electron pair to a nucleus and is, therefore, called **nucleophilic** (Greek, nucleus loving). Base displacements are nucleophilic displacements.

Nucleophilic displacements may be identified among reactions that are not Brønsted acid-base reactions. The formation of $Cu(NH_3)_4^{2+}$ has been previously used as an illustration of a Lewis acid-base reaction. Since the reaction occurs in water, the formation of this complex is more accurately interpreted as the displacement of the base H_2O from the complex $Cu(H_2O)_4^{2+}$ by the stronger base NH_3.

$$Cu(H_2O)_4^{2+} + 4NH_3 \rightarrow Cu(NH_3)_4^{2+} + 4H_2O$$

Lewis acids accept an electron pair in a reaction with a base; they are **electrophilic** (Greek, electron loving). Acid displacements, or electrophilic displacements, are not so common as base displacements, but this type of reaction is known. For example, if $COCl_2$ is viewed as a combination of $COCl^+$ (an acid) with Cl^- (a base), the reaction

$$COCl_2 + AlCl_3 \rightarrow COCl^+ + AlCl_4^-$$

is an electrophilic displacement in which the acid $AlCl_3$ displaces the weaker acid $COCl^+$ from its complex with the base Cl^- (Table 13.1). The reaction

$$SeOCl_2 + BCl_3 \rightarrow SeOCl^+ + BCl_4^-$$

may be similarly interpreted.

SOME SUGGESTED READINGS

Holliday, A. K., and Massey, A. G., *Inorganic Chemistry in Non-Aqueous Solvents,* New York, Pergamon, 1965 (paper).

Kolthoff, I. M., and Bruckenstein, S., *Acid-Bases in Analytical Chemistry,* New York, Wiley, 1964 (paper).

Luder, W. F., and Zuffanti, S., *The Electronic Theory of Acids and Bases,* New York, Dover, 1961 (paper).

Sisler, H. H., *Chemistry in Non-Aqueous Solvents,* New York, Reinhold, 1961 (paper).

Vander Werf, C. A., *Acids, Bases and the Chemistry of the Covalent Bond,* New York, Reinhold, 1961 (paper).

PROBLEMS

13.1   Write equations analogous to the following but employing compounds of the nitrogen system in place of the oxygen-system compounds.
(a) $KOH + HNO_3 \rightarrow KNO_3 + H_2O$
(b) $CaO + H_2O \rightarrow Ca(OH)_2$
(c) $xP_2O_5 + xH_2O \rightarrow (HPO_3)_{2x}$
(d) $Cl_2 + H_2O \rightarrow HCl + HOCl$
(e) $Pb(OH)_2 \rightarrow PbO + H_2O$
(f) $2Na + 2H_2O \rightarrow 2NaOH + H_2$
(g) $Zn(OH)_2 + 2NaOH \rightarrow Na_2[Zn(OH)_4]$

13.2   What is the conjugate base of (a) HSO_4^-, (b) H_2SO_4, (c) H_2S, (d) $HClO_2$, (e) $H_2PO_4^-$, (f) NH_3?

13.3   What is the conjugate acid of (a) HSO_4^-, (b) SO_4^{2-}, (c) S^{2-}, (d) $H_2PO_4^-$, (e) HCO_3^-, (f) NH_3?

13.4   Each of the following reactions is displaced to the right. (a) Arrange all of the Brønsted acids that appear in these equations according to decreasing acid strength. (b) Make a similar list for the Bronsted bases.
(a) $HC_2H_3O_2 + HS^- \rightleftharpoons H_2S + C_2H_3O_2^-$
(b) $H_3O^+ + H_2PO_4^- \rightleftharpoons H_3PO_4 + H_2O$
(c) $H_2S + OH^- \rightleftharpoons H_2O + HS^-$
(d) $H_3PO_4 + C_2H_3O_2^- \rightleftharpoons HC_2H_3O_2 + H_2PO_4^-$

13.5   On the basis of your lists from Problem 13.4, would you expect an appreciable reaction (over 50%) between the species listed in each of the following?
(a) $H_3O^+ + HS^- \rightarrow$ (c) $H_3PO_4 + HS^- \rightarrow$
(b) $H_2S + C_2H_3O_2^- \rightarrow$ (d) $HC_2H_3O_2 + H_2PO_4^- \rightarrow$

13.6   Which compound of each of the following pairs is the stronger acid?
(a) H_3PO_4 or H_3AsO_4 (d) H_3BO_3 or H_2CO_3
(b) H_3AsO_3 or H_3AsO_4 (e) H_2Se or HBr
(c) H_2SO_4 or H_2SO_3

13.7   Which compound of each of the following pairs is the stronger base?
(a) P^{3-} or S^{2-} (d) NO_2^- or NO_3^-
(b) PH_3 or NH_3 (e) Br^- or F^-
(c) SiO_3^{2-} or SO_3^{2-}

13.8   Ammonium chloride (NH_4Cl) reacts with sodium amide ($NaNH_2$) in liquid ammonia to produce sodium chloride and ammonia. Interpret this reaction in terms of the solvent system, Brønsted, and Lewis theories of acids and bases. State clearly what acid(s) and base(s) are involved in each case.

13.9 Interpret the following reactions in terms of the Lewis theory.

(a) $Ag^+ + 2NH_3 \rightarrow Ag(NH_3)_2^+$

(b) $S^{2-} + S \rightarrow S_2^{2-}$

(c) $HgCl_2 + 2Cl^- \rightarrow HgCl_4^{2-}$

(d) $H^- + H_2C{=}O \rightarrow H_3CO^-$

13.10 Interpret the following as Lewis displacement reactions. For each, state the type of displacement, what is displaced, and the agent for the displacement.

(a) $CH_3Cl + AlCl_3 \rightarrow CH_3^+ + AlCl_4^-$

(b) $NH_3 + H^- \rightarrow H_2 + NH_2^-$

(c) $HONO_2 + H_2SO_4 \rightarrow NO_2^+ + H_2O + HSO_4^-$

(d) $CH_3I + OH^- \rightarrow CH_3OH + I^-$

(e) $[Al(H_2O)_6]^{3+} + H_2O \rightarrow [Al(H_2O)_5(OH)]^{2+} + H_3O^+$

(f) $[Co(NH_3)_5(H_2O)]^{3+} + Cl^- \rightarrow [CO(NH_3)_5Cl]^{2+} + H_2O$

(g) $Br_2 + FeBr_3 \rightarrow Br^+ + FeBr_4^-$

(h) $O^{2-} + H_2O \rightarrow 2OH^-$

14

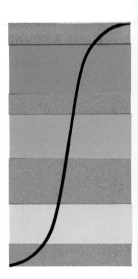

Ionic Equilibria

The principles of chemical equilibrium may be applied to equilibria involving ions in aqueous solution. The most important types of such equilibrium systems are: homogeneous equilibria between dissolved molecules of weak electrolytes and their ions, heterogeneous equilibria between slightly soluble solids and their ions in solutions, and homogeneous equilibria between oxidizing and reducing agents. An understanding of such equilibria is especially important to the study of analytical chemistry.

14.1 Weak Electrolytes

Strong electrolytes are completely ionic in water solution. For example, a $0.01\,M$ solution of $CaCl_2$ is $0.01\,M$ in calcium ions and $0.02\,M$ in chloride ions. Interionic attractions (the Debye-Hückel effect, Section 8.12) account for the observed deviations in the properties of solutions of strong electrolytes from the properties calculated on the basis of complete dissociation; such deviations are not large.

Weak electrolytes, however, are incompletely ionized in water solution; dissolved molecules exist in equilibrium with ions in such solutions. For example, the following equation represents the dissociation of acetic acid in water

$$HC_2H_3O_2 + H_2O \rightleftharpoons H_3O^+ + C_2H_3O_2^-$$

and the equilibrium constant for this reaction as written is

$$K' = \frac{[H_3O^+][C_2H_3O_2^-]}{[HC_2H_3O_2][H_2O]}$$

In dilute solutions, the molar concentration of water is virtually a constant (approximately 1000/18, or $55.5\,M$); the number of moles of water consumed in the formation of hydronium ion (approximately 10^{-3} mole per liter in a $0.1\,M$ acetic acid solution) is negligible in comparison with the large number of moles of water present. Thus

$$K = K'[H_2O] = \frac{[H_3O^+][C_2H_3O_2^-]}{[HC_2H_3O_2]}$$

We shall follow the practice of representing the concentration of hydronium ion by the symbol $[H^+]$, and thus the expression for the equilibrium constant reduces to a form consistent with the simplified equation

$$HC_2H_3O_2 \rightleftharpoons H^+ + C_2H_3O_2^-$$

$$K = \frac{[H^+][C_2H_3O_2^-]}{[HC_2H_3O_2]}$$

For complete accuracy, equilibrium constants should be expressed in terms of activities instead of concentrations. However, the concentrations of ions present in dilute solutions of weak electrolytes are so small that interionic attractions are negligible. Under these conditions, molar concentrations may be used, rather than activities, to give reasonably accurate results. By convention, the ions are written on the right of an equation for the reversible dissociation of a weak electrolyte; hence, the concentration terms for ions appear in the numerator of the expression for the equilibrium constant.

The degree of dissociation, α, of a weak electrolyte in aqueous solution may be determined by conductance measurements (Section 9.5) or, not as accurately, by measurements of colligative properties (Section 8.11). Potentiometric methods for such determinations are also used (Section 14.4, Example 14.10; Section 9.9, Example 9.6). From the degree of dissociation, the value of the equilibrium constant (or ionization constant) may be calculated.

Example 14.1 At $25°C$, a $0.100\,M$ solution of acetic acid is 1.34% ionized. What is the ionization constant for acetic acid?

Solution Since $\alpha = 0.0134$, in 1 liter of solution $(0.0134)\,(0.100) = 0.00134$ mole of acetic acid would be in ionic form, and $0.100 - 0.00134 = 0.09866$ mole of acetic acid would remain in molecular form. According to the chemical equation for the ionization, 1 mole of H^+ and 1 mole of $C_2H_3O_2^-$ are produced for every mole of acetic acid that ionizes. Therefore the equilibrium concentrations are

$$\underset{0.09866\,M}{HC_2H_3O_2} \rightleftharpoons \underset{0.00134\,M}{H^+} + \underset{0.00134\,M}{C_2H_3O_2^-}$$

These constants may be used to find the numerical value of the equilibrium constant.

$$K = \frac{[H^+][C_2H_3O_2^-]}{[HC_2H_3O_2]}$$

$$= \frac{(0.00134)(0.00134)}{(0.09866)}$$

$$= 1.81 \times 10^{-5}$$

In future problem work, we shall express equilibrium constants to two significant figures; higher accuracy is generally not warranted when molar concentrations are used instead of activities.

Example 14.2   What are the concentrations of all species present in $1.0M$ acetic acid at 25°C? What is the degree of ionization?

Solution   If we let x equal the number of moles of acetic acid in ionic form in 1 liter of solution, the equilibrium concentrations are

$$\underset{(1.0 - x)M}{HC_2H_3O_2} \rightleftharpoons \underset{(x)M}{H^+} + \underset{(x)M}{C_2H_3O_2^-}$$

Hence, we find

$$1.8 \times 10^{-5} = \frac{[H^+][C_2H_3O_2^-]}{[HC_2H_3O_2]}$$

$$= \frac{x^2}{(1.0 - x)}$$

which can be expanded to

$$x^2 + 1.8 \times 10^{-5}x - 1.8 \times 10^{-5} = 0$$

This equation may be solved by means of the quadratic formula; we find

$$x = [H^+] = [C_2H_3O_2^-] = 4.2 \times 10^{-3}M$$

$$(1.0 - x) = [HC_2H_3O_2] = 9.958 \times 10^{-1}M$$

(Note that this last concentration is $1.0M$ to two significant figures.) The degree of ionization can be calculated by dividing the number of ionized moles of acetic acid in 1 liter of solution by the total number of moles of acetic acid present in 1 liter.

$$\alpha = \frac{4.2 \times 10^{-3}}{1.0} = 4.2 \times 10^{-3}$$

The use of the quadratic formula in problem solving may be avoided by making an approximation which is frequently employed in calculations involving aqueous equilibria. The subtraction of a very small number from a larger number does not significantly alter the value of the larger number and may be neglected. Thus in the preceding example, such a small amount of acetic acid is ionized (x) that the quantity ($1.0 - x$) used to represent the concentration of undissociated acetic acid molecules is, for all practical purposes, equal to 1.0 (as previously noted).

By using 1.0 instead of $(1.0 - x)$ for the concentration of $HC_2H_3O_2$, we find

$$1.8 \times 10^{-5} = \frac{[H^+][C_2H_3O_2^-]}{[HC_2H_3O_2]}$$

$$= \frac{x^2}{1.0}$$

$$x = 4.2 \times 10^{-3} M$$

which is the same as the result obtained through the use of the quadratic formula.

The subtraction of a small number from another small number may not be neglected; therefore the quadratic formula must be employed to solve some problems. As a rule of thumb, if the number to be subtracted is more than 5% of the number from which it is to be subtracted, the simplified procedure should not be used; the final result of such a calculation would not have two significant figures. Thus the result of a calculation obtained by the use of the simplified procedure may be used to check whether the use of the procedure was justified.

In Table 14.1, the molar concentrations of ions are listed for solutions of acetic acid of various concentrations. The percent ionized increases with dilution; at infinite dilution, all electrolytes are completely dissociated. This is consistent with Le Chatelier's principle. Addition of water to an equilibrium system of a weak electrolyte,

$$HC_2H_3O_2 + H_2O \rightleftharpoons H_3O^+ + C_2H_3O_2^-$$

shifts the equilibrium to the right so that proportionately more of the electrolyte is found in ionic form.

The values of ionization constants change with temperature; most values are reported at 25°C. At 25°C, K for acetic acid is 1.8×10^{-5}; at 100°C, the numerical value of the constant for this equilibrium is 1.1×10^{-5}.

TABLE 14.1.
ION CONCENTRATIONS AND PERCENT IONIZATION OF SOLUTIONS
OF ACETIC ACID AT 25°C.

Concentration of Solution (M)	$[H^+]$ or $[C_2H_3O_2^-]$ (M)	Percent Ionization
1.00	0.00420	0.420
0.100	0.00134	1.34
0.0100	0.000420	4.20
0.00100	0.000125	12.5

An equilibrium system of a weak electrolyte may not only be prepared from the pure compound but also from compounds that supply the component ions of the electrolyte; this is illustrated in the following example.

Example 14.3 What are the concentrations of all species present in a solution made by diluting 0.10 mole of HCl and 0.50 mole of $NaC_2H_3O_2$ to 1.0 liter?

Solution Hydrochloric acid and sodium acetate are strong electrolytes. We may assume, therefore, that before equilibrium is attained, the concentration of H^+ is $0.10M$, and the concentration of $C_2H_3O_2^-$ is $0.50M$. If we let x equal the number of moles per liter of acetic acid at equilibrium, the equilibrium concentrations are

$$HC_2H_3O_2 \rightleftharpoons H^+ + C_2H_3O_2^-$$
$$(x)M \qquad (0.10 - x)M \qquad (0.50 - x)M$$

If we solve the problem using these quantities, the quadratic formula must be employed since x is not negligible in comparison to 0.10 or 0.50.

A simpler way to solve the problem is to assume that the reaction goes as far to the left as is possible and that then a portion of the acetic acid thus formed dissociates into ions. In this instance, let y equal the number of moles of acetic acid that is dissociated at equilibrium.

$$HC_2H_3O_2 \rightleftharpoons H^+ + C_2H_3O_2^-$$

	$HC_2H_3O_2$	H^+	$C_2H_3O_2^-$
after mixing:	—	$0.10M$	$0.50M$
reaction to left:	$0.10M$	—	$0.40M$
equilibrium:	$(0.10 - y)M$	$(y)M$	$(0.40 + y)M$

Now, y is indeed negligible in comparison to both 0.10 and 0.40, and we may simplify the problem by neglecting y in the terms for the concentrations of acetic acid and acetate ion. Thus

$$1.8 \times 10^{-5} = \frac{[H^+][C_2H_3O_2^-]}{[HC_2H_3O_2]}$$

$$= \frac{y(0.40)}{(0.10)}$$

$$y = 4.5 \times 10^{-6}M$$

We can see from the value obtained for y, that the approximations applied to $[C_2H_3O_2^-]$ and $[HC_2H_3O_2]$ are warranted. To two significant figures, the equilibrium concentrations are

$$[H^+] = 4.5 \times 10^{-6}M$$
$$[C_2H_3O_2^-] = 0.40M$$
$$[HC_2H_3O_2] = 0.10M$$

The hydroxides of most metals are either strong electrolytes or slightly soluble compounds. There are some water-soluble compounds, however, that produce alkaline solutions in which equilibria exist between molecules and ions. The most important such compound is ammonia, and the chemical equation for the reversible reaction is

$$H_2O + NH_3 \rightleftharpoons NH_4^+ + OH^-$$

The expression for the equilibrium constant for this reaction

$$K' = \frac{[NH_4^+][OH^-]}{[NH_3][H_2O]}$$

simplifies to the following if the concentration of water is assumed to be a constant,

$$K = K'[H_2O] = \frac{[NH_4^+][OH^-]}{[NH_3]}$$

Formerly it was assumed that ammonia gas dissolves in water to produce ammonium hydroxide molecules, NH_4OH, and that these molecules dissociate into NH_4^+ and OH^- ions. Currently, however, the existence of such ammonium hydroxide molecules is questioned. Considerable experimental evidence suggests that in aqueous solutions of ammonia, each NH_3 molecule is hydrogen bonded to several H_2O molecules; if NH_4OH molecules exist at all in such solutions, they constitute a minor component. The ammonia equilibrium, therefore, is probably best represented in the manner employed in the preceding equation.

Table 14.2 lists the ionization constants of some weak acids and some weak bases. Since the terms for the ion concentrations appear in the numerator of the ionization-constant expression, the magnitude of the value of K gives a qualitative idea of the strength of the electrolyte. Thus HCNO ($K = 1.2 \times 10^{-4}$) is a stronger acid than HCN ($K = 4.0 \times 10^{-10}$). The relative acidity of solutions of the two acids, however, must be found by comparing the concentrations of hydrogen ion in the solutions and not by comparing the equilibrium constants.

Example 14.4 Compare the acidity of $0.10\,M$ HCNO with the acidity of $0.10\,M$ HCN.

Solution Let x equal the concentration of hydrogen ion in $0.10\,M$ HCNO and y equal the concentration of hydrogen ion in $0.10\,M$ HCN.

$$HCNO \rightleftharpoons H^+ + CNO^- \qquad\qquad HCN \rightleftharpoons H^+ + CN^-$$
$$0.10\,M \quad (x)\,M \quad (x)\,M \qquad\qquad 0.10\,M \quad (y)\,M \quad (y)\,M$$

$$1.2 \times 10^{-4} = \frac{[H^+][CNO^-]}{[HCNO]} \qquad\qquad 4.0 \times 10^{-10} = \frac{[H^+][CN^-]}{[HCN]}$$

$$= \frac{x^2}{0.10} \qquad\qquad\qquad\qquad = \frac{y^2}{0.10}$$

$$x = \sqrt{1.2 \times 10^{-4}(0.10)} \qquad\qquad y = \sqrt{4.0 \times 10^{-10}(0.10)}$$

$$\frac{\text{acidity } 0.10M \text{ HCNO}}{\text{acidity } 0.10M \text{ HCN}} = \frac{x}{y} = \frac{\sqrt{1.2 \times 10^{-4}(0.10)}}{\sqrt{4.0 \times 10^{-10}(0.10)}}$$

$$= \sqrt{0.30 \times 10^6}$$

$$= 5.5 \times 10^2$$

The solution of HCNO is 550 times more acidic than the solution of HCN.

TABLE 14.2. IONIZATION CONSTANTS AT 25°C.		
Weak Acids		
acetic	$HC_2H_3O_2 \rightleftharpoons H^+ + C_2H_3O_2^-$	1.8×10^{-5}
benzoic	$HC_7H_5O_2 \rightleftharpoons H^+ + C_7H_5O_2^-$	6.0×10^{-5}
chlorous	$HClO_2 \rightleftharpoons H^+ + ClO_2^-$	1.1×10^{-2}
cyanic	$HCNO \rightleftharpoons H^+ + CNO^-$	1.2×10^{-4}
formic	$HCHO_2 \rightleftharpoons H^+ + CHO_2^-$	1.8×10^{-4}
hydrazoic	$HN_3 \rightleftharpoons H^+ + N_3^-$	1.9×10^{-5}
hydrocyanic	$HCN \rightleftharpoons H^+ + CN^-$	4.0×10^{-10}
hydrofluoric	$HF \rightleftharpoons H^+ + F^-$	6.7×10^{-4}
hypobromous	$HBrO \rightleftharpoons H^+ + BrO^-$	2.1×10^{-9}
hypochlorous	$HClO \rightleftharpoons H^+ + ClO^-$	3.2×10^{-8}
nitrous	$HNO_2 \rightleftharpoons H^+ + NO_2^-$	4.5×10^{-4}
Weak Bases		
ammonia	$NH_3 + H_2O \rightleftharpoons NH_4^+ + OH^-$	1.8×10^{-5}
aniline	$C_6H_5NH_2 + H_2O \rightleftharpoons C_6H_5NH_3^+ + OH^-$	4.6×10^{-10}
dimethylamine	$(CH_3)_2NH + H_2O \rightleftharpoons (CH_3)_3NH_2^+ + OH^-$	7.4×10^{-4}
hydrazine	$N_2H_4 + H_2O \rightleftharpoons N_2H_5^+ + OH^-$	9.8×10^{-7}
methylamine	$CH_3NH_2 + H_2O \rightleftharpoons CH_3NH_3^+ + OH^-$	5.0×10^{-4}
pyridine	$C_5H_5N + H_2O \rightleftharpoons C_5H_5NH^+ + OH^-$	1.5×10^{-9}
trimethylamine	$(CH_3)_3N + H_2O \rightleftharpoons (CH_3)_3NH^+ + OH^-$	7.4×10^{-5}

14.2   The Ionization of Water

Pure water is itself a very weak electrolyte and ionizes according to the equation

$$H_2O + H_2O \rightleftharpoons H_3O^+ + OH^-$$

In simplified form, this is

$$H_2O \rightleftharpoons H^+ + OH^-$$

The expression for the ionization constant derived from this equation is

$$K = \frac{[H^+][OH^-]}{[H_2O]}$$

In dilute solutions, the concentration of water is virtually a constant, and we may combine $[H_2O]$ with the constant K. Thus

$$K[H_2O] = [H^+][OH^-]$$

This constant, $K[H_2O]$, is called the ion product of water, or the water constant, and is given the symbol K_w. At 25°C,

$$K_w = 1.0 \times 10^{-14} = [H^+][OH^-]$$

In pure water,

$$[H^+] = [OH^-] = x$$

$$[H^+][OH^-] = 1.0 \times 10^{-14}$$

$$x^2 = 1.0 \times 10^{-14}$$

$$x = 1.0 \times 10^{-7} M$$

Thus the concentrations of both of the ions of water are equal to $1.0 \times 10^{-7} M$ in pure water or in any neutral solution at 25°C. Hence, in 1 liter, only 10^{-7} mole of water is in ionic form out of a total of approximately 55.5 moles.

In any aqueous solution, both hydronium and hydroxide ions exist. In an acid solution, the concentration of hydronium ions is larger than $1.0 \times 10^{-7} M$ and larger than the hydroxide ion concentration. In an alkaline solution, the hydroxide ion concentration is larger than $1.0 \times 10^{-7} M$ and larger than the hydronium ion concentration.

Example 14.5 What are $[H^+]$ and $[OH^-]$ in a $0.02 M$ solution of HCl?

Solution The quantity of hydronium ion obtained from the ionization of water is negligible compared to that derived from the hydrochloric acid. Furthermore, since HCl is a strong electrolyte, $[H^+] = 0.02 M$.

$$[H^+][OH^-] = 1.0 \times 10^{-14}$$

$$(2 \times 10^{-2})[OH^-] = 1.0 \times 10^{-14}$$

$$[OH^-] = \frac{1.0 \times 10^{-14}}{2 \times 10^{-2}}$$

$$[OH^-] = 5 \times 10^{-13} M$$

Thus there are hydroxide ions present in this acidic solution. Notice, however, that $[OH^-]$ is extremely small; in this solution, there would be one hydroxide ion for every 40 billion hydronium ions.

Example 14.6 What are $[H^+]$ and $[OH^-]$ in a $0.005 M$ solution of NaOH?

Solution Sodium hydroxide is a strong electrolyte, and therefore $[OH^-] = 5 \times 10^{-3} M$.

$$[H^+][OH^-] = 1.0 \times 10^{-14}$$

$$[H^+](5 \times 10^{-3}) = 1.0 \times 10^{-14}$$

$$[H^+] = \frac{1.0 \times 10^{-14}}{5 \times 10^{-3}}$$

$$[H^+] = 2 \times 10^{-12} M$$

14.3 pH

A convenient method for expressing the hydronium ion concentration of a solution is in terms of the pH scale. The **pH** of a solution may be defined as the logarithm of the reciprocal of the hydronium ion concentration. Since the logarithm of 1 is 0, pH may also be defined as the negative logarithm of the hydronium ion concentration. Thus

$$pH = \log\left(\frac{1}{[H^+]}\right) = -\log[H^+]$$

or

$$[H^+] = 10^{-pH} = \text{antilog}(-pH)$$

For a neutral solution, therefore,

$$[H^+] = 1.0 \times 10^{-7}$$
$$pH = -\log(10^{-7}) = -(-7)$$
$$pH = 7$$

For a 0.001 M solution of HCl,

$$[H^+] = 1 \times 10^{-3}$$
$$pH = -\log(10^{-3}) = 3$$

We can define **pOH** in the same terms—as the negative logarithms of the hydroxide ion concentration. Such values generally are not quoted; the pH value of a solution is used to define the acidity or alkalinity of the solution. However, it is frequently convenient to use pOH's in calculations involving alkaline solutions or solutions for which the hydroxide ion concentration is known. The water constant is

$$[H^+][OH^-] = 10^{-14}$$

By taking the logarithm of each term and multiplying through by -1, we find

$$-\log[H^+] - \log[OH^-] = -\log(10^{-14})$$

or

$$pH + pOH = 14$$

Thus for a 0.01 M solution of NaOH, the pOH is 2. Since the sum of the pH and the pOH equals 14, the pH of this solution is 12.

Example 14.7   What is the pH of a solution 0.050 M in H^+?

Solution
$$[H^+] = 5.0 \times 10^{-2}$$
$$\log[H^+] = \log 5.0 + \log 10^{-2}$$
$$= 0.7 - 2.0 = -1.3$$
$$pH = 1.3$$

Example 14.8 What is the pH of a solution for which $[OH^-] = 0.15 M$?

Solution
$$[OH^-] = 1.5 \times 10^{-1}$$
$$\log[OH^-] = \log 1.5 + \log 10^{-1}$$
$$= 0.2 \times 1.0 = -0.8$$
$$pOH = 0.8$$
$$pH = 13.2$$

An alternative solution is

$$[H^+][OH^-] = 1.0 \times 10^{-14}$$
$$[H^+] = \frac{1.0 \times 10^{-14}}{1.5 \times 10^{-1}} = 6.7 \times 10^{-14}$$
$$\log[H^+] = \log 6.7 + \log 10^{-14}$$
$$= 0.8 - 14.0 = -13.2$$
$$pH = 13.2$$

Example 14.9 What is the $[H^+]$ of a solution with a pH of 10.6?

Solution
$$\log[H^+] = -10.6 = 0.4 - 11.0$$
$$[H^+] = \text{antilog}\, 0.4 \times \text{antilog}\, (-11)$$
$$[H^+] = 2.5 \times 10^{-11}$$

It should be kept in mind that pH relates to a power of 10. Hence, a solution of pH = 1 has a hydronium ion concentration 100 times that of a solution of pH = 3 (not three times). Furthermore, since the pH is related to a *negative* exponent, the lower the pH value, the larger the concentration of hydronium ion. At pH = 7, a solution is neutral. Solutions with pH's below 7 are acidic; those with pH's above 7 are alkaline. These relationships are summarized in Table 14.3.

14.4 Determination of pH

Potentiometric methods are commonly employed for pH determination. Since the emf of a cell is dependent upon activities and not concentrations, we redefine pH as the negative logarithm of the activity of the hydronium ion concentration. However, this redefinition introduces a problem since it is experimentally impossible to determine activities of single ions, and as we shall see, it is necessary to introduce an assumption into the treatment.

The following cell might be used for the determination of pH's

$$\text{Pt} \mid H_2(1\ \text{atm}) \mid H^+(a = ?) \parallel Cl^-(1N) \mid Hg_2Cl_2(s) \mid Hg$$

This cell is diagrammed in Figure 14.1. The left-hand electrode is a hydrogen electrode (Section 9.8) in which the electrolyte is the solution being studied. This electrode is connected by means of a salt bridge to a normal calomel electrode. The calomel electrode utilizes, as the electro-

TABLE 14.3.
THE pH SCALE

pH	$[H^+]$	$[OH^-]$	
14	10^{-14}	10^0	
13	10^{-13}	10^{-1}	
12	10^{-12}	10^{-2}	
11	10^{-11}	10^{-3}	increasing
10	10^{-10}	10^{-4}	alkalinity
9	10^{-9}	10^{-5}	
8	10^{-8}	10^{-6}	
7	10^{-7}	10^{-7}	neutrality
6	10^{-6}	10^{-8}	
5	10^{-5}	10^{-9}	
4	10^{-4}	10^{-10}	
3	10^{-3}	10^{-11}	increasing
2	10^{-2}	10^{-12}	acidity
1	10^{-1}	10^{-13}	
0	10^0	10^{-14}	

lyte, a normal solution of potassium chloride which is saturated with mercurous chloride (Hg_2Cl_2); the electrode proper consists of mercury metal, at the bottom of the tube, overlayed with a paste of mercurous chloride (calomel) and mercury.

The half reactions for the cell are:

$$H_2(g) \rightarrow 2H^+(aq) + 2e^-$$
$$2e^- + 2Hg_2Cl_2(s) \rightarrow 2Hg(l) + 2Cl^-(aq)$$

Figure 14.1   *Hydrogen electrode and normal calomel electrode.*

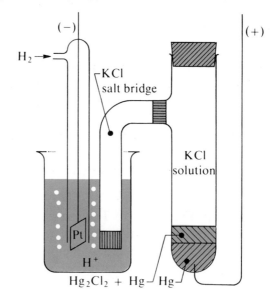

and the corresponding net chemical change is

$$H_2(g) + 2Hg_2Cl_2(s) \rightarrow 2H^+(aq) + 2Cl^-(aq) + 2Hg(l)$$

The cell is not thermodynamically reversible (Section 9.7). When the cell is discharging, $H^+(aq)$ ions leave the test solution and enter the salt bridge, and Cl^- ions leave the salt bridge and enter the test solution. When the operation of the cell is reversed, K^+ ions enter the test solution from the salt bridge, and anions from the test solution (not necessarily Cl^- ions) enter the salt bridge. Hence, there is an indeterminable liquid-junction potential at the salt bridge. The dependence of the emf of the cell upon the activities of the species present may be expressed by adapting the Nernst equation (Section 9.9),

$$E = E° - \frac{0.05916}{2} \log\left(\frac{(a_{H^+})^2(a_{Cl^-})^2}{(a_{H_2})}\right) + E_{\text{liquid junction}}$$

Upon expansion, this becomes

$$E = E° + \frac{0.05916}{2} \log(a_{H_2}) - 0.05916 \log(a_{Cl^-})$$

$$+ E_{\text{liquid junction}} - 0.05916 \log(a_{H^+})$$

We shall assume that the pressure of H_2 gas is maintained at 1 atm, that the salt bridge is effective in maintaining a constant Cl^- ion concentration in the calomel electrode, and that the liquid-junction potential is a constant value that is negligibly small. Hence, the first four terms of the expression for the emf of the cell may be combined into an experimentally determined constant, E'.

$$E = E' - 0.05916 \log(a_{H^+})$$

For the normal calomel electrode in air at 25°C, E' is 0.2825 v.* Therefore

$$E = 0.2825 + 0.05916 \, (\text{pH})$$

$$\text{pH} = \frac{E - 0.2825}{0.05916}$$

This expression may be regarded as an operational definition of pH. For problem work, we shall use pH's based on concentrations and activities interchangeably, since the activities of $H^+(aq)$ approximate the concentrations of $H^+(aq)$ in dilute solutions.

In place of the hydrogen electrode, a glass electrode is usually employed for the determination of pH's. The hydrogen electrode is easily poisoned and requires the use of gaseous hydrogen. A glass electrode

---

*In the absence of air, the normal potassium chloride-calomel electrode has an E' of 0.2812 v. Frequently, a saturated solution of KCl is employed; the generally accepted value of E' for such an electrode is 0.2415 v.

consists of a reference electrode containing a solution of known pH sealed in a membrane of special glass. In the determination of the pH of a solution, the glass electrode and another reference electrode are immersed in the solution being studied.

The emf of the complete cell depends upon the difference in potential across the glass membrane that separates solutions of different pH's and is found to respond to changes in pH in the same way that an assembly using a hydrogen electrode does. The value of E' for a cell using a glass electrode depends upon the electrode used in the construction of the glass electrode as well as the other reference electrode employed in the complete cell. Instruments known as pH meters employ glass electrodes and are usually calibrated in pH units rather than volts; such instruments are standardized with solutions of known pH.

Example 14.10 For a cell containing a solution of unknown pH and utilizing a hydrogen electrode and a normal calomel electrode, the potential is 0.608 v at 25°C. Calculate the pH of the solution and the approximate concentration of $H^+(aq)$.

Solution

$$pH = \frac{E - 0.283}{0.0592}$$

$$= \frac{0.608 - 0.283}{0.0592}$$

$$pH = 5.5$$

$$\log[H^+] = -5.5 = 0.5 - 6.0$$

$$[H^+] = 3.1 \times 10^{-6} M$$

An approximate value of the ionization constant of a weak acid or a weak base may be determined by measuring the pH of a solution of known concentration of the weak electrolyte. A more exact method for the determination of ionization constants based on pH determinations is described in Section 14.15.

Example 14.11 The pH of a 0.10M solution of a weak base, B, is 10.6. What is the ionization constant of B?

Solution

$$\log[H^+] = -10.6 = 0.4 - 11.0$$

$$[H^+] = 2.5 \times 10^{-11}$$

$$[OH^-] = \frac{1.0 \times 10^{-14}}{2.5 \times 10^{-11}} = 4.0 \times 10^{-4} M$$

Since the solution was prepared from the base alone,

$$[BH^+] = [OH^-] = 4.0 \times 10^{-4} M$$

The concentration of **B** in the solution is, for all practical purposes, equal to $0.10\,M$; the small quantity of **B** dissociated need not be considered. Thus the equilibrium concentrations are

$$\underset{0.10\,M}{\text{B}} \;+\; \text{H}_2\text{O} \rightleftharpoons \underset{4.0\,\times\,10^{-4}\,M}{\text{BH}^+} \;+\; \underset{4.0\,\times\,10^{-4}\,M}{\text{OH}^-}$$

The value of the ionization constant is

$$K = \frac{[\text{BH}^+][\text{OH}^-]}{[\text{B}]}$$

$$= \frac{(4.0 \times 10^{-4})^2}{1.0 \times 10^{-1}} = \frac{16 \times 10^{-8}}{1.0 \times 10^{-1}}$$

$$K = 1.6 \times 10^{-6}$$

14.5 Indicators

Indicators are colored, organic compounds of complex structure that change color in solution as the pH of the solution changes. For example, methyl orange is red in solutions of pH below 3.1 and yellow in solutions of pH above 4.5; the color of this indicator is a varying mixture of yellow and red in the pH range between 3.1 and 4.5. Many indicators have been described and used; a few are listed in Table 14.4.

By the use of indicators, one may determine the pH of a solution. If thymol blue is yellow in a test solution and methyl orange is red in another sample of the same solution, the pH of the solution is between 2.8 and 3.1. Reference to Table 14.4 shows that thymol blue is yellow only in solutions of pH greater than 2.8, and methyl orange is red only in solutions of pH less than 3.1. If enough indicators are employed, it is possible to determine pH values that are accurate to the first decimal place; potentiometric measurements of pH's are, however, more accurate.

Indicators are weak acids or weak bases. Since they are intensely colored, only a few drops of a dilute solution of an indicator need be employed in any determination; hence, the acidity of the solution in question is not significantly altered by the addition of the indicator.

If we let the symbol HIn stand for the litmus molecule (which is red) and the symbol In$^-$ stand for the anion (which is blue) derived from the weak acid, the equation for the litmus equilibrium may be written

$$\underset{\text{(red)}}{\text{HIn}} \rightleftharpoons \text{H}^+ + \underset{\text{(blue)}}{\text{In}^-}$$

According to the principle of Le Chatelier, increasing the concentration of H$^+$ shifts the equilibrium to the left, and the red (or acid) color of HIn is observed. On the other hand, addition of OH$^-$ decreases the concentration of H$^+$; the equilibrium shifts to the right, and the blue (or alkaline) color of In$^-$ is observed.

TABLE 14.4 SOME INDICATORS.			
Indicator	Acid Color	pH Range of Color Change	Alkaline Color
thymol blue	red	1.2–2.8	yellow
methyl orange	red	3.1–4.5	yellow
bromcresol green	yellow	3.8–5.5	blue
methyl red	red	4.2–6.3	yellow
litmus	red	5.0–8.0	blue
bromthymol blue	yellow	6.0–7.6	blue
phenolphthalein	colorless	8.3–10.0	red
alizarin yellow	yellow	10.0–12.1	lavender

The ionization constant for litmus is approximately equal to 10^{-7}.

$$10^{-7} = \frac{[H^+][In^-]}{[HIn]}$$

We may rearrange this expression in the following manner

$$\frac{10^{-7}}{[H^+]} = \frac{[In^-]}{[HIn]}$$

At a pH of 5 or below, the red color of litmus is observed. If we substitute $[H^+] = 10^{-5}$, which corresponds to pH = 5, into the preceding expression, we get

$$\frac{10^{-7}}{10^{-5}} = \frac{1}{100} = \frac{[In^-] \leftarrow \text{(blue)}}{[HIn] \leftarrow \text{(red)}}$$

Thus, the mixture appears red to the eye when the concentration of the red HIn is 100 times (or more) that of the blue In^-.

The blue color of litmus is observed in solutions of pH = 8 or higher. If $[H^+] = 10^{-8}$, then

$$\frac{10^{-7}}{10^{-8}} = \frac{10}{1} = \frac{[In^-] \leftarrow \text{(blue)}}{[HIn] \leftarrow \text{(red)}}$$

When the concentration of the blue In^- ion is 10 times that of the red HIn, or approximately 91% of the indicator is in ionic form, the blue color of the, In^- ions completely masks the red color of the HIn molecules, and the mixture appears blue.

Thus the blue color predominates when the concentration of the blue species is 10 times that of the red, whereas the red color predominates only when the concentration of the red form is 100 times that of the blue. This is not surprising since the blue color of litmus is a much stronger color than the red. Only when $[H^+] = K = 10^{-7}$ will the factor

$K/[H^+] = 1$ and $[In^-] = [HIn]$. Hence, at pH $= 7$, litmus exhibits its "neutral" color (purple).

Therefore the pH range over which a given indicator changes color depends upon the ionization constant of the indicator. For indicators that are weak acids, the smaller the value of K, the higher is the pH range of the color change.

Example 14.12 An indicator is a weak acid and the pH range of its color change is 3.1 to 4.5. Assuming that the neutral point of the indicator is in the center of this range, calculate the ionization constant of the indicator.

Solution The center of the range may *not* be calculated by averaging the pH values since pH's are exponential in form. We may find the center of the range by averaging the corresponding concentrations of H^+, however.

$$pH = 3.1$$
$$\log[H^+] = -3.1 = 0.9 - 4.0$$
$$[H^+] = 7.9 \times 10^{-4}$$

$$pH = 4.5$$
$$\log[H^+] = -4.5 = 0.5 - 5.0$$
$$[H^+] = 3.2 \times 10^{-5}$$

To average these two hydronium ion concentrations, we must express both to the same power of 10. Thus

$$\frac{79.0 \times 10^{-5} + 3.2 \times 10^{-5}}{2} = 4.1 \times 10^{-4}$$

When $[H^+] = 4.1 \times 10^{-4} M$, $K = [H^+]$. Therefore

$$K = 4.1 \times 10^{-4}$$

14.6 The Common-Ion Effect

In a $0.1 M$ solution of acetic acid, methyl orange assumes its acid color, red. If sodium acetate is added to this solution, the color changes to yellow showing that the addition causes the acidity of the solution to decrease. This experimental observation is readily explained on the basis of Le Chatelier's principle. The equilibrium

$$HC_2H_3O_2 \rightleftharpoons H^+ + C_2H_3O_2^-$$

is shifted to the left by the addition of the acetate ion from the sodium acetate, and the concentration of hydronium ion correspondingly decreases. Since acetic acid and sodium acetate have the acetate ion in common, this phenomenon is called the **common-ion effect.**

The concentration of hydronium ion in a solution of acetic acid to which acetate ion has been added can be calculated by means of the ionization constant of acetic acid. This is illustrated by the following example.

Example 14.13 What is the concentration of hydronium ion in a $0.10\,M$ solution of acetic acid that has been made $0.15\,M$ in sodium acetate?

Solution Sodium acetate is a strong electrolyte; the concentration of acetate ion derived from this source is, therefore, $0.15\,M$. In a $0.10\,M$ solution of pure acetic acid, $[H^+] = [C_2H_3O_2]^- = 0.00134\,M$ (Table 14.1). In a $0:10\,M$ solution of acetic acid to which sodium acetate has been added, the concentration of acetate ion derived from the ionization of acetic acid is much less than $0.00134\,M$ due to the common-ion effect. Therefore the concentration of acetate ion may be regarded as $0.15\,M$ and the contribution from acetic acid ignored. Likewise, the concentration of acetic acid may be taken as equal to the total concentration of acetic acid present, $0.10\,M$, since such a small amount of the acetic acid is ionized. Thus

$$HC_2H_3O_2 \rightleftharpoons H^+ + C_2H_3O_2^-$$
$$\quad\; 0.10M \qquad\quad (x)\,M \qquad 0.15M$$

$$1.8 \times 10^{-5} = \frac{[H^+][C_2H_3O_2^-]}{[HC_2H_3O_2]}$$

$$= \frac{[H^+](0.15)}{(0.10)}$$

$$[H^+] = 1.2 \times 10^{-5}\,M$$

Thus when a $0.10\,M$ solution of acetic acid is made $0.15\,M$ in sodium acetate, the concentration of hydronium ion is reduced from $1.3 \times 10^{-3}\,M$ to $1.2 \times 10^{-5}\,M$.

Example 14.14 What is the concentration of hydroxide ions in a solution made by dissolving 0.020 mole of ammonium chloride in 100 ml of $0.15\,M$ ammonia? Assume that the addition of the solid does not cause the volume of the solution to change.

Solution Ammonium chloride is a strong electrolyte. The concentration of NH_4^+ from the NH_4Cl added, is

$$? \text{ moles } NH_4^+ = 1000 \text{ ml soln.}\left(\frac{0.020 \text{ mole } NH_4^+}{100 \text{ ml soln.}}\right) = 0.20 \text{ mole } NH_4^+$$

Therefore

$$NH_3 + H_2O \rightleftharpoons NH_4^+ + OH^-$$
$$0.15M \qquad\qquad 0.20M \quad\; (x)\,M$$

$$1.8 \times 10^{-5} = \frac{[NH_4^+][OH^-]}{[NH_3]}$$

$$= \frac{(0.20)[OH^-]}{(0.15)}$$

$$[OH^-] = 1.4 \times 10^{-5}\,M$$

14.7 Buffers

It is sometimes necessary that a solution of definite pH be prepared and stored. The preservation of such a solution is even more difficult than its preparation. If the solution comes in contact with the air, it will absorb carbon dioxide (an acid anhydride) and become more acidic. If the solution is stored in a glass bottle, alkaline impurities leached from the glass may alter the pH. **Buffer solutions** are capable of maintaining their pH at some fairly constant value even when small amounts of acid or base are added.

A buffer may be prepared from a weak acid or a weak base and a salt of the weak electrolyte. For example, a buffer can be prepared from acetic acid and sodium acetate. If both of these materials are present in the same concentration, for example, $1.00M$, then

$$1.8 \times 10^{-5} = \frac{[H^+][C_2H_3O_2^-]}{[HC_2H_3O_2]}$$

$$[H^+] = 1.8 \times 10^{-5}\left(\frac{[HC_2H_3O_2]}{[C_2H_3O_2^-]}\right) = 1.8 \times 10^{-5}M$$

$$pH = -\log(1.8 \times 10^{-5}) = 4.7$$

The pK of a weak electrolyte may be defined in a manner analogous to pH or pOH,

$$pK = -\log K$$

A solution of a weak acid in which the concentration of the anion is the same as the concentration of the undissociated acid has a pH equal to the pK of the acid.

In a sample of the buffer previously described, the quantities of acetic acid molecules and acetate ion are much larger than the quantity of hydronium ion present—approximately 50,000 times larger.

$$HC_2H_3O_2 \rightleftharpoons H^+ + C_2H_3O_2^-$$
$$1.0M \qquad 1.8 \times 10^{-5}M \qquad 1.0M$$

If a small quantity of hydronium ion is added, the large reservoir of acetate ion will quickly convert it to acetic acid. If a small amount of hydroxide ion is added to the buffer, it will neutralize hydronium ion, but the large quanity of acetic acid present will, by dissociation, replace any hydronium ion removed and maintain the pH at a fairly constant value.

The action of buffers may be interpreted in terms of the Brønsted concept. Thus an acetic acid-acetate buffer

$$\underset{\text{Acid}_1}{HC_2H_3O_2} + \underset{\text{Base}_2}{H_2O} \rightleftharpoons \underset{\text{Acid}_2}{H_3O^+} + \underset{\text{Base}_1}{C_2H_3O_2^-}$$

effectively neutralizes small additions of hydronium ion because of the presence of a relatively large concentration of the base $C_2H_3O_2^-$.

Similarly, small additions of hydroxide ion are effectively neutralized by the acid $HC_2H_3O_2$ which is present in relatively large concentration. In either instance, the change in the pH of the solution brought about by the addition is slight.

Buffers are not called upon to withstand the addition of large amounts of acids or alkalies. The addition of 0.01 mole per liter of H^+ or OH^- is about the maximum shock that any buffer can be expected to withstand. How successfully a buffer withstands such an addition is illustrated in the following example.

Example 14.15 The ionization constant of acetic acid to three significant figures is 1.81×10^{-5}. A buffer containing $1.00M$ concentrations of acetic acid and sodium acetate has a pH of 4.74. (a) What is the pH of the solution after 0.0100 mole of HCl has been added to 1 liter of the buffer? (b) What is the pH of the solution after the addition of 0.0100 mole/liter of NaOH?

Solution (a) The 0.0100 mole/liter of H^+ converts an equivalent amount of acetate ion into acetic acid. Thus the concentrations are

$$HC_2H_3O_2 \rightleftharpoons \quad H^+ \quad + \quad C_2H_3O_2^-$$

$1.00M$	$1.81 \times 10^{-5}M$	$1.00M$	buffer
$1.01M$	?	$0.99M$	after H^+ addition

$$\frac{[H^+][C_2H_3O_2^-]}{[HC_2H_3O_2]} = 1.81 \times 10^{-5}$$

$$\frac{[H^+](0.99)}{(1.01)} =$$

$$[H^+] = 1.81 \times 10^{-5}\frac{(1.01)}{(0.99)}$$

$$= 1.85 \times 10^{-5}M$$

$$pH = 4.73$$

Thus the addition causes the pH to change 0.01 pH units. A similar addition to pure water would change the pH from 7.0 to 2.0—a change of 5.0 pH units.

(b) The addition of 0.0100 mole of OH^- would change the concentration of acetate ion to $1.01M$ and the concentration of acetic acid to $0.99M$. Thus

$$\frac{[H^+][C_2H_3O_2^-]}{[HC_2H_3O_2]} = 1.81 \times 10^{-5}$$

$$\frac{[H^+](1.01)}{(0.99)} =$$

$$[H^+] = 1.81 \times 10^{-5}\frac{(0.99)}{(1.01)}$$

$$= 1.77 \times 10^{-5}M$$

$$pH = 4.75$$

A similar addition to water would have caused the pH to rise from 7.0 to 12.0.

Alkaline buffers may also be prepared. If the base and its derived ion are present in equal concentrations,

$$pOH = pK$$
$$pH = 14.0 - pK$$

A solution with $[NH_3] = 0.10M$ and $[NH_4{}^+] = 0.10M$ is an example of this type of buffer.

$$NH_3 + H_2O \rightleftharpoons NH_4{}^+ + OH^-$$

0.10M 0.10M ?

$$\frac{[NH_4{}^+][OH^-]}{[NH_3]} = 1.8 \times 10^{-5}$$

$$[OH^-] = 1.8 \times 10^{-5}M$$
$$pOH = 4.7$$
$$pH = 9.3$$

Buffers may also be prepared in which the ratio of the concentration of weak electrolyte to the concentration of common ion is not 1:1; this technique may be used to obtain a buffer that has a pH (or pOH) different from the pK of the weak acid (or base). The 1 to 1 buffer is equally efficient in its ability to handle either acid or alkaline additions.

Let us assume that a buffer is to be prepared from a hypothetical weak acid, HA,

$$HA \rightleftharpoons H^+ + A^-$$

for which

$$\frac{[H^+][A^-]}{[HA]} = K$$

The concentration of hydronium ion is

$$[H^+] = \frac{K[HA]}{[A^-]}$$

Taking the negative logarithm of each term, we get

$$-\log[H] = -\log K - \log\left(\frac{[HA]}{[A^-]}\right)$$

or

$$pH = pK - \log\left(\frac{[HA]}{[A^-]}\right)$$

In general, for an effective buffer, the ratio of the concentration of the molecular species to the concentration of the ionic species should be between 1/10 and 10/1. This concentration range is equivalent to the following pH range.

$$pH = pK - \log\left(\frac{1}{10}\right) = pK - \log 10^{-1}$$

$$= pK + 1$$

$$pH = pK - \log\left(\frac{10}{1}\right)$$

$$= pK - 1$$

Therefore an efficient buffer may be prepared from acetic acid ($pK = 4.7$) having any desired pH between 3.7 and 5.7.

The use of buffers is an important part of many industrial processes; examples are electroplating and the manufacture of leather, photographic materials, and dyes. In bacteriological research, culture media are generally buffered to maintain the pH required for the growth of the bacteria being studied. Buffers are used extensively in analytical chemistry and are used to calibrate pH meters. Human blood is buffered to a pH of 7.4 by means of bicarbonate, phosphate, and complex protein systems.

Example 14.16   What concentrations should be used to prepare a cyanic acid–cyanate buffer of pH = 3.50?

Solution

$$pH = 3.50$$

$$\log[H^+] = -3.50 = 0.50 - 4.00$$

$$[H^+] = 3.1 \times 10^{-4}M$$

$$HCNO \rightleftharpoons H^+ + CNO^-$$

$$1.2 \times 10^{-4} = \frac{[H^+][CNO^-]}{[HCNO]}$$

$$= \frac{3.1 \times 10^{-4}[CNO^-]}{[HCNO]}$$

$$\frac{[HCNO]}{[CNO^-]} = \frac{3.1 \times 10^{-4}}{1.2 \times 10^{-4}}$$

$$\frac{[HCNO]}{[CNO^-]} = 2.6$$

Any solution in which [HCNO]/[CNO$^-$] is 2.6 will have a pH of 3.5. For example, if [HCNO] = 0.26M, [CNO$^-$] must be 0.10M; or if [HCNO] = 0.52M, [CNO$^-$] = 0.20M.

An alternative solution of the problem utilizes the relationship

$$pH = pK - \log \frac{[HCNO]}{[CNO^-]}$$

$$3.50 = 3.92 - \log \frac{[HCNO]}{[CNO^-]}$$

$$\log \frac{[HCNO]}{[CNO^-]} = 0.42$$

$$\frac{[HCNO]}{[CNO^-]} = 2.6$$

Example 14.17 What is the pH of a solution made by mxing 100 ml of $0.15M$ HCl and 200 ml of $0.20M$ aniline ($C_6H_5NH_2$)? Assume that the volume of the final solution is 300 ml.

Solution The number of moles of HCl used and the number of moles of aniline used are

$$? \text{ moles HCl} = 100 \text{ ml soln.} \left(\frac{0.15 \text{ mole HCl}}{1000 \text{ ml soln.}} \right) = 0.015 \text{ mole HCl}$$

$$? \text{ moles aniline} = 200 \text{ ml soln.} \left(\frac{0.20 \text{ mole aniline}}{1000 \text{ ml soln.}} \right) = 0.040 \text{ mole aniline}$$

One mole of aniline reacts with 1 mole of H^+. Thus

$C_6H_5NH_2$ +	H^+	$\rightarrow C_6H_5NH_3^+$	
0.040 mole	0.015 mole	—	before reaction
0.025 mole	—	0.015 mole	after reaction

The molar concentrations in the final solution are

$$? \text{ moles } C_6H_5NH_3^+ = 1000 \text{ ml soln.} \left(\frac{0.015 \text{ mole } C_6H_5NH_3^+}{300 \text{ ml soln.}} \right)$$

$$= 0.050 \text{ mole } C_6H_5NH_3^+$$

$$? \text{ moles } C_6H_5NH_2 = 1000 \text{ ml soln.} \left(\frac{0.025 \text{ mole } C_6H_5NH_2}{300 \text{ ml soln.}} \right)$$

$$= 0.083 \text{ mole } C_6H_5NH_2$$

Therefore the concentrations in the solution are

$$C_6H_5NH_2 + H_2O \rightleftharpoons C_6H_5NH_3^+ + OH^-$$
$$0.083M \qquad\qquad 0.050M \qquad\quad ?$$

$$\frac{[C_6H_5NH_3^+][OH^-]}{[C_6H_5NH_2]} = 4.6 \times 10^{-10}$$

$$\frac{(0.050)[OH^-]}{(0.083)} =$$

$$[OH^-] = 7.6 \times 10^{-10}M$$

$$[H^+] = 1.3 \times 10^{-5}M$$

$$pH = 4.9$$

14.8   The Solubility Product

A type of heterogeneous equilibrium that is important to analytical chemistry is the equilibrium between a slightly soluble solid and its ions in solution. Most substances are soluble in water to at least some slight extent; it is the "insoluble" or "slightly soluble" materials with which we are concerned. If such materials are placed in water, an equilibrium is established when the rate of dissolution of ions from the solid equals the rate of precipitation of ions from the *saturated solution.*

Thus an equilibrium exists between solid silver chloride and a saturated solution of silver chloride.

$$AgCl(s) \rightleftharpoons Ag^+(aq) + Cl^-(aq)$$

The equilibrium constant is

$$K' = \frac{[Ag^+][Cl^-]}{[AgCl]}$$

Since the concentration of a pure solid is a constant, $[AgCl]$ may be combined with K' to give

$$K_{SP} = K'[AgCl] = [Ag^+][Cl^-]$$

The constant K_{SP} is called a **solubility product**; the ionic concentrations of the expression are those for a saturated solution at the reference temperature.

Since the solubility of a salt usually varies widely with temperature, the numerical value of K_{SP} for a salt changes with temperature; values are usually recorded at 25°C. The ionic concentrations of a saturated solution of a slightly soluble material are low; therefore concentrations may be satisfactorily employed in equilibrium expressions. For the more soluble salts, interionic attractions cause the activity coefficients to deviate significantly from unity, and activities, rather than concentrations, must be employed for the mathematical analysis of these systems. Fortunately, it is the slightly soluble substances that are of primary interest in analytical chemistry. A table of solubility products, at 25°C, is given in the appendix.

The numerical value of K_{SP} for a salt may be found from the molar solubility of the salt. The molar solubility may be found by mixing a weighed excess of the pure solid with a carefully measured volume of pure water at the reference temperature. After the solution is saturated, the excess solid is removed by filtration, dried, and weighed. The weight loss is the solubility of the solid in the volume of water used; from this, the molar solubility of the material may be calculated. Another technique involves the preparation of a saturated solution of the salt and the chemical analysis of this solution.

Example 14.18   At 25°C, 0.00188 g of AgCl dissolves in 1 liter of water. What is the K_{SP} of AgCl?

Solution   The molar solubility of AgCl (molecular weight, 143) is

$$? \text{ moles AgCl} = 0.00188 \text{ g AgCl}\left(\frac{1 \text{ mole AgCl}}{143 \text{ g AgCl}}\right) = 1.31 \times 10^{-5} \text{ moles AgCl}$$

For each mole of AgCl dissolving, 1 mole of Ag^+ and 1 mole of Cl^- are formed.

$$AgCl(s) \rightleftharpoons \underset{1.31 \times 10^{-5}M}{Ag^+} + \underset{1.31 \times 10^{-5}M}{Cl^-}$$

$$K_{SP} = [Ag^+][Cl^-]$$
$$= (1.31 \times 10^{-5})^2$$
$$= 1.7 \times 10^{-10}$$

The K_{SP} of a substance may also be found by conductance measurements (if the equivalent conductances of the ions are known) or by potentiometric measurements.

Example 14.19   Calculate the K_{SP} of AgCl from the electrode potentials

$$e^- + AgCl(s) \rightleftharpoons Ag(s) + Cl^-(aq) \qquad E° = +0.222 \text{ v}$$
$$e^- + Ag^+(aq) \rightleftharpoons Ag(s) \qquad E° = +0.799 \text{ v}$$

(See Example 12.6, Section 12.9.)

Solution   The theoretical cell

$$Ag \,|\, Ag^+, Cl^- \,|\, AgCl \,|\, Ag$$

would have the following electrode reactions

$$Ag \rightarrow Ag^+ \quad e^- \qquad E_{ox}° = -0.799 \text{ v}$$
$$e^- + AgCl \rightarrow Ag + Cl^- \qquad E° = +0.222 \text{ v}$$

The cell reaction is

$$AgCl \rightarrow Ag^+ + Cl^- \qquad E° = -0.577 \text{ v}$$

Notice that the reaction for the standard cell is not spontaneous as written. For this reaction, $n = 1$.

$$\Delta G° = -nFE°$$
$$= -1 (23.1 \text{ kcal/v})(-0.577 \text{ v})$$
$$= +13.3 \text{ kcal}$$
$$\Delta G° = -RT \ln K$$
$$+13.3 \text{ kcal} = -1.36 \text{ kcal} (\log K)$$
$$\log K = -9.78$$
$$K = 1.7 \times 10^{-10}$$

For salts that have more than two ions per formula unit, the ion concentrations must be raised to the powers indicated by the coefficients of the balanced chemical equation.

$$Mg(OH)_2(s) \rightleftharpoons Mg^{2+} + 2OH^- \qquad K_{SP} = [Mg^{2+}][OH^-]^2$$

$$Bi_2S_3(s) \rightleftharpoons 2Bi^{3+} + 3S^{2-} \qquad K_{SP} = [Bi^{3+}]^2[S^{2-}]^3$$

$$Hg_2Cl_2(s) \rightleftharpoons Hg_2^{2+} + 2Cl^- \qquad K_{SP} = [Hg_2^{2+}][Cl^-]^2$$

For a salt of this type, the calculation of the K_{SP} from the molar solubility is slightly more difficult.

Example 14.20   At 25°C, 7.8 × 10⁻⁵ moles of silver chromate dissolve in 1 liter of water. What is the K_{SP} of Ag_2CrO_4?

Solution   For each mole of Ag_2CrO_4 that dissolves, 2 moles of Ag^+ and 1 mole of CrO_4^{2-} are formed. Therefore

$$Ag_2CrO_4(s) \rightleftharpoons \quad 2Ag^+ \quad + \quad CrO_4^{2-}$$
$$2(7.8 \times 10^{-5})M + 7.8 \times 10^{-5}M$$

$$K_{SP} = [Ag^+]^2[CrO_4^{2-}]$$
$$= (1.56 \times 10^{-4})^2(7.8 \times 10^{-4})$$
$$= 1.9 \times 10^{-12}$$

Example 14.21   The K_{SP} of CaF_2 is 3.9 × 10⁻¹¹ at 25°C. How many grams of calcium fluoride will dissolve in 100 ml of water at 25°C?

Solution   Let x equal the molar solubility of CaF_2.

$$CaF_2(s) \rightleftharpoons Ca^{2+} + 2F^-$$
$$\qquad\qquad\qquad x \qquad 2x$$

$$K_{SP} = [Ca^{2+}][F^-]^2 = 3.9 \times 10^{-11}$$
$$x(2x)^2 = 3.9 \times 10^{-11}$$
$$4x^3 =$$
$$x = 2.1 \times 10^{-4}M$$

$$? \text{ g } CaF_2 = 100 \text{ ml } H_2O\left(\frac{2.1 \times 10^{-4} \text{ mole } CaF_2}{1000 \text{ ml } H_2O}\right)\left(\frac{78 \text{ g } CaF_2}{1 \text{ mole } CaF_2}\right)$$
$$= 1.6 \times 10^{-3} \text{ g } CaF_2$$

There is evidence that some salts ionize in a stepwise manner. For example, lead chloride

$$PbCl_2(s) \rightleftharpoons Pb^{2+}(aq) + 2Cl^-(aq) \qquad K_{SP} = [Pb^{2+}][Cl^-]^2$$

is thought to ionize according to the equations

$$PbCl_2(s) \rightleftharpoons PbCl_2(aq) \qquad\qquad K_1 = [PbCl_2(aq)]$$

$$PbCl_2(aq) \rightleftharpoons PbCl^+(aq) + Cl^-(aq) \qquad K_2 = \frac{[PbCl^+][Cl^-]}{[PbCl_2(aq)]}$$

$$PbCl^+(aq) \rightleftharpoons Pb^{2+}(aq) + Cl^-(aq) \qquad K_3 = \frac{[Pb^{2+}][Cl^-]}{[PbCl^+]}$$

The product of the stepwise constants is

$$K_1 K_2 K_3 = [PbCl_2(aq)]\left(\frac{[PbCl^+][Cl^-]}{[PbCl_2(aq)]}\right)\left(\frac{[Pb^{2+}][Cl^-]}{[PbCl^+]}\right) = [Pb^{2+}][Cl^-]^2 = K_{SP}$$

In these expressions, $PbCl_2(aq)$ is a neutral molecule in solution.

Thus the solubility product principle applies to all solutions of slightly soluble materials whether they dissociate in a stepwise manner or not. However, the K_{SP}'s of salts that dissociate in steps must be carefully interpreted. For example, in a saturated solution of $PbCl_2$, the concentration of Cl^- is not twice the concentration of Pb^{2+} as the expression for the K_{SP} might lead one to expect; such an erroneous deduction ignores the existence of $PbCl_2(aq)$ molecules and $PbCl^+$ ions. The value of the K_{SP} applies only if the *actual* concentrations of Pb^{2+} and Cl^- are employed, and the stepwise mechanism must be considered in order to deduce the correct concentration terms.

Other factors introduce errors into solubility calculations for certain salts. The solubility of lead chloride is enhanced in moderately concentrated solutions of chloride ion because of the formation of the *complex ion*, $PbCl_3^-$.

$$PbCl_2(s) + Cl^-(aq) \rightleftharpoons PbCl_3^-(aq)$$

Also, the hydrolysis of the Pb^{2+} ion

$$Pb^{2+}(aq) + H_2O \rightleftharpoons Pb(OH)^+(aq) + H^+(aq)$$

reduces the concentration of Pb^{2+} so that the solubility of $PbCl_2$ is actually higher than the value obtained from a calculation that ignores hydrolysis. Complex-ion and hydrolysis equilibria are discussed in Section 14.12 and Section 14.14.

The solubility of any solid is increased by the presence of the ions of another salt in the solution; thus $PbCl_2$ is more soluble in moderately concentrated solutions of $NaNO_3$ than it is in pure water. This **salt effect** also increases the degree of ionization of soluble weak electrolytes. The effect is due to interionic attractions, and these do not depend upon the nature of the dissolved ions but on their concentrations and charges. Therefore, foreign ions reduce the activities of the ions of the substance under study. Since the equilibrium constant is properly a function of activities (rather than concentrations), more of the substance ionizes to realize the activity required to satisfy the mathematical relationship.

14.9 Precipitation and the Solubility Product

The numerical value of the solubility product of a salt is a quantitative statement of the limit of solubility of the salt. For a specific solution of a salt, the product of the concentrations of the ions, each raised to the proper power, is called the **ion product** of the solution. Thus for a saturated solution in equilibrium with excess solid, the ion product equals the K_{SP}. If the ion product of a solution is less than the K_{SP}, the solution is unsaturated; additional solid can dissolve in this solution. On the other hand, if the ion product is greater than the K_{SP}, the solution is momentarily supersaturated; precipitation will occur until the ion product equals the K_{SP}.

Example 14.22   Will a precipitate form if 10 ml of $0.01\,M$ NaCl and 10 ml of $0.0001\,M$ AgNO$_3$ are mixed? Assume that the final volume of the solution is 20 ml. For AgCl, $K_{SP} = 1.7 \times 10^{-10}$.

Solution   Diluting a solution to twice its original volume reduces the concentrations of ions in the solution to half their original value. Therefore if there were no reaction, the ion concentration would be

$$[Ag^+] = 5 \times 10^{-5}M$$
$$[Cl^-] = 5 \times 10^{-3}M$$

The ion product is

$$[Ag^+][Cl^-] =$$
$$(5 \times 10^{-5})(5 \times 10^{-3}) = 2.5 \times 10^{-7}$$

Therefore the ion product is larger than the K_{SP} (1.7×10^{-10}), and precipitation of AgCl will occur.

Example 14.23   Will a precipitate of Mg(OH)$_2$ form in a $0.001\,M$ solution of Mg(NO$_3$)$_2$ if the pH of the solution is adjusted to 9? The K_{SP} of Mg(OH)$_2$ is 8.9×10^{-12}.

Solution   If the pH = 9,

$$[OH^-] = 1 \times 10^{-5}M$$

Since $[Mg^{2+}] = 1 \times 10^{-3}$, the ion product is

$$[Mg^{2+}][OH^-]^2 =$$
$$(1 \times 10^{-3})(1 \times 10^{-5})^2 = 1 \times 10^{-13}$$

Since the ion product is less than 8.9×10^{-12}, no precipitate will form.

The common-ion effect pertains to solubility equilibria. As an example, consider the system

$$BaSO_4(s) \rightleftharpoons Ba^{2+}(aq) + SO_4^{2-}(aq)$$

The addition of sulfate ion, from sodium sulfate, to a saturated solution of barium sulfate will cause the equilibrium to shift to the left; the concentration of Ba^{2+} will decrease, and BaSO$_4$ will precipitate. Since the product $[Ba^{2+}][SO_4^{2-}]$ is a constant, increasing $[SO_4^{2-}]$ will cause $[Ba^{2+}]$ to decrease.

The amount of barium ion in a solution may be determined by precipitating the Ba^{2+} as BaSO$_4$. The precipitate is then removed by filtration, dried, and weighed. The concentration of Ba^{2+} left in solution after the precipitation may be reduced to a very low value if excess sulfate ion is employed in the precipitation. As a general rule, however, too large an excess of the common ion should be avoided. At high ionic concentrations, the salt effect increases the solubility of a salt, and for certain precipitates, the formation of a complex ion may lead to enhanced solubility.

Example 14.24 At 25°C, a saturated solution of $BaSO_4$ is $3.9 \times 10^{-5}M$; the K_{SP} of $BaSO_4$ is 1.5×10^{-9}. What is the solubility of $BaSO_4$ in $0.050M$ Na_2SO_4?

Solution The sulfate ion derived from $BaSO_4$ may be ignored. Thus

$$BaSO_4(s) \rightleftharpoons Ba^{2+} + SO_4^{2-}$$
$$? \qquad 5.0 \times 10^{-2}$$

$$[Ba^{2+}][SO_4^{2-}] = 1.5 \times 10^{-9}$$
$$[Ba^{2+}](5.0 \times 10^{-2}) =$$
$$[Ba^{2+}] = 3.0 \times 10^{-8}M$$

The solubility of $BaSO_4$ has been reduced from $3.9 \times 10^{-5}M$ to $3.0 \times 10^{-8}M$ by the common ion effect.

Frequently, a solution contains more than one ion capable of forming a precipitate with another ion which is to be added to the solution. For example, a solution might contain both Cl^- and CrO_4^{2-} ions, both of which form insoluble salts with Ag^+. When Ag^+ is added to the solution, the less soluble silver salt will precipitate first. If the addition is continued, eventually a point will be reached where the more soluble salt will begin to precipitate along with the less soluble.

Example 14.25 A solution is $0.10M$ in Cl^- and $0.10M$ in CrO_4^{2-}. If solid $AgNO_3$ is gradually added to this solution, which will precipitate first, $AgCl$ or Ag_2CrO_4? Assume that the addition causes no change in volume. For $AgCl$, $K_{SP} = 1.7 \times 10^{-10}$; for Ag_2CrO_4, $K_{SP} = 1.9 \times 10^{-12}$.

Solution When a precipitate *begins* to form, the pertinent ion product *just* exceeds the K_{SP} of the solid. Therefore we calculate the concentrations of Ag^+ needed to precipitate $AgCl$ and Ag_2CrO_4.

$$AgCl(s) \rightleftharpoons Ag^+ + Cl^- \qquad\qquad Ag_2CrO_4(s) \rightleftharpoons 2Ag^+ + CrO_4^{2-}$$
$$? \quad 0.10M \qquad\qquad\qquad\qquad ? \qquad 0.10M$$

$$[Ag^+][Cl^-] = 1.7 \times 10^{-10} \qquad\qquad [Ag^+]^2[CrO_4^{2-}] = 1.9 \times 10^{-12}$$
$$[Ag^+](0.10) = \qquad\qquad\qquad\qquad [Ag^+]^2(0.10) =$$
$$[Ag^+] = 1.7 \times 10^{-9}M \qquad\qquad\qquad [Ag^+]^2 = 1.9 \times 10^{-11}$$
$$[Ag^+] = 4.4 \times 10^{-6}M$$

Therefore, $AgCl$ will precipitate first.

Example 14.26 (a) In the experiment described in Example 14.25, what will be the concentration of the Cl^- ion when Ag_2CrO_4 begins to precipitate? (b) At this point, what percent of the chloride ion originally present remains in solution?

Solution (a) From the preceding example, we see that $[Ag^+] = 4.4 \times 10^{-6}M$ when Ag_2CrO_4 starts to precipitate. At this point, the concentration of chloride ion will be

$$[Ag^+][Cl^-] = 1.7 \times 10^{-10}$$
$$(4.4 \times 10^{-6})[Cl^-] =$$
$$[Cl^-] = \frac{1.7 \times 10^{-10}}{4.4 \times 10^{-6}} = 3.9 \times 10^{-5}M$$

Thus until the $[Cl^-]$ is decreased to $3.9 \times 10^{-5}M$, no Ag_2CrO_4 will form.

(b) Since the original concentration of chloride ion was $0.10M$, the percent of Cl^- remaining in solution when Ag_2CrO_4 starts to precipitate is

$$\frac{3.9 \times 10^{-5}}{1.0 \times 10^{-1}}100 = 0.039\%$$

Chromate ion is used as a **precipitation indicator.** The concentration of chloride ion in a solution can be determined by titrating a sample of the solution against a standard $AgNO_3$ solution using a few drops of K_2CrO_4 as an indicator. In the course of the titration, white $AgCl$ precipitates. The appearance of red Ag_2CrO_4 indicates that the precipitation of chloride ion is essentially complete. In a quantitative procedure of this type, the concentration of CrO_4^{2-} used is much less than that employed in the preceding problem. Hence, a higher concentration of Ag^+ is required to start the precipitation of Ag_2CrO_4, and a lower concentration of Cl^- will be present in the solution when the Ag_2CrO_4 begins to precipitate.

Example 14.27 What concentration of NH_4^+, derived from NH_4Cl, is necessary to prevent the formation of a $Mg(OH)_2$ precipitate in a solution that is $0.050M$ in Mg^{2+} and $0.050M$ in NH_3? The K_{SP} of $Mg(OH)_2$ is 8.9×10^{-12}.

Solution We first calculate the maximum concentration of hydroxide ion that can be present in the solution without causing $Mg(OH)_2$ to precipitate.

$$[Mg^{2+}][OH^-]^2 = 8.9 \times 10^{-12}$$
$$(5.0 \times 10^{-2})[OH^-]^2 =$$
$$[OH^-]^2 = 1.8 \times 10^{-10}$$
$$[OH^-] = 1.3 \times 10^{-5}M$$

From the expression for the ionization constant for NH_3, we can derive the concentration of NH_4^+ that will maintain the concentration of OH^- at this level.

$$\frac{[NH_4^+][OH^-]}{[NH_3]} = 1.8 \times 10^{-5}$$

$$\frac{[NH_4^+](1.3 \times 10^{-5})}{(5.0 \times 10^{-2})} = 1.8 \times 10^{-5}$$

$$[NH_4^+] = 6.9 \times 10^{-2}M$$

Thus the minimum concentration of NH_4^+ that must be present is $0.069M$.

14.10 Polyprotic Acids

Polyprotic acids are those that contain more than one acid hydrogen per molecule; examples include sulfuric acid (H_2SO_4), oxalic acid ($H_2C_2O_4$), phosphoric acid (H_3PO_4), and arsenic acid (H_3AsO_4). Polyprotic acids ionize in a stepwise manner, and there is an ionization constant for each step. Subscripts are added to the symbol K in order to specify the step to which the constant applies.

Phosphoric acid is triprotic and ionizes in three steps.

$$H_3PO_4 \rightleftharpoons H^+ + H_2PO_4^- \qquad \frac{[H^+][H_2PO_4^-]}{[H_3PO_4]} = K_1 = 7.5 \times 10^{-3}$$

$$H_2PO_4^- \rightleftharpoons H^+ + HPO_4^{2-} \qquad \frac{[H^+][HPO_4^{2-}]}{[H_2PO_4^-]} = K_2 = 6.2 \times 10^{-8}$$

$$HPO_4^{2-} \rightleftharpoons H^+ + PO_4^{3-} \qquad \frac{[H^+][PO_4^{3-}]}{[HPO_4^{2-}]} = K_3 = 1 \times 10^{-12}$$

Thus in a solution of phosphoric acid, three equilibria occur together with the water equilibrium; H_3PO_4, $H_2PO_4^-$, HPO_4^{2-}, PO_4^{3-}, H^+, OH^-, and H_2O are present.

The ionization of phosphoric acid is typical of all polyprotic acids in that the primary ionization is stronger than the secondary, and the secondary ionization is stronger than the tertiary. This trend in the value of the ionization constant is consistent with the nature of the particle that ionizes in each step. One would predict that a proton would be released more readily by an uncharged molecule than by a uninegative ion and more readily by a uninegative ion than by a binegative ion.

No polyprotic acid is known for which all ionizations are strong. The primary ionization of sulfuric acid is essentially complete,

$$H_2SO_4 \rightarrow H^+ + HSO_4^-$$

but the secondary ionization is weak,

$$HSO_4^- \rightleftharpoons H^+ + SO_4^{2-} \qquad \frac{[H^+][SO_4^{2-}]}{[HSO_4^-]} = K_2 = 1.3 \times 10^{-2}$$

Solutions of carbon dioxide are acidic. Carbon dioxide reacts with water to form carbonic acid, H_2CO_3; however, the reaction is not complete, and most of the carbon dioxide exists in solution as CO_2 molecules. Therefore, we shall indicate the primary ionization as follows:

$$CO_2 + H_2O \rightleftharpoons H^+ + HCO_3^- \qquad \frac{[H^+][HCO_3^-]}{[CO_2]} = K_1 = 4.2 \times 10^{-7}$$

where the symbol $[CO_2]$ is used to represent the total concentration of $CO_2(aq)$ and H_2CO_3. The second ionization step is

$$HCO_3^- \rightleftharpoons H^+ + CO_3^{2-} \qquad \frac{[H^+][CO_3^{2-}]}{[HCO_3^-]} = K_2 = 4.8 \times 10^{-11}$$

An analogous situation exists for solutions of sulfur dioxide in water. The acidity of aqueous SO_2 has been attributed to the ionization of sulfurous acid, H_2SO_3. However, H_2SO_3 has never been isolated in pure form; in solution, it apparently exists in equilibrium with $SO_2(aq)$

$$SO_2(aq) + H_2O \rightleftharpoons H_2SO_3(aq)$$

and we shall represent the primary ionization of sulfurous acid as

$$SO_2 + H_2O \rightleftharpoons H^+ + HSO_3^-$$

The ionization constants for some polyprotic acids are listed in Table 14.5.

Polyprotic acids form more than one salt. Depending upon the stoichiometric ratio of reactants, the reaction of NaOH and H_2SO_4 yields either the normal salt, Na_2SO_4 (sodium sulfate) or the acid salt $NaHSO_4$ (sodium bisulfate or sodium hydrogen sulfate). Three salts may be

TABLE 14.5.
IONIZATION CONSTANTS OF SOME POLYPROTIC ACIDS AT 25°C.

arsenic	H_3AsO_4	$\rightleftharpoons H^+ + H_2AsO_4^-$	$K_1 = 2.5 \times 10^{-4}$
	$H_2AsO_4^-$	$\rightleftharpoons H^+ + HAsO_4^{2-}$	$K_2 = 5.6 \times 10^{-8}$
	$HAsO_4^{2-}$	$\rightleftharpoons H^+ + AsO_4^{3-}$	$K_3 = 3 \times 10^{-13}$
carbonic	$CO_2 + H_2O$	$\rightleftharpoons H^+ + HCO_3^-$	$K_1 = 4.2 \times 10^{-7}$
	HCO_3^-	$\rightleftharpoons H^+ + CO_3^{2-}$	$K_2 = 4.8 \times 10^{-11}$
hydrosulfuric	H_2S	$\rightleftharpoons H^+ + HS^-$	$K_1 = 1.1 \times 10^{-7}$
	HS^-	$\rightleftharpoons H^+ + S^{2-}$	$K_2 = 1.0 \times 10^{-14}$
oxalic	$H_2C_2O_4$	$\rightleftharpoons H^+ + HC_2O_4^-$	$K_1 = 5.9 \times 10^{-2}$
	$HC_2O_4^-$	$\rightleftharpoons H^+ + C_2O_4^{2-}$	$K_2 = 6.4 \times 10^{-5}$
phosphoric	H_3PO_4	$\rightleftharpoons H^+ + H_2PO_4^-$	$K_1 = 7.5 \times 10^{-3}$
	$H_2PO_4^-$	$\rightleftharpoons H^+ + HPO_4^{2-}$	$K_2 = 6.2 \times 10^{-8}$
	HPO_4^{2-}	$\rightleftharpoons H^+ + PO_4^{3-}$	$K_3 = 1 \times 10^{-12}$
phosphorous (diprotic)	H_3PO_3	$\rightleftharpoons H^+ + H_2PO_3^-$	$K_1 = 1.6 \times 10^{-2}$
	$H_2PO_3^-$	$\rightleftharpoons H^+ + HPO_3^{2-}$	$K_2 = 7 \times 10^{-7}$
sulfuric	H_2SO_4	$\rightleftharpoons H^+ + HSO_4^-$	strong
	HSO_4^-	$\rightarrow H^+ + SO_4^{2-}$	$K_2 = 1.3 \times 10^{-2}$
sulfurous	$SO_2 + H_2O$	$\rightleftharpoons H^+ + HSO_3^-$	$K_1 = 1.3 \times 10^{-2}$
	HSO_3^-	$\rightleftharpoons H^+ + SO_3^{2-}$	$K_2 = 5.6 \times 10^{-8}$

derived from phosphoric acid: NaH_2PO_4 (sodium dihydrogen phosphate), Na_2HPO_4 (sodium hydrogen phosphate), and Na_3PO_4 (sodium phosphate).

Example 14.28 Calculate $[H^+]$, $[H_2PO_4^-]$, $[HPO_4^{2-}]$, $[PO_4^{3-}]$, and $[H_3PO_4]$ in a $0.10M$ solution of phosphoric acid.

Solution The principal source of H^+ is the primary ionization; the H^+ produced by the other ionizations, as well as that from the ionization of water, is negligible in comparison. Furthermore, the concentration of $H_2PO_4^-$ derived from the primary ionization is not significantly diminished by the secondary ionization. Thus we write

$$H_3PO_4 \rightleftharpoons H^+ + H_2PO_4^-$$
$$(0.10 - x)M \quad (x)M \quad (x)M$$

The problem must be solved by means of the quadratic formula.

$$\frac{[H^+][H_2PO_4^-]}{[H_3PO_4]} = 7.5 \times 10^{-3}$$

$$\frac{x^2}{(0.10 - x)} =$$

$$x = [H^+] = [H_2PO_4^-]2.4 \times 10^{-2}M$$

$$(0.10 - x) = [H_3PO_4] = 7.6 \times 10^{-2}M$$

The $[H^+]$ and $[H_2PO_4^-]$ apply to the secondary ionization. Therefore

$$H_2PO_4^- \rightleftharpoons H^+ + HPO_4^{2-}$$
$$2.4 \times 10^{-2}M \quad 2.4 \times 10^{-2}M \quad ?$$

$$\frac{[H^+][HPO_4^{2-}]}{[H_2PO_4^-]} = 6.2 \times 10^{-8}$$

$$\frac{(2.4 \times 10^{-2})[HPO_4^{2-}]}{(2.4 \times 10^{-2})} =$$

$$[HPO_4^{2-}] = 6.2 \times 10^{-8}M$$

In any solution of H_3PO_4 that does not contain ions derived from another electrolyte, the concentration of the secondary ion is equal to K_2.

For the tertiary ionization,

$$HPO_4^{2-} \rightleftharpoons H^+ + PO_4^{3-}$$
$$6.2 \times 10^{-8}M \quad 2.4 \times 10^{-2}M \quad ?$$

$$\frac{[H^+][PO_4^{3-}]}{[HPO_4^{2-}]} = 1 \times 10^{-12}$$

$$\frac{(2.4 \times 10^{-2})[PO_4^{3-}]}{(6.2 \times 10^{-8})} =$$

$$[PO_4^{3-}] = 3 \times 10^{-18}M$$

Example 14.29 What are $[H^+]$, $[HS^-]$, $[S^{2-}]$, and $[H_2S]$ in a $0.10M$ solution of H_2S?

Solution K_1 for H_2S is 1.1×10^{-7}; therefore the small amount of H_2S that ionizes is negligible in comparison to the original concentration of H_2S. In addition, the concentrations of H^+ and HS^- are not significantly altered by the secondary ionization ($K_2 = 1.0 \times 10^{-14}$). Therefore

$$H_2S \rightleftharpoons H^+ + HS^-$$
$$0.10M \quad (x)M \quad (x)M$$

$$\frac{[H^+][HS^-]}{[H_2S]} = 1.1 \times 10^{-7}$$

$$\frac{x^2}{0.10} =$$

$$x = [H^+] = [HS^-] = 1.0 \times 10^{-4}M$$

This fixes the concentrations of H^+ and HS^- in the secondary ionization.

$$HS^- \quad\rightleftharpoons\quad H^+ \quad + S^{2-}$$
$$1.0 \times 10^{-4}M \quad 1.0 \times 10^{-4}M \quad ?$$

$$\frac{[H^+][S^{2-}]}{[HS^-]} = 1.0 \times 10^{-14}M$$

$$\frac{(1.0 \times 10^{-4})[S^{2-}]}{(1.0 \times 10^{-4})} =$$

$$[S^{2-}] = 1.0 \times 10^{-14}M$$

The concentration of the secondary ion is equal to K_2 in any solution of H_2S that does not contain ions derived from another electrolyte.

The product of the expressions for the two ionizations of H_2S is

$$\left(\frac{[H^+][HS^-]}{[H_2S]}\right)\left(\frac{[H^+][S^{2-}]}{[HS^-]}\right) = K_1 K_2$$

$$\frac{[H^+]^2[S^{2-}]}{[H_2S]} = (1.1 \times 10^{-7})(1.0 \times 10^{-14}) = 1.1 \times 10^{-21}$$

This is a very convenient relationship, but it can be misleading. Superficially, it looks as though it applies to a process in which one sulfide ion is produced for every two hydronium ions. However, the ionization of H_2S does not proceed in this manner; in any solution of H_2S, the concentration of hydronium ion is much larger than the concentration of sulfide ion (Example 14.29). The majority of the H_2S molecules that ionize do so only to the HS^- stage, and S^{2-} ions result only from the small ionization of the secondary ion.

At 25°C, a saturated solution of H_2S is $0.10M$. For a *saturated solution*, therefore,

$$\frac{[H^+]^2[S^{2-}]}{(0.10)} = 1.1 \times 10^{-21}$$

$$[H^+]^2[S^{2-}] = 1.1 \times 10^{-22}$$

This relation can be used to calculate the sulfide ion concentration of a solution of known pH that has been saturated with H_2S. We shall see later that acidic solutions of H_2S are frequently employed laboratory reagents.

A similar relationship may be derived for carbonic acid.

$$\frac{[H^+][HCO_3^-]}{[CO_2]}\frac{[H^+][CO_3^{2-}]}{[HCO_3^-]} = K_1K_2$$

$$\frac{[H^+]^2[CO_3^{2-}]}{[CO_2]} = (4.2 \times 10^{-7})(4.8 \times 10^{-11}) = 2.0 \times 10^{-17}$$

Carbon dioxide is less soluble than H_2S; a saturated solution is $0.034M$ in CO_2.

$$\frac{[H^+]^2[CO_3^{2-}]}{(3.4 \times 10^{-2})} = 2.0 \times 10^{-17}$$

$$[H^+]^2[CO_3^{2-}] = 6.8 \times 10^{-19}$$

Example 14.30 What is the sulfide ion concentration of a dilute HCl solution that has been saturated with H_2S if the pH of the solution is 3.0?

Solution Since the pH = 3.0,

$$[H^+] = 1.0 \times 10^{-3}M$$

Therefore

$$[H^+]^2[S^{2-}] = 1.1 \times 10^{-22}$$
$$(1.0 \times 10^{-3})^2[S^{2-}] =$$
$$[S^{2-}] = 1.1 \times 10^{-16}M$$

In a saturated solution of pure H_2S (Example 14.29), $[S^{2-}] = 1.0 \times 10^{-14}M$. In the H_2S solution described in the problem, the common ion, H^+, has repressed the ionization of H_2S. In addition, since the solution contains H^+ ions from a source other than H_2S, $[H^+]$ does not equal $[HS^-]$, and consequently, $[S^{2-}]$ does not equal K_2.

14.11 Precipitation of Sulfides

The concentration of sulfide ion in an acidic solution saturated with H_2S is extremely low; in $0.3M$ acid saturated with H_2S there are approximately seven sulfide ions in every 10 ml of solution. Nevertheless, if an acid solution containing lead ions is saturated with H_2S, a precipitate of PbS forms immediately. Since the concentration of sulfide ions is so low, it seems unlikely that the precipitate is formed by the reaction

$$Pb^{2+}(aq) + S^{2-}(aq) \rightleftharpoons PbS(s)$$

There is evidence that in this and in similar sulfide precipitations, the hydrosulfide salt forms initially and then decomposes to give the normal sulfide.

$$Pb(HS)_2(s) \rightleftharpoons PbS(s) + H_2S(aq)$$

The hydroxides of many metals are known to decompose, upon heating, in a parallel manner.

$$Pb(OH)_2(s) \rightleftharpoons PbO(s) + H_2O$$

The hydrosulfide may form as a result of a reaction of the lead ion with the HS^- ion (the concentration of which is larger than the concentration of S^{2-} ion)

$$Pb^{2+}(aq) + 2HS^-(aq) \rightleftharpoons Pb(HS)_2(s)$$

or as a result of the reaction of Pb^{2+} with H_2S (the concentration of which is larger still)

$$Pb^{2+}(aq) + 2H_2S(aq) \rightleftharpoons Pb(HS)_2(s) + 2H^+(aq)$$

Undoubtedly, neither of these equations is representative of the mechanism of the hydrosulfide formation; each describes a three-body collision, and such a reaction is of low probability. If $Pb(HS)_2$ is the initial product, its formation probably goes through an intermediate $Pb(HS)^+$ ions and thus involves only two-body collisions.

$$Pb^{2+}(aq) + H_2S(aq) \rightleftharpoons Pb(HS)^+(aq) + H^+(aq)$$
$$Pb(HS)^+(aq) + H_2S(aq) \rightleftharpoons Pb(HS)_2(s) + H^+(aq)$$

However, an equilibrium constant does not depend upon the reaction mechanism by which the equilibrium is attained (Section 12.7). Provided the system is in equilibrium, the relationship expressed by the solubility product principle is valid no matter what series of reactions produces the precipitate. Thus we may use K_{SP}'s to calculate favorable reaction conditions for the formation of a desired precipitate or reaction conditions that will prevent the formation of a precipitate.

Example 14.31 A solution that is $0.30M$ in H^+, $0.050M$ in Pb^{2+}, and $0.050M$ in Fe^{2+} is saturated with H_2S; should PbS and/or FeS precipitate? The K_{SP} of PbS is 7×10^{-29} and the K_{SP} of FeS is 4×10^{-19}.

Solution For any saturated solution of H_2S,

$$[H^+]^2[S^{2-}] = 1.1 \times 10^{-22}$$

Since this solution is $0.30M$ in H,

$$(3.0 \times 10^{-1})^2[S^{2-}] = 1.1 \times 10^{-22}$$
$$[S^{2-}] = 1.2 \times 10^{-21}$$

Both Pb^{2+} and Fe^{2+} are 2+ ions, and the form of the ion product is

$$[M^{2+}][S^{2-}]$$

where M^{2+} stands for either metal ion. Since both are present in concentrations of $0.050M$,

$$[M^{2+}][S^{2-}]$$
$$(5.0 \times 10^{-2})(1.2 \times 10^{-21}) = 6.0 \times 10^{-23}$$

This ion product is greater than the K_{SP} of PbS; therefore PbS will precipitate. However, the ion product is less than the K_{SP} of FeS; the solubility of FeS has not been exceeded; no FeS will form.

Example 14.32 What must be the hydronium ion concentration of a solution that is $0.050M$ in Ni^{2+} to prevent the precipitation of NiS when the solution is saturated with H_2S? The K_{SP} of NiS is 3×10^{-21}.

Solution

$$[Ni^{2+}][S^{2-}] = 3 \times 10^{-21}$$
$$(0.050)[S^{2-}] =$$
$$[S^{2-}] = 6 \times 10^{-20}$$

Therefore the $[S^{2-}]$ must be less than 6×10^{-20} if NiS is not to precipitate. For a solution saturated with H_2S,

$$[H^+]^2[S^{2-}] = 1.1 \times 10^{-22}$$
$$[H^+]^2(6 \times 10^{-20}) =$$
$$[H^+] = 0.04M$$

The $[H^+]$ must be greater than $0.04M$ to prevent the precipitation of NiS.

The preceding examples illustrate an important analytical technique. In the usual qualitative analysis scheme, certain cations are separated into groups on the basis of whether their sulfides form in acidic solution. Thus, Hg^{2+}, Pb^{2+}, Cu^{2+}, Bi^{3+}, Cd^{2+}, and Sn^{2+} form acid-insoluble sulfides, whereas the sulfides of Fe^{2+}, Co^{2+}, Ni^{2+}, Mn^{2+}, and Zn^{2+} are soluble in $0.3M$ acid solutions; when such a solution is made alkaline, however, the corresponding sulfides precipitate.

It must be emphasized that calculations such as the preceding, although illustrative of principles, are only approximate; we have ignored hydrolysis (Section 14.14) and complex-ion formation (Section 14.12). Furthermore, the solubility-product constants for the sulfides are generally less reliable than those for other slightly soluble solids. The precipitated sulfides of some cations (notably Ni^{2+}, Co^{2+}, and Zn^{2+}) become more stable, and less soluble, upon standing. The decrease in solubility may be due to the transition from hydrosulfide to sulfide, but more probably, it is due to the rearrangement of the ions into a more stable crystalline form. Thus for all practical purposes, the K_{SP}'s for some sulfides change with time. Two different crystalline modifications of CoS are known; the α form has a K_{SP} of 5.0×10^{-22}, and the β form has a K_{SP} of 1.9×10^{-27}. The values of the solubility products of the sulfides listed in the appendix are for the freshly precipitated, or more soluble, modifications.

The precipitation of a sulfide causes the hydrogen ion concentration to increase; this is best seen by means of the overall equation for a specific change.

$$Pb^{2+}(aq) + H_2S(aq) \rightarrow PbS(s) + 2H^+(aq)$$

Hence, throughout the precipitation, the $[H^+]$ is steadily increasing, and since $[S^{2-}]$ is dependent upon $[H^+]$, the $[S^{2-}]$ is decreasing. This effect is particularly important for calculations involving solutions containing more than one cation. The most insoluble sulfide precipitates first, and by the time that the most soluble sulfide might be expected to start to precipitate, the sulfide ion concentration may be too low to effect this precipitation. This is illustrated in the following approximation.

Example 14.33 The sulfides of Fe^{2+} and Zn^{2+} do not precipitate from solutions that are $0.30M$ in H^+. However, when a solution $0.001M$ in H^+, $0.05M$ in Fe^{2+}, and $0.05M$ in Zn^{2+} is saturated with H_2S, white ZnS precipitates, but black FeS does not. Explain. The K_{SP} of ZnS is 2.5×10^{-22}, and K_{SP} of FeS is 4×10^{-19}.

Solution If the original concentration of H^+ is $1 \times 10^{-3}M$, the concentration of S^{2-} may be found.

$$[H^+]^2[S^{2-}] = 1.1 \times 10^{-22}$$
$$(1 \times 10^{-3})^2[S^{2-}] =$$
$$[S^{2-}] = 1.1 \times 10^{-16}$$

Since the concentration of each metal ion is $0.05M$, the ion product for either FeS or ZnS is

$$[M^{2+}][S^{2-}]$$
$$(5 \times 10^{-2})(1.1 \times 10^{-16}) = 5.5 \times 10^{-18}$$

It would appear that both ZnS and FeS should precipitate since the ion product for each salt exceeds its K_{SP}.

Let us assume, however, that only the ZnS precipitates (it has the lower K_{SP}). For each Zn^{2+} precipitated, two H^+ ions are added to the solution.

$$Zn^{2+}(aq) + H_2S(aq) \rightleftharpoons ZnS(s) + 2H^+(aq)$$

If x is the number of moles of Zn^{2+} that precipitate from a liter of solution, then $2x$ is the number of moles of H^+ per liter added to the solution by the precipitation. Thus

$$[Zn^{2+}] = (0.05 - x)M$$

$$[H^+] = (0.001 + 2x)M$$

$$[Zn^{2+}][S^{2-}] = 2.5 \times 10^{-22}$$

$$[S^{2-}] = \frac{2.5 \times 10^{-22}}{(0.05 - x)}$$

From the relationship

$$[H^+]^2[S^{2-}] = 1.1 \times 10^{-22}$$

we derive

$$(0.001 + 2x)^2 \frac{2.5 \times 10^{-22}}{(0.05 - x)} = 1.1 \times 10^{-22}$$

$$x = 0.037$$

Even in a solution containing only Zn^{2+} ions, not all of the Zn^{2+} precipitates as the sulfide.

$$[Zn^{2+}] = 0.05 - x = 0.013M$$

$$[H^+] = 0.001 + 2x = 0.075M$$

$$[S^{2-}] = \frac{2.5 \times 10^{-22}}{1.3 \times 10^{-2}} = 2 \times 10^{-20}M$$

Therefore the ion product for FeS is

$$[Fe^{2+}][S^{2-}]$$

$$(0.05)(2 \times 10^{-20}) = 1 \times 10^{-21}$$

Therefore FeS does not precipitate since the ion product is less than the K_{SP} for FeS (4×10^{-19}).

14.12 Equilibria Involving Complex Ions

Coordination compounds will be discussed in Chapter 16. However, complex ions, derived from coordination compounds, take part in some important aqueous equilibria that properly constitute a part of the topic of this chapter. A **complex ion** is a cation or an anion that is formed from a central metal cation together with either neutral molecules, anions, or a combination of molecules and anions, for example, $Co(NH_3)_6^{3+}$, $Cu(H_2O)_4^{2+}$, $CdCl_4^{2-}$, $Fe(CN)_6^{4-}$, $Ag(S_2O_3)_2^{3-}$, and $Co(NH_3)_5Cl^{2+}$. The groups attached to the central cation are called **ligands,** and the number of these groups in a given ion is the **coordination number** of the central ion. The charge on a complex ion is obtained by adding the charges of its constituent particles.

In general, a ligand must have an unshared pair of electrons with which it can bond to the central ion. Thus the ammonia molecule, NH_3, functions as a ligand in the formation of complex ions—the ammonium ion, NH_4^+, does not.

$$
H\!:\!\overset{\cdots}{\underset{}{N}}\!:\!H \qquad
\left[\; H\!:\!\overset{\overset{\textstyle H}{\cdots}}{N}\!:\!H \;\right]^{+}
$$

In addition to ammonia, the requirement is met by many neutral molecules and anions.

$$
H\!:\!\overset{\cdots}{\underset{H}{O}}\!: \qquad
[\,:\!C\!:\!:\!:\!N\!:\,]^{-} \qquad
:\!\overset{\cdots}{\underset{}{Cl}}\!:^{-} \qquad
\left[\; :\!\overset{\overset{\textstyle :\ddot{O}:}{}}{\underset{\underset{\textstyle :\ddot{O}:}{}}{S}}\!:\!\ddot{S}\!:\!\ddot{O}: \;\right]^{2-} \qquad
\left[\; :\!\ddot{O}\!:\!H \;\right]^{-}
$$

The stabilities of complex ions vary widely. The group I A and group II A cations only form aggregates that are loosely held together by weak ion-dipole or ion-ion electrostatic attractions; these are probably better described as ion pairs rather than complex ions. At the other extreme are the very stable complex ions, such as $Co(NH_3)_6^{3+}$ and $Fe(CN)_6^{4-}$, in which the strength of the attractions between the central ions and the ligands is of the same order as the covalent bond. In fact, the ammonium ion and the hydronium ion may be regarded as complex ions of a more stable type. We shall restrict our attention to those complex ions that are formed from their components in definite stoichiometric ratios and that exist in solution as reversibly dissociated entities.

All ions are hydrated in water solution (Section 3.17); many of these hydrated ions may be considered as complex ions. However, some ions (e.g., K^+, Na^+, and most anions) form loose aggregates with no fixed number of water molecules; the hydration of these ions varies with the concentration of the solution. On the other hand, most cations have a fixed number of water molecules bonded to them—although this number is difficult to determine and is not known with certainty for some species.

The copper(II) ion exists in crystalline hydrates as $Cu(H_2O)_4^{2+}$; there is evidence, however, that $Cu(H_2O)_6^{2+}$ is the hydrated form of the Cu^{2+} ion in aqueous solution and that two of the water molecules are at a greater distance from the central ion than the other four water molecules. Furthermore, a hydrated complex ion in water solution has a secondary sheath of water molecules that is loosely held by hydrogen bonding to the primary hydration shell; the number of water molecules in this secondary shell varies with the concentration of the solution, and these water molecules are not considered as a part of the complex ion.

There are many interlocking equilibria in a solution containing complex ions. A simple example of such a system is a solution of silver nitrate containing ammonia. Assuming that the coordination number of Ag^+ is four in all of its complex ions, we write the following equations for the equilibria that have been postulated to exist in this solution.

$$
Ag(H_2O)_4^+ + NH_3 \rightleftharpoons Ag(H_2O)_3(NH_3)^+ + H_2O \qquad (1)
$$

$$Ag(H_2O)_3(NH_3)^+ + NH_3 \rightleftharpoons Ag(H_2O)_2(NH_3)_2^+ + H_2O \quad (2)$$

$$NH_3 + H_2O \rightleftharpoons NH_4^+ + OH^- \quad (3)$$

$$2H_2O \rightleftharpoons H_3O^+ + OH^- \quad (4)$$

$$Ag(H_2O)_4^+ + OH^- \rightleftharpoons Ag(H_2O)_3(OH)(aq) + H_2O \quad (5)$$

$$Ag(H_2O)_3(OH)(aq) + OH^- \rightleftharpoons Ag(H_2O)_2(OH)_2^- + H_2O \quad (6)$$

The substance $Ag(H_2O)_3(OH)(aq)$ is a neutral molecule in solution.

We have adopted the common practice of not showing the water ligands of ions in aqueous solution; thus we have indicated the hydrated proton as H^+ and the hydrated zinc ion as Zn^{2+}. In the interest of simplicity, we shall continue this practice unless we are particularly interested in the coordinated water molecules of the ion under consideration. Therefore we shall write $Ag(NH_3)^+$ and $Ag(NH_3)_2^+$ for the ammonia complexes of Ag^+ found in equations (1) and (2).

Furthermore, we shall indicate the reversible dissociation of these ammonia complexes in the usual form rather than in the manner in which they are written in equations (1) and (2). Thus the ion $Ag(NH_3)_2^+$ dissociates in a stepwise manner similar to a weak diprotic acid such as H_2S.

$Ag(NH_3)_2^+ \rightleftharpoons$

$$Ag(NH_3)^+ + NH_3 \qquad K' = \frac{[Ag(NH_3)^+][NH_3]}{[Ag(NH_3)_2^+]} = 1.4 \times 10^{-4}$$

$Ag(NH_3)^+ \rightleftharpoons$

$$Ag^+ + NH_3^- \qquad K'' = \frac{[Ag^+][NH_3]}{[Ag(NH_3)^+]} = 4.3 \times 10^{-4}$$

The product of the two constants is called the **instability constant** of the $Ag(NH_3)_2^+$ ion.

$$\left(\frac{[Ag(NH_3)^+][NH_3]}{[Ag(NH_3)_2^+]}\right)\left(\frac{[Ag^+][NH_3]}{[Ag(NH_3)^+]}\right) = \frac{[Ag^+][NH_3]^2}{[Ag(NH_3)_2^+]}$$

$$K_{inst} = K'K'' = (1.4 \times 10^{-4})(4.3 \times 10^{-4}) = 6.0 \times 10^{-8}$$

For many complexes, the values of the equilibrium constants for the individual steps of the dissociations are not known although values for the overall dissociation may have been determined. However, overall instability constants for a complex ion must be cautiously interpreted since the chemical equation to which they apply does not take into account any intermediate species. The constants for the individual steps of a dissociation must be known in order to solve certain problems.

Example 14.34 A $1.0 \times 10^{-3}M$ solution of $AgNO_3$ is made $0.10M$ in NH_3. What are the concentrations of Ag^+, $Ag(NH_3)^+$, and $Ag(NH_3)_2^+$ in the resulting solution?

Solution   We shall assume that the Ag^+ is practically completely converted into the higher complex, $Ag(NH_3)_2^+$, by this excess of NH_3. Therefore

$$[Ag(NH_3)_2^+] = 1.0 \times 10^{-3} M$$

The formation of this concentration of $Ag(NH_3)_2^+$ would reduce the concentration of NH_3 by $2.0 \times 10^{-3} M$, but this, as well as the amount of NH_3 that reacts with H_2O to form NH_4^+, is negligible in comparison with the original concentration of NH_3. From the instability constant, we see

$$\frac{[Ag^+][NH_3]^2}{[Ag(NH_3)_2^+]} = 6.0 \times 10^{-8}$$

$$\frac{[Ag^+](1.0 \times 10^{-1})^2}{(1.0 \times 10^{-3})} =$$

$$[Ag^+] = 6.0 \times 10^{-9} M$$

The concentration of $Ag(NH_3)^+$ may be obtained from either of the stepwise dissociation constants. Thus

$$\frac{[Ag(NH_3)^+][NH_3]}{[Ag(NH_3)_2^+]} = 1.4 \times 10^{-4}$$

$$\frac{[Ag(NH_3)^+](1.0 \times 10^{-1})}{(1.0 \times 10^{-3})} =$$

$$[Ag(NH_3)^+] = 1.4 \times 10^{-6} M$$

By comparing the concentrations of all of the cations in the solution, we can see that the assumption that $Ag(NH_3)_2^+$ is the principal silver-containing ion is a valid one.

Example 14.35   What is the solubility of AgCl in $0.1 M$ NH_3?

Solution   If we let x equal the solubility of AgCl in moles per liter, then $[Cl^-] = x$. From the K_{SP} for AgCl, we derive

$$[Ag^+][Cl^-] = 1.7 \times 10^{-10}$$

$$[Ag^+] = \frac{1.7 \times 10^{-10}}{x}$$

If we assume that the majority of the dissolved Ag^+ goes into solution as $Ag(NH_3)_2^+$, then

$$[Ag(NH_3)_2^+] = x$$

Since two molecules of NH_3 are required for every $Ag(NH_3)_2^+$ ion formed,

$$[NH_3] = 0.10 - 2x$$

Therefore

$$\frac{[Ag^+][NH_3]^2}{[Ag(NH_3)_2^+]} = 6.0 \times 10^{-8}$$

$$\frac{\left(\dfrac{1.7 \times 10^{-10}}{x}\right)(0.10 - 2x)^2}{x} =$$

From which, we derive

$$\frac{(0.10 - 2x)^2}{x^2} = \frac{6.0 \times 10^{-8}}{1.7 \times 10^{-10}} = 3.5 \times 10^2$$

By extracting the square root of both sides of this equation, we get the relation

$$\frac{(0.10 - 2x)}{x} = 19$$

$$x = [Ag(NH_3)_2^+] = 4.8 \times 10^{-3} M$$

which is the solubility of AgCl in $0.10 M$ NH$_3$. The concentration of NH$_3$ is

$$[NH_s] = 0.10 - 2x = 9.0 \times 10^{-2} M$$

The concentration of Ag$^+$ is

$$[Ag^+] = \frac{1.7 \times 10^{-10}}{x}$$

$$= 3.5 \times 10^{-8} M$$

The concentration of Ag(NH$_3$)$^+$ can be derived from

$$\frac{[Ag(NH_3)^+][NH_3]}{[Ag(NH_3)_2^+]} = 1.4 \times 10^{-4}$$

$$\frac{[Ag(NH_3)^+](9.0 \times 10^{-2})}{4.8 \times 10^{-3}} =$$

$$[Ag(NH_3)^+] = 7.5 \times 10^{-6} M$$

Comparison of the concentrations of all of the species in the solution will show that our assumptions were justified.

Silver ion forms three complex ions with the thiosulfate ion. The stepwise equations for the dissociations of these ions and the corresponding equilibrium constants follow.

$$Ag(S_2O_3)_3^{5-} \rightleftharpoons Ag(S_2O_3)_2^{3-} + S_2O_3^{2-} \qquad K' = 2.0 \times 10^{-1}$$

$$Ag(S_2O_3)_2^{3-} \rightleftharpoons Ag(S_2O_3)^- + S_2O_3^{2-} \qquad K'' = 3.3 \times 10^{-5}$$

$$Ag(S_2O_3)^- \rightleftharpoons Ag^+ + S_2O_3^{2-} \qquad K''' = 1.5 \times 10^{-9}$$

The instability constant for the ion Ag(S$_2$O$_3$)$_3^{5-}$ is the product $K'K''K'''$ or

$$\frac{[Ag^+][S_2O_3^{2-}]^3}{[Ag(S_2O_3)_3^{5-}]} = 9.9 \times 10^{-15}$$

Example 14.36 What is [Ag$^+$] and [S$_2$O$_3^{2-}$] of a solution prepared by dissolving 1.0 mole of Ag(S$_2$O$_3$)$_3^{5-}$ in 1.0 liter of water?

Solution   The first step of the dissociation is much more extensive than any subsequent step.   Therefore the concentrations of $Ag(S_2O_3)_2^{3-}$ and $S_2O_3^{2-}$ may be calculated from this initial dissociation. If we let x equal $[Ag(S_2O_3)_2^{3-}]$, the following concentration terms for the first dissociation may be written.

$$Ag(S_2O_3)_3^{5-} \rightleftharpoons Ag(S_2O_3)_2^{3-} + S_2O_3^{2-}$$
$$1.0 - x \qquad\qquad x \qquad\qquad x$$

Therefore

$$\frac{[Ag(S_2O_3)_2^{3-}][S_2O_3^{2-}]}{[Ag(S_2O_3)_3^{5-}]} = 2.0 \times 10^{-1}$$

$$\frac{x^2}{(1.0 - x)} =$$

$$x = 0.36M$$

Consequently,

$$[Ag(S_2O_3)_2^{3-}] = [S_2O_3^{2-}] = 0.36M$$
$$[Ag(S_2O_3)_3^{5-}] = 1.0 - x = 0.64M$$

We can find the concentration of Ag^+ from the instability constant for $Ag(S_2O_3)_3^{5-}$.

$$\frac{[Ag^+][S_2O_3^{2-}]^3}{[Ag(S_2O_3)_3^{5-}]} = 9.9 \times 10^{-15}$$

$$\frac{[Ag^+](0.36)^3}{(0.64)} =$$

$$[Ag^+] = 1.4 \times 10^{-13}M$$

The concentration of $Ag(S_2O_3)^-$ may be calculated from K''.

$$\frac{[Ag(S_2O_3)^-][S_2O_3^{2-}]}{[Ag(S_2O_3)_2^{3-}]} = 3.3 \times 10^{-5}$$

$$\frac{[Ag(S_2O_3)^-](0.36)}{(0.36)} =$$

$$[Ag(S_2O_3)^-] = 3.3 \times 10^{-5}M$$

Comparison of the concentrations of the silver-containing ions shows that we were justified in neglecting the second step of the dissociation in order to calculate $[S_2O_3^{2-}]$, $[Ag(S_2O_3)_2^{3-}]$, and $[Ag(S_2O_3)_3^{5-}]$.

An important conclusion may be derived from this example.   When problems are solved using only the instability constant for the overall dissociation, the erroneous assumption is sometimes made that the chemical equation for the overall dissociation describes the stoichiometry of the solution.

$$Ag(S_2O_3)_3^{5-} \rightleftharpoons Ag^+ + 3S_2O_3^{2-}$$

Thus one might be tempted to say that $[S_2O_3^{2-}]$ is three times $[Ag^+]$ and solve the problem on the basis of this dubious supposition.   Notice that in the solution described in this example, the concentration of $S_2O_3^{2-}$ is not three times the concentration of Ag^+; rather, it is approximately 2.6 trillion times larger. The stepwise constants must be known in order to solve most problems accurately.

The principal complex ion in a solution is not always the one with the highest number of ligands as the following example will show.

Example 14.37 What are the concentrations of Ag^+, $S_2O_3^{2-}$, and all complex ions in a solution prepared from 0.010 mole of $Ag(S_2O_3)_3^{5-}$ in 1 liter of water?

Solution For the first step of the dissociation, we write

$$Ag(S_2O_3)_3^{5-} \rightleftharpoons Ag(S_2O_3)_2^{3-} + S_2O_3^{2-}$$
$$\quad\;\; 0.010 - x \qquad\qquad\quad x \qquad\quad\; x$$

$$\frac{[Ag(S_2O_3)_2^{3-}][S_2O_3^{2-}]}{[Ag(S_2O_3)_3^{5-}]} = 0.20$$

$$\frac{x^2}{0.010 - x} =$$

$$x = [Ag(S_2O_3)_2^{3-}] = [S_2O_3^{2-}] = 9.6 \times 10^{-3} M$$
$$(0.010 - x) = [Ag(S_2O_3)_3^{5-}] = 4 \times 10^{-4} M$$

For the second step of the dissociation,

$$\frac{[Ag(S_2O_3)^-][S_2O_3^{2-}]}{[Ag(S_2O_3)_2^{3-}]} = 3.3 \times 10^{-5}$$

$$\frac{[Ag(S_2O_3)^-](9.6 \times 10^{-3})}{(9.6 \times 10^{-3})} =$$

$$[Ag(S_2O_3)^-] = 3.3 \times 10^{-5} M$$

For the third step of the dissociation,

$$\frac{[Ag^+][S_2O_3^{2-}]}{[Ag(S_2O_3)^-]} = 1.5 \times 10^{-9}$$

$$\frac{[Ag^+](9.6 \times 10^{-3})}{(3.3 \times 10^{-5})} =$$

$$[Ag^+] = 5.2 \times 10^{-12} M$$

Whereas $Ag(S_2O_3)_3^{5-}$ was found to be the principal complex ion in the solution described in Example 14.36, in this example $Ag(S_2O_3)_2^{3-}$ is found to be the complex ion present in largest concentration. In the $0.01 M$ solution, $[Ag(S_2O_3)_3^{5-}]$ is only approximately 4% of $[Ag(S_2O_3)_2^{3-}]$, and $[Ag(S_2O_3)^-]$ is only approximately 0.3% of $[Ag(S_2O_3)_2^{3-}]$. Thus the method outlined above gives answers correct to two significant figures.

Slightly soluble substances can often be dissolved through the formation of complex ions. The dissolution of AgCl in NH_3 (Example 14.35) illustrates this technique, which is an important one in analytical chemistry. The equilibrium between solid AgCl and its ions

$$AgCl(s) \rightleftharpoons Ag^+(aq) + Cl^-(aq)$$

is forced to the right by the removal of Ag^+ ions through the formation of the silver-ammonia complex ion, and therefore AgCl dissolves.

A few metals (e.g., Hg, As, Sb, and Sn) form thio complex ions $(HgS_2^{2-}, AsS_3^{3-}, SbS_2^{3-}, SnS_3^{2-})$; the true structure of these anions may involve the HS^- ion. The formation of a thio complex ion may be used to separate sulfide precipitates. For example, a mixture of CuS (which does not form a thio complex) and As_2S_3 may be separated by dissolving the As_2S_3 in an alkaline solution containing S^{2-} ion. The solution must have a high pH to maintain a relatively high concentration of S^{2-}.

$$CuS(s) + S^{2-}(aq) \rightarrow \text{no reaction}$$
$$As_2S_3(s) + 3S^{2-}(aq) \rightleftharpoons 2AsS_3^{3-}(aq)$$

The reaction of As_2S_3 may involve HS^- ions or H_2S molecules, and the actual structure of the complex ion may be $As(SH)_4^-$.

If a solution containing Al^{3+} and Zn^{2+} is treated with a buffer of NH_3 at a controlled alkaline pH, $Al(OH)_3$ will precipitate, but Zn^{2+} will stay in solution as $Zn(NH_3)_4^{2+}$. The precipitation of $Zn(OH)_2$ is prevented by the formation of the complex ion; Al^{3+} does not form an ammonia complex.

$$Al^{3+}(aq) + 3OH^-(aq) \rightleftharpoons Al(OH)_3(s)$$
$$Zn^{2+}(aq) + 4NH_3(aq) \rightleftharpoons Zn(NH_3)_4^{2+}(aq)$$

Complex ions are frequently highly colored; $Fe(SCN)^{2+}$ is deep red. Thus the production of a deep red color when SCN^- is added to a solution serves as a test for the Fe^{3+} ion.

Example 14.38 Sodium thiosulfate ("hypo" in photography) is used to dissolve unreacted AgBr from an exposed and developed photographic plate or proof and thus "fix" the image. What is the solubility of AgBr in $0.010\,M\ S_2O_3^{2-}$?

Solution The principal complex ion produced is $Ag(S_2O_3)_2^{3-}$ (see Example 14.37). If x is the solubility of AgBr, then

$$AgBr(s) + 2S_2O_3^{2-} \rightleftharpoons Ag(S_2O_3)_2^{3-} + Br^-$$
$$\ 0.010 - 2x \qquad\qquad x \qquad\qquad x$$

We can derive an equilibrium constant for this equation by dividing the K_{SP} of AgBr by the product of $K'' \times K'''$.

$$K_{SP}\left(\frac{1}{K''}\right)\left(\frac{1}{K'''}\right) = [Ag^+][Br^-]\frac{[Ag(S_2O_3)_2^{3-}]}{[Ag(S_2O_3)^-][S_2O_3^{2-}]}\frac{[Ag(S_2O_3)^-]}{[Ag^+][S_2O_3^{2-}]}$$

$$(5.0 \times 10^{-13})\left(\frac{1}{3.3 \times 10^{-5}}\right)\left(\frac{1}{1.5 \times 10^{-9}}\right) = 10.$$

Therefore,

$$\frac{[Ag(S_2O_3)_2^{3-}][Br^-]}{[S_2O_3^{2-}]^2} = 10$$

$$\frac{x^2}{(0.010 - 2x)^2} = 10$$

$$\frac{x}{(0.010 - 2x)} = 3.16$$

$$x = 4.3 \times 10^{-3} M$$

14.13 Amphoterism

The hydroxides of certain metals react with both hydroxide ion and hydronium ion. Thus these water-insoluble compounds dissolve in solutions of both high and low pH. Examples of these compounds, which are called **amphoteric hydroxides,** are $Al(OH)_3$, $Zn(OH)_2$, $Sn(OH)_2$, $Cr(OH)_3$, $Be(OH)_2$, $Sb(\overline{O}H)_3$ (or Sb_2O_3), and $As(OH)_3$ (or As_2O_3); many other compounds including $Cu(OH)_2$ and $AgOH$ (or Ag_2O) exhibit this property to a lesser degree.

In alkaline solution, the metal of an amphoteric hydroxide forms the central atom of a complex anion. The formulas of these amphoterate anions are not known with certainty, and different formulas are sometimes written for the same ion. For example, the formulas AlO_2^-, $AlO(OH)_2^-$, and $Al(OH)_4^-$ are equivalent; they differ only in the amount of water represented.

$$AlO_2^- \xrightarrow{H_2O} AlO(OH)_2^- \xrightarrow{H_2O} Al(OH)_4^-$$
$$\underset{2H_2O}{\underline{}}\uparrow$$

The forms of some hydroxides themselves are in doubt. Most hydroxides, formed from OH^- ion and metal cations in solution, are precipitated as amorphous gels; upon aging, these materials generally crystallize. Their form, upon drying, varies from oxide, Cr_2O_3, to hydrated oxide, $Al_2O_3 \cdot H_2O$, to true hydroxide, $Mg(OH)_2$. Since true hydroxides form oxides upon strong heating,

$$Mg(OH)_2(s) \rightarrow MgO(s) + H_2O(g)$$

the form of the dried "hydroxide" precipitate does not necessarily tell anything about the form in which the substance was initially thrown out of solution. Nevertheless, a given "hydroxide" precipitate may be a hydrous oxide rather than a true hydroxide, and the oxy-anion formula of an amphoterate anion (such as AlO_2^-) is not without merit.

On the other hand, the metals that form amphoteric hydroxides also form cations that have a strong tendency to form complex ions through coordination with anions. Therefore the hydroxide-complex formula of an amphoterate anion (such as $Al(OH)_4^-$) is probably to be preferred.

This concept is supported by the existence of "basic salts" (such as $[Al(H_2O)_5(OH)]SO_4$).

If we regard amphoteric behavior in terms of the formation of hydroxide complexes, the following series of equations describe the successive reactions of the hydrated Al^{3+} ion (coordination number, 6) in a solution as the pH of the solution is increased.

$$Al(H_2O)_6^{3+} + OH^- \rightleftharpoons H_2O + Al(H_2O)_5OH^{2+}$$
$$Al(H_2O)_5OH^{2+} + OH^- \rightleftharpoons H_2O + Al(H_2O)_4(OH)_2^+$$
$$Al(H_2O)_4(OH)_2^+ + OH^- \rightleftharpoons H_2O + Al(H_2O)_3(OH)_3(s)$$
$$Al(H_2O)_3(OH)_3(s) + OH^- \rightleftharpoons H_2O + Al(H_2O)_2(OH)_4^-$$

Each of the preceding reactions may be interpreted as a replacement of a coordinated water molecule by a hydroxide ion or, in Brønsted terms, as the reaction of an acid (the aluminum complex) with the base OH^- in which a coordinated water molecule supplies the transferred proton. If these equations are read from right to left, they appear similar to equations for the ionizations of weak bases (such as NH_3) in water.

Starting with the aluminate ion, $Al(H_2O)_2(OH)_4^-$, a series of equations may be written for the reverse procedure—the lowering of the pH of the solution in which the reactions occur.

$$Al(H_2O)_2(OH)_4^- + H_3O^+ \rightleftharpoons H_2O + Al(H_2O)_3(OH)_3(s)$$
$$Al(H_2O)_3(OH)_3(s) + H_3O^+ \rightleftharpoons H_2O + Al(H_2O)_4(OH)_2^+$$
$$Al(H_2O)_4(OH)_2^+ + H_3O^+ \rightleftharpoons H_2O + Al(H_2O)_5OH^{2+}$$
$$Al(H_2O)_5OH^{2+} + H_3O^+ \rightleftharpoons H_2O + Al(H_2O)_6^{3+}$$

In this series of equations (forward direction), the aluminum complex functions as a Brønsted base and accepts a proton from the acid H_3O^+. Read from right to left, these equations are analogous to equations for the dissociations of weak acids.

Amphoteric hydroxides, then, are amphiprotic substances. They function as Brønsted acids when a proton is lost from a coordinated water molecule, or they function as Brønsted bases when a coordinated hydroxyl group accepts a proton.

Certain problems involving amphoteric hydroxides may be solved by using the solubility product constant of the hydroxide and the instability constant of the hydroxide complex ion. In the problem that follows, as well as in subsequent discussions, we shall follow the practice of not indicating the coordinated water molecules unless they are of particular importance to the topic under consideration.

> *Example 14.39* (a) At what minimum pH will 1.0×10^{-3} mole of $Al(OH)_3$ go into solution (1 liter) as $Al(OH)_4^-$? (b) At what maximum pH will 1.0×10^{-3} mole of $Al(OH)_3$ go into solution (1 liter) as Al^{3+}? K_{SP} of $Al(OH)_3$ is 5.0×10^{-33}, and K_{inst} of $Al(OH)_4^-$ is 1.3×10^{-34}.

Solution   (a) At the point at which $Al(OH)_3$ just dissolves,

$$K_{SP} = [Al^{3+}][OH^-]^3 = 5.0 \times 10^{-33} \tag{7}$$

If the $Al(OH)_3$ is substantially completely converted into $Al(OH)_4^-$, then,

and

$$[Al(OH)_4^-] = 1.0 \times 10^{-3} M$$

$$\frac{[Al^{3+}][OH^-]^4}{[Al(OH)_4^-]} = 1.3 \times 10^{-34}$$

$$\frac{[Al^{3+}][OH^-]^4}{(1.0 \times 10^{-3})} =$$

$$[Al^{3+}][OH^-]^4 = 1.3 \times 10^{-37} \tag{8}$$

If we divide equation (8) by equation (7), we get

$$\frac{[Al^{3+}][OH^-]^4}{[Al^{3+}][OH^-]^3} = \frac{1.3 \times 10^{-37}}{5.0 \times 10^{-33}}$$

$$[OH^-] = 2.6 \times 10^{-5} M$$

$$pH = 9.4$$

(b) The way the problem is stated, the $Al(OH)_3$ is to be completely converted into Al^{3+}. This may *not* be the pH at which the solid disappears into solution since the intermediate ions $(Al(OH)_2^+$ and $Al(OH)^{2+})$ are ignored. If, however,

$$[Al^{3+}] = 1.0 \times 10^{-3} M$$

Then,

$$[Al^{3+}][OH^-]^3 = 5.0 \times 10^{-33}$$

$$(1.0 \times 10^{-3})[OH^-]^3 =$$

$$[OH^-]^3 = 5.0 \times 10^{-30}$$

$$[OH^-] = 1.7 \times 10^{-10}$$

$$pH = 4.2$$

Too much credence must not be placed in the results obtained from calculations such as those of Example 14.39. In general, the constants are of doubtful validity, and the stepwise constants for many hydroxide systems are not known. Indeed, there is strong evidence that not all of the ions and equilibria in solutions of this type have been identified; probably the situation is much more complicated than we have depicted it. In theory, the ions $Al(OH)_5^{2-}$ and $Al(OH)_6^{3-}$ should be possible, but their existence in solution has never been firmly established.

We have considered only mononuclear complexes (complexes with only one central metal atom). However, polynuclear complexes have been identified in some hydroxide systems. For example, $Sn_2(OH)_2^{2+}$ and $Sn_3(OH)_4^{2+}$, as well as $SnOH^+$, are postulated as occurring in acidic solutions of Sn^{2+} ion. The structures of the polynuclear complexes involve hydroxide bridges between two tin atoms.

$$\left[\; (H_2O)_4Sn \underset{\underset{H}{O}}{\overset{\overset{H}{O}}{<\;\;>}} Sn(H_2O)_4 \;\right]^{2+}$$

$$\left[\; (H_2O)_4Sn \underset{\underset{H}{O}}{\overset{\overset{H}{O}}{<\;\;>}} Sn(H_2O)_2 \underset{\underset{H}{O}}{\overset{\overset{H}{O}}{<\;\;>}} Sn(H_2O)_4 \;\right]^{2+}$$

In these structures, each tin atom has a coordination number of six. In general, the identification of all of the constituents of most of these solutions is incomplete, and hence, reliable values for equilibrium constants are lacking.

Advantage is taken of the amphoteric nature of some hydroxides in analytical chemistry and in some commercial processes. For example, Mg^{2+} and Zn^{2+} may be separated from a solution containing the two ions by making the solution alkaline.

$$Mg^{2+} + 2OH^- \rightleftharpoons Mg(OH)_2(s)$$
$$Zn^{2+} + 4OH^- \rightleftharpoons Zn(OH)_4^{2-}$$

The insoluble magnesium hydroxide may be removed by filtration from the solution containing the zincate ion.

In the production of aluminum metal from bauxite (impure hydrated Al_2O_3), the ore is purified prior to its reduction to aluminum metal. This purification is accomplished by dissolving the aluminum oxide in a solution of sodium hydroxide and removing the insoluble impurities by filtration.

$$Al_2O_3(s) + 2OH^- + 3H_2O \longrightarrow 2Al(OH)_4^-$$

14.14 Hydrolysis

A solution of sodium acetate is alkaline because of the hydrolysis of the acetate ion (Section 13.5); the sodium ion does not hydrolyze.

$$\underset{Acid_1}{H_2O} + \underset{Base_2}{C_2H_3O_2^-} \rightleftharpoons \underset{Acid_2}{HC_2H_3O_2} + \underset{Base_1}{OH^-}$$

In the hydrolysis, $C_2H_3O_2^-$ (a Brønsted base) gains a proton from the acid H_2O which is converted into its conjugate base, OH^-. However, OH^- is a stronger base than $C_2H_3O_2^-$ (H_2O is a weaker acid than $HC_2H_3O_2$). Therefore the position of the preceding equilibrium is far to the left. In other words, since water is a weaker electrolyte than acetic acid, water does a better job of tying up protons than acetic acid does, and the backward reaction is more complete than the forward reaction. The hydrolysis, however, does proceed to an extent sufficient to cause a measurable effect on the pH of the solution.

An alternative view of hydrolysis is that the acetate ion disturbs the water equilibrium

$$2H_2O \rightleftharpoons H_3O^+ + OH^-$$

by removing H_3O^+ ions to form acetic acid.

$$H_3O^+ + C_2H_3O_2^- \rightleftharpoons HC_2H_3O_2 + H_2O$$

The removal of H_3O^+ ions causes the water equilibrium to shift to the right, producing a higher concentration of OH^- than is normally present in water.

It is obvious that ions derived from acids or alkalies that are strong electrolytes do not hydrolyze, and the weaker the electrolyte from which an ion is derived the more extensive is its hydrolysis. Provided the cation does not hydrolyze, the weaker the acid from which the anion of a salt is derived, the more alkaline is the aqueous solution of the salt. In other words, the stronger the Brønsted base (the anion), the weaker is the conjugate acid (the compound from which the anion is derived).

An equilibrium constant (K_H) may be derived for a hydrolysis equilibrium. For example, the equilibrium constant for the reaction

$$H_2O + C_2H_3O_2^- \rightleftharpoons HC_2H_3O_2 + OH^-$$

may be obtained by dividing the water constant by the ionization constant for acetic acid.

$$([H^+][OH^-])\left(\frac{[HC_2H_3O_2]}{[H^+][C_2H_3O_2^-]}\right) = \frac{[HC_2H_3O_2][OH^-]}{[C_2H_3O_2^-]}$$

$$K_w\left(\frac{1}{K_{HC_2H_3O_2}}\right) = K_H$$

$$(1.0 \times 10^{-14})\left(\frac{1}{1.8 \times 10^{-5}}\right) = 5.6 \times 10^{-10}$$

Example 14.40   What is the pH and the degree of hydrolysis of a $0.10M$ solution of $NaC_2H_3O_2$?

Solution   If we let x equal the equilibrium concentration of $HC_2H_3O_2$, we derive the following concentration terms.

$$C_2H_3O_2^- + H_2O \rightleftharpoons HC_2H_3O_2 + OH^-$$
$$0.10M \qquad\qquad\qquad (x)M \qquad (x)M$$

In arriving at these concentration expressions, we assume that the decrease in the concentration of $C_2H_3O_2^-$ because of hydrolysis is negligible in comparison with the original concentration of $C_2H_3O_2^-$; also, we assume that the contribution to the concentration of OH^- from the ionization of water is negligible in comparison to that derived from the hydrolysis.

$$\frac{[HC_2H_3O_2][OH^-]}{[C_2H_3O_2^-]} = 5.6 \times 10^{-10}$$

$$\frac{x^2}{0.10} =$$

$$x^2 = 5.6 \times 10^{-11}$$

$$x = [HC_2H_3O_2] = [OH^-] = 7.5 \times 10^{-6} M$$

We can see that our assumptions were justified; 7.5×10^{-6} is indeed negligible in comparison to 0.10, and for all practical purposes $[C_2H_3O_2^-] = 0.10 M$. Also the concentration of OH^- in pure water is only approximately 1.3% of the concentration of OH^- determined here; in a solution of sodium acetate, the OH^- produced by the hydrolysis would repress the ionization of water so that any additional OH^- from this source would be even more insignificant.

Since,

$$[OH^-] = 7.5 \times 10^{-6} M$$

$$[H^+] = 1.3 \times 10^{-9} M$$

$$pH = 8.9$$

The degree of hydrolysis is the fraction of the hydrolyzed species in the molecular form. Hence,

$$\text{degree of hydrolysis} = \frac{[HC_2H_3O_2]}{[C_2H_3O_2^-]}$$

$$= \frac{7.5 \times 10^{-6}}{1.0 \times 10^{-1}}$$

$$= 7.5 \times 10^{-5}$$

The acetate ion is said to be 7.5×10^{-3}% hydrolyzed.

The hydrolysis of cations is treated in an analogous manner. In a solution of ammonium chloride, the chloride ion (which is the conjugate base of the strong acid HCl) does not hydrolyze; however, the ammonium ion reacts with water

$$H_2O + NH_4^+(aq) \rightleftharpoons NH_3(aq) + H_3O^+(aq)$$

The NH_4^+ ion is a Brønsted acid, conjugate to the base NH_3. In the hydrolysis reaction, the acid NH_4^+ loses a proton to the base H_2O which is then converted into its conjugate acid H_3O^+. Ammonia is a stronger base than water; in this competition for protons, NH_3 is more effective than H_2O, and the concentration of NH_4^+ is higher than the concentration of H_3O^+. Nevertheless, a solution of ammonium chloride is acidic.

The equilibrium constant for this hydrolysis equilibrium is obtained by dividing the water constant by the ionization constant for ammonia.

$$K_H = \frac{[NH_3][H_3O^+]}{[NH_4^+]}$$

$$K_H = \frac{K_w}{K_{NH_3}} = \frac{1.0 \times 10^{-14}}{1.8 \times 10^{-5}} = 5.6 \times 10^{-10}$$

Example 14.41   What is the pH of a $0.30M$ solution of NH_4Cl?

Solution

$$H_2O + NH_4^+ \rightleftharpoons NH_3 + H_3O^+$$
$$0.30M \qquad (x)M \qquad (x)M$$

$$\frac{[NH_3][H_3O^+]}{[NH_4^+]} = 5.6 \times 10^{-10}$$

$$\frac{x^2}{0.30} =$$

$$x^2 = 1.7 \times 10^{-10}$$

$$x = [NH_3] = [H_3O^+] = 1.3 \times 10^{-5}M$$

$$pH = 4.9$$

The hydrolysis of metal cations is similar to that of NH_4^+ but much more complicated. Usually more than one hydrolytic product results from the hydrolysis of a metal cation, and often the values of the successive equilibrium constants do not decrease from step to step in the manner characteristic of the polyprotic acids. In some systems, hydrolysis proceeds to the point where the hydroxide of the metal cation precipitates. Furthermore, the constants have not been accurately determined for many systems, and in some systems, polynuclear complexes are thought to exist (Section 14.13).

A solution of iron(II) chloride is acidic because of the hydrolysis of the Fe^{2+} ion. The principal reaction is

$$2H_2O + Fe^{2+}(aq) \rightleftharpoons Fe(OH)^+(aq) + H_3O^+(aq)$$

although a second step occurs to a lesser extent

$$2H_2O + Fe(OH)^+(aq) \rightleftharpoons Fe(OH)_2(aq) + H_3O^+(aq)$$

The species $Fe(OH)_2(aq)$ is a neutral molecule in solution.

Example 14.42   What is the pH of a $0.10M$ solution of $Fe(NO_3)_2$?

Solution   The stepwise constants for the ionization of $Fe(OH)_2$ are

$Fe(OH)_2(s) \rightleftharpoons Fe(OH)_2(aq)$	$K_1 = 7.2 \times 10^{-6}$	
$Fe(OH)_2(aq) \rightleftharpoons Fe(OH)^+ + OH^-$	$K_2 = 1.0 \times 10^{-4}$	
$Fe(OH)^+ \rightleftharpoons Fe^{2+} + OH^-$	$K_3 = 2.5 \times 10^{-6}$	

From these, we derive the constants for the steps of the hydrolysis.

$$Fe^{2+} + H_2O \rightleftharpoons Fe(OH)^+ + H^+ \qquad K_{H_1} = \frac{K_w}{K_3} = 4.0 \times 10^{-9}$$

$$Fe(OH)^+ + H_2O \rightleftharpoons Fe(OH)_2(aq) + H^+ \qquad K_{H_2} = \frac{K_w}{K_2} = 1.0 \times 10^{-10}$$

From the values of the constants, we see that the first step of the hydrolysis proceeds to a limited extent only and that the concentration of $Fe(OH)^+$, from this step, is low. The hydrolysis of this low concentration of $Fe(OH)^+$, described in the second hydrolysis step (which also occurs to a very limited extent), is therefore negligible, and we shall ignore the second step in our calculations.

$$Fe^{2+} + H_2O \rightleftharpoons Fe(OH)^+ + H^+$$
$$(0.10 - x)M \qquad\qquad (x)M \quad (x)M$$

The x is negligible in comparison to 0.10 in the term for the concentration of Fe^{2+}.

$$\frac{[Fe(OH)^+][H^+]}{[Fe^{2+}]} = 4.0 \times 10^{-9}$$

$$\frac{x^2}{0.10} =$$

$$x = [H^+] = 2.0 \times 10^{-5}M$$

$$pH = 4.7$$

The concentrations of the species of interest present in this solution are

$$[H^+] = 2.0 \times 10^{-5}M$$
$$[Fe^{2+}] = 1.0 \times 10^{-1}M$$
$$[Fe(OH)^+] = 2.0 \times 10^{-5}M$$
$$[Fe(OH)_2(aq)] = 1.0 \times 10^{-10}M$$

The concentration of $Fe(OH)_2(aq)$ is readily calculated by means of K_{H_2}. From these concentration figures, we see that we were justified in neglecting the second step of the hydrolysis.

Notice that the equilibrium

$$Fe(OH)_2(s) \rightleftharpoons Fe(OH)_2(aq) \qquad K_1 = 7.2 \times 10^{-6}$$

defines the concentration of $Fe(OH)_2(aq)$ that exists in equilibrium with solid $Fe(OH)_2$ in a saturated solution. Since the concentration of $Fe(OH)_2(aq)$ in this 0.10M solution of $Fe(NO_3)_2$ is less than $7.2 \times 10^{-6}M$, the solution is not saturated with respect to $Fe(OH)_2$, and $Fe(OH)_2$ does not precipitate. The same conclusion could be reached by use of the K_{SP} of $Fe(OH)_2$.

Example 14.43   What is the pH of a solution prepared from 0.10 mole of $Hg(NO_3)_2$ in 1 liter of water?

Solution The stepwise constants for the ionization of $Hg(OH)_2$ are

$$Hg(OH)_2(s) \rightleftharpoons Hg(OH)_2(aq) \qquad K_1 = 2.5 \times 10^{-4}$$
$$Hg(OH)_2(aq) \rightleftharpoons Hg(OH)^+ + OH^- \qquad K_2 = 1.0 \times 10^{-14}$$
$$Hg(OH)^+ \rightleftharpoons Hg^{2+} + OH^- \qquad K_3 = 1.2 \times 10^{-8}$$

Therefore the constants for the steps in the hydrolysis of Hg^{2+} are

$$Hg^{2+} + H_2O \rightleftharpoons Hg(OH)^+ + H^+ \qquad K_{H_1} = \frac{K_w}{K_3} = 8.3 \times 10^{-7}$$

$$Hg(OH)^+ + H_2O \rightleftharpoons Hg(OH)_2(aq) + H^+ \qquad K_{H_2} = \frac{K_w}{K_2} = 1.0$$

In this system, the second hydrolysis step occurs to such an extent that the precipitation of $Hg(OH)_2$ appears likely, and we shall proceed on the basis of this assumption. Let x equal the number of moles of $Hg(OH)_2(s)$ precipitated and y equal the concentration of $Hg(OH)^+$. In any saturated solution of $Hg(OH)_2$, the concentration of $Hg(OH)_2(aq)$ is $2.5 \times 10^{-4}M$ (from K_1). The concentration of Hg^{2+} is, then

$$[Hg^{2+}] = 0.10 - [Hg(OH)^+] - [Hg(OH)_2(aq)] - \text{no. moles } Hg(OH)_2(s)$$
$$= 0.10 - y - (2.5 \times 10^{-4}) - x$$

It is easy to see that 2.5×10^{-4} is negligible in comparison with 0.10; in addition, y (which is even smaller than 2.4×10^{-4}) is also negligible. Therefore

$$[Hg^{2+}] = 0.10 - x$$

For each mole of $Hg(OH)^+$ formed, 1 mole of H^+ is formed; also, for each mole of $Hg(OH)_2$ formed (whether in solution or precipitated), 2 moles of H^+ are formed. Therefore

$$[H^+] = [Hg(OH)^+] + 2[Hg(OH)_2(aq)] + 2 \text{ (no. moles } Hg(OH)_2(s))$$
$$= y + 2(2.5 \times 10^{-4}) + 2x$$

We shall assume that the terms 5.0×10^{-4} and y are negligible with respect to $2x$ and that

$$[H^+] = 2x$$

From K_{H_2},

$$Hg(OH)^+ + H_2O \rightleftharpoons Hg(OH)_2(aq) + H^+$$
$$(y)M \qquad\qquad 2.5 \times 10^{-4}M \qquad (2x)M$$

$$\frac{[Hg(OH)_2(aq)][H^+]}{[Hg(OH)^+]} = 1.0$$

$$\frac{(2.5 \times 10^{-4})2x}{y} =$$

$$y = 5.0 \times 10^{-4}x$$

From K_{H_1},

$$Hg^{2+} \quad + \ H_2O \rightleftharpoons Hg(OH)^+ + \ H^+$$
$$(0.10 - x)M \qquad\qquad (y)M \qquad (2x)M$$

$$\frac{[Hg(OH)^+][H^+]}{[Hg^{2+}]} = 8.3 \times 10^{-7}$$

$$\frac{(y)(2x)}{(0.10 - x)} =$$

$$\frac{(5.0 \times 10^{-4}x)(2x)}{(0.10 - x)} =$$

$$x = 8.7 \times 10^{-3}$$
$$y = 5.0 \times 10^{-4}x$$
$$= (5.0 \times 10^{-4})(8.7 \times 10^{-3})$$
$$= 4.4 \times 10^{-6}$$

Therefore

$$[Hg^{2+}] = 0.10 - x = 9.1 \times 10^{-2}M$$
$$[Hg(OH)^+] = y = 4.4 \times 10^{-6}M$$
$$[Hg(OH)_2(aq)] = 2.5 \times 10^{-4}M$$
$$\text{moles } Hg(OH)_2(s) = x = 8.7 \times 10^{-3}\,\text{moles}$$
$$[H^+] = 2x = 1.7 \times 10^{-2}M$$
$$pH = 1.8$$

We can see that the concentrations of $Hg(OH)^+$ and $Hg(OH)_2(aq)$ are small in comparison to the concentrations of Hg^{2+} and H^+ and that we were justified in neglecting them.

The hydrolyses of anions derived from weak polyprotic acids are similar to the hydrolyses of multivalent cations. Generally, however, the values of the successive constants for the hydrolysis of an anion derived from a polyprotic acid decrease in magnitude from step to step. The ionization constants for H_2S are

$$H_2S \rightleftharpoons H^+ + HS^- \qquad K_1 = 1.1 \times 10^{-7}$$
$$HS^- \rightleftharpoons H^+ + S^{2-} \qquad K_2 = 1.0 \times 10^{-14}$$

Therefore the hydrolysis constants for the sulfide ion are

$$S^{2-} + H_2O \rightleftharpoons HS^- + OH^- \qquad K_{H_1} = \frac{K_w}{K_2} = 1.0$$

$$HS^- + H_2O \rightleftharpoons H_2S + OH^- \qquad K_{H_2} = \frac{K_w}{K_1} = 9.1 \times 10^{-8}$$

Notice that the *first* hydrolysis constant is obtained by dividing the water constant by the *second* ionization constant of H_2S.

In solutions of a soluble sulfide, the first step of the hydrolysis of the sulfide ion is so nearly complete that it far overshadows the second, and the acidity of the solution may be calculated by neglecting the hydrolysis of the HS^- ion. Frequently, the second step in the hydrolysis of an anion derived from a weak polyprotic acid may be neglected in problem solving.

Example 14.44   What is the pH of a $0.10M$ solution of Na_2S?

Solution

$$S^{2-} + H_2O \rightleftharpoons HS^- + OH^-$$
$$(0.10 - x)M \qquad (x)M \quad (x)M$$

$$\frac{[HS^-][OH^-]}{[S^{2-}]} = 1.0$$

$$\frac{x^2}{(0.10 - x)} =$$

$$x = 9.16 \times 10^{-2}$$
$$(0.10 - x) = [S^{2-}] = 8.4 \times 10^{-3}M$$
$$[HS^-] = [OH^-] = 9.2 \times 10^{-2}M$$
$$[H^+] = 1.1 \times 10^{-13}M$$
$$pH = 13.0$$

The exact mathematical treatment of systems in which both the cation and the anion hydrolyze is complicated. However, many such solutions may be analyzed by means of a simple approximation. In a solution of ammonium cyanide, the following hydrolyses are involved.

$$H_2O + NH_4^+ \rightleftharpoons NH_3 + H_3O^+ \qquad K_H = 5.6 \times 10^{-10}$$
$$H_2O + CN^- \rightleftharpoons HCN + OH^- \qquad K_H = 2.5 \times 10^{-5}$$

In separate solutions, the cyanide ion is hydrolyzed much more extensively than the ammonium ion. In a solution containing both ions, the hydrolyses interlock since the OH^- produced by the hydrolysis of the CN^- ion reacts with the H_3O^+ produced by the hydrolysis of the NH_4^+ ion. This reaction causes both hydrolyses to shift to the right and the degree of hydrolysis is increased in both cases.

In any solution, the sum of the concentrations of the cations must equal the sum of the concentrations of the anions.

$$[NH_4^+] + [H^+] = [CN^-] + [OH^-] \qquad (9)$$

We may assume that the concentrations of H^+ and OH^- are negligible in comparison to the concentrations of NH_4^+ and CN^- in solutions where the concentration of the salt is not too low. Therefore from equation (9),

$$[NH_4^+] = [CN^-]$$

If we let c equal the number of moles of NH_4CN used to prepare 1 liter of solution, before hydrolysis, $[NH_4^+] = [CN^-] = c$. At equilibrium,

$$c = [NH_4^+] + [NH_3]$$

$$c = [CN^-] + [HCN]$$

or

$$[NH_4^+] + [NH_3] = [CN^-] + [HCN] \tag{10}$$

By subtracting equation (10) from equation (9), we get

$$[H^+] - [NH_3] = [OH^-] - [HCN]$$

or

$$[H^+] + [HCN] = [OH^-] + [NH_3]$$

Provided the concentration of NH_4CN is large enough, the concentrations of H^+ and OH^- are negligible in comparison to the concentrations of HCN and NH_3, and

$$[HCN] = [NH_3]$$

The equation for the combined hydrolyses is

$$NH_4^+ + CN^- \rightleftharpoons HCN + NH_3$$

and the equilibrium constant for this equation may be found by dividing the water constant by the product of the ionization constants of HCN and NH_3. Thus

$$([H^+][OH^-])\left(\frac{[NH_3]}{[NH_4^+][OH^-]}\right)\left(\frac{[HCN]}{[H^+][CN^-]}\right) = K_w\left(\frac{1}{K_{NH_3}}\right)\left(\frac{1}{K_{HCN}}\right)$$

$$\frac{[NH_3][HCN]}{[NH_4][CN^-]} = \frac{K_w}{K_{NH_3}K_{HCN}}$$

If we let $x = [NH_3] = [HCN]$, then $(c - x) = [NH_4^+] = [CN^-]$, and the concentrations of these substances may be found from the preceding relationship.

$$\frac{x^2}{(c-x)^2} = \frac{K_w}{K_{NH_3}K_{HCN}}$$

$$\frac{x}{(c-x)} = \sqrt{\frac{K_w}{K_{NH_3}K_{HCN}}}$$

The pH of the solution may be found by noting that since $[NH_3] = [HCN]$ and $[NH_4^+] = [CN^-]$, then

$$\frac{[NH_3][HCN]}{[NH_4^+][CN^-]} = \frac{K_w}{K_{NH_3}K_{HCN}}$$

$$\frac{[HCN]^2}{[CN^-]^2} =$$

$$\frac{[HCN]}{[CN^-]} = \sqrt{\frac{K_w}{K_{NH_3}K_{HCN}}}$$

The expression for the ionization of HCN is

$$\frac{[H^+][CN^-]}{[HCN]} = K_{HCN}$$

$$[H^+] = K_{HCN}\left(\frac{[HCN]}{[CN^-]}\right)$$

$$= K_{HCN}\sqrt{\frac{K_w}{K_{NH_3}K_{HCN}}}$$

$$[H^+] = \sqrt{\frac{K_w K_{HCN}}{K_{NH_3}}}$$

Thus the pH is independent of the concentration of the solution in solutions of NH_4CN of moderate concentration.

Example 14.45 What is the pH of a $0.10M$ solution of NH_4CN?

Solution

$$[H^+] = \sqrt{\frac{K_w K_{HCN}}{K_{NH_3}}}$$

$$= \sqrt{\frac{(1.0 \times 10^{-14})(4.0 \times 10^{-10})}{(1.8 \times 10^{-5})}}$$

$$= 4.7 \times 10^{-10}M$$

$$pH = 9.3$$

14.15 Titration of Acids and Alkalies

We are now in a position to study acid-alkali titrations in some detail. Let us consider the titration of a 50.0 ml sample of $0.100N$ HCl with a solution of $0.100N$ NaOH. Since HCl and NaOH are both strong electrolytes, the only equilibrium to be considered is the water equilibrium. Furthermore, for either solution, the molarity is equal to the normality. We shall assume in the calculations that follow, that when a sample of NaOH solution is added to 50.0 ml of the HCl solution, the resulting volume is equal to the sum of the volumes of the two solutions.

The concentration of H^+ in the original 50.0 ml sample of acid in the titration flask is $0.100M$, and therefore the pH is 1.00.

After 10.0 ml of $0.100N$ NaOH has been added from the buret, the total volume of the solution is 60.0 ml, and the equivalent of 40.0 ml of $0.100N$ HCl remains unneutralized.

$$VN = VN$$

$$40.0(0.100) = 60.0x$$

$$x = [H^+] = 0.0667N$$

$$pH = 1.18$$

When 50.0 ml of $0.100N$ NaOH has been added, the "end point" of the titration is reached; all of the acid is neutralized, and the pH = 7.00.

As NaOH solution is added beyond the equivalence point, the solution in the titration flask becomes increasingly alkaline. For example, when 60.0 ml of 0.100N NaOH has been added (total volume, 110 ml), the solution contains the equivalent of 10.0 ml of 0.100N NaOH.

$$VN = VN$$
$$10.0(0.100) = 110.0x$$
$$x = [OH^-] = 0.00909N$$
$$pOH = 2.04$$
$$pH = 11.96$$

The values in Table 14.6 were obtained from calculations such as these, and the data of Table 14.6 are plotted in Figure 14.2. Notice that the curve rises sharply in the section around the equivalence point. Whereas the first 49.9 ml of NaOH solution added causes the pH to change by three units, the next 0.2 ml added cause a change of *six* units in the pH. If an indicator is to be used in this titration to locate the equivalence point, any indicator may be employed that changes color in the pH range of the straight portion of the curve. Around this point, the addition of one drop of NaOH solution causes a sharp increase in the pH. Any one of the three indicators indicated in Figure 14.2 would be satisfactory.

Let us now consider the titration of 50.0 ml of 0.100N acetic acid—a weak acid—with 0.100N sodium hydroxide. The concentration of H^+ in the original 50.0 ml sample of acid may be calculated by using the

TABLE 14.6.
TITRATION OF 50.0 ML OF 0.100N
HCL WITH 0.100N NaOH.

Volume of 0.100N NaOH Added (ml)	pH
0.0	1.00
10.0	1.18
20.0	1.37
30.0	1.60
40.0	1.96
49.0	3.00
49.9	4.00
50.0	7.00
50.1	10.00
51.0	11.00
60.0	11.96
70.0	12.22
80.0	12.36
90.0	12.46
100.0	12.52

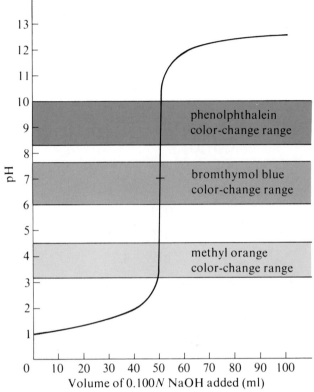

Figure 14.2   Titration of 50.0 ml of 0.100N HCl with 0.100N NaOH.

equilibrium constant (Example 14.2). From Table 14.1, we see that $[H^+] = 1.34 \times 10^{-3}M$, and the pH of the solution is, therefore, 2.87.

The solution resulting from the addition of 10.0 ml of 0.100N NaOH to the 50.0 ml sample of 0.100N $HC_2H_3O_2$ is, in effect, a buffer since it contains a mixture of $C_2H_3O_2^-$ ions produced by the neutralization together with unneutralized $HC_2H_3O_2$. The pH of a buffer is conveniently calculated by use of the relation

$$pH = pK - \log\left(\frac{[HA]}{[A^-]}\right)$$

which was derived in Section 14.7. For acetic acid, the pK is 4.75 (the negative logarithm of 1.80×10^{-5}). The ratio $[HC_2H_3O_2]/[C_2H_3O_2^-]$ is easily calculated. After 10.0 ml of NaOH is added, 40/50 of the acid of the original 50.0 ml sample remains unneutralized and 10/50 has, in effect, been converted into the salt sodium acetate. The ratio is, therefore, 4 to 1. Thus

$$pH = pK - \log\left(\frac{[HC_2H_3O_2]}{[C_2H_3O_2^-]}\right)$$
$$= 4.75 - \log(4/1)$$
$$= 4.15$$

At the equivalence point, all of the acid has been neutralized, and the solution (100 ml) is effectively $0.0500M$ in sodium acetate. The calculation of the pH of this solution must take into account the hydrolysis of the $C_2H_3O_2^-$ ion (Example 14.40).

$$C_2H_3O_2^- + H_2O \rightleftharpoons HC_2H_3O_2 + OH^-$$

$$0.0500M \qquad\qquad\qquad (x)M \qquad (x)M$$

$$\frac{[HC_2H_3O_2][OH^-]}{[C_2H_3O_2^-]} = 5.56 \times 10^{-10}$$

$$\frac{x^2}{5.00 \times 10^{-2}} =$$

$$x = [OH^-] = 5.27 \times 10^{-6}$$

$$pOH = 5.28$$

$$pH = 8.72$$

Notice that the equivalence point in this titration does not occur at the "neutral" pH, 7.

After the equivalence point, the addition of NaOH causes the solution to become increasingly alkaline. The added OH^- represses the hydrolysis of the acetate ion, and the contribution of the hydrolysis to the concentration of OH^- is negligible in comparison to the added OH^-. Thus the calculations from this point on are identical to those for the HCl–NaOH titration.

TABLE 14.7.
TITRATION OF 50.0 ML OF 0.100N
$HC_2H_3O_2$ WITH 0.100N NaOH.

Volume of 0.100N NaOH added (ml)	pH
0.0	2.87
10.0	4.15
20.0	4.57
30.0	4.93
40.0	5.35
49.0	6.44
49.9	7.45
50.0	8.72
50.1	10.00
51.0	11.00
60.0	11.96
70.0	12.22
80.0	12.36
90.0	12.46
100.0	12.52

Data for a $HC_2H_3O_2$–NaOH titration are summarized in Table 14.7 and plotted in Figure 14.3. The equivalence point of this titration occurs at a higher pH than that of the preceding titration, and all pH values on the acid side of the equivalence point are higher. Therefore the rapidly ascending portion of the curve around the equivalence point is reduced in length. From the curve of Figure 14.3, we can see that methyl orange is not a suitable indicator for this titration. Neither is bromthymol blue since its color change would start after 47.34 ml of NaOH has been added and continue until 49.97 ml has been added; this would hardly constitute a sharp end point for a titration. Phenolphthalein, however, would be a satisfactory indicator to employ.

Other titration curves may be drawn following the general line of approach outlined here. Figure 14.4 represents the titration curve for the titration of 50.0 ml of $0.100N$ NH_3 with $0.100N$ HCl. In this instance, methyl orange could be used as the indicator. Figure 14.5 is the titration curve for the titration of 50.0 ml of $0.100N$ $HC_2H_3O_2$ with $0.100N$ NH_3; both solutes are weak electrolytes. No indicator can be found that would function satisfactorily for this titration, and such titrations—between weak electrolytes—are not usually run.

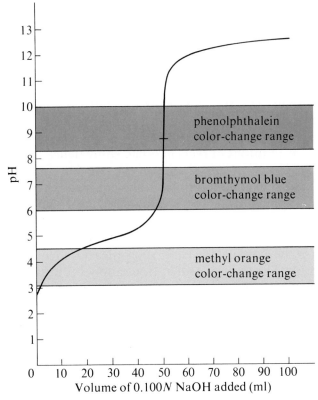

Figure 14.3   Titration of 50.0 ml of 0.100N $HC_2H_3O_2$ with 0.100N NaOH.

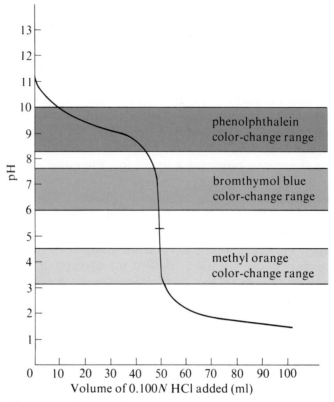

Figure 14.4   Titration of 50.0 ml of 0.100N NH_3 with 0.100N HCl.

Titrations may be conducted potentiometrically. For example, a titration may be performed with the electrodes of a pH meter immersed in the solution being analyzed. The pH of the solution is determined after successive additions of reagent. The equivalence point of the titration is indicated by an abrupt change in the pH, but additions and readings are continued beyond this point. The equivalence point may be determined by graphing the data and estimating the volume corresponding to the midpoint of the steeply rising portion of the titration curve. A plot of cell potential has the same shape as a titration curve based on pH, and titrations may be conducted using such measurements instead of pH determinations. The same considerations apply for the determination of the equivalence point for curves based on either type of measurement.

The potentiometric titration of a weak electrolyte serves as an important method of determining the dissociation constant of the electrolyte. Since

$$\text{pH} = \text{p}K - \log([\text{HA}]/[\text{A}^-])$$

the pK of the electrolyte is equal to the pH of the solution at half neutralization (where $[\text{HA}] = [\text{A}^-]$), but the pK, and hence the K itself, may be determined from any point on the titration curve.

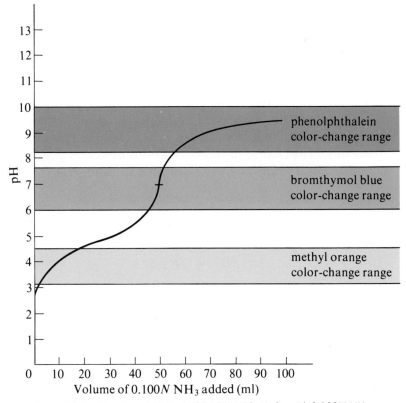

Figure 14.5   Titration of 50.0 ml of 0.100N HC$_2$H$_3$O$_2$ with 0.100N NH$_3$.

Example 14.46   The equivalence point in a titration of 40.00 ml of a solution of a weak monoprotic acid occurs when 35.00 ml of a 0.100N NaOH solution has been added. The pH of the solution is 5.75 after 20.00 ml of the NaOH solution has been added. What is the dissociation constant of the acid?

Solution   Since 35.00 ml of NaOH is required for complete neutralization, the acid has been 20/35 neutralized after 20.00 ml of NaOH has been added. In other words, 15/35 of the acid is in the form HA, and 20/35 is in the form A$^-$. The ratio [HA]/[A$^-$] is, therefore, 15 to 20 or 0.75.

$$pH = pK - \log\left(\frac{[HA]}{[A^-]}\right)$$
$$5.75 = pK - \log(0.75)$$
$$pK = 5.63$$
$$K = 2.4 \times 10^{-6}$$

14.16 Oxidation-Reduction Equilibria

The ionic equilibria we have thus far considered in this chapter have not involved oxidation and reduction. Electrochemical measurements are the principal source of data for the study of oxidation-reduction equilibria. As we have seen, electrochemical measurements are used in the study of certain equilibria that do not involve oxidation-reduction—such as the determination of pH (Section 14.4), K_{SP}'s (Section 14.8), and titration curves (Section 14.15).

The equilibrium constant for an oxidation-reduction equilibrium is readily calculated from the standard cell potential of the reaction which in turn may be calculated from the standard electrode potentials for the half reactions. The change in standard Gibbs free energy for the reaction under consideration is given by the equation (Section 9.7)

$$\Delta G° = -nFE° \tag{11}$$

and $\Delta G°$ is related to the equilibrium constant by the expression (Section 12.9)

$$\Delta G° = -RT \ln K \tag{12}$$

(See examples 12.6 and 14.19.) An expression that relates the equilibrium constant directly to the cell potential is obtained by combining equations (11) and (12).

$$E° = \left(\frac{RT}{nF}\right)\ln K$$

At 25°C,

$$E° = \frac{0.05916}{n}\log K$$

This expression may also be derived from the Nernst equation (Section 9.9). A convenient, and equivalent expression is

$$\log K = 16.90\, nE°$$

As a rule, an ionic reaction that does not involve oxidation-reduction reaches equilibrium very rapidly—usually in the time that it takes to prepare the solution. Although many oxidation-reduction reactions occur rapidly in solution, a large number do not; in this latter instance, equilibrium is attained very slowly. Therefore even a large value for an equilibrium constant does not necessarily mean that the reaction to which it pertains will occur at an appreciable rate.

Most oxidation–reduction reactions essentially go to completion, and therefore, these systems have very large equilibrium constants.

Example 14.47 A solution is made $0.100M$ in Fe^{2+}, $0.020M$ in MnO_4^-, and $1.000M$ in H^+. What are the concentrations of the ions at equilibrium?

Solution The reduction potentials are

$$e^- + Fe^{3+} \rightleftharpoons Fe^{2+} \qquad\qquad E° = +0.77 \text{ v}$$
$$5e^- + 8H^+ + MnO_4^- \rightleftharpoons Mn^{2+} + 4H_2O \qquad E° = +1.51 \text{ v}$$

The complete reaction is

$$5Fe^{2+} + MnO_4^- + 8H^+ \rightleftharpoons 5Fe^{3+} + Mn^{2+} + 4H_2O$$

for which,

$$E° = 1.51 - 0.77 = 0.74 \text{ v}$$
$$\log K = 16.9 \, n \, E°$$
$$= 16.9 \, (5) \, (0.74)$$
$$= 62.53$$
$$K = 3.4 \times 10^{62}$$

From the size of the equilibrium constant, we see that it may be assumed that this reaction essentially goes to completion. Notice that stoichiometrically equivalent amounts of Fe^{2+} and MnO_4^- have been used to prepare the solution. Therefore

$5Fe^{2+} +$	$MnO_4^- +$	$8H^+$	$\rightleftharpoons 5Fe^{3+} +$	$Mn^{2+} +$	$4H_2O$	
$0.100M$	$0.020M$	$1.00M$	—	—	—	initially
$5x$	x	$(1.00 - 0.16)M$	$0.100M$	$0.020M$	—	equilibrium

$$\frac{[Fe^{3+}]^5[Mn^{2+}]}{[Fe^{2+}]^5[MnO_4^-][H^+]^8} = 3.4 \times 10^{62}$$

$$\frac{(10^{-1})^5(2.0 \times 10^{-2})}{(5x)^5(x)(0.84)^8} =$$

$$x^6 = 7.6 \times 10^{-73}$$
$$x = [MnO_4^-] = 9.6 \times 10^{-13} M$$
$$5x = [Fe^{2+}] = 4.8 \times 10^{-12} M$$
$$[Mn^{2+}] = 2.0 \times 10^{-2} M$$
$$[Fe^{3+}] = 1.0 \times 10^{-1} M$$

An alternative solution is based on the fact that at equilibrium

$$[Mn^{2+}] = \left(\tfrac{1}{5}\right)[Fe^{3+}]$$
$$[MnO_4^-] = \left(\tfrac{1}{5}\right)[Fe^{2+}]$$

Therefore

$$\frac{[Fe^{3+}]^5[Mn^{2+}]}{[Fe^{2+}]^5[MnO_4^-][H^+]^8} = 3.4 \times 10^{62}$$

$$\frac{[Fe^{3+}]^5 (1/5)[Fe^{3+}]}{[Fe^{2+}]^5(1/5)[Fe^{2+}]} = (3.4 \times 10^{62})(0.84)^8$$

$$\frac{[Fe^{3+}]^6}{[Fe^{2+}]^6} = 8.4 \times 10^{61}$$

$$\frac{[Fe^{3+}]}{[Fe^{2+}]} = 2.1 \times 10^{10}$$

$$\frac{(10^{-1})}{[Fe^{2+}]} =$$

$$[Fe^{2+}] = 4.8 \times 10^{-12}M$$

$$[MnO_4^-] = (1/5)(4.8 \times 10^{-12}) = 9.6 \times 10^{-13}M$$

Oxidation-reduction reactions can be followed potentiometrically in much the same way as acid-alkali reactions, and redox titrations are extensively used in analysis. For example, the amount of iron in a sample of an ore can be determined by dissolving the ore, converting all of the iron in the resulting solution into the ferrous state, and titrating this solution against a standard solution of an oxidizing agent (such as ceric sulfate, potassium permanganate, or potassium dichromate). Let us consider the titration of 50.0 ml of $0.10M$ Fe^{2+} solution with a $0.10M$ solution of Ce^{4+}.

Example 14.48 A 50.0 ml sample of $0.10M$ ferrous sulfate is titrated with $0.10M$ ceric sulfate. (a) What is the equilibrium constant for the reaction? (b) What are the concentrations of ions in equilibrium at the equivalence point?

Solution The electrode potentials for the half-reactions are

$$e^- + Fe^{3+} \rightleftharpoons Fe^{2+} \qquad E^\circ = +0.77 \text{ v}$$
$$e^- + Ce^{4+} \rightleftharpoons Ce^{3+} \qquad E^\circ = +1.61 \text{ v}$$

and the potential for the reaction is

$$Fe^{2+} + Ce^{4+} \rightleftharpoons Fe^{3+} + Ce^{3+} \qquad E^\circ = +0.84 \text{ v}$$

$$\log K = 16.9 \, nE^\circ$$
$$= 16.9 \,(1)\,(0.84)$$
$$K = 1.6 \times 10^{14}$$

(b) To reach the equivalence point, as much Ce^{4+} will have to be added as there is Fe^{2+} in the original solution. At the equivalence point, therefore,

$$[Fe^{3+}] = [Ce^{3+}]$$

and

$$[Fe^{2+}] = [Ce^{4+}]$$

From the equilibrium constant,

$$\frac{[Fe^{3+}][Ce^{3+}]}{[Fe^{2+}][Ce^{4+}]} = 1.6 \times 10^{14}$$

$$\frac{[Fe^{3+}]^2}{[Fe^{2+}]^2} =$$

$$\frac{[Fe^{3+}]}{[Fe^{2+}]} = 1.3 \times 10^7$$

We can see that the reaction proceeds essentially to completion, and on this basis, we can calculate the concentrations of ions. Since the volume of the solution equals 100 ml at the equivalence point, $[Fe^{3+}] = [Ce^{3+}] = 0.050M$. If we let $x = [Fe^{2+}] = [Ce^{4+}]$,

$$\frac{(0.050)}{x} = 1.3 \times 10^7$$

$$x = [Fe^{2+}] = [Ce^{4+}] = 3.8 \times 10^{-9} M$$

and

$$[Fe^{3+}] = [Ce^{3+}] = 5.0 \times 10^{-2} M$$

At every point in the titration of Fe^{2+} with Ce^{4+}, the E of a theoretical cell

$$Pt \mid Ce^{4+}, Ce^{3+} \mid Fe^{3+}, Fe^{2+} \mid Pt$$

would be zero since equilibrium is established at each point. However, if the titration is run in a cell containing a standard hydrogen electrode (the reference electrode) and a platinum electrode (the indicator electrode) a difference in potential may be read as the titration proceeds.

The E of the cell

$$Pt \mid H_2 \mid H^+ \mid Fe^{3+}, Fe^{2+} \mid Pt$$

where the left-hand electrode is a standard hydrogen electrode, varies with the concentrations of the iron ions

$$E = E^\circ - \left(\frac{0.059}{1}\right) \log \frac{[Fe^{2+}]}{[Fe^{3+}]}$$

Initially, before any Ce^{4+} is added to the 50.0 ml sample of $0.10M$ Fe^{2+}, E is theoretically equal to $-\infty$, although traces of Fe^{3+}, due to air oxidation, will give a small positive reading.

After 10.0 ml of $0.10M$ Ce^{4+} is added, 40/50 of the iron is in the original form, Fe^{2+}, and 10/50 of the iron is in the oxidized form, Fe^{3+}. The ratio of $[Fe^{2+}]$ to $[Fe^{3+}]$ is, therefore, 4 to 1, and

$$E = +0.77 - (0.059) \log 4$$

$$= +0.77 - (0.059)(0.60)$$

$$= +0.73 \text{ v}$$

At the half-titration point, when 25.0 ml of Ce^{4+} has been added, $[Fe^{2+}] = [Fe^{3+}]$, and $[Fe^{2+}]/[Fe^{3+}] = 1$. Since the logarithm of 1 is 0,

$$E = +0.77 \text{ v}$$

At the equivalence point, $[Fe^{3+}]/[Fe^{2+}] = 1.3 \times 10^7$ (Example 14.48). Therefore

$$\frac{[Fe^{2+}]}{[Fe^{3+}]} = \frac{1}{1.3 \times 10^7} = 7.7 \times 10^{-8}$$

and

$$E = +0.77 - 0.059 \log (7.7 \times 10^{-8})$$
$$= +0.77 - 0.059(-7.11)$$
$$= +1.19 \text{ v}$$

After the equivalence point, the concentration of Fe^{2+} becomes vanishingly small. We may calculate points for the titration curve by remembering that at each point of the curve the E for the reduction of Ce^{4+} equals the E for the reduction of Fe^{3+} since E for the couple is zero whenever equilibrium is established. Prior to the equivalence point, the Ce^{4+} is consumed in the oxidation of Fe^{2+} as fast as it is added; after the equivalence point, Ce^{4+} is present in excess. The cell, in effect, is

$$Pt \mid H_2 \mid H^+ \mid Ce^{4+}, Ce^{3+} \mid Pt$$

After 60.0 ml of $0.100M$ Ce^{4+} has been added, 10.0 ml is present in excess. The concentration of Ce^{4+} is proportional to the 10.0 ml added above the amount needed for equivalence, and the concentration of Ce^{3+} is proportional to 50.0 ml (the volume needed to react with the 50.0 ml of Fe^{2+}). Therefore the ratio of $[Ce^{3+}]$ to $[Ce^{4+}]$ is equal to 50/10 or 5.

$$E = +1.61 - 0.059 \log \left(\frac{[Ce^{3+}]}{[Ce^{4+}]} \right)$$
$$= +1.61 - 0.059 \log (5)$$
$$= +1.56 \text{ v}$$

Notice that $E°$ for the $Ce^{4+} - Ce^{3+}$ couple (1.61 v) is reached when 100.0 ml of Ce^{4+} solution has been added.

The titration curve of Figure 14.6 was plotted from data obtained from calculations such as the foregoing. The equivalence point of an actual titration may be obtained by taking readings of the potential after successive additions of the oxidizing agent, plotting the data, and finding the inflection point of the titration curve in the same manner as that employed for acid-alkali titrations.

In addition to potentiometric determinations, oxidation-reduction indicators may be used to locate the end point of an oxidation-reduction titration. For the titration of Fe^{2+} by Ce^{4+}, ferroin is a suitable indicator. Ferroin undergoes a conversion from a pale blue form to a red form at at approximately 1.11 v, a value suitably close to the equivalence point voltage of 1.19 v.

The data plotted in Figure 14.6 were calculated for a cell utilizing a standard hydrogen electrode ($E° = 0.00$ v) as a reference electrode. In actual practice calomel electrodes (Section 14.4) or silver-silver chloride electrodes are generally employed in place of hydrogen electrodes since the latter are inconvenient to use. If a normal calomel electrode is

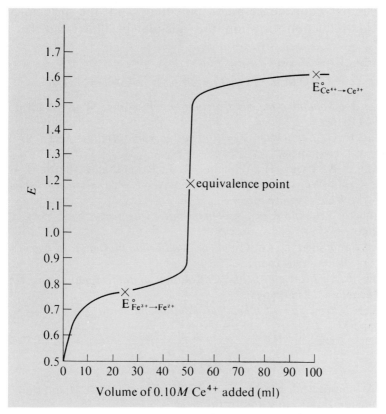

Figure 14.6   Titration of 50.0 ml 0.10M Fe^{2+} with 0.10M Ce^{4+}. Potential of a platinum electrode is referred to a standard hydrogen electrode.

employed as the reference electrode ($E = +0.283$ v), every potential measured will be displaced by 0.283 v. For example, the equivalence point of the titration would occur at 0.91 v instead of 1.19 v. The actual E measurements are of no concern since the equivalence point is derived from the titration curve and the curve is merely displaced to lower E values by the use of a calomel electrode in place of a hydrogen electrode.

As a matter of fact, for a given oxidation-reduction reaction, a titration curve based on actual E measurements would be slightly different from a titration curve derived from $E°$ values. $E°$ values are based on activities rather than concentrations; the difference between the activity and the concentration of a multivalent ion can be appreciable. If so-called "formal potentials" are used instead of standard potentials, a titration curve is obtained that is more in harmony with that plotted from the data obtained from an actual titration. Formal potentials are based on concentrations rather than activities. In any event, the equivalence point is located from the titration curve rather than from a calculated equivalence-point potential, and the principles of an oxidation-reduction titration are adequately illustrated by the use of $E°$'s.

SOME SUGGESTED READINGS

Butler, J. N., *Solubility and pH Calculations,* Reading, Mass., Addison-Wesley, 1964 (paper).

Clark, R. E. D., *Semi-Micro Qualitative Inorganic Analysis,* New York, Pergamon, 1965 (paper).

Hermann, J. A., Irving, H., Williams, R. J., Rosenthal, I., Suttle, J. F., Usdin, V. R., and Weiss, A. R., *Separation Methods in Analytical Chemistry,* New York, Wiley, 1964 (paper).

Klingenberg, J. J., and Reed, K., *Quantitative Chemistry,* New York, Reinhold, 1965.

Lee, T. S., and Sillen, L. G., *Chemical Equilibrium in Analytical Chemistry,* New York, Wiley, 1964 (paper).

Margolis, E. J., *Principles in the Calculation of Ionic Equilibrium,* New York, Macmillan, 1966 (paper).

Morris, K., *Principles of Chemical Equilibrium,* New York, Reinhold, 1965 (paper).

PROBLEMS

14.1 Arsenious acid, $HAsO_2$, is 0.0055% ionized in $0.20 M$ solution. What is the ionization constant for this acid?

14.2 (a) What are the concentrations of H^+, ClO^-, and $HClO$ in $0.10 M$ hypochlorous acid? (b) What is the degree of ionization of a $0.10 M$ solution of $HClO$?

14.3 A weak acid, HX, is 0.20% ionized in $0.50 M$ solution. What percent of HX is ionized in $0.010 M$ solution?

14.4 What are the concentrations of all species present in a solution prepared by the addition of 10 ml of $0.60 M$ sodium benzoate, $NaC_7H_5O_2$, to 10 ml of $0.40 M$ HCl? Assume that the total volume of the solution is 20 ml.

14.5 How many moles of nitrous acid, HNO_2, must be used to prepare 1.0 liter of a solution that has a pH of 3.0?

14.6 What is the pH of each of the following solutions? (a) $[H^+] = 0.25 M$, (b) $[OH^-] = 4.0 \times 10^{-3} M$, (c) $[OH^-] = 6.3 \times 10^{-10} M$.

14.7 What is the $[H^+]$ of each of the following solutions? (a) pH = 12.3, (b) pOH = 6.5, (c) pH = 6.7.

14.8 A cell consisting of a hydrogen electrode and a normal calomel electrode contains a solution of unknown pH. The potential is 0.833 v at 25°C. Calculate (a) the pH of the solution and (b) the $[H^+]$.

14.9 The cell described in Problem 14.8 is filled with a solution that has a pH of 3.9. What is the potential of the cell at 25°?

14.10 A $0.045 M$ solution of a weak acid, HX, has a pH of 4.7. What is the ionization constant of the acid?

14.11 An indicator, HIn, has an ionization constant of 5.0×10^{-8}. The acid color of the indicator is yellow, and the alkaline color is blue. The yellow color is visible when the ratio of yellow form to blue form is 20 to 1, and the blue color is predominant when the ratio of blue form to yellow form is 2 to 1. What is the pH range of color change for the indicator?

14.12 A solution is prepared by the addition of 0.040 mole of solid sodium cyanate, NaCNO, to 250 ml of 0.025 M cyanic acid, HCNO. Assume that no volume change occurs. Calculate (a) the pH of the solution and (b) the percent ionization of HCNO.

14.13 The solution prepared from 0.050 moles of a weak acid, HX, diluted to 200 ml has a pH of 3.6. What is the pH of the solution after 0.080 mole of solid NaX is dissolved in this solution? Assume that no significant volume change occurs.

14.14 A solution is prepared from 0.20 moles of a weak base, B, and 0.30 moles of the chloride of the base, (BH)Cl. The volume of the solution is 400 ml, and the pH is 8.2. What is the ionization constant for the reaction $B + H_2O \rightleftharpoons BH^+ + OH^-$?

14.15 How many moles of pyridinium chloride, $(C_5H_5NH)Cl$, should be added to 500 ml of 0.40M pyridine, C_5H_5N, to produce a buffer with pH = 4.6? Assume a negligible volume change in the preparation of the buffer.

14.16 At 25°C, 1.3×10^{-4} mole of $Mg(OH)_2$ dissolves in 1.0 liter of water. Calculate the K_{SP} of $Mg(OH)_2$.

14.17 The K_{SP} of $PbSO_4$ is 1.3×10^{-8}. What is the molar solubility of $PbSO_4$?

14.18 The K_{SP} of $Ag_2(C_2O_4)$ is 1.1×10^{-11}. What is the molar solubility of $Ag_2(C_2O_4)$?

14.19 Calculate the K_{SP} of lead iodide from the standard electrode potentials.

$$2e^- + PbI_2(s) \rightleftharpoons Pb(s) + 2I^-(aq) \qquad E° = -0.365 \text{ v}$$
$$2e^- + Pb^{2+}(aq) \rightleftharpoons Pb(s) \qquad E° = -0.126 \text{ v}$$

14.20 The K_{SP} of HgS is 1.6×10^{-54} and the Hg^{2+}/Hg electrode potential is

$$2e^- + Hg^{2+} \rightleftharpoons Hg \qquad E° = +0.854 \text{ v}$$

Calculate the $E°$ for the half reaction

$$2e^- + HgS \rightleftharpoons Hg + S^{2-}$$

14.21 A solution is prepared by the addition of 100 ml of 0.10M Na_3PO_4 to 150 ml of 0.15M $CaCl_2$. Calculate the concentrations of (a) Ca^{2+}, (b) PO_4^{3-}, (c) Na^+, and (d) Cl^- in the final solution, which may be assumed to have a volume of 250 ml. Neglect the hydrolysis of the phosphate ion.

14.22 How many moles of $Ag_2(C_2O_4)$ will dissolve in 100 ml of 0.050M $Na_2(C_2O_4)$? Neglect the hydrolysis of ions.

14.23 How many moles of $Cd(OH)_2$ will dissolve in 200 ml of a solution with a pH of 12.8?

14.24 Calculate the concentrations of (a) Ba^{2+}, (b) Cl^-, (c) K^+, and (d) CrO_4^{2-} in a solution prepared by the addition of 100 ml of 0.20M $BaCl_2$ to 100 ml of 0.60M K_2CrO_4. Assume that the final volume is 200 ml, and neglect the hydrolysis of ions.

14.25 (a) A solution is 0.20M in Ca^{2+} and 0.10M in Sr^{2+}. If solid Na_2SO_4 is very slowly added to this solution, which will precipitate first, $CaSO_4$

or $SrSO_4$? Neglect volume changes. (b) The addition of Na_2SO_4 is continued until the second cation just starts to precipitate as the sulfate. What is the concentration of the first cation at this point? (c) What percentage of the original concentration of this cation remains in solution at this point?

14.26 (a) A solution is $0.10M$ in Pb^{2+} and $0.10M$ in Ag^+. Solid NaI is gradually added to the solution. Neglect volume changes, and calculate the concentrations of I^- required to start the precipitation of PbI_2 and AgI. Which iodide precipitates first? (b) What is the concentration of Ag^+ when PbI_2 starts to precipitate? (c) What is the concentration of Ag^+ when half of the Pb^{2+} has been precipitated as PbI_2?

14.27 What minimum concentration of NH_4^+ is necessary to prevent the formation of a $Mn(OH)_2$ precipitate from a solution that is $0.020M$ in in Mn^{2+} and $0.050M$ in NH_3?

14.28 A solution is $0.020M$ in Mg^{2+} and $0.050M$ in NH_4^+. What should the concentration of NH_3 be in order to cause $Mg(OH)_2$ to start to precipitate?

14.29 Calculate the concentrations of (a) H^+, (b) $H_2AsO_4^-$, (c) $HAsO_4^{2-}$, (d) AsO_4^{3-} ions, and (e) H_3AsO_4 molecules in a $0.30M$ solution of H_3AsO_4.

14.30 Calculate the concentrations of (a) H^+, (b) $HC_2O_4^-$, (c) $C_2O_4^{2-}$, and (d) $H_2C_2O_4$ in a 1.0 liter solution containing 0.30 moles of HCl and 0.10 moles of $Na_2C_2O_4$.

14.31 What is the pH of a $0.040M$ H_2S solution?

14.32 What is the lowest $[H^+]$ that must be present to prevent the formation of a precipitate of ZnS when a solution that is $0.10M$ in Zn^{2+} is saturated with H_2S?

14.33 What sulfides will precipitate from a solution containing $0.050M$ concentrations of Fe^{2+}, Zn^{2+}, Pb^{2+}, and Mn^{2+} and which is $0.50M$ in $HC_2H_3O_2$ and $0.50M$ in $NaC_2H_3O_2$ when the solution is saturated with H_2S?

14.34 A solution that is $0.10M$ in Cd^{2+} and $0.050M$ in H^+ is saturated with H_2S. What concentration of Cd^{2+} remains in solution after CdS has precipitated? Note that it is necessary to take into account the increase in $[H^+]$ caused by the precipitation.

14.35 A solution has a pH of 1.0 and contains Cu^{2+} and Fe^{2+} in $0.50M$ con--centrations. Calculate the concentrations of (a) H^+, (b) Cu^{2+}, and (c) Fe^{2+} in the solution after it has been saturated with H_2S. Take into consideration any change in $[H^+]$ caused by precipitation.

14.36 A 10.0 ml sample of a solution is $0.26M$ in H^+ and contains 0.017 g Bi^{3+} and 0.021 g Pb^{2+}. The solution is saturated with H_2S and essentially quantitative precipitation of the sulfides occurs. Take into account any change in acidity due to reactions and calculate the final: (a) $[H^+]$, (b) $[S^{2-}]$, (c) $[Bi^{3+}]$, and (d) $[Pb^{2+}]$. (e) What total weight of solid precipitates out of solution?

14.37 A solution is $0.10M$ in H^+, $0.020M$ in MnO_4^-, and $0.030M$ in Fe^{3+}. Saturation of the solution with H_2S reduces MnO_4^- to Mn^{2+} and Fe^{3+} to Fe^{2+}; in these reactions H_2S is oxidized to sulfur. These redox reactions may be considered to be complete. In subsequent calculations, do not neglect any change in acidity caused by reactions. (a) What sulfides precipitate, if any? (b) What is the final $[H^+]$? (c) What is the total weight of solid that precipitates out of 50.0 ml of solution?

14.38 What concentration of H^+ is present in a solution containing $0.10M$ concentrations of Ni^{2+} and Cd^{2+} if upon saturation with H_2S the maximum amount of CdS precipitates but no NiS precipitates at any stage?

14.39 Compare the molar solubilities of (a) AgCl, (b) AgBr, and (c) AgI in $1.0M$ ammonia solution.

14.40 Calculate the molar solubility of AgI in a solution that is $1.0M$ in CN^-.

14.41 (a) At what minimum $[OH^-]$ will 1.0×10^{-3} moles of $Zn(OH)_2$ go into solution (1.0 liter) as $Zn(OH)_4^{2-}$? (b) At what maximum $[OH^-]$ will 1.0×10^{-3} moles of $Zn(OH)_2$ go into solution (1.0 liter) as Zn^{2+}?

14.42 (a) What is the pH of a $0.10M$ solution of $NaNO_2$? (b) What is the degree of hydrolysis?

14.43 What concentration of NH_4Cl will produce a solution with a pH of 5.0?

14.44 The pH of a $0.50M$ solution of NaX is 9.7. What is the ionization constant of the weak acid HX?

14.45 What is the pH of a $0.20M$ solution of $ZnCl_2$? Take only the first step of the hydrolysis into account.

14.46 How many moles of $AlCl_3$ are present in 100 ml of a solution that has a pH of 3.1? Consider only the first step of the hydrolysis.

14.47 What is the $[H^+]$ of a $0.10M$ solution of $NaHSO_4$?

14.48 Calculate (a) the $[H^+]$ and (b) the degree of hydrolysis of a $0.10M$ solution of Na_2CO_3. The second step of the hydrolysis may be neglected.

14.49 Determine pH values for the titration curve pertaining to the titration of 30.00 ml of $0.0500N$ NH_3 with $0.0500N$ HCl (a) after 10.00 ml of the HCl solution has been added, (b) after 30.00 ml has been added, and (c) after 40.00 ml has been added.

14.50 The equivalence point in a titration of 50.00 ml of a weak acid HX occurs when 20.00 ml of $0.200N$ NaOH solution has been added. The pH of the solution is 5.10 after 13.42 ml of the NaOH solution has been added. What is the equilibrium constant of HX?

14.51 A 40.00 ml sample of a $0.100N$ solution of hypochlorous acid, HClO, is titrated with $0.100N$ NaOH. What is the pH of the solution after 30.00 ml of NaOH solution has been added?

14.52 When metallic iron is added to a $0.200M$ Cd^{2+} solution, the following reaction occurs:

$$Fe(s) + Cd^{2+} \rightleftharpoons Fe^{2+} + Cd(s)$$

(a) Calculate the equilibrium constant for the reaction. (b) Calculate the concentrations of ions present at equilibrium.

14.53 What is the equilibrium constant for the reaction of $Cr_2O_7^{2-}$ with Fe^{2+} in acid solution?

15

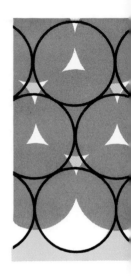

Metals

More than three quarters of all the known elements are metals. Although metals vary widely with respect to a given property, several chemical and physical properties are typical of metals and generally serve as the basis of the definition of this class of elements. Metals have superior electrical and thermal conductivities, characteristic luster, and the ability to be deformed, without cleaving, under stress. Among the chemical characteristics of most metals is their tendency to donate electrons thus producing positive ions and their formation of basic oxides. Much of the chemistry of the metals has been included in the discussion of the nonmetals of Chapter 10.

15.1 Properties of Metals

In the overwhelming majority of cases, metal crystals belong to one of three classifications: face-centered cubic, hexagonal close packed, and body-centered cubic (Table 15.1). The geometric arrangement of atoms in the face-centered cubic and the hexagonal close packed crystals is such that each atom has a coordination number of 12 (is adjoined by 12 other atoms). If the atoms are viewed as spheres, there is a minimum of empty space in these two types of crystals, and both of the crystal lattices are spoken of as close-packed structures. The body-centered cubic arrangement is more open than either of the close-packed arrangements; each atom of a body-centered cubic crystal has a coordination number of 8. The unit cells of the three crystal types are illustrated in Figure 15.1.

The division between the three crystalline forms is about even; approximately two-thirds of the metals crystallize in one of the close-packed arrangements. The difference between the two close-packed structures may be derived from a consideration of Figure 15.2. The shaded circles of the diagram represent the first layer of spheres which

TABLE 15.1.
CRYSTAL STRUCTURE OF METALS.[a]

Li bcc hcp	Be hcp												
Na bcc	Mg hcp											Al fcc	
K bcc	Ca fcc hcp bcc	Sc hcp fcc	Ti hcp bcc	V bcc	Cr bcc fcc	Mn	Fe bcc fcc	Co hcp fcc	Ni fcc	Cu fcc	Zn hcp	Ga	Ge
Rb bcc	Sr fcc hcp bcc	Y hcp	Zr hcp bcc	Nb bcc	Mn bcc	Tc hcp	Ru hcp	Rh fcc	Pd fcc	Ag fcc	Cd hcp	In	Sn
Cs bcc	Ba bcc	La hcp fcc	Hf hcp bcc	Ta bcc	W bcc	Re hcp	Os hcp	Ir fcc	Pt fcc	Au fcc	Hg	Tl hcp bcc	Pb fcc

Ce fcc hcp	Pr hcp fcc	Nd hcp	Pm	Sm	Eu bcc	Gd hcp	Tb hcp	Dy hcp	Ho hcp	Er hcp	Tm hcp	Yb fcc	Lu hcp

[a] fcc, face-centered cubic; bcc, body-centered cubic; hcp, hexagonal close packed.

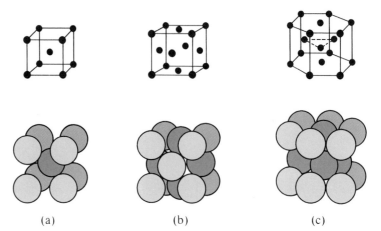

Figure 15.1 (a) Body-centered cubic, (b) face-centered cubic, and (c) hexagonal close-packed structures.

are placed as close together as possible. The second layer of spheres (open circles of Figure 15.2) are placed in the hollows formed by adjacent spheres of the first layer. The first two layers of both the face-centered cubic and the hexagonal close-packed arrangements are the same; the difference arises in the third and subsequent layers.

In the hexagonal close packed arrangement, the spheres of the third layer are placed so that they are directly over those of the first layer; the sequence of layers may be represented as *ababab*.... However, in the face-centered cubic structure, the spheres of the third layer are placed over the holes (marked *x* in Figure 15.2) formed by the arrangements of the first two layers. The spheres of the fourth layer of the body-centered cubic structure are placed so that they are directly over those of the first

Figure 15.2 Schematic representation of the first two layers of the close-packed arrangements.

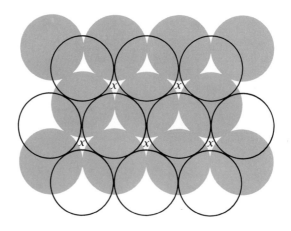

layer, and the sequence of layers is *abcabc*. . . . Notice that in the hexagonal close-packed arrangement the *x* holes are not capped, and there are tunnels, or channels, that run through the entire structure.

The crystal forms of the elements for which there is no entry in Table 15.1 either are unknown or, as is the case of manganese and mercury, do not fall into one of the three categories. Some of the metals exhibit crystal allotropy and different crystal forms are stable under different conditions; the first form listed in Table 15.1 is the stable one under ordinary conditions. In most cases, all of the members of a given group crystallize in the same type of crystal lattice. For example, the I A metals (which have low densities) all crystallize in the body-centered cubic system (which is more open than either of the close-packed structures).

The densities of the metals show a wide variation; of all the *solid* elements, lithium has the lowest density and osmium has the highest density. The range of densities of the solid nonmetallic elements is much narrower, and the large majority of metals have considerably higher densities than any solid nonmetal. The metals of groups I A and II A are referred to as the light metals because they are exceptions to the preceding generalization. The close-packed arrangement of the atoms of most metallic crystals helps to explain the relatively high densities encountered.

The trend in the magnitude of the density across a period (Figure 15.3) reflects the variation in atomic radius of the elements of the period. Thus the atomic radii of the elements of the fourth, fifth, and sixth periods reach a minimum approximately at group VIII, and the densities are at a maximum at this point. The I A metals have the largest atomic radii and the smallest atomic masses of their periods; these factors coupled with their crystal structure give them comparatively low densities.

The densities of the elements of a group increase with increasing atomic number; this trend corresponds to an increase in atomic mass which is not offset by a proportionate increase in atomic radius. Data for the lanthanides of period 6 are not plotted in Figure 15.3, but the lanthanide contraction causes the pronounced difference between the curves for period 5 and period 6.

The melting points and boiling points of the nonmetals show extreme variation—from the very low values of the gaseous elements to the extremely high values of the elements that crystallize in covalent network lattices such as the diamond. There is considerable variation in the melting and boiling points of the metals although low values, such as those of the gaseous nonmetals, are not observed. In general, most metals have comparatively high melting and boiling points.

The striking feature of the curves of Figures 15.4 and 15.5 is the maximum that occurs at approximately the center of each curve. Curves for

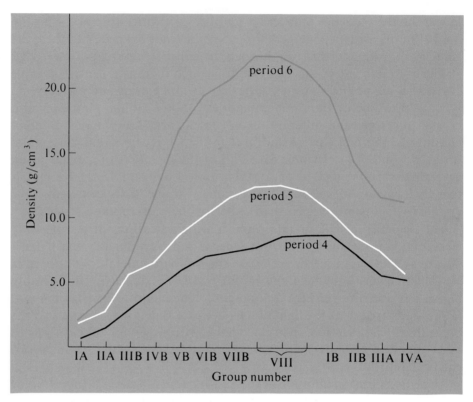

Figure 15.3   Densities of the metals of the fourth, fifth, and sixth periods.

the heat of fusion, heat of vaporization, and hardness of metals have approximately the same appearance. For a given period, therefore, the strength of the metallic bonding (Section 3.15) must reach a maximum around the center of the transition series.

The strength of the metallic bonding is, of course, related to the number of delocalized electrons per atom used in the bonding. If we count only the ns, np, and unpaired $(n - 1)$ d electrons of a metal as bonding electrons, we get an order that approximates that of the properties under discussion. This analysis is a decided oversimplification; other factors, such as atomic radius, nuclear charge, number of bonding orbitals, overlap of orbital energies, and crystal form, are involved.

The deformability, luster, thermal conductivity, and electrical conductivity of metals are the properties most characteristic of metallic bonding and the metallic state (Section 3.15). Electrical conductivity is measured in units of 1/ohm cm; a conductivity of 1.0/ohm cm means that a current of 1.0 amp flows when a potential of 1.0 v is applied to opposite faces of 1.0 cm^3 cube of the material being studied (Section 9.1). The conductivities of metals, or conductors, lie in the general range of 10^4 to 10^6/ohm cm at room temperature and decrease with increasing temperature. This is approximately 1 million to 1 billion times the con-

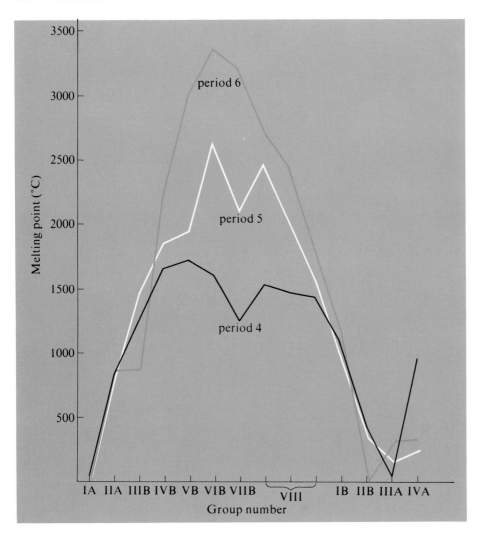

Figure 15.4 *Melting points of the metals of the fourth, fifth, and sixth periods.*

ductivities of the semimetals, or semiconductors, which range from 10^{-5} to 10/ohm cm at room temperature and increase with rising temperature. The nonmetals, or insulators, have negligible conductivities—from 10^{-22} to 10^{-10}/ohm cm at room temperature, increasing with increasing temperature.

The way in which the conductivities of the three classes of elements vary with temperature reflects the electronic structures of the three classes. The conductivity of metals is attributable to the delocalized electrons of the metallic bonding and the fact that either the valence band is not filled or the conduction band lies close to the valence band with no intervening forbidden zone (Section 3.15). Increasing the temperature increases the vibration of the metal ions of the crystal lattice

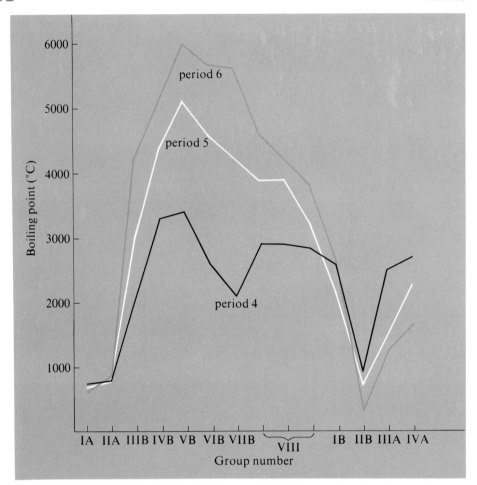

Figure 15.5   Boiling points of the metals of the fourth, fifth, and sixth periods.

and impedes the flow of electrons. Thus the conductivities of metals generally decrease with increasing temperature.

For semiconductors, heat excites electrons from the valence band, across a forbidden zone, into the conduction band (Section 3.15). Therefore rising temperature facilitates conduction.

In the case of nonmetals, conduction is next to impossible at room temperature; the valence electrons are employed in covalent bonding and are not free to move throughout the crystal. However, the covalent bonding is broken by heating, and this permits electronic motion and conduction.

The conductivities of some metals are listed in Table 15.2. The metals of group I B (copper, silver, and gold) are outstanding electrical conductors. Except for similarities in the relative standing in a period of elements of the same group, periodic trends in the conductivities are difficult to discern. Nor is it easy to explain the lack of a close correlation

TABLE 15.2.
ELECTRICAL CONDUCTIVITIES OF THE METALS AT 0°C IN UNITS OF 10^4/OHM CM.

1	2	3	4	5	6	7	8	9	10	11	12	13	14	15
Li 11.8	Be 18													
Na 23	Mg 25											Al 40		
K 15.9	Ca 23	Sc	Ti 1.2	V 0.6	Cr 6.5	Mn 20	Fe 11.2	Co 16	Ni 16	Cu 65	Zn 18	Ga 2.2		
Rb 8.6	Sr 3.3	Y	Zr 2.4	Nb 4.4	Mo 23	Tc	Ru 8.5	Rh 22	Pd 10	Ag 66	Cd 15	In 12	Sn 10	Sb 2.8
Cs 5.6	Ba 1.7	La 1.7	Hf 3.4	Ta 7.2	W 20	Re 5.3	Os 11	Ir 20	Pt 10	Au 49	Hg 4.4	Tl 7.1	Pb 5.2	Bi 1

between the general trend in melting points and the pattern of the conductivities.

The thermal conductivity, luster, and deformability of metals have been discussed in Section 3.15. In general, thermal conductivities parallel electrical conductivities. The nondirectional character of metallic bonding accounts for the ease with which planes of atoms slide across one another under stress so that the crystal may be deformed without shattering. When the planes of an ionic crystal are displaced (Figure 15.6), the new alignment brings ions of the same charge into proximity and results in the cleavage of the crystal. Covalent network crystals are deformed only by breaking the covalent bonds of the crystal, a process which also results in the fragmentation of the crystal.

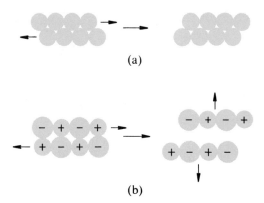

(a)

(b)

Figure 15.6   Effect of deformation on (a) a metallic
crystal, and (b) an ionic crystal.

15.2   Natural Occurrence of Metals

An **ore** is a naturally occurring material from which one or more metals can be profitably extracted. The principal types of ores and examples of each are listed in Table 15.3. A few of the less reactive metals occur in nature in elementary form; for many of these metals, native ores constitute the most important source. The greatest tonnage of metals is derived from oxides—either oxide ores or metal oxides that are produced by the calcining of carbonate or sulfide ores.

Silicate minerals are abundant in nature. However, the extraction of metals from silicates is difficult, and the cost of such processes may be prohibitive. Consequently, only the less common metals are commercially derived from silicate ores. Phosphate minerals are, in general, rare and frequently occur in low concentrations.

A number of metals occur as impurities in the ores of other metals so that both metals are derived from the same commercial operation. For example, cadmium metal is obtained as a by-product in the production of zinc.

Ores, as mined, generally contain variable amounts of unwanted

TABLE 15.3. OCCURRENCE OF METALS.	
Type of Ore	**Examples**
native metals	Cu, Ag, Au, As, Sb, Bi, Pd, Pt
oxides	Al_2O_3, Fe_2O_3, Fe_3O_4, SnO_2, MnO_2, TiO_2, $FeO \cdot Cr_2O_3$, $FeO \cdot WO_3$, Cu_2O, ZnO
carbonates	$CaCO_3$, $CaCO_3 \cdot MgCO_3$, $MgCO_3$, $FeCO_3$, $PbCO_3$, $BaCO_3$, $SrCO_3$, $ZnCO_3$, $MnCO_3$, $CuCO_3 \cdot Cu(OH)_2$, $2CuCO_3 \cdot Cu(OH)_2$
sulfides	Ag_2S, Cu_2S, CuS, PbS, ZnS, HgS, $FeS \cdot CuS$, FeS_2, Sb_2S_3, Bi_2S, MoS_2, NiS, CdS
halides	NaCl, KCl, AgCl, $KCl \cdot MgCl_2 \cdot 6H_2O$, NaCl and $MgCl_2$ in sea water
sulfates	$BaSO_4$, $SrSO_4$, $PbSO_4$, $CaSO_4 \cdot 2H_2O$, $CuSO_4 \cdot 2Cu(OH)_2$
silicates	$Be_3AlSi_6O_{18}$, $ZrSiO_4$, $Sc_2Si_2O_7$, $(NiSiO_3, MgSiO_3)$[a]
phosphates	$(CePO_4, LaPO_4, NdPO_4, PrPO_4, Th_3(PO_4)_4)$[a], $LiF \cdot AlPO_4$

[a] Occur in a single mineral but not in fixed proportions.

materials (such as silica, clay, and granite) which are called **gangue.** The concentration of the desired metal must be high enough to make its extraction chemically feasible and economically competitive. Ores of low concentration are worked only if they can be processed comparatively easily and inexpensively or if the metal product is scarce and valuable. The required concentration varies greatly from metal to metal. For aluminum or iron, it should be 30% or more; for copper, it may be 1% or less.

15.3 Metallurgy: Preliminary Treatment of Ores

Metallurgy is the science of extracting metals from their ores and preparing them for use. Metallurgical processes may be conveniently divided into three principal operations: (1) **preliminary treatment,** in which the desired component of the ore is concentrated, specific impurities removed, and/or the mineral is put into a suitable form for subsequent treatment, (2) **reduction,** in which the metal compound is reduced to the free metal, and (3) **refining,** in which the metal is purified and, in some cases, substances added to give desired properties to the final product. The problems encountered in each step vary from metal to metal so that many different metallurgical procedures exist.

The processing of many ores requires, as a first step, that much of the gangue be removed. Such **concentration** procedures, which are usually carried out on ores that have been crushed and ground, may be based on physical or chemical properties. **Physical separations** are based on differences between the physical properties of the mineral and the gangue. Thus through washing with water, the particles of rocky impurities may often be separated from the heavier mineral particles. This may be accomplished by shaking the crushed ore in a stream of water on an inclined table; the heavier mineral particles settle to the bottom and are collected. Adaptations of this process exist.

Flotation is a method of concentration applied to many ores, especially those of copper, lead, and zinc. The finely crushed ore is mixed with a suitable oil and water in large tanks. The mineral particles are wetted by the oil, whereas the gangue particles are wetted by the water. Agitation of the mixture with air produces a froth, containing the oil and mineral particles, which floats on the top of the water and which is then skimmed off.

Since Fe_3O_4 is ferromagnetic, particles of this material (the ore magnetite) can be magnetically separated from particles of gangue. Some finely divided particles become charged in an electrostatic field, and electrostatic separations are employed.

The removal of free metals from native ores may be considered to be a type of concentration. Certain ores, such as native bismuth and native copper, are heated to a temperature just above the melting point of the metal and the liquid metal poured away from the gangue.

Mercury will dissolve silver and gold to form what are called **amalgams.** Hence, the native ores of silver and gold are treated with mercury, the resulting amalgam collected, and the free silver or gold recovered from the amalgam by distilling away the mercury.

The **Parkes process** for refining lead, which also is a concentration method for silver, relies upon the selective dissolution of silver in molten zinc. A small amount of zinc (1 to 2%) is added to molten lead which contains silver as an impurity. Silver is much more soluble in zinc than in lead; lead and zinc are insoluble in each other. Hence, most of the silver concentrates in the zinc which comes to the top of the molten lead. The zinc layer solidifies first upon cooling; it is removed and the silver obtained by distilling away the zinc.

The chemical properties of minerals are the basis of **chemical separations.** An important example is the **Bayer method** of obtaining pure aluminum oxide from the ore bauxite. Since aluminum hydroxide is amphoteric, the alumina is dissolved away from the ore impurities (principally ferric oxide and silicates) by treatment of the crushed ore with hot sodium hydroxide solution.

$$Al_2O_3(s) + 2OH^-(aq) + 3H_2O \rightarrow 2Al(OH)_4^-(aq)$$

The solution of sodium aluminate is filtered and cooled; its pH is adjusted downward by dilution and/or neutralization with carbon dioxide so that aluminum hydroxide precipitates (Section 14.13). Pure aluminum oxide, ready for reduction, is obtained by heating the aluminum hydroxide.

$$2Al(OH)_3(s) \rightarrow Al_2O_3(s) + 3H_2O(g)$$

The first step in the extraction of magnesium from sea water is a chemical concentration. The Mg^{2+} in sea water (approximately 0.13%) is precipitated as magnesium hydroxide by treatment of the sea water with a slurry of calcium hydroxide. The calcium hydroxide is produced by roasting oyster shells.

$$CaCO_3(s) \rightarrow CaO(s) + CO_2(g)$$
$$CaO(s) + H_2O \rightarrow Ca(OH)_2(s)$$

The magnesium hydroxide is converted to magnesium chloride by reaction with hydrochloric acid, and the magnesium chloride solution is evaporated to produce the dry $MgCl_2$ necessary for electrolytic reduction.

The metal component of some ores may be obtained by leaching. Thus low grade carbonate and oxide ores of copper may be leached with dilute sulfuric acid

$$CuO(s) + 2H^+(aq) \rightarrow Cu^{2+}(aq) + H_2O$$
$$CuCO_3(s) + 2H^+(aq) \rightarrow Cu^{2+}(aq) + CO_2(g) + H_2O$$

and the resulting copper sulfate solutions directly subjected to electrolysis.

Silver and gold ores are leached with solutions of sodium cyanide in the presence of air since these metals form very stable complex ions with the cyanide ion. For native silver, argentite (Ag_2S), and cerargyrite ($AgCl$), the reactions are

$$4Ag(s) + 8CN^-(aq) + O_2(g) + 2H_2O \rightarrow 4Ag(CN)_2^-(aq) + 4OH^-(aq)$$
$$Ag_2S(s) + 4CN^-(aq) \rightarrow 2Ag(CN)_2^-(aq) + S^{2-}(aq)$$
$$AgCl(s) + 2CN^-(aq) \rightarrow Ag(CN)_2^-(aq) + Cl^-(aq)$$

After concentration, many ores are **roasted** in air. The sulfide ores of the less reactive metals are directly reduced to the free metal by heating (see Section 15.4). However, the majority of the sulfide ores, as well as the carbonate ores, are converted into oxides by roasting.

$$2ZnS(s) + 3O_2(g) \rightarrow 2ZnO(s) + 2SO_2(g)$$
$$PbCO_3(s) \rightarrow PbO(s) + CO_2(g)$$

Oxides are more readily reduced than sulfides or carbonates.

15.4 Metallurgy: Reduction

By far the largest quantity of metals, as well as the largest number of metals, are produced by **smelting** operations—high temperature reduction processes in which the metal is usually secured in a molten state. In most of these processes, a **flux** (such as limestone, $CaCO_3$) is added to the ore and the reducing agent to remove the gangue that remains after ore concentration. The flux forms a **slag** with the silica and silicate impurities; for limestone and silica the simplified equations are

$$CaCO_3(s) \rightarrow CaO(s) + CO_2(g)$$
$$CaO(s) + SiO_2(s) \rightarrow CaSiO_3(l)$$

The slag is liquid at the smelting temperatures, generally floats on top of the molten metal, and hence is readily separated from the metal.

The reducing agent employed for a given smelting operation is, of course, the least expensive material that is capable of yielding a product of the required purity. For the ores of the metals of low reactivity, no chemical agent is needed. For metal ores that require a reducing agent, carbon, in the form of coke, is most often used. When carbon is incapable of bringing about the desired reduction, more powerful reducing agents (such as hydrogen, sodium, or aluminum) are employed. The most electropositive metals (such as sodium, magnesium, and aluminum) are not obtained by smelting with chemical agents but are produced by electrochemical means.

The sulfides of mercury, copper, and lead are examples of ore that require no reducing agent. Mercury is produced by roasting cinnabar, HgS, in air.

$$HgS(s) + O_2(g) \rightarrow Hg(g) + SO_2(g)$$

The mercury vapor is condensed in a receiver and requires no further purification.

Copper sulfide ores, after concentration by flotation, are smelted not to the metal but to a material called matte which is essentially cuprous sulfide, Cu_2S. In this operation, a flux is employed to remove ore impurities in the form of a slag composed principally of calcium and ferrous silicates. A prior roasting may be used to reduce the sulfur content of the ore. The matte is reduced by blowing air through the molten material.

$$Cu_2S(l) + O_2(g) \rightarrow 2Cu(l) + SO_2(g)$$

The cuprous oxide that forms is reduced by stirring the molten metal by poles of green wood. The copper produced by this method (blister copper) is about 99% pure and is refined by electrolysis.

Lead sulfide ores (galena) are subjected to a roasting operation in which a portion of the PbS is converted into lead oxide and lead sulfate.

$$2PbS(s) + 3O_2(g) \rightarrow 2PbO(s) + 2SO_2(g)$$
$$PbS(s) + 2O_2(g) \rightarrow PbSO_4(s)$$

The resulting PbS, PbO, and PbSO$_4$ mixture, together with fluxes, is smelted in the absence of air. The reactions, in which sulfur is oxidized and lead reduced, are

$$PbS(s) + 2PbO(s) \rightarrow 3Pb(l) + SO_2(g)$$
$$PbS(s) + PbSO_4(s) \rightarrow 2Pb(l) + 2SO_2(g)$$

Some lead is also produced by carbon reduction in a blast furnace. In this process, the sulfide ore is roasted in an excess of air so that virtually complete conversion to the oxide results. The oxide is smelted with coke

$$PbO(s) + C(s) \rightarrow Pb(l) + CO(g)$$
$$PbO(s) + CO(g) \rightarrow Pb(l) + CO_2(g)$$

The lead from this process may be refined by the Parkes process (Section 15.5), or electrolytically.

Oxides (obtained as ores or from roasting operations) of iron, zinc, tin, cadmium, antimony, nickel, cobalt, molybdenum, and other metals are reduced by carbon. Examples are

$$SnO_2(s) + 2C(s) \rightarrow Sn(l) + 2CO(g)$$
$$ZnO(s) + C(s) \rightarrow Zn(g) + CO(g)$$

In the production of zinc, the metal vapor distills from the retort in which the reduction is carried out and is condensed in a receiver.

The reactions that occur in a high-temperature carbon reduction are complex. In most cases, the reduction is effected principally by carbon monoxide, not carbon. Since both the mineral and coke are solids that are not readily fusible, contact between them is poor and direct reaction slow.

$$MO(s) + C(s) \rightarrow M(l) + CO(g)$$

(M stands for a metal.) However, a gas and a solid make better contact and react more readily.

$$2C(s) + O_2(g) \rightarrow 2CO(g)$$
$$MO(s) + CO(g) \rightarrow M(l) + CO_2(g)$$

The carbon dioxide produced is converted into carbon monoxide by reaction with coke.

$$C(s) + CO_2(g) \rightarrow 2CO(g)$$

The most important commercial metal, iron, is produced by carbon reduction in a blast furnace designed to operate continuously (Figure 15.7). The ore, coke, and a limestone flux are charged into the top of the furnace and heated air, which is sometimes enriched with oxygen, is

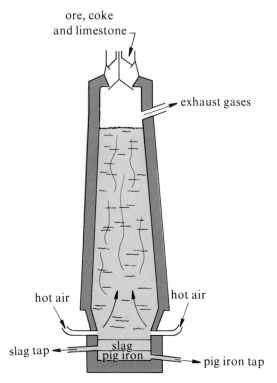

Figure 15.7   Diagram of a blast furnace (schematic).

blown in at the bottom. The incoming air reacts with carbon to form carbon monoxide and liberate considerable amounts of heat; at this point, the temperature of the furnace is the highest (ca., 1500°C).

The iron ore (usually Fe_2O_3) is reduced in stages depending upon the temperature. Near the top of the furnace, where the temperature is lowest, Fe_3O_4 is the reduction product.

$$3Fe_2O_3(s) + CO(g) \rightarrow 2Fe_3O_4(s) + CO_2(g)$$

The descending Fe_3O_4 is reduced to FeO in a lower, hotter, zone.

$$Fe_3O_4(s) + CO(g) \rightarrow 3FeO(s) + CO_2(g)$$

In the hottest zone, reduction to metallic iron occurs.

$$FeO(s) + CO(g) \rightarrow Fe(l) + CO_2(g)$$

The molten iron collects in the bottom of the furnace. Molten slag, principally calcium silicate which is produced by the ultimate action of the flux on the gangue, also collects on the bottom. The slag floats on top of the molten iron, thus protecting the metal from oxidation by the incoming air. The slag and iron are periodically drawn off. The hot exhaust gases are used to heat incoming air and some slag is used in making cement.

The impure iron produced by the blast furnace (**pig iron**) contains up to 4% carbon, up to 2% silicon, some phosphorus, and a trace of sulfur. In the manufacture of steel (Section 15.5), these impurities are removed or their concentrations adjusted; in addition, certain metallic ingredients are added. The presence of some carbon in steel is desirable, and the amount of carbon in the final product is readily controlled in the refining process.

The carbon reduction of some oxides yields products (such as chromium, manganese, and tungsten) that contain an appreciable quantity of carbon. If these metals are to be used in the manufacture of steel, the carbon content does not matter, and an alloy of iron and chromium as well as alloys of iron with manganese and other metals are prepared by the carbon reduction of mixed oxides for use in the manufacture of steel. Chromite, a mixed oxide of iron and chromium, is the only important ore of chromium.

However, since carbon impurities are difficult to remove from many metals, carbon reduction is not a satisfactory method for preparing these metals in a pure form. In such instances, as well as those in which carbon is incapable of effecting a reduction, reactive metals (such as Na, Mg, and Al) may be used as reducing agents. Processes that use metals as reducing agents are more expensive than those that employ carbon since the cost of the production of the metal used as a reducing agent must be taken into account.

The reduction of an oxide by aluminum is called the **Goldschmidt,** or **thermite, process.**

$$Cr_2O_3(s) + 2Al(s) \rightarrow 2Cr(l) + Al_2O_3(l)$$
$$3MnO_2(s) + 4Al(s) \rightarrow 3Mn(l) + 2Al_2O_3(l)$$
$$3BaO(s) + 2Al(s) \rightarrow 3Ba(l) + Al_2O_3(l)$$

The reactions are highly exothermic, and molten metals are produced. The reaction of Fe_2O_3 and aluminum

$$Fe_2O_3(s) + 2Al(s) \rightarrow 2Fe(l) + Al_2O_3(l)$$

is used at times for the production of molten iron in welding operations and as the basis of incendiary (thermite) bombs.

Other oxides commercially reduced by metals include: UO_3 (by Al or Ca), V_2O_5 (by Al), Ta_2O_5 (by Na), MoO_3 (by Al), ThO_2 (by Ca), and WO_3 (by Al).

The **Kroll process** involves the reduction of metal halides (such as $TiCl_4$, $ZrCl_4$, UF_4, and $LaCl_3$) by magnesium, sodium, or calcium. In the production of titanium, titanium tetrachloride is prepared by the reaction of titanium dioxide, carbon, and chlorine. The chloride is a liquid and is readily purified by distillation. Purified $TiCl_4$ is passed into molten magnesium or sodium at approximately 700°C under an atmosphere of argon or helium (which prevents oxidation of the product).

$$TiCl_4(g) + 2Mg(l) \rightarrow Ti(s) + 2MgCl_2(l)$$

On a minor scale, scrap iron is used to effect certain reductions. Some stibnite (Sb_2S_3) is reduced by iron (Section 10.15) and some galena, PbS, is reduced by iron. Iron is added to the solutions of copper sulfate obtained by leaching low-grade copper ores with sulfuric acid

$$Cu^{2+}(aq) + Fe(s) \rightarrow Cu(s) + Fe^{2+}(aq)$$

Copper is also obtained by electrolysis of these copper sulfate solutions.

A metal displacement reaction employing zinc is used to obtain silver and gold from solutions resulting from cyanide leaching operations.

$$2Ag(CN)_2^-(aq) + Zn(s) \rightarrow 2Ag(s) + Zn(CN)_4^{2-}(aq)$$

Hydrogen can be used, at high temperatures, in place of carbon for metallurgical reductions, but it is more expensive than coke. Hydrogen is used for the preparation of some metals when carbon reduction yields an unsatisfactory product. Examples are

$$GeO_2(s) + 2H_2(g) \rightarrow Ge(s) + 2H_2O(g)$$
$$WO_3(s) + 3H_2(g) \rightarrow W(s) + 3H_2O(g)$$
$$MoO_3(s) + 3H_2(g) \rightarrow Mo(s) + 3H_2O(g)$$

The metals are produced as powders by this method. Germanium is melted and cast into ingots, but tungsten (wolfram) and molybdenum have high melting points. They are heated and pounded into compact form. Hydrogen cannot be used to reduce the oxides of some metals because of the formation of undesirable hydrides.

The most reactive metals are prepared by electrolytic reduction of molten compounds. Sodium and magnesium (as well as the other I A and II A metals) are prepared by electrolysis of the fused chlorides. Sodium chloride is electrolyzed in a **Downs cell** (Figure 15.8), which is designed to keep the products separate from one another so that they do not react.

cathode: $\qquad$ $e^- + Na^+ \rightarrow Na(l)$

anode: $\qquad$ $2Cl^- \rightarrow Cl_2(g) + 2e^-$

Purified Al_2O_3 is electrolyzed in the **Hall process** for the production of aluminum (Figure 15.9). Alumina dissolved in cryolite, Na_3AlF_6, produces a solution that will conduct electric current. The carbon lining of the cell serves as the cathode, and carbon anodes are used. The primary reaction at the anode may be considered to be the discharge of oxygen from oxide ions. However, the oxygen reacts with the carbon anodes so

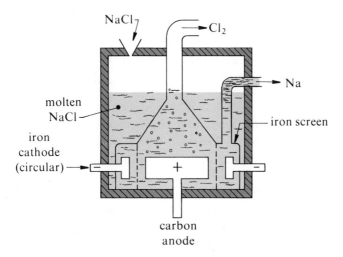

Figure 15.8   Schematic diagram of the Downs cell for the production
of sodium and chlorine.

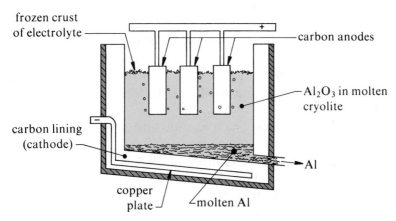

Figure 15.9   Schematic diagram of an electrolytic cell for the production of
aluminum.

that the cell reactions are

cathode: $3e^- + Al^{3+} \longrightarrow Al(l)$

anode: $C(s) + 2O^{2-} \longrightarrow CO_2(g) + 4e^-$

The molten aluminum collects at the bottom of the cell and is periodically withdrawn.

Some metals are prepared by the electrolysis of aqueous solutions of
their salts. Very pure zinc is produced by the electrolysis of zinc sulfate
solutions. The zinc sulfate is obtained by treating zinc oxide (from zinc
sulfide ores, by roasting) with sulfuric acid, and the sulfuric acid for the

process is made from the sulfur dioxide derived from the roasting of the sulfide ore.

cathode: $2e^- + Zn^{2+}(aq) \rightarrow Zn(s)$

anode: $2H_2O \rightarrow O_2(g) + 4H^+(aq) + 4e^-$

Aqueous solutions of salts of copper, cadmium, chromium, cobalt, gallium, indium, manganese, and thorium are electrolyzed to produce the corresponding metals. Electrolytically prepared metals generally require no further refining.

15.5 Metallurgy: Refining

Most of the metals obtained from reduction operations require refining to rid them of objectionable impurities. Refining processes vary widely from metal to metal, and for a given metal, the method employed may vary with the proposed use of the final product. Along with the removal of materials which impart undesirable properties to the metal, the refining step may include the addition of substances to give the product desired characteristics. Some refining processes are designed to recover valuable metal impurities, such as gold, silver, and platinum.

Crude tin, lead, and bismuth are purified by **liquation.** Ingots of the impure metals are placed at the top of a sloping hearth maintained at a temperature slightly above the melting point of the metal. The metal melts and flows down the inclined hearth into a well leaving behind the solid impurities.

Some low-boiling metals (such as zinc and mercury) are purified by distillation.

The Parkes process for the refining of lead, in which silver and gold are removed by extraction with molten zinc, is discussed in Section 15.3.

In the **Mond process,** impure nickel is treated with carbon monoxide at 60° to 80°C. The nickel reacts to form gaseous nickel carbonyl leaving solid impurities, including cobalt, behind.

$$Ni(s) + 4CO(g) \rightarrow Ni(CO)_4(g)$$

Pure nickel is recovered from the carbonyl by heating the gas to temperatures of from 180° to 200°C.

$$Ni(CO)_4(g) \rightarrow Ni(s) + 4CO(g)$$

The carbon monoxide is recirculated.

The **Van Arkel process** is also based upon the thermal decomposition of a metal compound. The method, which is used for the purification of titanium, hafnium, and zirconium, involves the decomposition of a metal iodide on a hot metal filament. For example, impure zirconium is heated with a limited amount of iodine in an evacuated glass apparatus.

$$Zr(s) + 2I_2(g) \rightarrow ZrI_4(g)$$

The gaseous zirconium tetraiodide is decomposed upon contact with a hot filament and pure zirconium metal is deposited upon the filament.

$$ZrI_4(g) \rightarrow Zr(s) + 2I_2(g)$$

The regenerated iodine reacts with more zirconium. The process is very expensive and is employed for the preparation of limited amounts of very pure metals for special uses.

Another process capable of producing metals of very high purity is **zone refining** (Section 10.23). A circular heater is fitted around a rod of an impure metal, such as germanium (Figure 15.10). The heater, which is slowly moved down the rod, melts a band of the metal. As the heater moves along, pure metal recrystallizes out of the melt, and impurities are swept along in the molten zone to one end of the rod which is subsequently discarded. More than one pass of the heater may be made on the same rod.

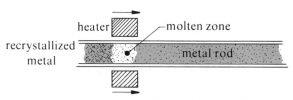

Figure 15.10   Schematic diagram of zone refining.

Electrolytic refining is an important, and widely used, method of purification. Many metals, including copper, tin, lead, gold, zinc, chromium, and nickel, are refined electrolytically. Plates of the impure metal are used as anodes, the electrolyte is a solution of a salt of the metal, and the pure metal plates out on the cathode. For copper, copper sulfate is employed as the electrolyte, and the electrode reactions are

anode: $\quad\quad\quad\quad\quad\quad$ $Cu(s) \rightarrow Cu^{2+}(aq) + 2e^-$

cathode: $\quad\quad$ $2e^- + Cu^{2+}(aq) \rightarrow Cu(s)$

The more reactive metals in the crude copper anode, such as iron, are oxidized and pass into solution where they remain; they are not reduced at the cathode. The less reactive metals, such as silver, gold, and platinum, are not oxidized. As the copper anode dissolves away, they fall to the bottom of the cell from where they are recovered as a valuable "anode sludge."

Pig iron is refined into steel by the **Bessemer process** or the **open hearth process.** In both these processes, the impurities (carbon from the coke used in the reduction, and such substances as silicon, phosphorus, and sulfur from the ore) are oxidized and volatilize out of the iron or go into the slag.

In the Bessemer process, molten pig iron from the blast furnace is poured into egg-shaped converters and a blast of air blown through the melt to oxidize the impurities. The heat required to keep the charge molten is supplied by these oxidations. The process is rapid (10 to 15 min); however, it is difficult to control, and the quality of the product is variable.

By far the largest percentage of steel is manufactured by the open hearth process. A charge of pig iron, scrap iron, and iron oxide is heated in a shallow hearth lined with calcium oxide or magnesium oxide. A blast of burning fuel and hot air is directed on the molten iron, and the oxidation of the impurities is accomplished by reaction with excess air or with iron oxide. The carbon monoxide escapes and burns, and the oxides of silicon, phosphorus, and sulfur combine with the oxides of the hearth lining to form a slag.

Since it takes about 8 to 10 hours to produce a batch of steel by the open hearth process, the quality of the final product is readily controlled and is uniform. Alloying metals, such as manganese, chromium, nickel, tungsten, molybdenum, and vanadium may be added before the charge is poured.

15.6   The Group I A Metals

The I A metals, also called the **alkali metals,** constitute the most reactive group of metals. None of the elements is found free in nature, and all are prepared by the electrolysis of dry, molten salts. The element francium, $Z = 87$, is formed in certain natural radioactive processes; all of its isotopes are radioactive with short half lives, and the element is extremely rare.

The group I A elements are silvery metals; cesium has a slight golden-yellow cast. The elements are comparatively soft (they can be cut by a knife) and have low melting points and boiling points (Table 15.4).

TABLE 15.4. SOME PROPERTIES OF THE I A METALS.	Lithium	Sodium	Potassium	Rubidium	Cesium
outer electronic configuration	$2s^1$	$3s^1$	$4s^1$	$5s^1$	$6s^1$
melting point (°C)	179	97.5	63.7	39.0	28.5
boiling point (°C)	1336	880	760	700	670
density (g/cm³)	0.53	0.97	0.86	1.53	1.90
atomic radius (Å)	1.23	1.57	2.03	2.16	2.35
ionic radius, M^+ (Å)	0.60	0.95	1.33	1.48	1.69
ionization potential (ev)					
first	5.4	5.1	4.3	4.2	3.9
second	75.6	47.3	31.8	27.4	23.4
Electrode potential, $E°$,					
(M^+/M) (v)	−3.05	−2.71	−2.93	−2.93	−2.92

Melting point, boiling point, and hardness decrease with increasing atomic number. The metals are good conductors of heat and electricity. They have very low densities. For comparison, consider the densities of the metals of the first transition series which range from 2.5 g/cm^3 for $_{21}$Sc to 8.9 g/cm^3 for $_{30}$Cu.

The alkali metals emit electrons when irradiated (the photoelectric effect). Cesium, which ejects electrons most readily, is used in the manufacture of photocells (employed in light meters and electric eyes) which convert light signals into electric signals.

The electronic configuration of each of the alkali metals is that of the preceding noble gas (a noble gas core) plus a single s valence electron in the outer shell. These valence electrons are easily lost to give 1+ ions that are isoelectronic with noble gases. Thus the elements of group I A have lower first ionization potentials than any other group of the periodic table. The ease with which these elements lose electrons makes them extremely strong reducing agents.

The second ionization potentials of the I A metals are so much higher than the first ionization potentials that the 1+ oxidation state is the only one observed for these metals. With few exceptions, alkali metal compounds are ionic.

In general, the reactivity of the elements increases with increasing atomic number paralleling the decrease in first ionization potential. Thus in most cases, cesium is the most reactive element of the group and lithium is the least reactive. This order of reactivity is expected since a large atom holds its valence electron less tightly than a small atom; in a large atom, the electron is farther from the nucleus and is screened from the positive nuclear charge by a large number of underlying electron shells.

Each I A element has the largest atomic radius and largest ionic radius of any element of its period. This comparatively large size combined with the low charge of the I A ions leads to species that have little polarizing ability (and hence form strongly ionic compounds) and that do not readily form complex ions.

Since the alkali metal ions have comparatively low charge/size ratios, the hydration energies of the ions are low. The enthalpy change of the transformations

$$M^+(g) + xH_2O(l) \rightarrow M^+(aq)$$

cannot be measured directly but may be estimated by means of calculations involving other measurable quantities. The lithium ion, which is the smallest ion and has the least effectively screened nuclear charge of the group, has the largest hydration energy. The hydration energies decrease with increasing ion size (Table 15.5).

Although all of the I A ions are loosely hydrated in water solution, only salts of lithium and sodium (the two smallest ions) form hydrates in

TABLE 15.5. ENTHALPY CHANGES OF SOME I A METAL TRANSFORMATIONS (KCAL).					
	Li	Na	K	Rb	Cs
$M(s) \rightarrow M(g)$	+37	+26	+22	+20	+19
$M(g) \rightarrow M^+(g) + e^-$	+124	+118	+100	+96	+89
$M^+(g) \rightarrow M^+(aq)$	−121	−95	−76	−69	−62
$M(s) \rightarrow M^+(aq) + e^-$	+40	+49	+46	+47	+46

which the water may be considered to be coordinated around the cation, and in these substances the metal ion–water attractions are electrostatic. Hydrates of salts of the other I A metals are known, but the water is not present in these crystals as coordination water.

The trend in the magnitudes of the hydration energies of the ion helps to explain why the order of the electrode potentials is different from that of the ionization potentials (Table 15.5). Of all the alkali metals, lithium is the most difficult to oxidize to the 1+ state, and lithium has the highest ionization potential of any member of the group. On the other hand, lithium is the I A metal most readily converted to *hydrated* 1+ ions, and lithium has the lowest standard electrode potential.

The relationship between ionization potential and electrode potential may be clarified by means of a Born-Haber treatment of the half reaction

$$M(s) \rightarrow M^+(aq) + e^-$$

For the purpose of analysis, the enthalpy change for this half reaction may be considered to be derived from the enthalpy of sublimation (energy absorbed),

$$M(s) \rightarrow M(g)$$

the ionization energy (energy absorbed),

$$M(g) \rightarrow M^+(g) + e^-$$

and the enthalpy of hydration (energy evolved),

$$M^+(g) \rightarrow M^+(aq)$$

The sums of these energy effects actually apply to transformations in which the electrons are left in the gaseous state; however, the values derived, which are listed in Table 15.5, permit some valid comparisons to be made. Each of the factors listed in Table 15.5 varies in a regular, and predictable, manner. The sums of the energy effects, however, indicate that the oxidation of lithium to produce hydrated lithium ions requires less energy than the oxidation of any other I A metal and that the corresponding oxidation of sodium requires more energy than the oxidation of any other I A metal. This conclusion is supported by the electrode potentials of the alkali metals. In an oxidation-reduction reaction involving the alkali metals, the energy required to effect one of these oxidation half reactions is usually more than adequately supplied by the reduction.

Rigorously, electrode potentials can only be derived from changes in Gibbs free energy, which include not only changes in enthalpy but also changes in entropy. These entropy effects are not large; but since we have ignored them, and also used ΔH values correct only to 1 kcal, not much importance should be attached to the order of the values for K, Rb, and Cs recorded in Table 15.5, other than to note that they lie between the values for Li and Na.

All of the hydroxides of the alkali metals are strong electrolytes. Alkali metal compounds are generally quite soluble in water. However, the hydroxide, carbonate, phosphate, and fluoride of lithium are much less soluble than the corresponding salts of the other I A metals. Sodium ion may be precipitated from solution as sodium zinc uranyl acetate, $NaZn(UO_2)_3(C_2H_3O_2)_9 \cdot 6H_2O$, and the perchlorate ion, ClO_4^-, the hexachloroplatinate ion, $[PtCl_6]^{2-}$, and the cobaltinitrite ion, $[Co(NO_2)_6]^{3-}$, may be used to precipitate K^+, Rb^+, and Cs^+.

The unipositive ammonium ion has a radius that lies between those of K^+ and Rb^+, and ammonium salts have solubilities that resemble those of the alkali metal salts. The ionic radius of the thallous ion, Tl^+, is similar to that of the rubidium ion. Not only do thallous compounds resemble rubidium compounds in solubility, but TlOH is also a strong electrolyte.

Some of the reactions of the I A metals are summarized in Table 15.6. Whereas the properties of lithium are similar in most respects to those of the other members of group I A, there are some dissimilarities which may be traced to the comparatively small size of Li and Li^+. The first members of the groups of the periodic table often deviate slightly in character from the remaining members of their groups. In addition, similarities may be observed between these first members and elements that adjoin them diagonally on the periodic table (diagonal relationships).

$$\begin{array}{cccc} Li & Be & B & C \\ Na & Mg & Al & Si \end{array}$$

Thus lithium resembles magnesium in some of its properties. The magnesium ion has a slightly larger ionic radius (0.65 Å) than the lithium ion (0.60 Å), but the charge on the magnesium ion is 2+.

Following are some of the ways in which lithium resembles magnesium and differs from its congeners. The carbonate, phosphate, and fluoride of lithium are but slightly soluble in water. Lithium forms a normal oxide, rather than a peroxide or a superoxide, upon burning in oxygen. Lithium ions are more strongly hydrated than those of any other I A element. Lithium reacts directly with nitrogen to give a nitride.

TABLE 15.6.
REACTION OF THE I A METALS.[a]

Reaction	Remarks
$2M + X_2 \rightarrow 2MX$	X_2 = all halogens
$4Li + O_2 \rightarrow 2Li_2O$	excess oxygen
$2Na + O_2 \rightarrow Na_2O_2$	
$M + O_2 \rightarrow MO_2$	M = K, Rb, Cs
$2M + S \rightarrow M_2S$	also with Se and Te
$6Li + N_2 \rightarrow 2Li_3N$	Li only
$12M + P_4 \rightarrow 4M_3P$	also with As, Sb
$2M + 2C \rightarrow M_2C_2$	M = Li and Na; other I A metals give nonstoichiometric interstitial compounds
$2M + H_2 \rightarrow 2MH$	
$2M + 2H_2O \rightarrow 2MOH + H_2$	room temperature
$2M + 2H^+ \rightarrow 2M^+ + H_2$	violent reaction
$2M + 2NH_3 \rightarrow 2MNH_2 + H_2$	liquid NH_3 in presence of catalysts such as Fe; gaseous NH_3, heated

[a] M = any I A metal, except where noted.

Lithium hydroxide may be decomposed to Li_2O and water upon heating, and lithium carbonate decomposes to Li_2O and CO_2 upon ignition. Lithium nitrate decomposes upon heating.

$$4LiNO_3(s) \rightarrow 2Li_2O(s) + 4NO_2(g) + O_2(g)$$

The nitrates of the other alkali metals form nitrites upon heating,

$$2MNO_3(s) \rightarrow 2MNO_2(s) + O_2(g)$$

and the hydroxides and carbonates of Na, K, Rb, and Cs are thermally stable.

15.7 The Group II A Metals

The group II A metals, or **alkaline earth metals,** are highly electropositive and constitute the second most reactive group of metals. They are not found free in nature and are commonly produced by the electrolysis of molten chlorides. Radium is a comparatively scarce element and all of its isotopes are radioactive.

Because of its larger nuclear charge, each II A metal has a smaller atomic radius than that of the I A metal of its period. Since atoms of the II A metals are smaller and have two bonding electrons instead of one, the II A metals have higher melting and boiling points and greater densities than the I A metals (Table 15.7). In addition, the alkaline earth metals are harder than the alkali metals. Beryllium is hard enough to scratch glass and has a tendency toward brittleness; the degree of hardness declines with increasing atomic number. The alkaline earth metals are white metals with a silvery luster. They are good conductors of electricity.

Each of the II A metals has an electronic configuration consisting of a noble gas core plus two s electrons in the outer, valence, level. The loss of the two valence electrons produces an ion that is isoelectronic not only with a noble gas but also with the I A metal ion of the same period. However, the alkaline earth metal ions have a larger nuclear charge than the alkali metal ions and are therefore considerably smaller. The beryllium ion is an exceptionally small cation, and as is the case with atomic radii, the ionic radii increase with increasing atomic number.

In comparison to the I A metal ions, the II A metal ions, therefore, have considerably greater ratios of ionic charge to ionic radius. There are several important consequences of this fact. The hydration energy of a given alkaline earth ion is about five times that of the alkali metal ion of the same period. Furthermore, whereas the compounds of calcium, strontium, and barium are essentially ionic, the compounds of the smaller members of the group, magnesium and beryllium, have appreciable covalent character because the cations of these metals have a stronger polarizing effect on anions. This tendency for covalent bond

TABLE 15.7.
SOME PROPERTIES OF THE II A METALS.

	Beryllium	Magnesium	Calcium	Strontium	Barium
outer electronic configuration	$2s^2$	$3s^2$	$4s^2$	$5s^2$	$6s^2$
melting point (°C)	1280	651	851	800	850
boiling point (°C)	1500	1107	1440	1366	1537
density (g/cm³)	1.86	1.75	1.55	2.6	3.59
atomic radius (Å)	0.89	1.36	1.74	1.91	1.98
ionic radius, M^{2+} (Å)	0.31	0.65	0.99	1.13	1.35
ionization potential (ev)					
first	9.3	7.6	6.1	5.7	5.2
second	18.2	15.0	11.9	11.0	10.0
third	153.9	80.1	51.2	—	—
electrode potential, E^0, (M^{2+}/M) (v)	−1.85	−2.36	−2.87	−2.89	−2.91

formation is particularly pronounced for beryllium; all compounds of this metal, even those with the most electronegative elements such as oxygen and fluorine, have significant covalent character. Beryllium has the greatest tendency of the group toward the formation of complex ions; examples are $[Be(H_2O)_4]^{2+}$, $[Be(NH_3)_4]^{2+}$, BeF_4^{2-}, and $[Be(OH)_4]^{2-}$. Beryllium hydroxide is the only amphoteric hydroxide formed by a group II A metal.

The covalent nature of beryllium halides is indicated by the poor electrolytic conduction of the anhydrous molten compounds; NaCl is generally added to anhydrous molten $BeCl_2$ in the electrolytic preparation of beryllium.

Gaseous $BeCl_2$ molecules are linear and presumably of the sp hybrid type. In most solid compounds, beryllium is tetrahedrally disposed, in many through sp^3 hybrid bonding. Such a configuration is observed in the complex ions of beryllium. Beryllium chloride is polymeric; each beryllium atom is joined to four chlorine atoms.

The BeO crystal may be considered to be composed of BeO_4 tetrahedra.

The ionization potentials of the II A metals are higher than those of the I A metals because of differences in atomic size and nuclear charge. Nevertheless, the II A metals are very reactive, although not so reactive as the I A metals. The ionization potentials recorded in Table 15.7 show that it is distinctly more difficult to remove three electrons than it is to remove two; hence, the production of 3+ ions is not likely. However, these values also show that the second electron is significantly more difficult to remove than the first; the production of 1+ ions might appear reasonable.

A 1+ ion would have a much smaller hydration energy than a 2+ ion. In addition, because of the less intense electric field surrounding a 1+ ion (the 1+ ion would be larger as well as having a lower positive charge), the lattice energies of crystalline compounds of such ions would be smaller. Therefore the additional energy required to remove the second electron is more than supplied by the larger hydration energy of the 2+ ion or, in the case of solids, by the larger lattice energy of the M^{2+} salt. Stable 1+ ions of the II A metals do not exist in the solid state or in solution.

It is because of these comparatively large hydration energies that the electrode potentials of the II A metals (despite larger enthalpies of sublimation and larger ionization energies) are rather similar in magnitude to those of the I A metals. The hydration energy is largest for Be^{2+}

and smallest for Ba^{2+}, but nevertheless the electrode potentials fall in the same order as the ionization potentials: Ba is the strongest reducing agent of the group and Be is the weakest.

This order of reactivity is illustrated by the reactions of the alkaline earth metals with water. Beryllium fails to react at red heat. Magnesium will react with boiling water or steam. Calcium, strontium, and barium react vigorously with cold water. Some chemical reactions of the group II A metals are summarized in Table 15.8.

Almost all the salts of the I A metals are very soluble in water. In contrast, a number of II A metal compounds are not appreciably water soluble; the solubility products of some of these insoluble compounds are listed in Table 15.9.

The solubility of a salt depends upon the lattice energy of the salt (energy absorbed in the solution process)

$$MA(s) \longrightarrow M^{2+}(g) + A^{2-}(g)$$

TABLE 15.8.
REACTIONS OF THE II A METALS.[a]

Reactions	Remarks
$M + X_2 \longrightarrow MX_2$	X_2 = all halogens
$2M + O_2 \longrightarrow 2MO$	Ba also gives BaO_2
$M + S \longrightarrow MS$	also with Se and Te
$3M + N_2 \longrightarrow M_3N_2$	at high temperatures
$6M + P_4 \longrightarrow 2M_3P_2$	at high temperatures
$M + 2C \longrightarrow MC_2$	all except Be which forms Be_2C; high temperatures
$M + H_2 \longrightarrow MH_2$	M = Ca, Sr, Ba; high temperatures; Mg with H_2 under pressure
$M + 2H_2O \longrightarrow M(OH)_2 + H_2$	M = Ca, Sr, Ba; room temperature
$Mg + H_2O \longrightarrow MgO + H_2$	steam; Be does not react at red heat
$M + 2H^+ \longrightarrow M^{2+} + H_2$	
$Be + 2OH^- + 2H_2O \longrightarrow Be(OH)_4^{2-} + H_2$	Be only
$M + 2NH_3 \longrightarrow M(NH_2)_2 + H_2$	M = Ca, Sr, Ba; liquid ammonia in presence of catalysts
$3M + 2NH_3 \longrightarrow M_3N_2 + 3H_2$	gaseous NH_3; high temperatures

[a] M = any II A metal, except where noted.

TABLE 15.9.
SOLUBILITY PRODUCT CONSTANTS OF SOME II A METAL SALTS.

	OH^-	SO_4^{2-}	CO_3^{2-}	$C_2O_4^{2-}$	F^-	CrO_4^{2-}
Be^{2+}	1.6×10^{-26}	—	—	—	—	—
Mg^{2+}	8.9×10^{-12}	—	10^{-5}	8.6×10^{-5}	8×10^{-8}	—
Ca^{2+}	1.3×10^{-6}	2.4×10^{-5}	4.7×10^{-9}	1.3×10^{-9}	1.7×10^{-10}	7.1×10^{-4}
Sr^{2+}	3.2×10^{-4}	7.6×10^{-7}	7×10^{-10}	5.6×10^{-8}	7.9×10^{-10}	3.6×10^{-5}
Ba^{2+}	5.0×10^{-3}	1.5×10^{-9}	1.6×10^{-9}	1.5×10^{-8}	2.4×10^{-5}	8.5×10^{-11}

and the hydration energies of the ions (energy evolved)

$$M^{2+}(g) \rightarrow M^{2+}(aq)$$
$$A^{2-}(g) \rightarrow A^{2-}(aq)$$

When the solubilities of salts containing the same anion are compared, the hydration energy of the anion may be neglected and solubility differences attributed to the combination of the other two factors.

The solubility of the alkaline earth sulfates decreases with increasing cation size; $BeSO_4$ is very soluble, and $BaSO_4$ is very insoluble. The sulfate ion has a radius that is more than twice that of the largest II A cation, Ba^{2+}. The lattice energies of the sulfates do not change greatly in the sequence from $BeSO_4$ to $BaSO_4$ presumably because the anion is so much larger than any II A cation. The trend in the solubility of the sulfates, therefore, parallels the trend in hydration energies of the ions. The hydration of the small Be^{2+} ion is by far the most exothermic of any ion of the group, and $BeSO_4$ is by far the most soluble sulfate formed by any ion of the group.

The trend in the solubility of hydroxides is the reverse of that of the sulfates; $Be(OH)_2$ is the least soluble alkaline earth hydroxide, and the solubility increases down the group. For hydroxides, the lattice energy is dependent upon cation size. The strength of the crystal forces decreases with increasing cation size; $Be(OH)_2$ has the largest lattice energy of any alkaline earth hydroxide. Apparently, the trend in lattice energy (energy required) overshadows the trend in hydration energy (energy released).

Solubility data cannot always be so simply interpreted. In the preceding solubility considerations, we have ignored entropy effects. In addition, even though the lattice energies and hydration energies of a group of salts may vary regularly, the sum of the two energy effects, and hence the solubilities of the salts, may vary in an irregular manner in the same way that the standard electrode potentials of the I A metals vary.

The lattice energies of the oxides of the II A metals decrease regularly from BeO to BaO, and the effect of this trend is seen in the series of reactions of the alkaline earth oxides with water. Beryllium oxide is insoluble in, and unreactive toward, water. Magnesium oxide reacts very slowly with water; MgO that has been ignited at high temperatures, however, is practically inert. The oxides of calcium, strontium, and barium readily react with water to form hydroxides

$$MO + H_2O \rightarrow M(OH)_2$$

The carbonates of the alkaline earth metals decompose upon heating

$$MCO_3(s) \rightarrow MO(s) + CO_2(g)$$

The thermal stability of the carbonates varies directly with the size of the cation. Beryllium carbonate is very unstable and can be prepared only in an atmosphere of carbon dioxide presumably because of the enhanced stability of BeO over $BeCO_3$.

The tendency of the II A metals ions toward hydration causes a number of the compounds of these ions to hydrate with ease; $Mg(ClO_4)_2$, $CaCl_2$, $CaSO_4$, and $Ba(ClO_4)_2$ are used as desiccants.

The beryllium ion hydrolyzes in solution

$$[Be(H_2O)_4]^{2+} + H_2O \rightleftharpoons [Be(H_2O)_3(OH)]^+ + H_3O^+$$

but the other cations do not hydrolyze. The hydroxides of beryllium and magnesium may be regarded as insoluble (Table 15.9). Even though the hydroxides of calcium, strontium, and barium are limitedly soluble in water, these compounds are completely dissociated in aqueous solution.

The sulfides of the group are water soluble, and solutions of these compounds are alkaline due to the hydrolysis of the sulfide ion. In quantitative determinations, barium ion is usually precipitated as barium sulfate, strontium ion as strontium sulfate or strontium oxalate, and calcium ion as calcium oxalate. Magnesium ion is precipitated as $Mg(NH_4)PO_4 \cdot 6H_2O$ by the HPO_4^{2-} ion in the presence of ammonia. Beryllium may be determined as the hydroxide.

Barium ion may be separated from Sr^{2+}, Ca^{2+}, and Mg^{2+} in solution, by taking advantage of the fact that the chromate of barium is the least soluble chromate of any ion of the group. The chromate ion, CrO_4^{2-}, exists in equilibrium with the dichromate ion, $Cr_2O_7^{2-}$, in acid solution.

$$2CrO_4^{2-}(aq) + 2H^+(aq) \rightleftharpoons Cr_2O_7^{2-}(aq) + H_2O$$

The pH of the solution is carefully adjusted by means of an acetic acid buffer so that the concentration of CrO_4^{2-} is maintained at a low value. This concentration is sufficient to precipitate only $BaCrO_4$.

After the $BaCrO_4$ has been removed, $SrCrO_4$ may be made to precipitate by the addition of ammonia and ethyl alcohol. Increasing the pH of the solution increases the concentration of chromate ions by shifting the chromate-dichromate equilibrium. When the concentration of CrO_4^{2-} is high enough, $SrCrO_4$ precipitates. Calcium chromate does not precipitate under these conditions.

The calcium ion may be separated from the magnesium ion by the careful addition of ammonium oxalate. Magnesium oxalate is much more soluble than calcium oxalate. The magnesium ion may be precipitated as magnesium ammonium phosphate.

Because of the extremely small size of Be and Be^{2+}, beryllium is even more exceptional with regard to the other members of group II A than lithium is with regard to the other members of group I A. The diagonal relationship between beryllium and aluminum is particularly striking. Although Al^{3+} is larger than Be^{2+}, the two ions have similar electric fields because of the higher charge of Al^{3+}.

Both elements have a strong tendency toward the formation of covalent compounds. The halides are largely covalent in nature, soluble in organic solvents, and strong Lewis acids. Both aluminum hydroxide and beryllium hydroxide are amphoteric, and both metals dissolve in solutions of hydroxides to give hydrogen. The standard electrode potential of beryllium is similar in magnitude to that of aluminum but much smaller than those of the other II A metals.

The carbides of beryllium and aluminum yield methane, CH_4, on hydrolysis

$$Be_2C(s) + 4H_2O \rightarrow 2Be(OH)_2(s) + CH_4(g)$$
$$Al_4C_3(s) + 12H_2O \rightarrow 4Al(OH)_3(s) + 3CH_4(g)$$

The hydrolysis of the other II A metal carbides yields acetylene, C_2H_2.

Aluminum and beryllium (as well as magnesium in this case) have thin protective oxide coatings which make them resistant to attack by dilute nitric acid. Beryllium oxide and aluminum oxide are hard, extremely high melting, insoluble solids. Beryllium and aluminum form the stable fluoro complex anions BeF_4^{2-} and AlF_6^{3-}. The other II A metals do not form complexes with the fluoride ion that are stable in solution. Normal beryllium carbonate is unstable, and aluminum carbonate cannot be made at all.

15.8 The Transition Metals

The transition metals are found in groups III B to II B in the periodic table. Some chemists do not include group II B (the zinc group) in this classification, and some exclude group I B (the copper group) as well. However, there are advantages in classifying the copper- and zinc-group elements as transition elements, and we shall follow this practice.

In general, the transition metals have high melting and boiling points, high heats of fusion, and high heats of vaporization (Section 15.1). The group II B elements (zinc, cadmium, and mercury) are exceptions to this generalization. Mercury is a liquid under ordinary conditions, and all of the II B elements are comparatively low melting and relatively easy to volatilize (distillation constitutes a method of refining the metals). Most of the transition metals are good conductors of heat and electricity; the I B elements are outstanding in these respects (Table 15.2).

The significant feature of the electronic configurations of the transition elements (Table 15.10) is the gradual build up of the d subshell of the next to the outer shell. Included in the sixth and seventh periods are the lanthanides and actinides, respectively. These are the inner-transition elements in which inner f orbitals are being filled (Section 15.9).

TABLE 15.10.
POSTULATED ELECTRONIC CONFIGURATIONS OF THE VALENCE SUBSHELLS OF THE TRANSITION METALS.

Sc	$3d^1 4s^2$	Y	$4d^1 5s^2$	La	$5d^1 6s^2$
Ti	$3d^2 4s^2$	Zr	$4d^2 5s^2$	Hf	$5d^2 6s^2$
V	$3d^3 4s^2$	Nb	$4d^4 5s^1$	Ta	$5d^3 6s^2$
Cr	$3d^5 4s^1$	Mo	$4d^5 5s^1$	W	$5d^4 6s^2$
Mn	$3d^5 4s^2$	Tc	$4d^6 5s^1$	Re	$5d^5 6s^2$
Fe	$3d^6 4s^2$	Ru	$4d^7 5s^1$	Os	$5d^6 6s^2$
Co	$3d^7 4s^2$	Rh	$4d^8 5s^1$	Ir	$5d^9$
Ni	$3d^8 4s^2$	Pd	$4d^{10}$	Pt	$5d^9 6s^1$
Cu	$3d^{10} 4s^1$	Ag	$4d^{10} 5s^1$	Au	$5d^{10} 6s^1$
Zn	$3d^{10} 4s^2$	Cd	$4d^{10} 5s^2$	Hg	$5d^{10} 6s^2$

The transition elements exhibit a wide variation in chemical properties. Many compounds of the transition elements are colored and paramagnetic because of unpaired electrons. Since the inner d orbitals are energetically close to the s orbital of the outer level, both ns and $(n-1)d$ electrons are involved in compound formation. With the exceptions of zinc, cadmium, and the elements of group III B, all of the transition elements exhibit more than one oxidation state in compound formation. The largest number of oxidation states, as well as the maximum oxidation number, is observed for the fifth transition element of period 4 (Mn) and the sixth elements of periods 5 and 6 (Ru and Os, respectively). For these elements and the ones preceding them in each transition series, the maximum oxidation number corresponds to the total number of ns and $(n-1)d$ electrons (Table 15.11). The higher oxidation numbers of a given element are most frequently seen in compounds containing the more electronegative elements: fluorine, oxygen, and chlorine (Tables 15.12, 15.13, and 15.14).

After the maximum oxidation state of a period is reached in each transition series, there is a decrease in the highest oxidation number observed for each subsequent element, and these oxidation states are, in general, difficult to obtain and unstable. Less common and unstable oxidation states are enclosed in parentheses in Table 15.11.

TABLE 15.11.
OXIDATION STATES OF THE TRANSITION ELEMENTS
(LESS COMMON, OR UNSTABLE, STATES IN PARENTHESES).

Sc	Ti	V	Cr	Mn	Fe	Co	Ni	Cu	Zn
								1+	
	(2+)	(2+)	2+	2+	2+	2+	2+	2+	2+
3+	3+	3+	3+	(3+)	3+	3+	(3+)	(3+)	
	4+	4+	(4+)	4+	(4+)	(4+)	(4+)		
		5+	(5+)		(5+)				
			6+	(6+)	(6+)				
				7+					

Y	Zr	Nb	Mo	Tc	Ru	Rh	Pd	Ag	Cd
						(1+)		1+	
	(2+)	(2+)	(2+)	(2+)	2+	(2+)	2+	(2+)	+2
3+	(3+)	(3+)	3+	(3+)	3+	3+	(3+)	(3+)	
	4+	(4+)	4+	4+	4+	4+	4+		
		5+	5+	5+	(5+)	(5+)			
			6+	(6+)	(6+)	(6+)			
				7+	(7+)				
			(8+)		(8+)				

La	Hf	Ta	W	Re	Os	Ir	Pt	Au	Hg
						(1+)		1+	1+
		(2+)	(2+)		(2+)	(2+)	2+		2+
3+	(3+)	(3+)	(3+)	3+	(3+)	3+	(3+)	3+	
	4+	(4+)	4+	4+	4+	4+	4+		
		5+	5+	(5+)	(5+)	(5+)	(5+)		
			6+	(6+)	6+	(6+)	(6+)		
				7+					
					8+				

In general, the lowest oxidation number observed is 2+; notable exceptions are: Cu^+, Ag^+, Au^+, and Hg_2^{2+}. The mercury(I), or mercurous, ion is unique; evidence for its dimeric structure includes the following. Mercurous salts are diamagnetic in agreement with the formula Hg_2^{2+}; the ion Hg^+ would have one unpaired electron. X-ray studies of mercurous salts indicate discrete Hg_2^{2+} ions. The interpretations of certain equilibria involving the mercurous ion are in agreement with experimentally derived values for the equilibrium constants only if the formula Hg_2^{2+} is used.

Within each group, the higher oxidation states become more stable, and more important, with increasing atomic number; a corresponding decline in the stability and importance of the lower oxidation states is also observed. The gain in stability of the higher states with increasing

OXIDATION STATES OF THE TRANSITION ELEMENTS OF THE FOURTH PERIOD WITH EXAMPLES (UNSTABLE OR UNIMPORTANT STATES IN PARENTHESES).

Ox.	Sc	Ti	V	Cr	Mn	Fe	Co	Ni	Cu	Zn
1+									Cu_2O, $CuCl$, Cu_2S, Cu_2SO_4, $CuCN$	
2+		$(2+)$ TiO, $TiCl_2$	$(2+)$ VO, VSO_4, VCl_2	CrO, CrS, $CrCl_2$, $Cr(OH)_2$, $CrSO_4$, $Cr(C_2H_3O_2)_2$	MnO, MnS, $MnCl_2$, $Mn(OH)_2$, $MnSO_4$, $Mn(CN)_6^{4-}$	FeO, FeS, $FeCl_2$, $Fe(OH)_2$, $FeSO_4$	CoO, CoS, $CoCl_2$, $Co(OH)_2$, $CoSO_4$	NiO, NiS, $NiCl_2$, $Ni(OH)_2$, $NiSO_4$	CuO, CuS, $CuCl_2$, $Cu(OH)_2$, $CuSO_4$, $Cu(NH_3)_4^{2+}$, $CuCl_4^{2-}$	ZnO, ZnS, $ZnCl_2$, $Zn(OH)_2$, $ZnSO_4$, $Zn(OH)_4^{2-}$, $Zn(NH_3)_4^{2+}$
3+	Sc_2O_3, $ScCl_3$, $ScOCl$, $ScO(OH)$, Sc_2S_3, $Sc(OH)_6^{3-}$, ScF_6^{3-}	Ti_2O_3, $TiCl_3$, $Ti_2(SO_4)_3$, TiF_6^{3-}	V_2O_3, VCl_3, $VOCl$, $V_2(SO_4)_3$, $VOSO_4$, VF_6^{3-}	Cr_2O_3, $CrCl_3$, $Cr(OH)_3$, $Cr_2(SO_4)_3$, $Cr(OH)_4^-$	$(3+)$ Mn_2O_3, $MnO(OH)$, $Mn(C_2H_3O_2)_3$	Fe_2O_3, Fe_2S_3, $FeCl_3$, $Fe(OH)_3$	Co_2O_3, CoF_3, $Co(CN)_6^{3-}$	$(3+)$ Ni_2O_3	$(3+)$ CuO_2^-, CuF_6	
4+		TiO_2, $TiCl_4$, $TiO(SO_4)$, TiF_6^{2-}	VO_2, VCl_4, $VOCl_2$, $VO(SO_4)$, VOF_4^{2-}	$(4+)$ CrF_4, CrF_6^{2-}, CrO_4^{4-}	MnO_2, MnO_3^{2-}, MnF_6^{2-}	$(4+)$ FeO_3^{2-}, FeO_4^{4-}	$(4+)$ CoO_2, CoO_4^{4-}	$(4+)$ NiO_2, NiF_6^{2-}		
5+			V_2O_5, VF_5, $VOCl_3$, VO_4^{3-}, VF_6^-, VOF_4^-	$(5+)$ Cr_2O_5, CrF_5, CrO_4^{3-}, $CrOF_4^-$		$(5+)$ FeO_4^{3-}				
6+				CrO_3, CrO_2Cl_2, CrO_4^{2-}, $Cr_2O_7^{2-}$, CrO_3F^-	$(6+)$ MnO_4^{2-}	$(6+)$ FeO_4^{2-}				
7+					MnO_4^-, MnO_3F					

559

TABLE 15.13.
OXIDATION STATES OF THE TRANSITION ELEMENTS OF THE FIFTH PERIOD WITH EXAMPLES (UNSTABLE OR UNIMPORTANT STATES IN PARENTHESES).

Y	Zr	Nb	Mo	Tc	Ru	Rh	Pd	Ag	Cd
						(1+) $Rh(CO)_2Cl$		1+ Ag_2O, Ag_2S, $AgCl$, $AgNO_3$, Ag_2SO_4, $Ag(NH_3)_2^+$, $Ag(CN)_2^-$	
	(2+) $ZrCl_2$	(2+) NbO	(2+) $MoCl_2$	(2+)	2+ $Ru(CN)_6$	(2+)	2+ PdO, $PdCl_2$, $PdSO_4$, $Pd(NH_3)_4^{2+}$, $PdCl_4^{2-}$	(2+) AgO, AgF_2	2+ CdO, CdS, $CdCl_2$, $Cd(OH)_2$, $CdSO_4$, $Cd(NH_3)_4^{2+}$, $Cd(CN)_4^{2-}$
3+ Y_2O_3, Y_2S_3, YCl_3, $Y(OH)_3$, $Y_2(SO_4)_3$	(3+) $ZrCl_3$, $ZrBr_3$	(3+) $NbCl_3$	3+ Mo_2S_3, $MoCl_3$, $MoCl$, MoF_4^-, $Mo(CN)_7^{4-}$	(3+)	3+ $RuCl_3$, $Ru(NH_3)_6^{3+}$	3+ Rh_2O_3, Rh_2S_3, $RhCl_3$, $Rh_2(SO_4)_3$, RhF_6^{3-}	(3+): PdF_3	(3+) AgF_4^-	
	4+ ZrO_2, $ZrCl_4$, $Zr(SO_4)_2$, $ZrO(NO_3)_2$, ZrF_6^{2-}, ZrF_7^{3-}	(4+) NbO_2, $NbCl_4$	4+ MoO_2, MoS_2, $MoCl_4$, $Mo(CN)_8^{4-}$	4+ TcO_2, TcS_2, $TcCl_4$, $TcCl_6^{2-}$	4+ RuO_2, RuS_2, $RuCl_4$, RuF_6^{2-}	4+ RhO_2, RhF_4, RhF_6^{2-}	4+ PdO_2, PdS_2, $PdCl_6^{2-}$		
		5+ Nb_2O_5, $NbCl_5$, NbF_6^-, NbO_3^-, NbF_7^{2-}, $NbOF_5^{2-}$	5+ Mo_2S_5, $MoCl_5$, $Mo(CN)_8^{3-}$, $MnOF_5^{2-}$	(5+)	(5+) RuF_5	(5+) Rh_2S_5			
			6+ MoO_3, MoS_3, MoF_6, MoO_2Cl_2, MoO_4^{2-}	(6+) $TcCl_6$, TcF_6	(6+) RuF_6, RuO_4^{2-}	(6+) RhF_6			
				7+ Tc_2O_7, Tc_2S_7, TcO_4^-, TcO_3Cl	(7+) RuO_4^-				

TABLE 15.14.
OXIDATION STATES OF THE TRANSITION ELEMENTS OF THE SIXTH PERIOD WITH EXAMPLES (UNSTABLE OR UNIMPORTANT STATES IN PARENTHESES).

La	Hf	Ta	W	Re	Os	Ir	Pt	Au	Hg
						(1+) $IrCl$		1+ Au_2S AuI, $AuCN$ $Au(CN)_2^-$	1+ Hg_2Cl_2 $Hg_2(NO_3)_2$ Hg_2SO_4
		(2+) $TaCl_2$	(2+) WCl_2		(2+) $OsCl_2$ $Os(CN)_6^{4-}$	(2+) IrS $Ir(CN)_6^{4-}$ $Ir(NH_3)_4^{2+}$	2+ PtO $PtCl_2$ $Pt(NH_3)_4^{2+}$ $PtCl_4^{2-}$		2+ HgO HgS, $HgCl_2$ $HgSO_4$ $Hg(CN)_4^{2-}$
3+ La_2O_3 La_2S_3, $LaCl_3$ $La(OH)_3$ $La_2(SO_4)_3$	(3+) $HfBr_3$	(3+) $TaCl_3$ $TaBr_3$	(3+) $W_2Cl_9^{3-}$	3+ Re_2O_3 Re_2Cl_6 $ReCl_4^-$	(3+) $OsCl_3$ $Os(NH_3)_6^{3+}$	3+ Ir_2O_3 Ir_2S_3, $IrCl_3$ $Ir_2(SO_4)_3$	(3+) $PtCl_3$ $PtBr_3$	3+ Au_2O_3 Au_2S_3, $AuCl_3$ $AuCl_4^-$, AuO_2^- $Au(NH_3)_4^{3+}$	
	4+ HfO_2 $HfCl_4$ HfF_7^{3-}	(4+) TaO_2 $TaCl_4$	4+ WO_2 WCl_4, WS_2	4+ ReO_2 ReS_2, ReF_4 ReF_6^{2-}, ReO_3^{2-}	4+ OsO_2 $OsCl_4$, OsS_2 OsF_6^{2-}	4+ IrO_2 IrS_2, IrF_4 IrF_6^{2-}	4+ PtO_2 $PtCl_4$ PtO_3^{2-}, $PtCl_6^{2-}$		
		5+ Ta_2O_5 $TaCl_5$ TaO_4^{3-} TaF_7^{2-}	5+ WCl_5 $WOCl_5^{2-}$ $WOCl_4^-$ $W(CN)_8^{3-}$	(5+) $ReOF_3$ ReO_3^-	(5+) OsF_5 OsF_6^-	(5+) IrF_6^-	(5+) PtF_5		
			6+ WO_3 WS_3, WCl_6 WO_2Cl_2 WO_4^{2-}, WF_7^-	(6+) ReO_3 ReF_6 $ReOCl_4$	6+ OsF_6 OsP_2 OsO_4^{2-}	(6+) IrF_6	(6+) PtO_3 PtF_6		
				7+ Re_2O_7 Re_2S_7, ReF_7 ReO_3Cl, ReO_4^-					
					8+ OsO_4 $OsO_4(OH)_2^{2-}$				

561

atomic number may be attributed to the increasing atomic size which makes the d electrons more available for compound formation.

Thus the 2+ ions of many of the fourth period transition elements are stable and characteristic of the elements, whereas the 2+ states of the heavier elements are not particularly common nor stable. The most important oxidation states of iron are 2+ and 3+; for osmium, the heaviest member of the same group, the most important states are 4+, 6+, and 8+.

The maximum oxidation number of manganese (which is the first member of its group) is attained in the permanganate ion, MnO_4^-. This ion is a strong oxidizing agent in acidic solution.

$$5e^- + 8H^+ + MnO_4^- \rightarrow Mn^{2+} + 4H_2O \qquad E° = +1.51 \text{ v}$$

In contrast, the analogous perrhenate ion, ReO_4^-, formed by the heaviest member of the group, is stable under comparable conditions.

The transition elements of group VI B form series of oxy anions in which the central metal ion is in an oxidation state of 6+; the simplest members of these series are the chromate ion, CrO_4^{2-}, the molybdate ion, MoO_4^{2-}, and the tungstate ion, WO_4^{2-}. Only a few polynuclear complexes of chromium have been reported; the most important of these is the dichromate ion, $Cr_2O_7^{2-}$ which results when chromate solutions are acidified.

$$2H^+ + CrO_4^{2-} \rightarrow Cr_2O_7^{2-} + H_2O$$

The dichromate ion is easily reduced in acid and consequently is a strong oxidizing agent.

$$6e^- + 14H^+ + Cr_2O_7^{2-} \rightarrow 2Cr^{3+} + 7H_2O \qquad E° = +1.33 \text{ v}$$

In contrast, molybdenum and tungsten form very extensive series of polynuclear molybdates and tungstates, and these compounds, as well as the corresponding acids, are very stable and without significant oxidizing power. The formation of such polynuclear oxy anions is not a common phenomenon in transition metal chemistry.

With increasing oxidation number, the oxides of a given element become less basic and more acidic. Thus CrO is an exclusively basic oxide and dissolves in acids to form Cr^{2+} salts; Cr_2O_3 is amphoteric and forms Cr^{3+} salts with acids and the chromite ion, $Cr(OH)_4^-$, in alkaline solution; CrO_3 is entirely acidic in character and gives rise to chromates, CrO_4^{2-}, and dichromates, $Cr_2O_7^{2-}$.

The atomic and ionic radii of the transition elements are, in general, smaller than those of the representative elements of the same period (Figure 3.3) since, for the transition elements, electrons are being added to an inner d sublevel where they feel the effect of the nuclear charge more than they would in the outer shell. This relatively small size causes the transition element ions to have comparatively high charge densities;

this, plus the availability of d orbitals for bonding, accounts for the pronounced tendency of most transition elements to form numerous stable complex ions (Chapter 16).

There are horizontal (or period) similarities as well as vertical (or group) similarities between the transition metals. The elements Cr through Cu, of the first transition series, have very similar atomic radii and ionic radii for ions of the same charge (Table 15.15), and horizontal similarities follow (such as the formation of compounds of formula MO, MS, MCl_2, etc.). Among the heavier elements, horizontal similarities are also evident (e.g., the formation of MO_2 compounds), and such similarities are particularly striking among the transition triads of group VIII (Fe, Co, and Ni; Ru, Rh, and Pd; and Os, Ir, and Pt). The elements of the two heavier triads are similar both physically and chemically.

The lanthanides occur at the beginning of the transition series of the sixth period. For the lanthanides, electrons are being added to the $4f$ sublevel without significant change in the $5s$, $5p$, $5d$, and $6s$ sublevels. The nuclear charge increases as this $4f$ sublevel deep within the atom is being filled, and there is a consequent decrease in the atomic and ionic radii of the lanthanides (Table 15.18) which is known as the **lanthanide contraction.**

The lanthanide contraction has an important effect on the properties of the transition elements following the lanthanides in the sixth period. Because of the lanthanide contraction, the atomic radii of these elements are not much different from those of the corresponding elements of the fifth period (Figure 15.11). Consequently, the second and third members of each group resemble each other much more than they resemble the first member of the group; there is no regular increase in size with increasing atomic number such as is observed for the A family elements.

Even though 32 elements intervene, hafnium ($Z = 72$) is notably similar to zirconium ($Z = 40$). Both elements have approximately the same atomic and ionic radii, and the chemical properties of the two elements are very similar; the separation of the two elements, which occur together in nature, is extremely difficult.

Some of the standard electrode potentials of the transition elements

**TABLE 15.15.
ATOMIC AND IONIC RADII OF THE TRANSITION ELEMENTS OF THE FOURTH PERIOD.**

	Sc	Ti	V	Cr	Mn	Fe	Co	Ni	Cu	Zn
atomic radii	1.44	1.32	1.22	1.17	1.17	1.17	1.16	1.15	1.17	1.25
ionic radii										
M^{2+}	—	0.90	0.88	0.84	0.80	0.76	0.74	0.72	0.72	0.74
M^{3+}	0.81	0.76	0.74	0.69	0.66	0.64	0.63	—	—	—

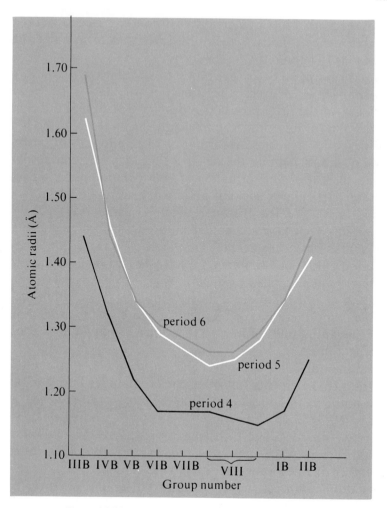

Figure 15.11   Atomic radii of the transition elements.

are listed in Table 15.16. For the most part, the potentials listed for the heavier elements, since they are for lower oxidation states, are not particularly important; however, they do serve to illustrate several trends.

Many of the metals react with dilute acids, as well as water or steam, to liberate hydrogen. Some of the metals, however, are poor reducing agents—notably, mercury, the group I B elements (copper, silver and gold), and the transition triads of the fifth and sixth periods (ruthenium, rhodium, palladium, osmium, iridium, and platinum). Frequently, these six elements of the transition triads, silver, and gold are referred to as noble metals.

Thus the elements of low reactivity appear to be concentrated toward the end of the transition series particularly those of the fifth and sixth periods, and in general, there is a decrease in electropositive character (or strength of the metals as reducing agents) across a period and down a group. The decreasing size of the atoms across a period causes the elec-

TABLE 15.16.
STANDARD ELECTRODE POTENTIALS OF THE TRANSITION ELEMENTS (VOLTS).

	Sc	Ti	V	Cr	Mn	Fe	Co	Ni	Cu	Zn
M^+/M	—	—	—	—	—	—	—	—	+0.52	—
M^{2+}/M	—	−1.63	−1.19	−0.91	−1.18	−0.44	−0.28	−0.25	+0.34	−0.76
M^{3+}/M	−2.08	−1.21	−0.88	−0.74	−0.28	−0.04	+0.42	—	—	—

	Y	Zr	Nb	Mo	Tc	Ru	Rh	Pd	Ag	Cd
M^+/M	—	—	—	—	—	—	+0.6	—	+0.80	—
M^{2+}/M	—	—	—	—	+0.4	+0.45	+0.6	+0.99	—	−0.40
M^{3+}/M	−2.37	—	−1.1	−0.2	—	—	+0.8	—	—	—

	La	Hf	Ta	W	Re	Os	Ir	Pt	Au	Hg
M^+/M	—	—	—	—	—	—	—	—	+1.69	+0.79
M^{2+}/M	—	—	—	—	—	+0.85	—	+1.2	—	+0.85
M^{3+}/M	−2.52	—	—	−0.11	+0.3	—	+1.15	—	+1.50	—

trons to be held increasingly tightly. The vertical trend is more surprising in view of the trends established by the A families. However, for transition elements, the increasing nuclear charge with increasing atomic number down a group is not accompanied by a large increase in atomic size, and the electrons are held more tightly. This is particularly true of the transition elements of the sixth period that follow the lanthanides. Here, the unusually small sizes of the atoms cause the electrons to be very tightly held; with the exceptions of La and Hf, the least electropositive member of each group is the sixth period element.

Although a given electrode potential may indicate a thermodynamic tendency for a reaction to occur, at times the rates at which some transition elements react are extremely slow. Thus chromium is a moderately strong reducing agent and reacts with nonoxidizing acids, such as HCl, to liberate hydrogen. Chromium does not, however, react with nitric acid, a strong oxidizing agent. It is said that the metal is made passive by the nitric acid. The phenomenon of passivity, which is displayed by many transition elements is not well understood. In some instances, it may be that the metal is protected by a thin, transparent, impervious, oxide coating.

The products of some of the reactions of the transition metals of the fourth period, which are the most common of the transition elements, are given in Table 15.17.

15.9 The Lanthanides

Postulated electronic configurations for the lanthanides are given in Table 15.18; there is some uncertainty to the assignment listed. The

TABLE 15.17.
PRODUCTS OF SOME REACTIONS OF THE TRANSITION ELEMENTS OF THE FOURTH PERIOD.

	Sc	Ti	V	Cr	Mn
O_2	Sc_2O_3	TiO_2	V_2O_5, VO_2	Cr_2O_3	Mn_3O_4
X_2	ScX_3	TiX_4	VF_5, VCl_4, VBr_3, VI_3	CrX_3 (except CrI_2)	MnX_2
S	Sc_2S_3	TiS_2	V_2S_5, VS_2	CrS	MnS
N_2	ScN	TiN	VN	CrN	Mn_3N_2
HCl	$Sc^{3+} + H_2$	$Ti^{3+} + H_2$	—	$Cr^{2+} + H_2$	$Mn^{2+} + H_2$
H_2O	$Sc(OH)_3 + H_2$	$TiO_2 + H_2$[a]	—	$Cr_2O_3 + H_2$[a]	$Mn(OH)_2 + H_2$
NaOH	—	—	—	$Cr(OH)_6^{3-} + H_2$	

	Fe	Co	Ni	Cu	Zn
O_2	Fe_3O_4, Fe_2O_3	Co_3O_4	NiO	Cu_2O, CuO	ZnO
X_2	FeX_3 (except FeI_2)	CoX_2	NiX_2	CuX_2 (except CuI)	ZnX_2
S	FeS	CoS	NiS	Cu_2S	ZnS
N_2	—	—	—	—	—
HCl	$Fe^{2+} + H_2$	$Co^{2+} + H_2$	$Ni^{2+} + H_2$	—	$Zn^{2+} + H_2$
H_2O	$Fe_3O_4 + H_2$[a]	$CoO + H_2$[a]	$NiO + H_2$[a]	—	$ZnO + H_2$[a]
NaOH	—	—	—	—	$[Zn(OH)_4]^{2-} + H_2$

[a]Steam

TABLE 15.18.
SOME PROPERTIES OF THE LANTHANIDES

	Z	Postulated Electronic Configurations of Valence Subshells	Oxidation States	Atomic Radius, Å	Ionic Radius, M^{3+}, Å	$E°$ $3e^- +$ $M^{3+} \rightarrow M$ (volts)
La	57	$5d^1 6s^2$	3+	1.69	1.06	−2.52
Ce	58	$4f^2 6s^2$	3+, 4+	1.65	1.03	−2.48
Pr	59	$4f^3 6s^2$	3+, 4+	1.65	1.01	−2.46
Nd	60	$4f^4 6s^2$	2+, 3+, 4+	1.64	1.00	−2.43
Pm	61	$4f^5 6s^2$	3+	—	0.98	−2.42
Sm	62	$4f^6 6s^2$	2+, 3+	1.66	0.96	−2.41
Eu	63	$4f^7 6s^2$	2+, 3+	1.85	0.95	−2.41
Gd	64	$4f^7 5d^1 6s^2$	3+	1.61	0.94	−2.40
Tb	65	$4f^9 6s^2$	3+, 4+	1.59	0.92	−2.39
Dy	66	$4f^{10} 6s^2$	3+, 4+	1.59	0.91	−2.35
Ho	67	$4f^{11} 6s^2$	3+	1.58	0.89	−2.32
Er	68	$4f^{12} 6s^2$	3+	1.57	0.88	−2.30
Tm	69	$4f^{13} 6s^2$	2+, 3+	1.56	0.87	−2.28
Yb	70	$4f^{14} 6s^2$	2+, 3+	1.70	0.86	−2.27
Lu	71	$4f^{14} 5d^1 6s^2$	3+	1.56	0.85	−2.26

differentiating electrons of the lanthanides, or inner-transition elements, are lodged in the third from the outer shell in $4f$ orbitals. This factor accounts for some of the unusual aspects of the chemistry of these elements. The atomic and ionic radii of the elements show a regular decrease with increasing atomic number (the lanthanide contraction).

The outstanding feature of the chemistry of the lanthanides is their similarity. The differentiating $4f$ electrons lie deep within the lanthanide atoms; thus these f electrons are shielded from the surroundings of the atom and do not cause strong variations in properties. This is to be contrasted with the wide variation in transition-element properties. The d electrons project from transition element atoms and ions and interact with the surroundings (Chapter 16). Hence, the number and arrangement of the d electrons of the transition elements is significant, whereas the number and arrangement of the f electrons of the inner-transition elements cause only minor variations in properties.

All the lanthanides form ions in the characteristic group III B oxidation state, 3+ (Table 15.18). For some of the elements, other oxidation states are known, but these are less stable. The 3+ ions are formed through the loss of the two $6s$ electrons and one $4f$ electron (or one $5d$ electron, if such is available).

There is some evidence that f^0, f^7 (half-filled), and f^{14} (filled) ions have stable configurations. Thus, La^{3+}, (f^0), Gd^{3+} (f^7), and Lu^{3+} (f^{14}) are the only ions that these elements form, and the most stable 2+ and 4+ ions are Eu^{2+} (f^7), Yt^{2+} (f^{14}), Ce^{4+} (f^0), and Tb^{4+} (f^7). The ceric ion, Ce^{4+}, is a good oxidizing agent.

The elements occur together in nature because of their great chemical similarity. Promethium, which is radioactive and probably occurs only in trace amounts, is an exception. The elements are extremely difficult to separate; repeated fractional crystallization and ion-exchange techniques have been employed to effect separations.

All of the lanthanides are silvery white, very reactive metals. The electrode potentials for the reduction of the 3+ ions are strikingly similar (Table 15.18). The metals react slowly with cold water, and rapidly with acids, to liberate hydrogen. They react with the halogens, carbon, silicon, nitrogen, and sulfur at elevated temperatures. Saltlike hydrides are produced by the reactions with hydrogen. They react with oxygen to give oxides of general formula M_2O_3 (except for cerium, which gives CeO_2). The M_2O_3 oxides react with water to form insoluble hydroxides, $M(OH)_3$, that are not amphoteric. Insoluble carbonates, $M_2(CO_3)_3$, may be produced by the reaction of carbon dioxide with the oxides or hydroxides. The sulfates, nitrates, and chlorates of the 3+ ions are water soluble; the phosphates, fluorides, and oxalates are insoluble. The precipitation of the elements as oxalates serves as the basis of an analytical determination. Generally, the compounds are paramagnetic and highly colored.

15.10 The Metals of Group III A

The characteristics of the group III A elements have been discussed in Section 10.28, and some of the properties of the metals are listed in Table 10.26.

Aluminum, the most abundant metal of the earth's crust (approximately 8%), is obtained by the electrolysis of molten Al_2O_3 (the Hall Process, Section 15.4). Gallium, indium, and thallium are widely distributed in nature but occur only in trace amounts; they may be prepared by the electrolysis of aqueous solutions of salts of the metals. They are soft, white metals with relatively low melting points (Figure 15.4). Gallium has an unusually low melting point (30°C). Since its boiling point is not abnormally low (2070°C), gallium has an exceptional liquid range and has found use as a thermometer fluid.

The metals are fairly reactive (Table 15.19). Aluminum, gallium, and indium (but not thallium) have protective oxide coatings and are passive toward nitric acid. However, all of the metals react with nonoxidizing acids to liberate hydrogen. As expected from their $ns^2 np^1$ electronic configurations, the most important oxidation state is 3+. Most of the compounds of the metals in the 3+ oxidation state are covalent. In water, however, the M^{3+} ions are stabilized through hydration (Section 10.28), and the heats of hydration are high.

The sulfates, nitrates, and halides are water soluble, but the M^{3+} ions hydrolyze readily.

$$[M(H_2O)_6]^{3+} + H_2O \rightarrow [M(H_2O)_5(OH)]^{2+} + H_3O^+$$

TABLE 15.19.
REACTIONS OF ALUMINUM, GALLIUM, INDIUM, AND THALLIUM.[a]

Reaction	Remarks
$2M + 3X_2 \rightarrow 2MX_3$	X_2 = all halogens; Tl also gives TlX; no iodide of Tl^{3+}
$4M + 3O_2 \rightarrow 2M_2O_3$	High temperatures; Tl also gives Tl_2O
$2M + 3S \rightarrow M_2S_3$	High temperatures; Tl also gives Tl_2S; also with Se and Te
$2Al + N_2 \rightarrow 2AlN$	Al only; GaN and InN may be prepared indirectly
$2M + 6H^+ \rightarrow 2M^{3+} + 3H_2$	M = Al, Ga, and In; Tl gives Tl^+
$2M + 2OH^- + 6H_2O \rightarrow 2M(OH)_4^- + 3H_2$	M = Al and Ga

[a] M = Al, Ga, In, and Tl, except where noted.

For this reason, salts of weak acids (such as acetates, carbonates, sulfides, and cyanides) do not exist in water solution. Such salts are completely hydrolyzed.

$$[M(H_2O)_6]^{3+} + 3C_2H_3O_2^- \rightarrow M(OH)_3(s) + 3H_2O + 3HC_2H_3O_2$$

In addition, complexes with ammonia do not exist in water.

$$[M(H_2O)_6]^{3+} + NH_3 \rightarrow [M(H_2O)_5(OH)]^{2+} + NH_4^+$$

The hydroxides, $M(OH)_3$, are insoluble in water. Aluminum hydroxide and gallium hydroxide are amphoteric.

$$Al(OH)_3 + OH^- \rightarrow [Al(OH)_4]^-$$
$$Ga(OH)_3 + OH^- \rightarrow [Ga(OH)_4]^-$$

Aluminum sulfate forms an important series of double salts called alums, $MAl(SO_4)_2 \cdot 12H_2O$ (or $M_2SO_4 \cdot Al_2(SO_4)_3 \cdot 24H_2O$) where M may be almost any univalent cation (Na^+, K^+, Rb^+, Cs^+, NH_4^+, Ag^+, and Tl^+) except Li^+ (which is too small). In addition to Al^{3+}, other M^{3+} species form series of such double sulfates: Fe^{3+}, Cr^{3+}, Mn^{3+}, Ti^{3+}, Co^{3+}, Ga^{3+}, In^{3+}, Rh^{3+}, and Ir^{3+}.

Hydrides, analogous to those of boron, are not formed by aluminum, gallium, indium, and thallium. However, $[MH_4]^-$ ions, analogous to the borohydride ion, are formed.

Among the heavier members of the group, compounds with the metal in a 1+ oxidation state are known. The np^1 electron is more readily removed than the ns^2 electrons, which comprise an inert pair. This effect is also seen for the M^{2+} ions of group IV A, and the low reactivity of mercury has been ascribed to the $6s^2$, inert pair, of its valence level.

Unlike the transition elements, however, the 1+ state of the III A elements (their lowest state) is most stable among the heavier members of the group. No 1+ compounds of aluminum are known. Gallium and indium form a few such compounds (such as Ga_2S, Ga_2O at high temperatures, InCl, InBr, and In_2O). The Ga^+ and In^+ ions are not stable in water solution.

For thallium, however, the 1+ state is important and stable. In fact, Tl^+ is more stable in water than Tl^{3+} (which is a strong oxidizing agent).

$$2e^- + Tl^{3+} \rightleftharpoons Tl^+ \qquad E° = +1.25 \text{ v}$$

The oxide Tl_2O dissolves in water to form the soluble hydroxide TlOH. Whereas the Tl^{3+} ion is extensively hydrolyzed in aqueous solution, the Tl^+ ion is not. A wide variety of Tl^+ compounds are known. The sulfate, nitrate, acetate, and fluoride are water soluble; the chloride, bromide, iodide, sulfide, and chromate are insoluble. In its chemistry, the Tl^+ ion has been compared to the Ag^+ ion.

15.11   The Metals of Group IV A

Of the elements of group IV A, germanium, tin, and lead are classi-fied as metals. The characteristics of the group as a whole are discussed in Section 10.22, and some of the properties of the metals are listed in Table 10.23. The metals are not abundant in nature; germanium is a rare element.

Germanium is a semiconductor and is used in the manufacture of transistors. It is a hard, brittle, white metal and has the highest melting point of the metals of the group. Tin and lead have relatively low melt-ing points and low tensile strengths. Lead is especially soft and malleable.

The metals are fairly reactive (Table 15.20). Lead frequently appears less reactive than the electrode potential

$$2e^- + Pb^{2+} \rightleftharpoons Pb \qquad E° = -0.13 \text{ v}$$

would indicate because of the formation of surface coatings. Thus the reaction of lead with sulfuric acid or hydrochloric acid is impeded by the formation of insoluble lead sulfate or lead chloride on the surface of the metal.

Since the elements have $ns^2\, np^2$ valence shell configurations, two oxidation states are observed: 4+ and 2+ (inert pair species). The 4+ state declines in importance, and the 2+ state becomes increasingly im-portant down the series: Ge, Sn, Pb. Thus only a few 2+ germanium compounds are of importance (GeO, GeS, $GeCl_2$, $GeBr_2$, and GeI_2),

TABLE 15.20.
REACTIONS OF GERMANIUM, TIN, AND LEAD.[a]

Reaction	Remarks
$M + 2X_2 \rightarrow 2MX_4$	X_2 = any halogen; M = Ge and Sn; Pb yields PbX_2
$M + O_2 \rightarrow MO_2$	M = Ge and Sn; high tem-peratures; Pb yields PbO or Pb_3O_4
$M + 2S \rightarrow MS_2$	M = Ge and Sn; high tem-peratures; Pb yields PbS
$M + 2H^+ \rightarrow M^{2+} + H_2$	M = Sn and Pb
$3M + 4H^+ + 4NO_3^- \rightarrow 3MO_2 + 4NO + 2H_2O$	M = Ge and Sn
$3Pb + 8H^+ + 2NO_3^- \rightarrow 3Pb^{2+} + 2NO + 4H_2O$	
$M + OH^- + 2H_2O \rightarrow M(OH)_3^- + H_2$	M = Sn and Pb; slow
$Ge + 2OH^- + 4H_2O \rightarrow Ge(OH)_6^{2-} + 2H_2$	

[a] M = Ge, Sn, and Pb, except where noted.

whereas only a few 4+ lead compounds are important (PbO_2, $Pb(C_2H_3O_2)_4$, PbF_4, and $PbCl_4$). The Sn^{2+} (stannous, or tin(II) ion) and Pb^{2+} (plumbous, or lead(II) ion) are the only cationic species of the group that exist in water; 4+ ions probably do not exist. Most of the pure 2+ and 4+ compounds are covalent, although PbF_2 is known to be ionic.

All of the metals form dioxides; GeO_2 and SnO_2 are the products of the reactions of the metals with oxygen. Lead dioxide may be prepared by the oxidation of PbO or Pb^{2+} salts in alkaline solution.

$$Pb(OH)_3^-(aq) + OCl^-(aq) \longrightarrow PbO_2(s) + Cl^-(aq) + OH^-(aq) + H_2O$$

Lead dioxide is a strong oxidizing agent.

$$2e^- + 4H^+ + PbO_2 \longrightarrow Pb^{2+} + 2H_2O \qquad E° = +1.46\,v$$

In acid solution, PbO_2 oxidizes Mn^{2+} to MnO_4^- and Cl^- to Cl_2. In contrast to GeO_2 and SnO_2, PbO_2 is thermally unstable. Upon gentle heating, PbO_2 decomposes to Pb_3O_4 (red lead); stronger heating gives PbO (litharge). The compound Pb_3O_4 contains lead in two oxidation states and may be represented as $Pb^{II}_2Pb^{IV}O_4$ like the compounds Fe_3O_4 and Co_3O_4, both of which conform to the formula $M^{II}(M^{III}O_2)_2$.

Germanates, stannates, and plumbates may be derived from the dioxides by reactions with aqueous alkali or, in the case of PbO_2, fusion with alkali metal oxides or alkaline earth oxides. The stannates and plumbates form trihydrates in which the anion is an octahedral hydroxy complex: $[M(OH)_6]^{2-}$; a few germanates of similar structure are known (e.g., $Fe[Ge(OH)_6]$). Crystalline metagermanates (e.g., Na_2GeO_3) and orthogermanates (e.g., Mg_2GeO_4) are known; these compounds have structures analogous to the meta- and orthosilicates. There are no hydroxides of formula $M(OH)_4$, but hydrous MO_2 oxides may be prepared.

Treatment of the Sn^{2+} and Pb^{2+} ions, in water solution, with OH^- ion gives hydrous-oxide precipitates that are commonly assigned the formulas $Sn(OH)_2$ and $Pb(OH)_2$. By heating these products, SnO and PbO can be prepared; PbO is also the product of the reaction of lead and oxygen as well as the decompositions of Pb_3O_4 and PbO_2. The compound GeO may be prepared by the hydrolysis of $GeCl_2$.

All of the monoxides, as well as the hydrous oxides (or hydroxides) are amphoteric and dissolve in either acid or alkaline solution. In excess alkali, germanites, stannites, and plumbites are produced. For example,

$$PbO(s) + OH^-(aq) + H_2O \longrightarrow Pb(OH)_3^-(aq)$$

The stannite ion is a strong reducing agent.

$$2e^- + Sn(OH)_6^{2-} \longrightarrow Sn(OH)_3^- + 3OH^- \qquad E° = -0.93\,v$$

All of the metals form monosulfides, MS, but only germanium and tin form disulfides, MS_2. The disulfides of germanium and tin may be prepared by the reactions of the metals and sulfur and may be precipitated from solutions of Ge^{IV} or Sn^{IV} compounds by H_2S. The disulfides, like the dioxides, are amphoteric. In solutions of alkali metal sulfides or ammonium sulfide, GeS_2 and SnS_2 dissolve to form thioanions; compounds of the SnS_3^{2-} and SnS_4^{4-} ions have been isolated from such solutions, but thiogermanates have not been obtained in pure form.

$$SnS_2(s) + S^{2-}(aq) \rightarrow SnS_3^{2-}(aq)$$

Insoluble PbS and SnS may be precipitated from solutions by means of H_2S. Lead(II) sulfide is also the product of the direct union of the elements, and SnS may be prepared by the thermal decomposition of SnS_2. Germanium(II) sulfide may be derived from the disulfide of germanium by the reaction

$$GeS_2 + Ge \rightarrow 2GeS$$

None of the monosulfides is soluble in sulfide solutions.

Complete series of the tetrahalides of germanium, tin, and lead are known except for $PbBr_4$ and PbI_4. Lead in a 4+ state has strong oxidizing power and cannot exist in a compound with bromine and iodine in 1− states (which have reducing abilities). Lead(IV) chloride readily decomposes at 100°C.

$$PbCl_4(l) \rightarrow PbCl_2(s) + Cl_2(g)$$

The tetrahalides, in general, are volatile covalent substances. They hydrolyze readily producing hydrous dioxides.

The tetrahalides of germanium and tin form complex anions, such as GeF_6^{2-} and $SnCl_6^{2-}$; a few compounds containing such anions of lead(IV) have been prepared. Whereas the halo complexes GeF_6^{2-}, SnF_6^{2-}, and $SnCl_6^{2-}$ are stable in water, the others are readily hydrolyzed to give the corresponding dioxides.

All of the dihalides of germanium, tin, and lead are known. Germanium(II) halides, as well as tin(II) halides, may be prepared by the reaction of the appropriate tetrahalide and metal.

$$GeCl_4 + Ge \rightarrow 2GeCl_2$$

The reactions of tin and the hydrohalic acids yield tin(II) halides. Lead(II) halides may be produced by the direct reaction of the elements, and since all PbX_2 compounds are insoluble in water, they may be precipitated from solutions containing Pb^{2+} by the addition of halide ions.

The dihalides are much less volatile than the tetrahalides indicating an increased degree of ionic character; PbF_2, $PbCl_2$, and $PbBr_2$ are ionic in the solid state. The dihalides of germanium are not particularly stable. Complex anions, such as $GeCl_3^-$, $SnCl_4^{2-}$, $PbCl_3^-$, $PbCl_4^{2-}$, and $PbCl_6^{4-}$ are known. Both Sn^{2+} and Pb^{2+} form such ions in aqueous solution in the presence of halide ions; in general, the ions MX^+ and MX_3^- are most important. Insoluble lead(II) halides dissolve in solutions containing excess halide ions because of the formation of such complexes.

All three metals form covalent, volatile hydrides: GeH_4, germane; SnH_4, stannane; and PbH_4, plumbane. The hydride of lead is thermally unstable and decomposes to the elements at $0°C$; SnH_4 decomposes at approximately $150°C$. Continuing the trend established by carbon and silicon, germanium forms catenated hydrides of formula Ge_nH_{2n+2}, where n is any number from 2 to 8. Tin or lead form only the simple hydrides.

The Sn^{2+} and Pb^{2+} ions are extensively hydrolyzed in water.

$$[Sn(H_2O)_6]^{2+} + H_2O \rightleftharpoons [Sn(H_2O)_5(OH)]^+ + H_3O^+ \qquad K_H \simeq 10^{-2}$$

$$[Pb(H_2O)_6]^{2+} + H_2O \rightleftharpoons [Pb(H_2O)_5(OH)]^+ + H_3O^+ \qquad K_H \simeq 10^{-8}$$

The hydrolysis is particularly pronounced in the case of tin(II) compounds; excess acid is generally added to aqueous solutions of such compounds to inhibit hydrolysis and prevent the precipitation of basic salts, such as $Sn(OH)Cl$.

Lead(II) nitrate and lead(II) acetate are soluble in water; the acetate is only slightly dissociated. The sulfate, chromate, carbonate, sulfide, and all of the halides, of Pb^{2+} are only slightly soluble in water.

SOME SUGGESTED READINGS

Cooper, D. G., *The Periodic Table,* Washington, D. C., Butterworth, 1964 (paper).

Cotton, F. A., and Wilkinson, G., *Advanced Inorganic Chemistry,* 2nd ed., New York, Wiley, 1966.

Emeleus, H. J., and Anderson, J. S., *Modern Aspects of Inorganic Chemistry,* 3rd ed., Princeton, N. J., Van Nostrand, 1960.

Heslop, R. B., and Robinson, P. L., *Inorganic Chemistry,* New York, Elsevier, 1963.

Hume-Rothery, W., *Electrons, Atoms, Metals and Alloys,* New York, Dover, 1963 (paper).

Kleinberg, J., Argersinger, W. J., Jr., and Griswold, E., *Inorganic Chemistry,* Boston, Heath, 1960.

Larsen, E. M., *Transitional Elements,* New York, Benjamin, 1965 (paper).

Latimer, W., *Reference Book in Inorganic Chemistry,* 3rd ed., New York, Macmillan, 1964 (paper).

Lingane, J. J., *Analytical Chemistry of Selected Metallic Elements,* New York, Reinhold, 1965 (paper).

Mellor, J. W., and Parkes, G. D., *Modern Inorganic Chemistry,* 5th ed., New York, Wiley, 1961.

Moeller, T., *The Chemistry of the Lanthanides*, New York, Reinhold, 1963 (paper).

Mott, N. F., and Jones, H., *The Theory of the Properties of Metals and Alloys*, New York, Dover, 1958 (paper).

Rich, R. L., *Periodic Correlations*, New York, Benjamin, 1965 (paper).

Sanderson, R. T., *Inorganic Chemistry*, New York, Reinhold, 1967.

Shrager, A. M., *Elementary Metallurgy and Metallography*, New York, Dover, 1961 (paper).

Weeks, M. E., and Leicester, H. M., *Discovery of the Elements,* 6th ed., Easton, Penna., Chemical Education Publishing Co., 1956.

PROBLEMS

15.1   List as many chemical and physical properties of metals as you can. Explain the relationships of atomic structure and crystal structure to these properties.

15.2   What diameter of iron wire must be used so that a given length will have an electrical conductivity equal to that of the same length of copper wire that is 1.0 cm in diameter? Electrical conductivities are listed in Table 16.2.

15.3   Describe, with equations, the steps in the metallurgy of (a) Mg (from sea water), (b) Al (from bauxite), (c) Cu (from CuS), (d) Zn (from ZnS), (e) Pb (from $PbCO_3$), (f) Fe (from Fe_2O_3).

15.4   Explain why it is not surprising that the following ores are found in nature: (a) native ores of platinum, gold, and silver, (b) sulfate ores of barium, strontium, and lead, (c) Na^+ and Mg^{2+} in sea water, (d) sulfide ores of lead, bismuth, and nickel.

15.5   Give equations for the reactions that occur in a blast furnace for the production of pig iron.

15.6   Describe the following metallurgical processes. Use equations where possible. (a) froth flotation, (h) Parkes process, (c) Mond process, (d) Van Arkel process, (e) Kroll process, (f) leaching, (g) roasting, (h) liquation, (i) zone refining, (j) thermite process.

15.7   What is meant by a "diagonal relationship?" Give an example of such a relationship with evidence to support the validity of the concept.

15.8   Lithium reacts slowly with water; sodium reacts vigorously; potassium reacts still more vigorously (the hydrogen produced bursts into flame); and rubidium and cesium react explosively. This order of reactivity is contrary to the order of $E°$ values that presumably pertain to aqueous reactions. Explain. Notice the melting points of the I A metals.

15.9   What reason can you give for the fact that Li_2CO_3 decomposes upon heating to give Li_2O and CO_2 whereas the carbonates of the other I A metals are thermally stable? Why does $LiNO_3$ decompose in a different manner from every other I A nitrate?

15.10   The second ionization potentials of the II A metals are much larger than the first ionization potentials. Why don't these elements form $1+$ ions in their reactions?

15.11   The standard electrode potential, $E°$, for the Hg_2^{2+}/Hg half reaction is +0.788 v. For the cell

$$Pt \mid Hg \mid Hg_2^{2+}(10^{-3}m) \parallel Hg_2^{2+}(10^{-2}m) \mid Hg \mid Pt$$

E equals 0.0296 v. (a) How does the potential of the concentration cell prove that the formula of the mercurous ion is Hg_2^{2+} and not Hg^+? (b) What would the potential of this cell be if the mercurous ion had the formula Hg^+? Notice that the concentrations given apply to the formula Hg_2^{2+}. (c) What would the standard electrode potential of the mercurous ion/mercury couple be if the formula of the mercurous ion were Hg^+?

15.12   The K_{sp} of Hg_2Cl_2 is 1.1×10^{-18}. What would be the value of the K_{sp} of mercurous chloride if the compound had the formula $HgCl$?

15.13   Why are the transition triads of group VIII so much alike physically and chemically? Cite evidence for your explanation and give examples of the similarity.

15.14   The corrosion of iron is thought to occur by an electrochemical mechanism. Explain why an underground iron pipe may be protected from rusting by buried bars of magnesium connected to the pipe by wires.

15.15   What reasons can you give to explain the low order of reactivity of the noble metals?

15.16   What explanation may be given for the fact that the atomic radii of europium and ytterbium are out of line in comparison to the atomic radii of the other lanthanides? (See Table 15.18.)

15.17   Write equations for the reactions of CrO, Cr_2O_3, and CrO_3 with $H^+(aq)$ and $OH^-(aq)$.

15.18   One method for waterproofing fabrics consists of coating the fabric with aluminum acetate and then treating the coated fabric with steam. Explain, using equations, what occurs during this process. Why is the final product waterproof?

15.19   A solution contains both Sn^{2+} and Pb^{2+}. How may these ions be separated?

16

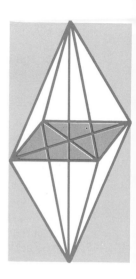

Complex
Compounds

The chemistry of complex compounds is the subject of much of the current research in inorganic chemistry. Innumerable practical applications have derived from these studies; advances have occurred in such fields as metallurgy, analytical chemistry, biochemistry, water softening, textile dyeing, ion exchange, electrochemistry, and bacteriology. In addition, the study of complex compounds has enlarged our understanding of chemical bonding, certain physical properties (such as spectral and magnetic properties), minerals (many minerals are complex compounds), and metabolic processes (both heme of blood and chlorophyll of plants are complex compounds).

16.1 Structure

A complex ion, or complex compound, consists of a central metal cation to which several anions and/or molecules (called **ligands**) are bonded. With few exceptions, free ligands have at least one electron pair that is not engaged in bonding.

$$:\ddot{\text{C}}\text{l:}^- \qquad :\text{C}:::\text{N}:^- \qquad \text{H}:\ddot{\text{O}}: \qquad \text{H}:\ddot{\text{N}}:\text{H}$$
$$\qquad\qquad\qquad\qquad\qquad\quad \text{H} \qquad\quad \text{H}$$

It is these electron pairs that may be considered to be donated to the electron-deficient metal ions in the formation of complexes, and ligands are substances capable of acting as Lewis bases. The bonding of complexes, however, shows a wide variation in character—from strongly covalent to predominantly ionic (Section 16.4).

The ligands are said to be coordinated around the central cation in a **first coordination sphere**; in the formulas of complex compounds (such as $K_3[Fe(CN)_6]$ and $[Cu(NH_3)_4]Cl_2$), the first coordination sphere is indicated by square brackets. The ligands are disposed about the central

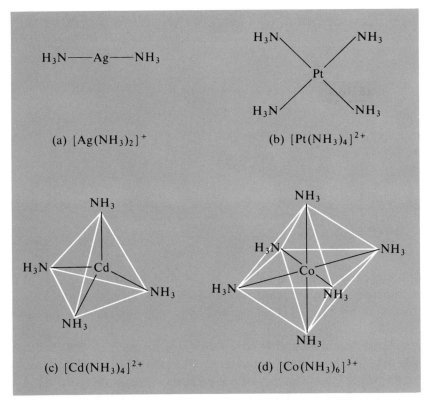

Figure 16.1 Common configurations of complex ions: (a) linear, (b) square planar, (c) tetrahedral, and (d) octahedral.

ion in a regular geometric manner (Figure 16.1), and the number of atoms *directly* bonded to the central metal ion, or the number of co-ordination positions, is called the **coordination number** of the central ion.

The charge of a complex is the sum of the charges of the constituent parts, and complexes may be cations, anions, or neutral molecules. Thus in each of the following complexes of platinum (IV): $[Pt(NH_3)_5Cl]^{3+}$, $[Pt(NH_3)_2Cl_4]^0$, and $[PtCl_6]^{2-}$, the platinum contributes $4+$, each chlorine contributes $1-$, and the coordinated ammonia molecules do not contribute to the charge of the whole.

An interesting series of platinum(IV) complexes appears in Table 16.1. The list is headed by the chloride of the $[Pt(NH_3)_6]^{4+}$ ion, and in each subsequent entry an ammonia molecule of the coordination sphere is replaced by a chloride ion. The coordinated ammonia molecules and chloride ions are tightly held and do not dissociate in water solution; however, those chloride ions of the compound that are not coordinated to the platinum are ionizable. Hence, aqueous solutions of the last three compounds of the table do not precipitate silver chloride upon the addi-tion of silver nitrate, whereas solutions of the first four precipitate AgCl

TABLE 16.1.
SOME PLATINUM(IV) COMPLEX COMPOUNDS.

	Molar Conductance 0.001N Solution, 25°C[a]	Number of Ions per Formula Unit	Number of Cl⁻ Ions per Formula Unit
$[Pt(NH_3)_6]Cl_4$	523	5	4
$[Pt(NH_3)_5Cl]Cl_3$	404	4	3
$[Pt(NH_3)_4Cl_2]Cl_2$	228	3	2
$[Pt(NH_3)_3Cl_3]Cl$	97	2	1
$[Pt(NH_3)_2Cl_4]$	0	0	0
$K[Pt(NH_3)Cl_5]$	108	2	0
$K_2[PtCl_6]$	256	3	0

[a] cm^2/ohm mole

in amounts proportional to 4/4, 3/4, 2/4, and 1/4, respectively, of their total chlorine content. In addition, in each case, the total number of ions per formula unit derived from conductance data agrees with the formula listed in the table.

In general, the most stable complexes are formed by metal ions that have a high positive charge and a small ionic radius. The transition elements and the metals immediately following (notably the III A and IV A metals) have a marked tendency to form complexes. Few complexes are known for the lanthanides and the I A and II A metals (with the exception of beryllium). The bonding of transition-metal complexes involves the d orbitals of the central metal atom.

Complexes are known containing metal ions with coordination numbers of from two to nine. However, the majority of complexes are two-, four-, and sixfold coordinate (Figure 10.1), and the coordination number six is by far the most common.

Six-coordinate complexes are octahedral. The regular octahedral arrangement of atoms is frequently represented

This is a convenient way to create a three-dimensional illusion in the depiction of this configuration. However, no difference between the bonds of the vertical axis and the other bonds should be inferred from this drawing; all of the bonds are equivalent. Tetragonal geometry is a distorted form of the octahedral in which the bond distances along one of the axes are longer or shorter than the remaining bonds.

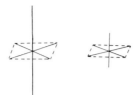

Four-coordinate complexes are known in tetrahedral and square-planar configurations. The square-planar configuration is the usual one for Pt^{II}, Pd^{II}, and Au^{III}, and is assumed by many complexes of Ni^{II} and Cu^{II}. Examples include $[Pt(NH_3)_4]^{2+}$, $[PdCl_4]^{2-}$, $[AuCl_4]^-$, $[Ni(CN)_4]^{2-}$, and $[Cu(NH_3)_4]^{2+}$. There is evidence that square complexes may be, in reality, tetragonal forms with two groups, along a vertical axis, located at greater distances from the central ion than the ligands of the plane. Thus $[Cu(NH_3)_4]^{2+}$, in water solution, may have two water molecules coordinated in the manner shown in Figure 16.2. Hence, square-planar and octahedral geometries may be considered to merge.

The tetrahedral configuration, for four-coordinate complexes, is encountered more frequently than the square-planar, and is particularly common for complexes of the nontransition elements. Certain complexes of Cu^I, Ag^I, Au^I, Be^{II}, Zn^{II}, Cd^{II}, Hg^{II}, Al^{III}, Ga^{III}, In^{III}, Fe^{III}, Co^{II}, and Ni^0 are of this type; examples include $[Cu(CN)_4]^{3-}$, $[BeF_4]^{2-}$, $[AlF_4]^-$, $[FeCl_4]^-$, $[Cd(CN)_4]^{2-}$, $[ZnCl_4]^{2-}$, and $[Ni(CO)_4]^0$. The oxyanions of certain transition metals (such as VO_4^{3-}, CrO_4^{2-}, FeO_4^{2-}, and MnO_4^-) are tetrahedral resembling the tetrahedral oxyanions of nonmetals (such as SiO_4^{4-}, PO_4^{3-}, AsO_4^{3-}, SO_4^{2-}, and ClO_4^-). Whereas a number of tetrahedral complexes of transition elements are known, the majority of complexes of these elements are octahedral.

Linear, two-coordinate, complexes are not as common as the other forms previously mentioned. However, well-characterized complexes

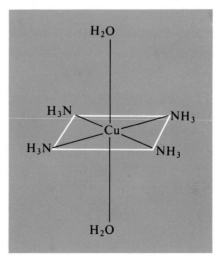

Figure 16.2 Configuration of $[Cu(NH_3)_4 \cdot (H_2O)_2]^{2+}$.

of this type are known for Cu^I, Ag^I, and Hg^{II}; examples are $[CuCl_2]^-$, $[Ag(NH_3)_2]^+$, $[Au(CN)_2]^-$, $[Hg(NH_3)_2]^{2+}$, and $[Hg(CN)_2]^0$.

In general, there is no one characteristic coordination number and geometry for each metal ion. Whereas all of the known complexes of Co^{III} are octahedral, most cations form more than one type of complex. Thus tetrahedral and octahedral complexes of Al^{III} are known; Cu^I forms linear and tetrahedral complexes; and square-planar, tetrahedral, and octahedral complexes of Ni^{II} exist.

Complexes of the transition elements are frequently highly colored. Examples of complexes that exhibit a wide range of colors are $[Co(NH_3)_6]^{3+}$ (yellow), $[Co(NH_3)_5(H_2O)]^{3+}$ (pink), $[Co(NH_3)_5Cl]^{2+}$ (violet), $[Co(H_2O)_6]^{3+}$ (purple), and $[Co(NH_3)_4Cl_2]^+$ (a violet form and a green form—see Section 16.3).

The ligands we have discussed thus far have been capable of forming only one bond with the central ion; they are referred to as **unidentate** (Latin, one toothed) ligands. Certain ligands are capable of occupying more than one coordination position of a metal ion. Ligands that coordinate through two bonds from different parts of the molecule or anion are called **bidentate**. Examples are

carbonate ion   oxalate ion   ethylenediamine

The carbonate and oxalate ions each coordinate through two oxygen atoms; the ethylenediamine molecule (abbreviated *en*) coordinates through both nitrogen atoms.

Bidentate ligands form rings with the central metal ions

and the resulting metal complexes are called **chelates** (Greek, claw). The formation of five- or six-membered rings is generally favored.

Multidentate ligands have been prepared that can coordinate at 2, 3, 4, 5, or 6 positions. In general, chelates are more stable than complexes containing only unidentate ligands. Thus the sexadentate complexing agent ethylenediaminetetraacetate ion (versene)

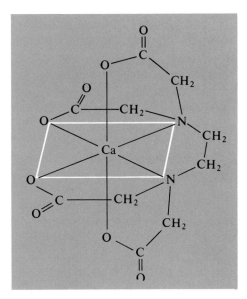

Figure 16.3   Ethylenediaminetetraacetate complex of Ca^{2+} ($[Ca(EDTA)]^{2-}$).

is capable of forming a very stable complex with the calcium ion—an ion with one of the least tendencies toward the formation of complexes (Figure 16.3).

Certain complexes (which are called **labile**) rapidly undergo reactions in which ligands are replaced; other complexes (**nonlabile**, or **inert, complexes**) do not undergo these substitution reactions or do so only slowly. The distinction applies to the rate of attainment of equilibrium and has no bearing on the position of equilibrium. With the exception of the complexes of Cr^{III} and Co^{III}, most of the octahedral complexes of the fourth period transition elements are very labile; exchange reactions come to equilibrium almost as fast as the reagents are mixed. The reason that the complexes of Co^{III} have been studied more than any other group of complexes is that these substances undergo ligand exchange reactions at a slower, more convenient, rate.

The inertness of a complex should not be confused with its thermodynamic stability. Although $[Co(NH_3)_6]^{3+}$ is stable in aqueous solution

$$[Co(NH_3)_6]^{3+} + 6H_2O \rightleftharpoons [Co(H_2O)_6]^{3+} + 6NH_3 \qquad K \cong 10^{-34}$$

the complex is unstable in aqueous acid

$$[Co(NH_3)_6]^{3+} + 6H_3O^+ \rightleftharpoons [Co(H_2O)_6]^{3+} + 6NH_4^+ \qquad K \cong 10^{22}$$

Nevertheless, the $[Co(NH_3)_6]^{3+}$ ion can exist in dilute acid for weeks; the latter reaction must have a high activation energy. Thus the complex is thermodynamically unstable and, at the same time, inhert.

Examples of the reverse situation are also known. The stable complex $[FeCl_6]^{3-}$ is very labile and undergoes rapid exchange with radioactive chloride in aqueous solution.

In many cases, complex formation results in the stabilization of metal ions toward oxidation or reduction. Electrode potentials for Zn^{2+} and some complexes of this ion are

$$2e^- + Zn^{2+}(aq) \rightleftharpoons Zn(s) \qquad\qquad E° = -0.763 \text{ v}$$
$$2e^- + [Zn(NH_3)_4]^{2+} \rightleftharpoons Zn(s) + 4NH_3 \qquad\qquad E° = -1.04 \text{ v}$$
$$2e^- + [Zn(CN)_4]^{2-} \rightleftharpoons Zn(s) + 4CN^- \qquad\qquad E° = -1.26 \text{ v}$$

The increasing stability toward reduction observed in this series parallels increasing stability of the complexes toward dissociation in aqueous solution. The instability constant of $[Zn(NH_3)_4]^{2+}$ is approximately 10^{-10} and that of the $[Zn(CN)_4]^{2-}$ ion is about 10^{-18}.

It is tempting to ascribe the lower electrode potentials of the complexes to the decreased concentrations of $Zn^{2+}(aq)$ in the solutions of these complexes, and such an interpretation is in agreement with the concentration effects predicted by the Nernst equation (Section 9.9). However, this explanation implies a mechanism for the reductions that has not been confirmed. The "free" zinc ion, $Zn^{2+}(aq)$, is in reality an aquo complex, and it is difficult to see why the reduction of every other complex of Zn^{2+} should be required to proceed through, and be dependent upon, the aquo complex. Mechanism studies of the oxidation-reduction reactions of complexes indicate that the actual situation is not this simple. There is, however, a relationship between the stability of a complex toward dissociation and its tendency to undergo oxidation or reduction.

In many instances, complex formation results in the stabilization of a metal in a rare, or otherwise unknown, oxidation state. A classic example is afforded by the complexes of Co^{III}. Simple compounds containing cobalt in an oxidation state of $3+$ are rare. The electrode potential

$$e^- + [Co(H_2O)_6]^{3+} \rightleftharpoons [Co(H_2O)_6]^{2+} \qquad E° = +1.81 \text{ v}$$

indicates that the hydrated Co^{3+} ion is a strong oxidizing agent, capable of oxidizing water to oxygen and hence incapable of prolonged existence in water.

In the presence of many complexing agents, such as NH_3, the $3+$ oxidation state of cobalt is much more stable toward reduction.

$$e^- + [Co(NH_3)_6]^{3+} \rightleftharpoons [Co(NH_3)_6]^{2+} \qquad E° = +0.11 \text{ v}$$

The $[Co(NH_3)_6]^{3+}$ ion can exist in aqueous solution. It does not oxidize water to oxygen, and in fact, the reverse reaction—the oxidation of Co^{II} complexes by a stream of air—is used to prepare Co^{III} complexes. The ammonia complex of Co^{III}, with an instability constant of about 10^{-34}, is much more stable toward dissociation than the ammonia complex of Co^{II}, which has an instability constant of approximately 10^{-5}.

The electrode potentials for copper and its ions may be diagrammed

$$Cu^{2+} \xrightarrow{\;E^\circ\; =\; 0.153\; v\;} Cu^+ \xrightarrow{\;E^\circ\; =\; 0.521\; v\;} Cu$$

from which we can see that the Cu^+ ion is unstable in water solution and disproportionates (Section 9.11).

$$2Cu^+(aq) \rightleftharpoons Cu^{2+}(aq) + Cu(s) \qquad E^\circ = 0.368\; v$$

The equilibrium constant for this disproportionation may be derived from the cell potential.

$$K = \frac{[Cu^{2+}]}{[Cu^+]^2} \cong 10^6$$

With certain complexing agents, the stability of the 1+ state is enhanced more than that of the 2+ state. For example, with ammonia $K \cong 10^{-2}$, and the $[Cu(NH_3)_2]^+$ ion is stable toward disproportionation. Other complexing agents, such as ethylenediamine, have a greater affinity for Cu^{II} than Cu^{I}. For ethylenediamine, $K \cong 10^5$, and an ethylenediamine complex of Cu^{I} does not exist in water solution.

A similar situation is observed for the ions of gold; Au^+ is theoretically unstable toward disproportionation into Au^{3+} and Au metal. In addition, this case is complicated by the fact that both ions are strong oxidizing agents and are capable of oxidizing water. However, stable complexes of both Au^{I} and Au^{III} are known.

The stability of complex ions toward dissociation in aqueous solution is discussed in Section 14.12.

16.2 Nomenclature

Since there are thousands of complexes known and the number is constantly expanding, a system of nomenclature has been adopted for these compounds. The following paragraphs summarize the important rules of the I.U.P.A.C. system; they are adequate for naming the simple, and frequently encountered, complexes.

1. If the complex compound is a salt, the cation is named first whether or not it is the complex ion.

2. The constituents of the complex are named in the following order: anions, neutral molecules, central metal ion.

3. Anionic ligands are given -o endings; examples are: OH^-, hydroxo; S^{2-}, thio; Cl^-, chloro; F^-, fluoro; CO_3^{2-}, carbonato; CN^-, cyano; CNO^-, cyanato; $C_2O_4^{2-}$, oxalato; NO_3^-, nitrato; NO_2^-, nitro; SO_4^{2-}, sulfato; and $S_2O_3^{2-}$, thiosulfato.

4. The names of neutral ligands are not changed. Exceptions to this rule are: H_2O, aquo; NH_3, ammine; CO, carbonyl; and NO, nitrosyl.

-5. The number of ligands of a particular type is indicated by a prefix: di-, tri-, tetra-, penta-, and hexa- (for two to six). For complicated ligands (such as ethylenediamine), the prefixes bis-, tris-, and tetrakis- (two to four) are employed.

6. The oxidation number of the central ion is indicated by a Roman numeral, set off by parentheses, and placed after the name of the complex.

7. If the complex is an anion, the ending -ate is employed. If the complex is a cation or a neutral molecule, the name is not changed. Examples follow:

$[Ag(NH_3)_2]Cl$	Diamminesilver(I) chloride
$[Co(NH_3)_3Cl_3]$	Trichlorotriamminecobalt(III)
$K_4[Fe(CN)_6]$	Potassium hexacyanoferrate(II)
$[Ni(CO)_4]$	Tetracarbonylnickel(0)
$[Cu(en)_2]SO_4$	Bis(ethylenediamine)copper(II)sulfate
$[Pt(NH_3)_4][PtCl_6]$	Tetraammineplatinum(II) hexachloroplati-nate(IV)
$[Co(NH_3)_4(H_2O)Cl]Cl_2$	Chloroaquotetraamminecobalt(III) chloride

Common names are frequently employed where they are clearly more convenient than the systematic name (e.g., ferrocyanide rather than hexacyanoferrate(II) for $[Fe(CN)_6]^{4-}$) or where the structure of the complex is not certain (e.g., the aluminate ion).

16.3 Isomerism

Two compounds with the same molecular formula but different arrangements of atoms are called **isomers;** such compounds, of course, differ in their chemical and physical properties. **Structural isomerism** is displayed by compounds that have different ligands within their coordination spheres; several types of structural isomers may be identified.

The following pair of compounds of Co^{III} serve as an example of **ionization isomers.**

(a) $[Co(NH_3)_5(SO_4)]Br_2$ (b) $[Co(NH_3)_5Br]SO_4$
(red)   (violet)

Conductance data show that both compounds dissociate into two ions in aqueous solution. In the first compound, the SO_4^{2-} ion is a part of the coordination sphere, and the Br^- ion is ionizable. Hence, an aqueous solution of compound (a) gives an immediate precipitate of AgBr upon the addition of $AgNO_3$, but since the SO_4^{2-} ion is not free, no precipitate forms upon the addition of $BaCl_2$. For compound (b), the reverse is true. An aqueous solution of this compound gives a precipitate of

$BaSO_4$ but not $AgBr$ since the SO_4^{2-} is ionizable and the Br^- is co-ordinated. Note that SO_4^{2-} functions as a unidentate ligand and that the charge on the complex ion of compound (a) is $1-$ and of compound (b) is $2-$.

There are numerous additional examples of ionization isomers; for example,

$$[Pt(NH_3)_4Cl_2]Br_2 \qquad [Pt(NH_3)_4Br_2]Cl_2$$

Hydrate isomerism is analogous to ionization isomerism and is probably best illustrated by the following series of compounds of formula $CrCl_3 \cdot 6H_2O$.

(a) $[Cr(H_2O)_6]Cl_3$
  (violet)

(b) $[Cr(H_2O)_5Cl]Cl_2 \cdot H_2O$
  (green)

(c) $[Cr(H_2O)_4Cl_2]Cl \cdot 2H_2O$
  (green)

In a mole of each of these compounds there are 6 moles of water. However, in compound (a) six water molecules are coordinated; in compound (b), five; and in compound (c), four. The uncoordinated water, which probably occurs in the crystals as lattice water, is readily lost when compounds (b) and (c) are exposed to desiccants; however, the coordinated water is not so easily removed. Further evidence for the structures of the compounds is afforded by conductance data (the compounds are composed of four, three, and two ions, respectively) and the quantity of $AgCl$ precipitated (the compounds have three, two, and one ionizable chloride ions, respectively).

Another example of hydrate isomerism is given by the following pair of compounds.

$$[Co(NH_3)_4(H_2O)Cl]Cl_2 \qquad [Co(NH_3)_4Cl_2]Cl \cdot H_2O$$

Coordination isomers are compounds that have at least two centers of coordination and which may be considered to have been formed through the exchange of ligands between these coordination centers. In simple examples, involving only two complex ions per compound, the coordinated metal ions may be the same

$$[Cr(NH_3)_6][Cr(SCN)_6] \qquad [Cr(NH_3)_4(SCN)_2][Cr(NH_3)_2(SCN)_4]$$

or different

$$[Cu(NH_3)_4][PtCl_4] \qquad [Pt(NH_3)_4][CuCl_4]$$

and the oxidation state of the metals may vary

$$[Pt(NH_3)_4][PtCl_6] \qquad\qquad [Pt(NH_3)_4Cl_2][PtCl_4]$$

tetraammineplatinum(II)   dichlorotetraammineplatinum(IV)
hexachloroplatinate(IV)   tetrachloroplatinate(II)

Linkage isomerism is a rare, but interesting type; it arises when ligands are capable of coordinating in two ways. For example, the nitrite ion, NO_2^-, can coordinate through an oxygen atom (—ONO, nitrito compounds) or through the nitrogen atom (—NO_2, nitro compounds).

$$[Co(NH_3)_5(NO_2)]Cl_2 \qquad [Co(NH_3)_5(ONO)]Cl_2$$

(yellow)   (red)
nitropentaamminecobalt(III)   nitritopentaamminecobalt(III)
chloride   chloride

Theoretically, many ligands might be capable of forming linkage isomers: CN^- might coordinate either through the C atom or the N atom; SCN^-, through N or S; CO, through C or O. However, few authentic cases of linkage isomerism are known.

Stereoisomerism is a second general classification of isomers. Compounds are stereoisomers when they both contain the same ligands in their coordination spheres but differ in the way that these ligands are arranged in space. One type of stereoisomerism is **geometric, or cis-trans, isomerism.**

An example of geometric isomerism is afforded by the *cis* and *trans* isomers of the square planar dichlorodiammineplatinum(II); see Figure 16.4. In the *cis* isomer, the chlorine atoms are situated on adjacent corners of the square (along an edge), whereas in the *trans* isomer, they occupy opposite corners (along the diagonal).

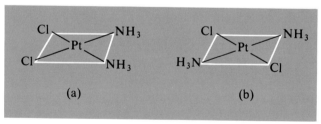

(a)   (b)

Figure 16.4   *(a) Cis and (b) trans isomers of dichlorodiammine-platinum(II).*

Since all the ligands of a tetrahedral complex have the same relationship to one another, *cis-trans* isomerism does not exist for this geometry. Many geometric isomers are known for octahedral complexes, however. There are two isomers of the dichlorotetraamminecobalt(III) ion: a violet *cis* form and a green *trans* form (Figure 16.5).

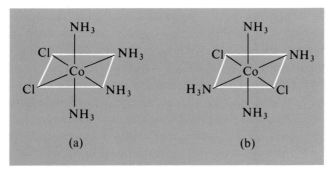

Figure 16.5 (a) Cis and (b) trans isomers of the dichlorotetraam-minecobalt(III) ion.

A second type of stereoisomerism is **optical isomerism.** A molecule, or ion, that possesses no element of symmetry is spoken of as asymmetric; it can exist in two forms that are not superimposable and that bear the same relationship that a right hand (or glove) bears to a left hand (or glove). That the hands, or gloves, are not superimposable is readily demonstrated by attempting to put a left-handed glove on a right hand. Such forms are called **enantiomorphs** (Greek, opposite forms) or **mirror images** (since the one may be considered to be a mirror reflection of the other).

Enantiomorphs have identical physical properties except for their effects on plane-polarized light. Light that has been passed through a polarizer consists of waves that vibrate in a single plane. One enantiomorph (the **dextro** form), pure or in solution, will rotate the plane of the plane-polarized light to the right; the other (the **levo** form) will rotate the plane an equal extent to the left.

It is for this reason that enantiomorphs are called optical isomers or **optical antipodes.** An equimolar mixture of enantiomorphs, called a **racemic modification,** has no effect on plane-polarized light since it contains an equal number of *dextro*rotatory and *levo*rotatory forms.

The tris(ethylenediamine)cobalt(III) ion exists in enantiomorphic forms. Examination of the diagrams of Figure 16.6 confirms that the

Figure 16.6 Dextro and levo forms of the tris(ethylenediamine)cobalt(III) ion.

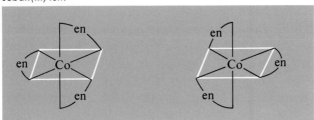

enantiomorphs are not superimposable and that the ions are asymmetric. Note that bidentate chelating agents can span only *cis* positions.

Both types of stereoisomerism—geometric and optical—are illustrated by the isomers of the dichlorobis(ethylenediamine)cobalt(III) ion (Figure 16.7). The *trans* configuration of this ion is optically inactive; the ion is symmetric, and a mirror image would be identical to the original. The *cis* arrangement, however, is asymmetric and exists in *dextro* and *levo* forms. The *trans* modification is said to be a *diastereoisomer* of either the *dextro* or *levo cis* modification.

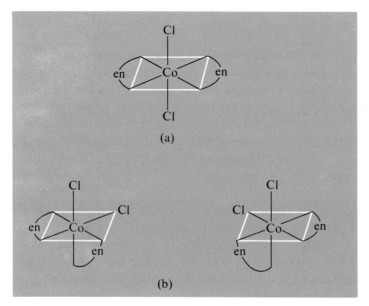

Figure 16.7   Isomers of the dichlorobis(ethylenediamine)cobalt(III) ion. (a) trans isomer, (b) optical isomers of the cis form.

Optical isomerism is especially important in organic chemistry (Chapter 17).

16.4   The Bonding in Complexes

There are several approaches to the theoretical treatment of the bonding in complexes. The **valence bond theory** describes the bonding in terms of hybridized orbitals of the central metal ion. The metal ion is assumed to have a number of unoccupied orbitals available for complex formation equal to its coordination number. Each ligand donates a pair of electrons toward the formation of a coordinate covalent bond, and a bond arises from the overlap of a vacant metal orbital and a filled orbital of a ligand. The bonds usually have an appreciable degree of polarity.

A strong bond results from the maximum overlap of the constituent orbitals. The atomic orbitals of the metal ion are hybridized to form a set of equivalent orbitals that have directional characteristics typical of the complex formed (Section 3.12). The types of hybridization commonly encountered are

sp linear
sp^3 tetrahedral
dsp^2 square planar
d^2sp^3 octahedral

In the formation of coordination compounds of the transition elements, d orbitals of the metal are generally involved. As we shall see, many of the properties of this large and important group of complexes depend upon the electrons in those d orbitals that are not employed in bonding. The conventional boundary surfaces of the d orbitals are illustrated in Figure 16.8; those of the s and p orbitals are shown in Figure 2.13. The d_{xy}, d_{xz}, and d_{yz} orbitals lie in the xy, xz, and yz planes,

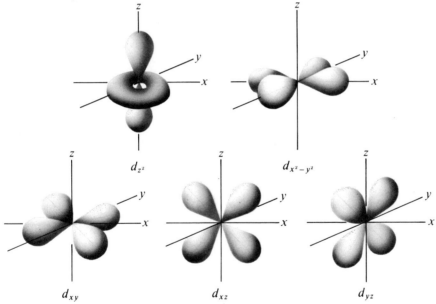

Figure 16.8   Conventional boundary surfaces of the d orbitals.

respectively with their lobes between the axes. The $d_{x^2-y^2}$ orbital is similar to the d_{xy} except that it is rotated so that its lobes are directed along the x and y axes. The d_{z^2} orbital is symmetrical about the z axis.

Figure 16.9 shows the arrangements of the ligands of octahedral and square planar complexes in relation to sets of Cartesian coordinates. For octahedral coordination, d_{z^2} and $d_{x^2-y^2}$ orbitals, as well as p_x,

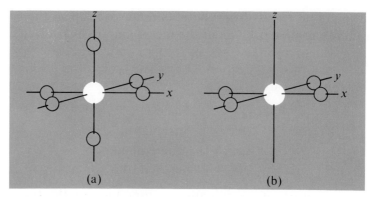

Figure 16.9   Arrangement of ligands of (a) octahedral and (b) square planar complexes in relation to sets of Cartesian coordinates.

p_y, and p_z orbitals, are directed toward ligands; it is these orbitals that are combined with an s orbital into a d^2sp^3 set. Square planar (dsp^2) hybridization utilizes the $d_{x^2-y^2}$, p_x, p_y, and s orbitals.

The valence bond diagrams of some simple complexes together with the electronic configurations of the central metal ions are shown in Figure 16.10. Hund's rule applies to the electrons occupying the non-

Figure 16.10   Valence bond diagrams for some simple complexes.

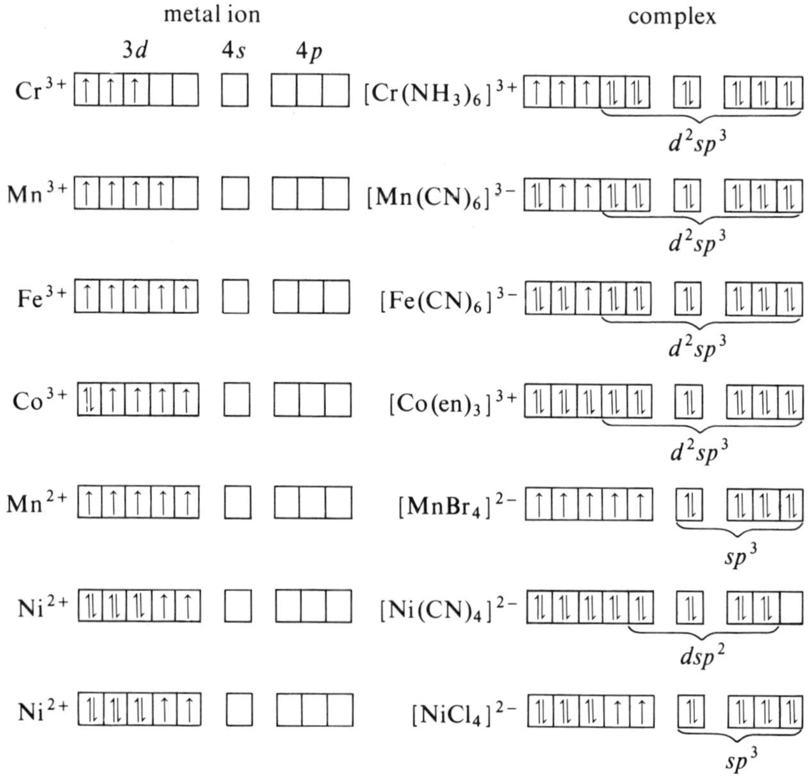

bonding d orbitals, and accordingly, some of these electrons are unpaired. In each of the complexes shown, the number of unpaired electrons determined by magnetic susceptibility measurement agrees with
the structure diagrammed. Thus $[Co(en)_3]^{3+}$ and $[Ni(CN)_4]^{2-}$ are diamagnetic, and the others are paramagnetic. In addition, the experimentally determined geometry of each complex agrees with that predicted on the basis of the type of hybridization displayed.

There are some defects in this attractively simple picture. From the
diagrams of Figure 16.10, one might suppose that all of the octahedral
complexes of Fe^{III} would have one unpaired electron (as in $[Fe(CN)_6]^{3-}$)
and that all of the octahedral complexes of Co^{III} would be diamagnetic
(like $[Co(en)_3]^{3+}$). This is not the case. The magnetic moments of
$[FeF_6]^{3-}$ and $[CoF_6]^{3-}$ indicate the existence of five and four unpaired
electrons, respectively, in these complexes; these are the same numbers
of unpaired electrons as are found in the free Fe^{3+} and Co^{3+} ions. At one
time, the bonding in this type of complex was thought to be ionic with
the d orbitals of the central ion undisturbed by complex formation.
According to a later explanation, the $4d$, rather than the $3d$, orbitals are
assumed to be used for the octahedral hybridization. Hence, **inner**
(d^2sp^3) and **outer** (sp^3d^2) **complexes** are postulated (Figure 16.11).
Since it is impossible to clear two inner d orbitals of the Ni^{2+} ion for
inner d^2sp^3 hybridization, all octahedral Ni^{II} complexes must be assumed to be of the outer type.

A further complication arises in the case of $[Co(NO_2)_6]^{4-}$—an octahedral complex with one unpaired electron. In order to fit this complex
into the d^2sp^3 category, it is necessary to postulate the promotion of an
electron into the $4d$ sublevel.

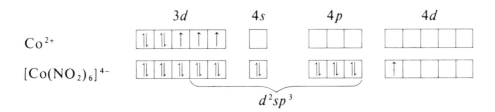

It is also necessary to assume such an unlikely promotion for all of the
square complexes of Cu^{II}.

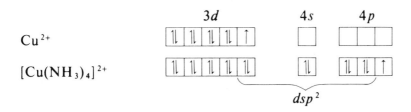

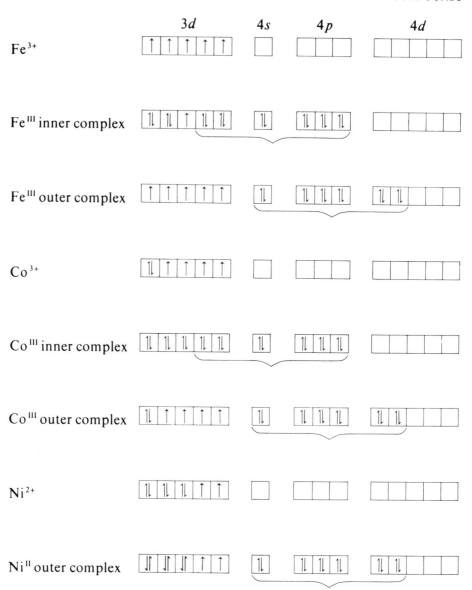

Figure 16.11   Inner and outer complexes of Fe^{III}, Co^{III}, and Ni^{II}.

The fundamental defect of the valence bond theory is that it fails to take into account the existence of antibonding molecular orbitals which are produced, along with bonding molecular orbitals, by the overlap of atomic orbitals. Many of the experimental observations that are difficult to explain on the basis of the valence bond approach are readily understood in terms of electrons occupying antibonding orbitals.

The **crystal field theory** and its more acceptable outgrowth, the **ligand field theory,** center on the d orbitals of the metal ion. In a free transition-metal ion, all five of the d orbitals have equal energies, or are **degenerate.** All of the d orbitals are not equivalent, however, when the metal ion engages in complex formation; the degeneracy is split.

Consider the relation of the d orbitals (Figure 16.8) to the ligands of an octahedral complex (Figure 16.9). The d_{z^2} and $d_{x^2-y^2}$ orbitals have lobes that point toward ligands, whereas the lobes of the d_{xy}, d_{xz}, and d_{yz} orbitals lie between ligands. Thus in the complex, two sets of d orbitals exist; the d_{xy}, d_{xz}, and d_{yz} orbitals (or t_{2g} orbitals) are equivalent to each other, and the d_{z^2} and $d_{x^2-y^2}$ orbitals (or e_g orbitals) are equivalent to each other and different from the first three. The symbols t_{2g} and e_g are applied to threefold degenerate and twofold degenerate sets of orbitals, respectively.

It is not immediately obvious that the d_{z^2} orbital is perfectly equivalent to the $d_{x^2-y^2}$ orbital. The d_{z^2} orbital may be regarded as a combination, in equal parts, of two hypothetical orbitals, $d_{z^2-y^2}$ and $d_{z^2-x^2}$, which have shapes exactly like that of the $d_{x^2-y^2}$ orbital (see Figure 16.12). Since the number of d orbitals is limited to five, the $d_{z^2-y^2}$ and $d_{z^2-x^2}$ orbitals have no independent existence.

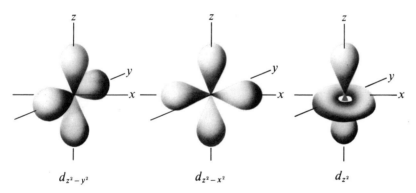

$$d_{z^2-y^2} \qquad\qquad d_{z^2-x^2} \qquad\qquad d_{z^2}$$

Figure 16.12 Diagrams showing that the d_{z^2} orbital may be considered to be a combination of $d_{z^2-y^2}$ and $d_{z^2-x^2}$ orbitals.

In a square planar complex (Figure 16.9), the d orbitals exhibit four different relationships: the lobes of the $d_{x^2-y^2}$ orbital point toward ligands; the lobes of the d_{xy} orbital lie between ligands but are coplanar with them; the lobes of the d_{z^2} orbital point out of the plane of the complex but the belt around the center lies in the plane; lastly, all of the lobes of the d_{yz} and d_{xz} orbitals, which are degenerate, point out of the plane of the complex.

The order of splitting of the d orbitals in a tetrahedral complex may be derived from an examination of Figure 16.13, which shows the relation of tetrahedrally arranged ligands to a system of Cartesian coordinates and a hypothetical cube. The lobes of the d_{xy}, d_{xz}, and d_{yz} orbitals

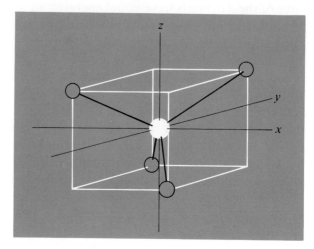

Figure 16.13   The relation of tetrahedrally arranged ligands to a set of Cartesian coordinates.

point toward cube edges, and the lobes of the d_{z^2} and $d_{x^2-y^2}$ orbitals point toward the centers of cube faces. Therefore a threefold degenerate set, t_{2g}, and a twofold degenerate set, e_g, exist.

The splitting of the d orbital energies by ligand fields of octahedral, tetrahedral, and square planar geometries are summarized in Figure 16.14. The crystal field theory and the ligand field theory differ in their interpretations of the origin of these splittings. In the crystal field treatment, it is assumed, for purposes of analysis, that the origin may be

Figure 16.14   The splitting of d-orbital energies by ligand fields of three different geometries.

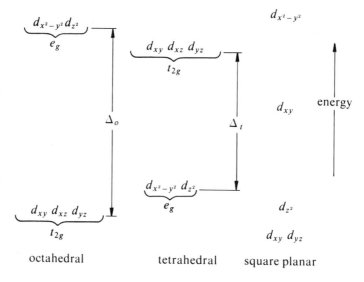

regarded as purely electrostatic. In this view, a field surrounding the positively charged central metal ion is produced by the negative ends of dipolar molecules or by anions which function as ligands.

In the central metal ion, an electron in a d orbital that has lobes directed toward ligands has a higher energy (owing to electrostatic repulsion) than an electron in an orbital with lobes that point between ligands. In octahedral complexes, the orbitals of the e_g group, therefore, have higher energies than those of the t_{2g} group, whereas in tetrahedral complexes, this order is reversed (Figure 16.14). The difference between the energies of the e_g and t_{2g} orbitals in an octahedral complex is called Δ_0, and the difference in tetrahedral complexes is labeled Δ_t.

The crystal field theory fails to take into account the mixing of metal and ligand orbitals and the covalent character of the bonding in complexes, and hence it is ultimately unsatisfactory. The ligand field theory offers a more realistic explanation which derives from molecular orbital theory.

In an octahedral complex, the $3d_{z^2}$ and $3d_{x^2-y^2}$ orbitals along with the $4s$ and three $4p$ orbitals are assumed to overlap the six ligand σ orbitals with the attendant formation of six bonding molecular orbitals and six antibonding molecular orbitals (Section 3.14).. The d_{xy}, d_{xz}, and d_{yz} orbitals (the t_{2g} set), which do not overlap the σ orbitals of the ligands, are essentially nonbonding. (The t_{2g} set can be used in π bonding, however.)

A bonding molecular orbital concentrates electron density between the atoms and is of relatively low energy in comparison to an antibonding molecular orbital which has a low electron density between the atoms and acts as a disruptive force. A molecular orbital energy level diagram for an octahedral complex with no π bonding is given in Figure 16.15.

Whenever two atomic orbitals of different energies combine, the character of the resulting bonding molecular orbital is predominantly that of the atomic orbital of lower energy, and the antibonding molecular orbital has mainly the character of the higher energy atomic orbital. In an octahedral complex, the bonding orbitals have predominantly the character of ligand orbitals. The antibonding orbitals resemble metal orbitals more than ligand orbitals and the t_{2g} set, which are nonbonding, may be considered as purely metal orbitals.

In an octahedral complex, the six electron pairs from the ligands completely occupy the bonding molecular orbitals. The d electrons of the central metal ion are accommodated in the t_{2g} nonbonding orbitals and the $(e_g)_a$ antibonding orbitals; the difference between the energies of these sets is Δ_0. The four remaining antibonding orbitals are never occupied in the ground states of any known complex.

Hence, the conclusion reached by this treatment is much the same as

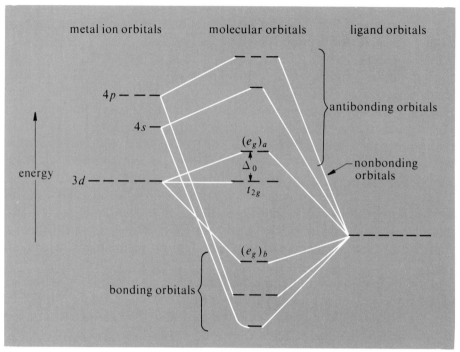

Figure 16.15 *Diagram indicating the formation of molecular orbitals for an octahedral complex with no π bonding.*

that postulated by the crystal field theory: in an octahedral complex, the degeneracy of the metal d orbitals may be considered to be split into a threefold degenerate set, t_{2g}, and a higher energy, metal-like, twofold degenerate set which may be labeled $(e_g)_a$ or simply e_g.

The molecular orbital treatment may be applied to tetrahedral and square planar complexes, but the applications are much more complicated. The conclusions reached are in essential agreement with the splittings diagrammed in Figure 16.14.

For the octahedral complexes of a given metal ion, the magnitude of Δ_o is different for each set of ligands, and the electronic configurations of many complexes depend upon the size of Δ_o.

For complexes of transition-element ions with one, two, or three d electrons (which are referred to as d^1, d^2, or d^3 ions), the orbital occupancy is certain and is independent of the magnitude of Δ_o. The electrons enter the lower energy t_{2g} orbitals singly with their spins parallel. For d^4, d^5, d^6, and d^7 ions, a choice of two configurations is possible (see Figure 16.16).

In the case of an octahedral complex of a d^4 ion, the fourth electron can singly occupy a higher energy e_g orbital, or it can enter a t_{2g} orbital, thus pairing with an electron already present. The former configuration

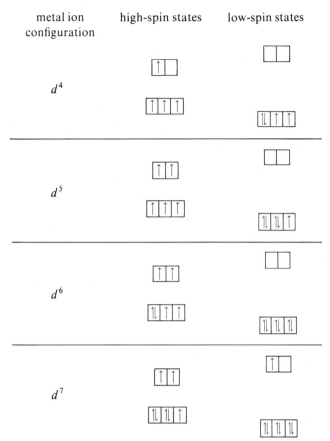

Figure 16.16 *Arrangements of electrons in high-spin and low-spin octahedral complexes of d^4, d^5, d^6, and d^7 ions.*

has four unpaired electrons and is called the **high-spin state**; the latter configuration, with two unpaired electrons, is called the **low-spin state**. Which configuration is assumed depends upon which is energetically more favorable.

If Δ_o is small, the electron may be promoted to the e_g level where it occupies an orbital singly. However, if Δ_o is large, the electron may be forced to pair with an electron in a t_{2g} orbital even though this pairing occurs against interelectronic repulsion and requires the expenditure of a pairing energy, P. Thus the high spin configuration results when

$$\Delta_o < P$$

and the low spin configuration is assumed when

$$\Delta_o > P$$

The value of P depends upon the metal ion; Δ_o is different for each complex.

This conclusion is also valid for complexes of d^5, d^6, and d^7 ions. For a complex of a d^8 ion, there is only one possible configuration: six electrons paired in the t_{2g} orbitals and two unpaired electrons in the e_g orbitals. Likewise, complexes of d^9 and d^{10} ions exist in only one configuration.

The complexes that were fitted into the valence bond scheme only with difficulty are readily classified by the ligand field theory. Hence, the inner complex $[Fe(CN)_6]^{3-}$ with one unpaired electron is in reality a low spin state of this d^5 ion, and the outer complex $[FeF_6]^{3-}$ with five unpaired electrons has the high spin configuration of a d^5 ion. The octahedral complexes of Ni^{II}, all of which must be assumed to be of the outer valence-bond type, have the only configuration possible for a complex of a d^8 ion: six electrons in the t_{2g} orbitals and two unpaired electrons in the e_g orbitals. The complex $[Co(NO_2)_6]^{4-}$, for which it was necessary to postulate the promotion of an electron to a $4d$ atomic orbital in the valence bond treatment, is a low spin d^7 complex according to the ligand field theory.

Values of Δ_o can be obtained from studies of the absorption spectra of complexes. In the complex $[Ti(H_2O)_6]^{3+}$, there is only one electron to be accommodated in either the t_{2g} or e_g orbitals. In the ground state, this electron occupies a t_{2g} orbital. However, excitation of the electron to an e_g orbital is possible when the energy required for this transition, Δ_o, is supplied, and the absorption of light by the complex can bring about such excitations. The wavelength of light absorbed most strongly by the $[Ti(H_2O)_6]^{3+}$ ion is approximately 4900 Å, which corresponds to a Δ_o of about 58 kcal/mole. The single absorption band of this complex spreads out over a considerable portion of the visible spectrum; however, most of the red and violet light is not absorbed, and this causes the red-violet color of the complex.

The interpretation of the absorption spectra of complexes with more than one d electron is considerably more complicated since more than two arrangements of d electrons are possible. In general, for a given metal ion, the replacement of one set of ligands by another causes a change in the energy difference between the t_{2g} and e_g orbitals, Δ_o, which gives rise to different light-absorption properties. Hence, in many instances, a striking color change is observed when the ligands of a complex are replaced by other ligands.

Ligands may be arranged in a **spectrochemical series** according to the magnitude of Δ_o they bring about. From the experimental study of the spectra of many complexes, it has been found that the order is the same for the complexes of all of the transition elements in their common oxidation states with only occasional inversions of order between ligands that stand near to one another on the list. The order of some common ligands is

$$I^- < Br^- < Cl^- < F^- < OH^- < C_2O_4^{2-} < H_2O < NH_3 < en < NO_2^- < CN^-$$

The values of Δ_o induced by the halide ions are generally low, and complexes of these ligands usually have high-spin configurations. The cyanide ion, which stands at the opposite end of the series from the halide ions, induces the largest d-orbital splittings of any ligand listed; cyano complexes generally have low-spin configurations.

A given ligand, however, does not always produce complexes of the same spin type. Thus the hexaammine complex of Fe^{2+} has a high-spin configuration, whereas the hexaammine complex of Co^{3+} (which is iso-electronic with Fe^{2+}) has a low-spin configuration.

For each metal ion, there is a point in the series that corresponds to the change from ligands that produce high-spin complexes to ligands that form low-spin complexes. For example, Co^{II} forms high-spin complexes with NH_3 and ethylenediamine, but the NO_2^- and CN^- complexes of Co^{II} have low-spin configurations. The actual position in the series where this change from high- to low-spin complex formation occurs depends upon the electron-pairing energy, P, for the metal ion as well as the values of Δ_o for the complexes under consideration.

SOME SUGGESTED READINGS

Ballhausen, C. J., *Introduction to Ligand Field Theory*, New York, McGraw-Hill, 1962.

Basolo, F., and Johnson, R. C., *Coordination Chemistry*, New York, Benjamin, 1964 (paper).

Day, M. C., and Selbin, J., *Theoretical Inorganic Chemistry*, New York, Reinhold, 1962.

Dunn, T. M. McClure, D. S., and Pearson, R. G., *Some Aspects of Crystal Field Theory*, New York, Harper, 1965 (paper).

Dwyer, F. P., and Mellor, D. P., *Chelating Agents and Metal Chelates*, New York, Academic, 1964.

Figgis, B. N., *Introduction to Ligand Fields*, New York, Wiley, 1966.

Jones, M., *Elementary Coordination Chemistry*, Englewood Cliffs, N. J., Prentice-Hall, 1964.

Kauffman, G. B., *Alfred Werner, Founder of Coordination Chemistry*, New York, Springer, 1966.

Klixbull-Jorgensen, C., *Inorganic Complexes,* New York, Academic, 1964.

Martin, D. F., and Martin, B. B., *Coordination Compounds*, New York, McGraw-Hill, 1964.

Murmann, R. K., *Inorganic Complex Compounds*, New York, Reinhold, 1964 (paper).

Orgel, L., *An Introduction to Transition-Metal Chemistry. Ligand Field Theory*, New York, Wiley, 1960.

Sanderson, R. T., *Inorganic Chemistry*, New York, Reinhold, 1967.

PROBLEMS

16.1 Name the following compounds:

(a) $K_2[PtCl_6]$ (e) $[Pt(NH_3)_2Cl_2]$

(b) $[Cr(H_2O)_5Cl]SO_4$ (f) $[Cr(NH_3)_6][Co(C_2O_4)_3]$

(c) $[Co(NH_3)_2(en)_2]Cl_3$ (g) $[Co(NH_3)_4SO_4]NO_3$

(d) $Na[Au(CN)_2]$

16.2 Write formulas for each of the following: (a) sodium hexacyanoferrate (III), (b) potassium tetracyanonickelate(0), (c) hexaamminecobalt(III) hexanitrocobaltate(II), (d) sulfatotetraammineplatinum(IV) hydroxide, (e) chlorothiocyanatobis (ethylenediamine) cobalt(III) nitrite.

16.3 Write a formula for an example of each of the following: (a) an ionization isomer of $[Co(NH_3)_4Cl_2]NO_2$, (b) a coordination isomer of $[Co(NH_3)_6][Cr(CN)_6]$, (c) a hydrate isomer of $[Co(NH_3)_4(H_2O)Cl]Cl_2$, (d) a linkage isomer of $[Co(en)_2(NO_2)_2]Cl$.

16.4 There is only one compound with the formula $Ce[Fe(CN)_6]$. Is this compound cerium(IV) hexacyanoferrate(II) or cerium(III) hexacyanoferrate(III)? What is the reason for your choice?

16.5 Diagram the structures of all of the possible stereoisomers of each of the following. Classify the structures as geometric or optical isomers. (a) $[Cr(H_2O)_4(SCN)_2]^+$, (b) $[Cr(NH_3)_3Cl_3]$, (c) $[Pt(NH_3)(py)ClBr]$ (py is pyridene, C_5H_5N, a unidentate ligand, and. the complex is square planar), (d) $[Co(en)_2(H_2O)OH]^{2+}$, (e) $[Co(NH_3)_4(C_2O_4)]^+$.

16.6 The complex $[Ni(CN)_4]^{2-}$ is square planar, and the complex $[NiCl_4]^{2-}$ is tetrahedral. Draw valence bond diagrams for these complexes and predict the number of unpaired electrons in each.

16.7 How does the valence bond theory explain the fact that all octahedral complexes of Ni^{2+} have two unpaired electrons? Contrast this with the ligand field theory explanation. Use diagrams.

16.8 Draw valence bond diagrams for the following, each of which is diamagnetic. What geometric configuration does each have? (a) $AgCl_2^-$, (b) $ZnCl_4^{2-}$, (c) $PdCl_4^{2-}$, (d) $RhCl_6^{3-}$.

16.9 Draw d-orbital splitting diagrams for the high- and low-spin octahedral complexes of Fe^{3+}. How many unpaired electrons are there in each?

16.10 For Fe^{2+} the electron pairing energy, P, is about 50 kcal/mole. Approximate values of Δ_o for the complexes $[Fe(NH_3)_6]^{2+}$ and $[Fe(CN)_6]^{4-}$ are 35 kcal/mole and 94 kcal/mole, respectively. (a) Do these complexes have high- or low-spin configurations? (b) Draw a d-orbital splitting diagram for each.

16.11 Draw d-orbital splitting diagrams for $[Co(NH_3)_6]^{2+}$ and $[Co(NH_3)_6]^{3+}$; the Δ_o values for these two complex ions are approximately 29 kcal/mole and 66 kcal/mole, respectively. The pairing energy of Co^{2+} is about 64 kcal/mole, and that of Co^{3+} is about 50 kcal/mole.

16.12 How can dipole moment measurement distinguish between geometric isomers of a square planar complex that is a neutral molecule?

16.13 How many unpaired electrons are present in octahedral complexes of Zn^{2+}, Ni^{2+}, Ni^{3+}, Mn^{2+}, Mn^{3+}, V^{2+}, V^{3+}, and V^{4+} with (a) ligands that induce a large Δ_o, and (b) ligands that induce a small Δ_o?

16.14 Identify all of the possible isomers (stereoisomers as well as coordination isomers) of the compound $[Pt(NH_3)_4][PtCl_6]$.

16.15 The $[Ti(H_2O)_6]^{3+}$ complex is red-violet. What change in color would be expected if the ligands of this complex were replaced by ligands that induce a larger Δ_o? Note that the color of the complex corresponds to light transmitted, not absorbed.

17

Organic
Chemistry

The name organic chemistry derives from the early concept that substances of plant or animal origin (organic substances) were different from those of mineral origin (inorganic substances). In the middle of the nineteenth century, however, the idea that organic substances could only be synthesized by living organisms was gradually discounted. Not only have a large number of natural products been synthesized in the laboratory, but also countless related materials have been made that do not occur in nature. All of these compounds contain carbon, and over a million carbon compounds are known.

Because it represents a convenient division of chemistry, the term organic chemistry is retained, but it is now commonly defined as the chemistry of carbon and its compounds. Some carbon compounds, such as carbonates, carbides, and cyanides, are traditionally classed as inorganic compounds, and organic chemistry is probably better defined as the chemistry of the hydrocarbons (compounds containing only carbon and hydrogen) and their derivatives.

Carbon forms an unusually large number of compounds because of its exceptional ability to catenate (Section 10.22). In addition, the carbon atom can form four, very stable, single-covalent bonds, and it also has the ability to form multiple bonds with other carbon atoms or with atoms of other elements (Section 10.22).

17.1 The Alkanes

The simplest hydrocarbon is methane, CH_4. The molecule contains four, equivalent, carbon-hydrogen bonds arranged tetrahedrally (Figure 17.1), and the bonding may be considered to arise through the use of sp^3 hybrid orbitals of the carbon atom. Each of the bonds of methane is of the same length (1.095 Å), and each of the H—C—H bond angles is 109° 28′ (the so-called tetrahedral angle). The commonly employed structural formula of methane,

$$
\begin{array}{c}
\text{H} \\
| \\
\text{H}-\text{C}-\text{H} \\
| \\
\text{H}
\end{array}
$$

does not accurately represent the tetrahedral arrangement of the molecule.

The **alkanes** are hydrocarbons in which all of the carbon–carbon bonds are single bonds; they may be considered to be derived from methane by the successive addition of —CH₂— units. Such a series of compounds is said to be **homologous**. Thus the formula of the second member of the family, ethane,

$$
\begin{array}{cc}
\text{H} & \text{H} \\
| & | \\
\text{H}-\text{C}-&\text{C}-\text{H} \\
| & | \\
\text{H} & \text{H}
\end{array}
$$

may be formally derived by the introduction of a —CH₂— unit between the carbon and a hydrogen of methane. This molecule is also represented by the formula CH_3—CH_3.

The alkanes conform to the general formula C_nH_{2n+2} where n is the number of carbon atoms in the compound. A few subsequent members of the family, and their names, are

$$
\begin{array}{ccc}
\text{H} & \text{H} & \text{H} \\
| & | & | \\
\text{H}-\text{C}-&\text{C}-&\text{C}-\text{H} \\
| & | & | \\
\text{H} & \text{H} & \text{H}
\end{array}
\qquad
\begin{array}{cccc}
\text{H} & \text{H} & \text{H} & \text{H} \\
| & | & | & | \\
\text{H}-\text{C}-&\text{C}-&\text{C}-&\text{C}-\text{H} \\
| & | & | & | \\
\text{H} & \text{H} & \text{H} & \text{H}
\end{array}
$$

$$CH_3CH_2CH_3 \qquad\qquad CH_3CH_2CH_2CH_3$$

propane   butane

Figure 17.1   Representations of the structure of methane, CH_4. The bonds in diagram (a) are of exaggerated length in comparison to the atomic sizes.

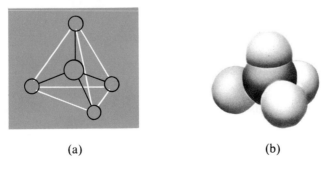

(a)   (b)

$$
\begin{array}{ccccc}
\text{H} & \text{H} & \text{H} & \text{H} & \text{H} \\
| & | & | & | & | \\
\text{H}-\text{C}-\text{C}-\text{C}-\text{C}-\text{C}-\text{H} \\
| & | & | & | & | \\
\text{H} & \text{H} & \text{H} & \text{H} & \text{H}
\end{array}
$$

$CH_3CH_2CH_2CH_2CH_3$

pentane

These compounds are spoken of as **straight-chain** compounds even though the carbon chains are far from linear (Figure 17.2); all of the bond angles are approximately tetrahedral, and axial rotation of any carbon atom around a single bond of the chain is possible.

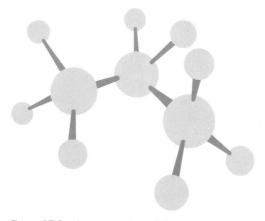

Figure 17.2   *Representation of the structure of propane,* $CH_3CH_2CH_3$.

There is only one compound for each of the formulas CH_4, C_2H_6, and C_3H_8. However, there are two compounds with the formula C_4H_{10}: the compound with a straight chain and one with a **branched chain**.

$$
\begin{array}{ccc}
\text{H} & \text{H} & \text{H} \\
| & | & | \\
\text{H}-\text{C}-\text{C}-\text{C}-\text{H} \\
| & | & | \\
\text{H} & | & \text{H} \\
 & | & \\
\text{H}-\text{C}-\text{H} \\
 & | & \\
 & \text{H} &
\end{array}
\qquad \text{or} \qquad
\begin{array}{c}
CH_3CHCH_3 \\
| \\
CH_3
\end{array}
$$

methylpropane

The two compounds of formula C_4H_{10} are **structural isomers** (compounds with the same molecular formula but different structural formulas); they have different properties.

There are three structural isomers of C_5H_{12}: pentane (the straight chain compound),

$$\underset{\text{methylbutane}}{CH_3CH_2\underset{|}{\overset{}{C}}HCH_3}\qquad\text{and}\qquad\underset{\text{dimethylpropane}}{CH_3-\underset{\underset{CH_3}{|}}{\overset{\overset{CH_3}{|}}{C}}-CH_3}$$

methylbutane · · · · · · · · · · · · · dimethylpropane

In the alkane series, the number of possible structural isomers increases rapidly: there are 5 structural isomers for C_6H_{14}, 9 for C_7H_{16}, 75 for $C_{10}H_{22}$, and it has been calculated that over 4 billion isomers are possible for $C_{30}H_{62}$.

A branched-chain compound may be named in terms of the longest straight chain in the molecule. The side chains are named as alkyl radicals, and their positions on the straight chain are usually indicated by a numbering system. Alkyl radicals are fragments of alkane molecules from which a hydrogen atom has been removed; their names are derived from the name of the parent alkane with the ending changed to $-yl$. A list of common alkyl radicals appears in Table 17.1.

TABLE 17.1.
SIMPLE ALKYL RADICALS.

Formula	Name
CH_3-	methyl
CH_3CH_2-	ethyl
$CH_3CH_2CH_2-$	*normal*-propyl or *n*-propyl
$CH_3\underset{\underset{CH_3}{\vert}}{C}H-$	isopropyl
$CH_3CH_2CH_2CH_2-$	*normal*-butyl or *n*-butyl
$CH_3\underset{\underset{CH_3}{\vert}}{C}HCH_2-$	isobutyl
$CH_3CH_2\underset{\underset{CH_3}{\vert}}{C}H-$	*secondary*-butyl or *sec*-butyl
$CH_3\underset{\underset{CH_3}{\vert}}{\overset{\overset{CH_3}{\vert}}{C}}-$	*tertiary*-butyl or *tert*-butyl

For example, the longest straight chain in the molecule

$$
\begin{array}{c}
CH_3 \\
| \\
CH_3C—CHCH_2CH_3 \\
|\quad\ | \\
CH_3\ CH_2 \\
| \\
CH_3
\end{array}
$$

consists of five carbon atoms, and the compound is named as a deriva-tive of pentane. The pentane chain is numbered starting at the end that will give the side chains the lowest numbers.

$$
\begin{array}{c}
CH_3 \\
| \\
CH_3C——CHCH_2CH_3 \\
|\quad\ \ | \\
CH_3\ \ CH_2 \\
| \\
CH_3
\end{array}
$$

$$\ \ 1\quad 2\quad\ 3\quad 4\quad 5$$

In the name, a number is used to indicate the position of each substituent radical. Thus the name of the compound is

2,2-dimethyl-3-ethylpentane

No numbers appear in the names of our earlier examples of structural isomers. The name methylpropane requires no number to indicate the position of the methyl radical with regard to the propane chain since there is only one possible position for the methyl group (number 2). If the methyl group were placed on either terminal carbon atom (number 1 or number 3), the compound would be the straight-chain isomer, butane. In like manner, the names methylbutane and dimethylpropane do not require the use of numbers; there is only one possible structure cor-responding to each name.

Names for some of the higher straight-chain homologs may be ob-tained from Table 17.2 which lists the melting points and boiling points of some of the straight-chain alkanes. With increasing molecular weight, the melting points and boiling points increase. The first four compounds are gases under ordinary conditions; higher homologs are liquids (C_5H_{12} to $C_{15}H_{32}$) and solids (from $C_{16}H_{34}$ on).

Aliphatic hydrocarbons are open-chain structures; in addition, **cyclic hydrocarbons** are known. The **cycloalkanes** are ring structures that contain only single carbon-carbon bonds; they have the general formula C_nH_{2n}. Examples are

cyclopropane   cyclohexane

Three- and four-membered rings are strained because the C—C—C bond angles of the ring deviate considerably from the tetrahedral angle (109° 28'). The carbon atoms of cyclopropane form an equilateral triangle, and the bond angles are 60°. The bond angles of cyclobutane are approximately 90° since the four carbon atoms are approximately coplanar and form a square. In cyclopentane, cyclohexane, and higher cycloalkanes, the bond angles of the ring are much nearer to the tetrahedral angle. The carbon atoms of the larger ring compounds are not coplanar; the rings are puckered so as to give bond angles of approximately 109° 28'.

TABLE 17.2.
PHYSICAL PROPERTIES OF SOME STRAIGHT-CHAIN ALKANES

Compound	Formula	Melting Point (°C)	Boiling Point (°C)
methane	CH_4	−183	−162
ethane	C_2H_6	−172	−88
propane	C_3H_8	−187	−42
butane	C_4H_{10}	−135	1
pentane	C_5H_{12}	−131	36
hexane	C_6H_{14}	−94	69
heptane	C_7H_{16}	−91	99
octane	C_8H_{18}	−57	126
nonane	C_9H_{20}	−54	151
decane	$C_{10}H_{22}$	−30	174
hexadecane	$C_{16}H_{34}$	20	288
heptadecane	$C_{17}H_{36}$	23	303

17.2 The Alkenes

The **alkenes**, or **olefins**, are aliphatic hydrocarbons that have a carbon–carbon double bond somewhere in their molecular structure. The first member of the series is ethene (or ethylene),

Each carbon atom of ethene may be considered to form sp^2 hybrid bonding orbitals; these three orbitals are employed in the formation of three σ bonds: one with the other carbon atom and two with hydrogen atoms. Molecules of the type AB_3

in which the bonding occurs through sp^2 hybrid orbitals of atom A, are triangular planar with bond angles of 120° (Section 3.12). In ethene, all six atoms lie in the same plane, and all bond angles are approximately 120°. Each carbon atom has an electron in a p orbital that is not engaged in the formation of sp^2 σ bonds. These two p orbitals are coplanar and perpendicular to the plane of the molecule; they overlap to form a π bonding orbital with regions of charge density above and below the plane of the molecule (Figure 17.3).

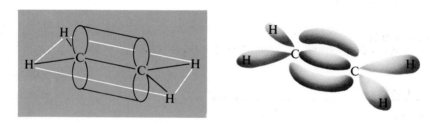

Figure 17.3   Schematic representation of the bonding in ethene.

The p orbitals can overlap and from a π bonding orbital only when they lie in the same plane. Consequently, free rotation around the carbon-carbon double bond is not possible without breaking the π bond. The carbon-carbon bond distance in ethene (1.33 Å) is shorter than that in ethane (1.54 Å) because of the double bond. The π bond is not so strong as the σ bond; the carbon–carbon bond energy in ethane is approximately 81 kcal/mole, and the bond energy of the carbon–carbon double bond in ethene is about 145 kcal/mole.

Alkanes are called **saturated** compounds because all the valence electrons of the carbon atoms are engaged in single bond formation, and no more hydrogen atoms, or atoms of other elements, can be accommodated by the carbon atoms of the chain. **Unsaturated** compounds, such as the alkenes, can undergo **addition reactions** (Section 17.5) because of the availability of the π electrons of the double bond. In one such reaction, hydrogen adds to ethene to form ethane.

$$CH_2\!\!=\!\!CH_2 + H_2 \rightarrow CH_3\!\!-\!\!CH_3$$

Alkenes conform to the general formula C_nH_{2n}. The name of an alkene is derived from the name of the corresponding alkane by changing the ending from -ane to -ene; a number is used, where necessary, to indicate the position of the double bonds. The second member of the series is propene.

$$CH_2{=}CH{-}CH_3$$

New types of isomerism arise in the alkene series. The type of structural isomerism displayed by the alkanes (e.g., butane and methylpropane) is known as **chain isomerism**. In addition to chain isomerism, **position isomerism** occurs in the olefin series. There is only one straight-chain butane. There are, however, two straight-chain butenes, and they differ in the *position* of the double bond.

$$CH_2{=}CH{-}CH_2{-}CH_3 \qquad CH_3{-}CH{=}CH{-}CH_3$$

1-butene   2-butene

In the first compound, the double bond is located between carbon atoms number 1 and number 2, and the lower number (1) is used to indicate its position. In like manner, the lower number is used to indicate the position of the double bond (which occurs between carbon atoms number 2 and number 3) in the name of the second compound. In each case the chain is numbered from the end that gives the lowest possible number for the name.

The alkenes also exhibit **geometric** (or **cis-trans**) **isomerism**, which is a type of **stereoisomerism**. Stereoisomers have the same structural formula but differ in the arrangement of the atoms in space. An example is provided by the isomers of 2-butene. Because of the restricted rotation around the double bond, one isomer exists with both methyl groups on the same side of the double bond (the *cis* isomer), and another isomer exists with the methyl groups on opposite sides of the double bond (the *trans* isomer). All of the carbon atoms of the molecule lie in the same plane.

cis-2-butene   trans-2-butene

boiling point, 1°C   boiling point, 2.5°C

The properties of the 2-butenes do not differ greatly. Other *cis-trans* isomers exhibit wider variation in their physical properties.

$$H \quad \diagdown \quad H$$

cis-1,2-dichloroethene
boiling point, 60.1°C

trans-1,2-dichloroethene
boiling point, 48.4°C

The physical properties of the alkenes are very similar to the alkanes. The C_2H_4, C_3H_6, and C_4H_8 compounds are gases under ordinary conditions; the C_5H_{10} to $C_{18}H_{36}$ compounds are liquids; and the higher alkenes are solids. All of the compounds are only slightly soluble in water.

Cycloalkenes are known, for example,

$$CH_2—CH_2$$
$$CH_2 \qquad\qquad CH_2$$
$$CH=CH$$
cyclohexene

17.3   The Alkynes

Molecules that contain carbon–carbon triple bonds are known as alkynes. These unsaturated hydrocarbons have the general formula C_nH_{2n-2} and constitute the **alkyne**, or **acetylene**, **series**. The first member of the series is ethyne, or acetylene.

$$H—C\equiv C—H$$

In acetylene, each carbon atom uses sp hybrid orbitals to form a σ bond with a hydrogen atom and a σ bond with the other carbon atom. Consequently, the four atoms of the molecule lie in a straight line. In addition to the carbon–carbon σ bond, two π bonds are formed between the carbon atoms by the overlap of p orbitals (Figure 17.4). The resultant carbon–carbon bond distance (1.21 Å) is shorter than the carbon–carbon double bond distance (1.33 Å). The π bonds are weaker than the C—C σ bond; the bond energy of the triple bond is approximately 198 kcal/mole (compared to the single bond energy of 81 kcal/mole). Alkynes readily undergo addition reactions across the triple bond because of the availability of the four electrons of the π bonds.

Figure 17.4   Schematic representation of the bonding in acteylene.

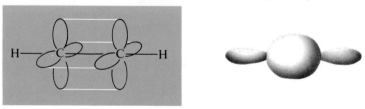

Alkynes are named in a manner analogous to that employed in naming alkenes; the ending -yne is used in place of -ene. Their physical properties are similar to those of the other aliphatic hydrocarbons. Both chain and position isomerism occur in the alkyne series, but *cis-trans* isomerism is not possible because of the linear geometry of the grouping $X—C\equiv C—X$, where X is a carbon atom or an atom of another element.

Notice that a branched-chain isomer of C_4H_6 is impossible; only two isomers of C_4H_6 exist

$$HC\equiv CCH_2CH_3 \qquad CH_3C\equiv CCH_3$$
1-butyne   2-butyne

Both branched-chain and straight-chain isomers of C_5H_8 are known.

$$HC\equiv CCH_2CH_2CH_3 \qquad CH_3C\equiv CCH_2CH_3 \qquad HC\equiv CCHCH_3$$
$$\underset{\text{methyl-1-butyne}}{\overset{\displaystyle \quad \qquad \qquad \qquad \qquad \qquad \qquad \qquad \qquad \qquad \qquad \qquad \;\; CH_3}{}}$$

1-pentyne   2-pentyne   methyl-1-butyne

17.4 Aromatic Hydrocarbons

Aromatic hydrocarbons are compounds that have molecular structures based on that of benzene, C_6H_6. The six carbon atoms of benzene are arranged in a ring from which the hydrogen atoms are radially bonded (Figure 17.5). The entire structure is planar, and all of the bond angles are 120°. The carbon-carbon bond distance is 1.39 Å, which is between the single bond distance of 1.54 Å and the double bond distance of 1.33 Å.

Figure 17.5 Geometry of the benzene molecule.

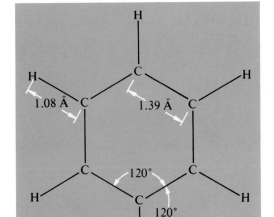

The electronic structure of benzene may be represented as a resonance hybrid

$$
\begin{array}{c}
\text{H} \\
\text{C} \\
\text{H---C} \quad \text{C---H} \\
\text{H---C} \quad \text{C---H} \\
\text{C} \\
\text{H}
\end{array}
\leftrightarrow
\begin{array}{c}
\text{H} \\
\text{C} \\
\text{H---C} \quad \text{C---H} \\
\text{H---C} \quad \text{C---H} \\
\text{C} \\
\text{H}
\end{array}
$$

This representation correctly shows that all of the carbon-carbon bonds are equivalent and that each one is intermediate between a single bond and a double bond.

Each carbon atom of the ring uses sp^2 hybrid orbitals to form σ bonds with two adjacent carbon atoms and a hydrogen atom; therefore the resulting framework of the molecule is planar with bond angles of 120°. A $2p$ electron of each carbon atom is not employed in the formation of these sp^2 hybrid bonds. The axes of these p orbitals are perpendicular to the plane of the molecule, and the p orbitals overlap to form a π bonding orbital (Figure 17.6). The resulting multicenter π bond contains six electrons with regions of charge density above and below the plane of the ring.

The electrons of the π bond are said to be delocalized in the sense that they are not engaged in the formation of electron-pair bonds between two specific atoms. The structure, which is reminiscent of that of

Figure 17.6   The π bonding system of benzene; σ bonds are indicated as black lines.

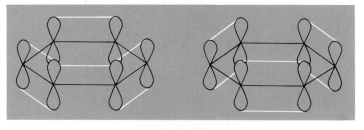

graphite (Section 10.23), is very stable and is responsible for the properties that are typical of aromatic compounds. The benzene ring does not
readily undergo addition reactions in the way that alkenes and alkynes
do.

Notice that the resonance and molecular-orbital pictures of benzene
are equivalent. If the overlap of the p orbitals is imagined to occur only
between orbitals of adjacent carbon atoms in such a way that traditional electron-pair bonds between only two atoms result, then the two
resonance forms are derived (Figure 17.6). According to the resonance
theory, neither of these forms is correct; the true structure is a hybrid of
both of them. Hence, the resonance representation leads to the same
result as the molecular orbital description; both call for the overlap of
all six p orbitals and the formation of a multicenter π bond.

The benzene ring is usually represented as

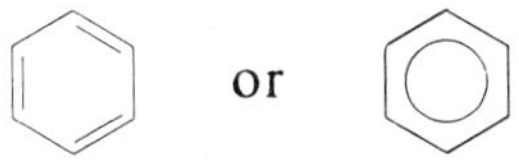

or

The carbon and hydrogen atoms of the ring are not shown. In benzene
derivatives, such as

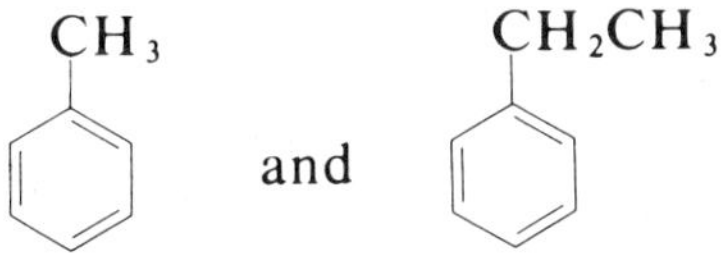

CH₃

and

CH₂CH₃

toluene
methylbenzene

ethylbenzene

it is understood that the substituents replace hydrogen atoms of the ring.
The radical formed from benzene by the removal of a hydrogen atom,

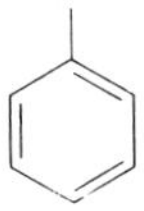

is called a **phenyl radical.**

There are three position isomers of any disubstituted benzene deriva-
tive. For example,

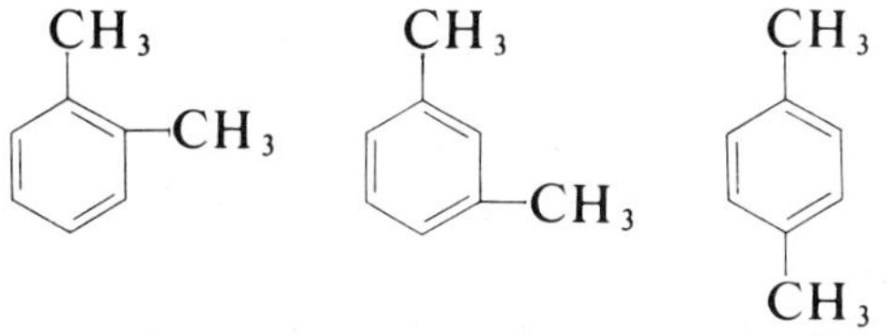

CH₃

—CH₃

CH₃

—CH₃

CH₃

CH₃

o-xylene   m-xylene   p-xylene

The prefixes *ortho-* (*o-*), *meta-* (*m-*), and *para-* (*p-*) are used to designate
the positions of the two substituent groups.

Compounds are known in which several rings are fused together. For example, naphthalene, $C_{10}H_8$, is a planar molecule that is a resonance hybrid,

There are no hydrogen atoms bonded to the carbon atoms through which the rings are fused.

17.5   Reactions of the Hydrocarbons

Combustion of any hydrocarbon in excess oxygen yields carbon dioxide and water.

$$CH_4(g) + 2O_2(g) \rightarrow CO_2(g) + 2H_2O(g)$$

The reactions are highly exothermic, which accounts for the use of hydrocarbons as fuels. Carbon compounds exist in oxidation states intermediate between the hydrocarbons and carbon dioxide. These compounds are discussed in sections that follow; they are not generally prepared by direct reaction with elementary oxygen.

The replacement of a hydrogen atom of a hydrocarbon molecule by another atom or group of atoms is called a **substitution reaction.** The alkanes react with chlorine, or bromine, in the presence of sunlight, or ultraviolet light, by means of a free-radical chain mechanism (Section 12.6). The chain is initiated by the light-induced dissociation of a chlorine molecule into atoms.

$$Cl_2 \rightarrow 2Cl\cdot$$

Propagation of the chain occurs by the reactions

$$Cl\cdot + CH_4 \rightarrow CH_3\cdot + HCl$$
$$CH_3\cdot + Cl_2 \rightarrow CH_3Cl + Cl\cdot$$

The chain is terminated by the reactions

$$CH_3\cdot + Cl\cdot \rightarrow CH_3Cl$$
$$Cl\cdot + Cl\cdot \rightarrow Cl_2$$
$$CH_3\cdot + CH_3\cdot \rightarrow CH_3CH_3$$

The reactions that terminate the chain occur at the walls of the container, which carry away the energy liberated by the formation of the new bond. In a collision between radicals in the gas phase, the united fragments fly apart almost immediately because of the lack of a third body to carry away the energy released by bond formation. Hence, the chain terminators do not occur with a great frequency, and all of the reactants are rapidly consumed in the reactions.

The overall reaction for the preceding mechanism is

$$CH_4 + Cl_2 \rightarrow CH_3Cl + HCl$$

In addition to chloromethane, CH_3Cl, the reaction produces dichloro-methane, CH_2Cl_2, trichloromethane (chloroform), $CHCl_3$, and tetra-chloromethane (carbon tetrachloride), CCl_4. In terms of the chain mechanism, these compounds arise through collisions of chlorine atoms with already chlorinated methane molecules. For example,

$$Cl\cdot + CH_3Cl \rightarrow CH_2Cl\cdot + HCl$$
$$CH_2Cl\cdot + Cl_2 \rightarrow CH_2Cl_2 + Cl\cdot$$

Complex mixtures of mono- and polysubstituted isomers are obtained as products of the chlorination of higher alkanes.

Addition reactions are characteristic of unsaturated hydrocarbons; examples follow.

$$CH_2 \begin{array}{c} CH_2-CH_2 \\ \diagdown \\ CH=CH \end{array} CH_2 + H_2 \xrightarrow{Pt} CH_2 \begin{array}{c} CH_2-CH_2 \\ \diagup \diagdown \\ CH_2-CH_2 \end{array} CH_2$$

$$CH_2{=}CH_2 + Br_2 \longrightarrow \underset{\text{1,2-dibromoethane}}{CH_2Br-CH_2Br}$$

$$HC{\equiv}CH + HCl \longrightarrow \underset{\text{1-chloroethene}}{CH_2{=}CHCl}$$

$$CH_2{=}CHCl + HCl \longrightarrow \underset{\text{1,1-dichloroethane}}{CH_3-CHCl_2}$$

$$\underset{}{\overset{\overset{\textstyle CH_3}{|}}{CH_3CH_2C}}{=}CH_2 + HOH \xrightarrow{H_2SO_4} \underset{\underset{\text{2-methyl-2-butanol}}{\overset{|}{OH}}}{\overset{\overset{\textstyle CH_3}{|}}{CH_3CH_2CCH_3}}$$

$$CH_3CH{=}CH_2 + HBr \longrightarrow \underset{\underset{\text{2-bromopropane}}{\overset{|}{Br}}}{CH_3CHCH_3}$$

When unsymmetrical molecules (such as HBr) add to the double bond of an olefin, two isomeric compounds are sometimes produced. Thus in the last reaction of the previous series, two compounds are obtained.

$$\underset{\underset{\text{2-bromopropane}}{\overset{|}{Br}}}{CH_3CHCH_3} \qquad \underset{\text{1-bromopropane}}{CH_3CH_2CH_2Br}$$

Over 90% of the product, however, is the 2-bromo- isomer. The principal product of such an addition is that in which the hydrogen atom of the addend is bonded to the carbon that originally had the larger number of hydrogen atoms (**Markovnikov's rule**).

The initial step of the mechanism of the addition of HBr is thought to be an electrophilic attack by a proton (a Lewis acid) on the π electrons of the double bond (a Lewis base). The product of this step is a positive ion called a **carbonium ion,** and for propene, two such ions are possible.

$$
\begin{array}{c}
\overset{\displaystyle H\ \ H}{\underset{\displaystyle H}{CH_3-\overset{+}{C}-C-H}} \\[2ex]
CH_3-\overset{\displaystyle H}{\underset{\displaystyle H}{C}}=\overset{\displaystyle H}{C}-H + H^+ \\[2ex]
\overset{\displaystyle H\ \ H}{\underset{\displaystyle H}{CH_3-C-\overset{+}{C}-H}}
\end{array}
$$

The π electrons are used to bond the incoming proton to one of the carbon atoms of the double bond which leaves the other carbon atom with a positive charge. The stability of carbonium ions is known to decrease in the order

$$
\underset{+}{R-\overset{\displaystyle R}{C}-R} \ > \ \underset{+}{R-\overset{\displaystyle H}{C}-R} \ > \ \underset{+}{R-\overset{\displaystyle H}{C}-H}
$$

where R is an alkyl radical. Consequently, in the reaction of propene with HBr, the carbonium ion produced in larger quantity is the first one shown.

Carbonium ions are highly reactive Lewis acids; they exist only transiently and rapidly combine with bromide ion (a Lewis base).

$$
CH_3\underset{+}{CH}CH_3 + Br^- \rightarrow \underset{\displaystyle Br}{CH_3CHCH_3}
$$

$$
CH_3CH_2CH_2^+ + Br^- \rightarrow CH_3CH_2CH_2Br
$$

Thus the relative stabilities of the carbonium ions are responsible for the fact that 2-bromopropane is the principal product of the reaction.

In contrast to unsaturated aliphatic hydrocarbons, the principal reactions of benzene are substitutions, not additions.

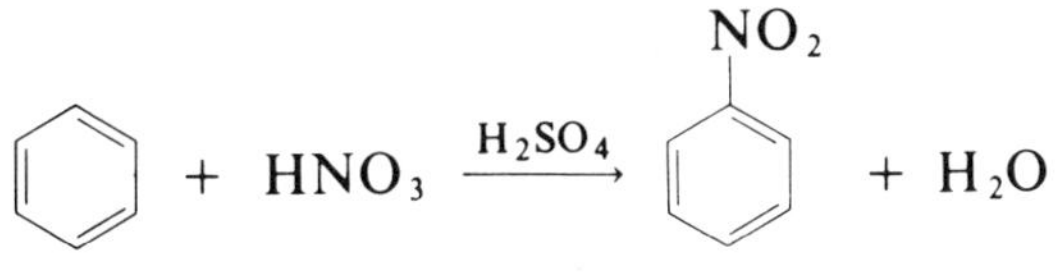

$$\text{benzene} + HNO_3 \xrightarrow{H_2SO_4} \text{nitrobenzene} + H_2O$$

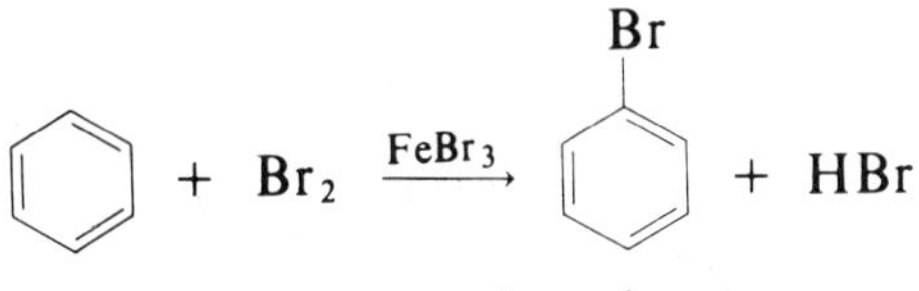

nitrobenzene

$$\text{benzene} + Br_2 \xrightarrow{FeBr_3} \text{bromobenzene} + HBr$$

bromobenzene

$$\text{benzene} + CH_3Cl \xrightarrow{AlCl_3} \text{toluene} + HCl$$

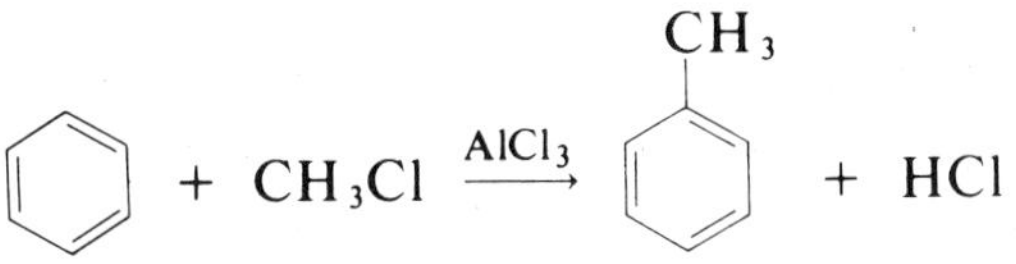

toluene

The last reaction is the Friedel-Crafts synthesis for the preparation of aromatic hydrocarbons.

The catalysts, which are indicated over the arrows in the preceding equations, produce powerful Lewis acids (NO_2^+, Br^+, and CH_3^+) as follows:

$$HNO_3 + 2H_2SO_4 \rightarrow NO_2^+ + H_3O^+ + 2HSO_4^-$$
$$Br_2 + FeBr_3 \rightarrow Br^+ + FeBr_4^-$$
$$CH_3Cl + AlCl_3 \rightarrow CH_3^+ + AlCl_4^-$$

These cationic Lewis acids, which are short-lived reaction intermediates, are electrophilic, and we shall indicate them as E^+ in the mechanism that follows.

The benzene ring is attacked by the electrophilic group, E^+, which bonds to a carbon atom by means of a pair of π electrons and creates an activated complex with a positive charge.

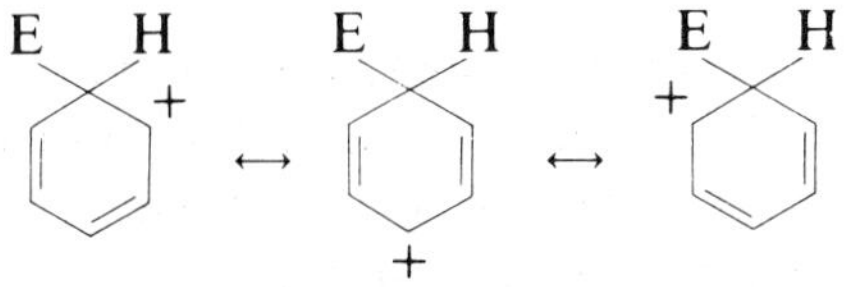

Notice that the carbon atom to which E is bonded holds two groups in the complex; the remaining five carbon atoms hold only their customary hydrogen atoms. The complex is a resonance hybrid, and the charge is delocalized, thus providing a degree of stability. The π bonding system of benzene is more stable, however, and is restored by the loss of a proton.

The proton is lost to the anion produced in the reaction that generated the cationic electrophile.

$$H^+ + HSO_4^- \rightarrow H_2SO_4$$

$$H^+ + FeBr_4^- \rightarrow HBr + FeBr_3$$

$$H^+ + AlCl_4^- \rightarrow HCl + AlCl_3$$

17.6   Alcohols and Ethers

The alcohols may be considered as derivatives of hydrocarbons in which a hydroxyl group, OH, replaces a hydrogen. The hydroxyl group is one of a number of **functional groups,** which are groups of atoms that give organic compounds bearing them characteristic chemical and physical properties.

The compounds are named by changing the ending -*ane* of the parent hydrocarbon to -*anol*; the lowest possible number is assigned to the hydroxyl group to indicate its position. Alcohols may be classified as *primary*, *secondary*, or *tertiary*, according to the number of alkyl radicals on the carbon atom holding the OH. Thus

| ·1-butanol | 3-methyl-2-butanol | 2-methyl-2-butanol |
| a primary alcohol | a secondary alcohol | a tertiary alcohol |

Alcohols associate through hydrogen bonding,

For this reason, the melting points and boiling points of the alcohols are higher than those of alkanes of corresponding molecular weight (Table 17.3). The lower alcohols are miscible with water in all proportions because of intermolecular hydrogen bonding.

However, as the size of the alkyl radical increases, the alcohols become more like alkanes in their physical properties, and the higher alcohols are only slightly soluble in water.

TABLE 17.3.
PHYSICAL PROPERTIES OF SOME ALCOHOLS.

Name	Formula	Melting Point (°C)	Boiling Point (°C)	Solubility in Water (g/100 g H_2O, 20°C)
methanol	CH_3OH	−98	65	miscible
ethanol	CH_3CH_2OH	−115	78	miscible
1-propanol	$CH_3(CH_2)_2OH$	−127	97	miscible
1-butanol	$CH_3(CH_2)_3OH$	−90	117	7.9
1-pentanol	$CH_3(CH_2)_4OH$	−79	138	2.4
1-hexanol	$CH_3(CH_2)_5OH$	−52	157	0.6

Alcohols, like water, are amphiprotic substances. They can act as Brønsted bases (proton acceptors) with very strong acids.

$$H_2SO_4 + ROH \rightleftharpoons ROH_2^+ + HSO_4^-$$

With very strong bases, they are Brønsted acids (proton donors).

$$ROH + H^- \rightarrow OR^- + H_2$$

Alcohols, however, are more weakly acidic and basic than water; consequently, the conjugate acids (ROH_2^+) and conjugate bases (OR^-) are stronger than H_3O^+ and OH^-. The anion OR^-, known as an alkoxide ion, results from the reaction of an alcohol with a reactive metal (compare the reaction of water with sodium).

$$2CH_3CH_2OH + 2Na \rightarrow 2CH_3CH_2ONa + H_2$$

The first member of the series, methanol or methyl alcohol, is known as wood alcohol because it may be obtained by the destructive distillation of wood. The principal commercial source of this alcohol is the catalytic hydrogenation of carbon monoxide.

$$CO + 2H_2 \rightarrow CH_3OH$$

The alcohol of alcoholic beverages is ethanol, or ethyl alcohol. It is prepared by the fermentation of starches or sugars. Ethanol is also commercially prepared from ethene. The indirect addition of water to olefins by means of sulfuric acid is a general method of preparing alcohols. The synthesis of ethanol proceeds by the following steps.

$$CH_2{=}CH_2 + H_2SO_4 \rightarrow CH_3CH_2OSO_2OH$$
$$CH_3CH_2OSO_2OH + H_2O \rightarrow CH_3CH_2OH + H_2SO_4$$

Alcohols may be prepared from alkyl halides by displacement, or nucleophilic substitution, reactions.

$$RX + OH^- \rightarrow ROH + X^-$$

This is an important classification of organic reactions and includes reactions of the alkyl halides, as well as the alcohols themselves, with a wide variety of nucleophilic substances. The reactions are usually reversible and are run under conditions that favor the formation of the desired compound; an excess of the nucleophilic reagent may be employed or the product removed from the reaction mixture as it forms (e.g., by distillation).

Primary and secondary halides or alcohols generally react by what is called an S_N2 mechanism, which can be illustrated by the reaction of hydroxide ion with methyl bromide. The hydroxide ion, a Lewis base, attacks the carbon atom and displaces the bromide ion (also a Lewis base) which takes along the electron pair with which it had been bonded.

$$OH^- + H{\underset{H}{\overset{H}{-}}}C{-}Br \quad \longrightarrow \quad \left[HO{---}\underset{H}{\overset{H \quad H}{C}}{---}Br \right]^- \quad \longrightarrow \quad HO{-}\underset{H}{\overset{H}{C}}{-}H + Br^-$$

activated complex

The attack of the OH^- ion takes place on the opposite side of the carbon atom from that holding the bromine atom. As the OH^- ion approaches, it begins to form a covalent bond, and the bromide ion begins to break away; the activated complex of the reaction is the form in which both nucleophilic groups are partially bonded to the carbon atom. The reaction causes inversion of the geometric arrangement of the groups attached to the carbon atom, a process that is customarily compared to the inversion of an umbrella in a high wind. The mechanism is given the designation S_N2 because it is the substitution of one nucleophilic group for another, and the rate-determining step (the formation of the activated complex) is bimolecular. The nucleophilic substitution reaction of HBr with CH_3OH proceeds through the formation of $CH_3OH_2^+$ and the displacement of H_2O from this ion by Br^-.

In the case of tertiary alkyl halides, the three alkyl groups bonded to the carbon atom bearing the halogen inhibit the rearward approach of the OH^- ion, and it is thought that tertiary alkyl halides undergo displacement reactions by a different mechanism. The rate-determining step is the formation of a carbonium ion,

$$CH_3{-}\underset{CH_3}{\overset{CH_3}{\underset{|}{\overset{|}{C}}}}{-}Br \quad \longrightarrow \quad CH_3{-}\underset{CH_3}{\overset{CH_3}{\underset{|}{\overset{|}{C}}}}^+ + Br^-$$

The central carbon atom of the carbonium ion has only six electrons in its valence level and displays sp^2 hybridization; the carbonium ion is, therefore, planar. It is a powerful Lewis acid and rapidly adds hydroxide ion (a Lewis base).

$$CH_3-\underset{\underset{CH_3}{|}}{\overset{\overset{CH_3}{|}}{C^+}} + OH^- \rightarrow CH_3-\underset{\underset{CH_3}{|}}{\overset{\overset{CH_3}{|}}{C}}-OH$$

This mechanism is given the designation S_N1 because it is a nucleophilic substitution in which the rate-determining step is unimolecular. The S_N1 mechanism is favored when the reaction is run in polar solvents (such as water) which aids the first-step ionization of the halide.

Tertiary alcohols also undergo S_N1 reactions. The steps of a typical substitution involving HBr are

$$(CH_3)_3COH + H^+ \rightleftharpoons (CH_3)_3COH_2^+ \qquad \text{(rapid, equilibrium)}$$

$$(CH_3)_3COH_2^+ \rightarrow (CH_3)_3C^+ + H_2O \qquad \text{(rate determining)}$$

$$(CH_3)_3C^+ + Br^- \rightarrow (CH_3)_3CBr$$

In all of these nucleophilic substitution reactions, appreciable quantities of olefins are formed along with the substitution products; this is particularly true of the reactions of the tertiary compounds, and olefin formation is thought to proceed by the elimination of a proton by a carbonium ion.

$$H-\underset{\underset{H}{|}}{\overset{\overset{H}{|}}{C}}-\underset{\underset{CH_3}{|}}{\overset{\overset{CH_3}{|}}{C^+}} \rightarrow H^+ + \underset{\underset{H}{|}}{\overset{\overset{H}{|}}{C}}=\underset{\underset{CH_3}{|}}{\overset{\overset{CH_3}{|}}{C}}$$

Tertiary carbonium ions are formed more readily than any other type (Section 17.5); elimination reactions of primary and secondary alcohols are thought to occur by a mechanism that does not involve the formation of carbonium ions.

The elimination of one water molecule from one molecule of an alcohol produces an olefin.

$$CH_3CH_2OH \xrightarrow[\text{above 150°C}]{H_2SO_4} CH_2{=}CH_2 + H_2O$$

Under milder conditions, only one molecule of water is removed from two molecules of alcohol, and an ether is produced.

$$CH_3CH_2OH + HOCH_2CH_3 \xrightarrow[130-140°C]{H_2SO_4} CH_3CH_2OCH_2CH_3 + H_2O$$
$$\text{diethyl ether}$$

Ethers may be regarded as derivatives of water, HOH, in which both hydrogen atoms are replaced by alkyl groups, ROR. The alkyl groups may be alike or different.   Ethers are also produced by nucleophilic substitution reactions involving alkoxide ions and alkyl halides.

$$CH_3CH_2O^- + CH_3CH_2CH_2Br \rightarrow CH_3CH_2OCH_2CH_2CH_3 + Br^-$$
ethyl propyl ether

Unlike alcohols, ethers do not associate by hydrogen bonding.   Therefore the boiling points of ethers are much lower than those of alcohols of corresponding molecular weight, and the ethers are much less soluble in water.

CH_3CH_2OH CH_3OCH_3

ethanol   dimethyl ether

boiling point, 78°C   boiling point, −24°C

Notice that ethanol and dimethyl ether are isomeric; the type of isomerism displayed by this pair of compounds is known as **functional group isomerism**.   The ethers are less reactive than the alcohols.

Polyhydroxy alcohols contain more than one OH group.   Examples include 1,2-ethanediol (ethylene glycol),

CH_2—CH_2

| | |

OH   OH

and 1,2,3-propanetriol (glycerol), which is derived from fats,

CH_2—CH—CH_2

OH   OH   OH

Unlike aliphatic alcohols, which do not dissociate in water solution, the aromatic alcohols are weak acids in water.

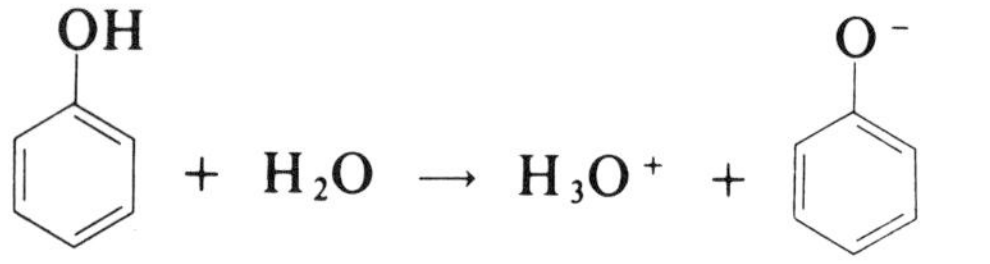

phenol   phenoxide ion

The acidity of phenol (carbolic acid) is attributed to the stability of the phenoxide ion in which the charge is delocalized by the π bonding system of the aromatic ring.

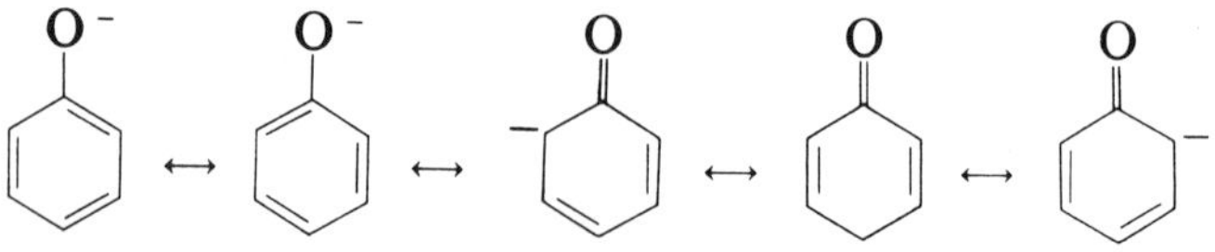

Aromatic halides do not readily undergo displacement reactions. Sodium phenoxide is commercially obtained from chlorobenzene by reaction with NaOH at elevated temperatures and under high pressure.

$$\underset{\text{Cl}}{\bigcirc} + 2\text{NaOH} \rightarrow \underset{\text{ONa}}{\bigcirc} + \text{NaCl} + H_2O$$

Phenol is derived by acidification of the phenoxide.

17.7 Carbonyl Compounds

A carbon atom can form a double bond with an oxygen atom to produce what is called a **carbonyl group**

$$\overset{O}{\underset{|}{\overset{\|}{-C-}}}$$

The double bond, like the carbon–carbon double bond, consists of a σ bond and a π bond between the bonded atoms. The carbon atom of the carbonyl group and the atoms bonded to it are coplanar and form bond angles of 120°, a geometry that is typical of sp^2 hybridized species. The carbonyl double bond differs from the olefinic double bond in that it is markedly polar since oxygen is more electronegative than carbon.

If the carbonyl group is bonded to one alkyl group and a hydrogen, or to two hydrogens, the compound is an **aldehyde**.

$$\underset{\substack{\text{formaldehyde}\\\text{methanal}}}{H-\overset{\overset{\displaystyle O}{\|}}{C}-H} \qquad \underset{\substack{\text{acetaldehyde}\\\text{ethanal}}}{CH_3-\overset{\overset{\displaystyle O}{\|}}{C}-H} \qquad \underset{\text{3-methylbutanal}}{CH_3-\overset{\overset{\displaystyle CH_3}{|}}{C}-CH_2-\overset{\overset{\displaystyle O}{\|}}{C}-H}$$

Systematic nomenclature of aldehydes employs the ending -*al*; substituent groups are given numbers based on the assignment of the number 1 (understood) to the carbonyl carbon.

In a **ketone**, the carbonyl groups is bonded to two alkyl groups which may be alike or different.

$$\underset{\substack{\text{acetone}\\\text{propanone}}}{CH_3-\overset{\overset{\displaystyle O}{\|}}{C}-CH_3} \quad \underset{\substack{\text{methyl ethyl ketone}\\\text{butanone}}}{CH_3-\overset{\overset{\displaystyle O}{\|}}{C}-CH_2CH_3} \quad \underset{\text{5-methyl-3-hexanone}}{CH_3CH_2-\overset{\overset{\displaystyle O}{\|}}{C}-CH_2\overset{\overset{\displaystyle CH_3}{|}}{C}HCH_3}$$

The ending-*one* is used to designate a ketone; numbers are employed to indicate the positions of substituents, the carbonyl group being assigned the lowest possible number.

Aldehydes may be prepared by the mild oxidation of primary alcohols. An oxidizing agent such as potassium dichromate in dilute sulfuric acid may be used.

$$3RCH_2OH + Cr_2O_7^{2-} + 8H^+ \rightarrow 3R\overset{\overset{\displaystyle O}{\|}}{C}-H + 2Cr^{3+} + 7H_2O$$

Equations for reactions such as this are usually written with the oxidizing agent indicated over the arrow and only the organic reactant and product shown. Thus

$$CH_3CH_2OH \xrightarrow{\text{Cr}_2\text{O}_7^{2-}/\text{H}^+} CH_3\overset{\displaystyle O}{\overset{\displaystyle \|}{C}}-H$$

When an aldehyde is prepared by the oxidation of a primary alcohol, provision must be made to prevent the aldehyde from being destroyed by further oxidation since aldehydes are easily oxidized to carboxylic acids (Section 17.8). Many aldehydes may be distilled out of the reaction mixture as they are formed.

Some aldehydes are made commercially by reacting alcohol vapors with air over a copper catalyst at elevated temperatures.

$$2CH_3OH + O_2 \xrightarrow{\text{Cu}} 2H-\overset{\displaystyle O}{\overset{\displaystyle \|}{C}}-H + 2H_2O$$

The oxidation of alcohols may also be conducted by passing the hot alcohol vapor over a heated copper catalyst in the absence of oxygen. This process results in the removal of a molecule of hydrogen from an alcohol molecule and is called a **dehydrogenation**; it avoids the danger of secondary oxidation of the aldehyde product.

$$CH_3CH_2CH_2OH \xrightarrow{\text{Cu}} CH_3CH_2\overset{\displaystyle O}{\overset{\displaystyle \|}{C}}-H + H_2$$

The oxidation of secondary alcohols produces ketones.

$$CH_3CH_2\overset{\displaystyle OH}{\overset{\displaystyle |}{C}}HCH_3 \xrightarrow{\text{Cr}_2\text{O}_7^{2-}/\text{H}^+} CH_3CH_2\overset{\displaystyle O}{\overset{\displaystyle \|}{C}}CH_3$$

Acetone (propanone) may be prepared by the oxidation of 2-propanol with oxygen or by the dehydrogenation of the alcohol.

$$CH_3\overset{\displaystyle OH}{\overset{\displaystyle |}{C}}HCH_3 \xrightarrow{\text{Cu}} CH_3\overset{\displaystyle O}{\overset{\displaystyle \|}{C}}CH_3 + H_2$$

The oxidation of tertiary alcohols results in the destruction of the carbon skeleton of the molecule.

The double bond of the carbonyl group readily undergoes many addition reactions. Reduction of aldehydes or ketones with hydrogen in the presence of a nickel or platinum catalyst yields primary or secondary alcohols.

$$R-\overset{\displaystyle O}{\overset{\displaystyle \|}{C}}-H + H_2 \rightarrow R-\overset{\displaystyle OH}{\overset{\displaystyle |}{C}}H_2$$

$$\underset{\text{R}}{\overset{\text{O}}{\overset{\|}{\text{C}}}}\text{R} + \text{H}_2 \rightarrow \underset{\text{R}}{\overset{\text{OH}}{\overset{|}{\text{CH}}}}\text{R}$$

When an unsymmetrical reagent (such as HCN) adds to the double bond, the positive part of the addend (the hydrogen) adds to the oxygen, and the negative part of the addend (the cyanide group) bonds to the carbon. This mode of addition reflects the polarity of a carbonyl double bond; the oxygen is negative with respect to the carbon.

$$\underset{\text{R}}{\overset{\text{O}}{\overset{\|}{\text{C}}}}\text{R} + \text{H}-\text{C}\equiv\text{N} \rightarrow \text{R}-\overset{\overset{\text{OH}}{|}}{\underset{\underset{\text{C}\equiv\text{N}}{|}}{\text{C}}}-\text{R}$$

a cyanohydrin

The proposed mechanism for additions of this type consists of the electrophilic attack of the anionic Lewis base

$$\underset{\text{R}}{\overset{\text{O}}{\overset{\|}{\text{C}}}}\text{R} + \text{CN}^- \rightarrow \text{R}-\overset{\overset{\text{O}^-}{|}}{\underset{\underset{\text{CN}}{|}}{\text{C}}}-\text{R}$$

followed by combination with a proton

$$\text{R}-\overset{\overset{\text{O}^-}{|}}{\underset{\underset{\text{CN}}{|}}{\text{C}}}-\text{R} + \text{H}^+ \rightarrow \text{R}-\overset{\overset{\text{OH}}{|}}{\underset{\underset{\text{CN}}{|}}{\text{C}}}-\text{R}$$

An important addition reaction involves organomagnesium compounds known as **Grignard reagents**. Alkyl halides react with magnesium metal in dry diethyl ether

$$\text{R}-\text{X} + \text{Mg} \rightarrow \text{R}-\text{Mg}-\text{X}$$

These reagents are usually given the formula RMgX; however, the materials possess a high degree of ionic character and may be mixtures of magnesium dialkyls (MgR_2) and magnesium halides (MgX_2). Water must be excluded from a Grignard reaction because these reagents are easily hydrolyzed.

$$\text{R}-\text{Mg}-\text{X} + \text{HOH} \rightarrow \text{R}-\text{H} + \text{Mg(OH)X}$$

The formula Mg(OH)X stands for an equimolar mixture of magnesium hydroxide and magnesium halide.

A Grignard reagent adds to an aldehyde as follows

$$R'\text{—}\overset{\overset{\textstyle O}{\|}}{C}\text{—}H + R\text{—}Mg\text{—}X \rightarrow R'\text{—}\overset{\overset{\textstyle OMgX}{|}}{\underset{\underset{\textstyle R}{|}}{C}}\text{—}H$$

where the alkyl groups R and R' may be alike or different. The addition compound is readily decomposed by water or by dilute acid.

$$R'\text{—}\overset{\overset{\textstyle OMgX}{|}}{\underset{\underset{\textstyle R}{|}}{C}}\text{—}H + HX \rightarrow R'\text{—}\overset{\overset{\textstyle OH}{|}}{\underset{\underset{\textstyle R}{|}}{C}}\text{—}H + MgX_2$$

Thus the ultimate product of the reaction of a Grignard reagent and an aldehyde is a secondary alcohol.

Hydrolysis of an addition compound formed by a Grignard reagent and a ketone yields a tertiary alcohol.

$$R'\text{—}\overset{\overset{\textstyle O}{\|}}{C}\text{—}R'' + RMgX \rightarrow R'\text{—}\overset{\overset{\textstyle OMgX}{|}}{\underset{\underset{\textstyle R}{|}}{C}}\text{—}R''$$

$$R'\text{—}\overset{\overset{\textstyle OMgX}{|}}{\underset{\underset{\textstyle R}{|}}{C}}\text{—}R'' + HX \rightarrow R'\text{—}\overset{\overset{\textstyle OH}{|}}{\underset{\underset{\textstyle R}{|}}{C}}\text{—}R'' + MgX_2$$

The alkyl groups may be alike or different.

In these reactions of Grignard reagents, new carbon–carbon bonds are formed, and the reactions are frequently useful as steps in organic syntheses. The alcohols produced may be oxidized to carbonyl compounds, subjected to displacement reactions, or dehydrated to olefins. Thus a series of reactions may be employed to synthesize a desired compound from compounds of lower molecular weight.

17.8 Carboxylic Acids and Esters

Oxidation of the aldehyde group yields a **carboxyl group**

$$\text{—}\overset{\overset{\textstyle O}{\|}}{C}\text{—}H \rightarrow \text{—}\overset{\overset{\textstyle O}{\|}}{C}\text{—}OH$$

Compounds containing the —COOH group are weak acids (**carboxylic acids**); ionization constants for some of these acids are listed in Table 17.4.

TABLE 17.4.
PROPERTIES OF SOME CARBOXYLIC ACIDS.

Acid	Formula	Melting Point (°C)	Boiling Point (°C)	Ionization Constant at 25°C
methanoic (formic)	$HCOOH$	8	101	1.8×10^{-4}
ethanoic (acetic)	CH_3COOH	17	118	1.8×10^{-5}
propanoic (propionic)	CH_3CH_2COOH	−22	141	1.4×10^{-5}
butanoic (butyric)	$CH_3(CH_2)_2COOH$	−8	164	1.5×10^{-5}
pentanoic (valeric)	$CH_3(CH_2)_3COOH$	−35	187	1.6×10^{-5}
benzoic	C_6H_5COOH	122	249	6.0×10^{-5}

$$R-\overset{\displaystyle O}{\overset{\|}{C}}-OH + H_2O \rightleftharpoons R-\overset{\displaystyle O}{\overset{\|}{C}}-O^- + H_3O^+$$

The charge of the carboxylate anion is delocalized.

$$R-\overset{\displaystyle O}{\overset{\|}{C}}-O^- \leftrightarrow R-\overset{\displaystyle O^-}{\overset{|}{C}}=O$$

The acids are associated through hydrogen bonding. Lower members of the series form dimers in the vapor state.

$$R-C\overset{\displaystyle O\text{---}H-O}{\underset{\displaystyle O-H\text{---}O}{}}C-R$$

According to systematic nomenclature, the name of a carboxylic acid is derived from the parent hydrocarbon by elision of the final -e, addition of the ending -oic, and addition of the separate word *acid*. The numbers used to designate the positions of substituents on the carbon chain are derived by numbering the chain starting with the carbon of the carboxyl group.

$$CH_3CH_2\overset{\displaystyle O}{\overset{\|}{C}}-OH \qquad CH_3\overset{\displaystyle CH_3}{\overset{|}{C}}HCH_2\overset{\displaystyle O}{\overset{\|}{C}}-OH$$

propanoic acid   3-methylbutanoic acid

Carboxylic acids may be prepared by the oxidation of primary alcohols or aldehydes. Potassium dichromate or potassium permanganate are frequently employed as the oxidizing agent.

$$CH_3CH_2CH_2CH_2OH \xrightarrow{Cr_2O_7^{2-}/H^+} CH_3CH_2CH_2\overset{\displaystyle O}{\overset{\|}{C}}-OH$$

Acetic acid is commercially prepared by the air oxidation of acetaldehyde.

$$2CH_3\overset{\overset{\displaystyle O}{\|}}{C}-H + O_2 \xrightarrow{Mn(C_2H_3O_2)_2} 2CH_3\overset{\overset{\displaystyle O}{\|}}{C}-OH$$

Vigorous oxidation of an alkyl-substituted aromatic compound converts the side chain to a carboxyl group and thus yields benzoic acid.

toluene   benzoic acid

These oxidations do not touch the aromatic ring, an illustration of the stability of this structure.

The oxidation of an unsaturated hydrocarbon yields a variety of products, including carboxylic acids, depending upon conditions. Dilute aqueous permanganate at room temperature oxidizes olefins to glycols.

$$R-CH=CH-R \xrightarrow{MnO_4^-} R-\underset{\underset{\displaystyle OH}{|}}{CH}-\underset{\underset{\displaystyle OH}{|}}{CH}-R$$

Under more vigorous conditions (more concentrated solutions and heating), the carbon chain is cleaved at the double bond and carboxylic acids produced.

$$R-CH=CH-R \xrightarrow{MnO_4^-} R-\overset{\overset{\displaystyle O}{\|}}{C}-OH + HO-\overset{\overset{\displaystyle O}{\|}}{C}-R$$

Alkynes also may be cleaved to yield acids.

$$R-C\equiv C-R \xrightarrow{MnO_4^-} R-\overset{\overset{\displaystyle O}{\|}}{C}-OH + HO-\overset{\overset{\displaystyle O}{\|}}{C}-R$$

Oxidation of some olefins yields ketones.

$$R-\underset{\underset{\displaystyle R}{|}}{C}=\underset{\underset{\displaystyle R}{|}}{C}-R \xrightarrow{MnO_4^-} R-\underset{\underset{\displaystyle R}{|}}{C}=O + O=\underset{\underset{\displaystyle R}{|}}{C}-R$$

Carboxylic acids may be produced by the alkaline hydrolysis of alkyl cyanides; the cyanides are the product of nucleophilic substitution reactions of the CN^- ion with alkyl halides.

$$CH_3CH_2Br + CN^- \rightarrow CH_3CH_2CN + Br^-$$

$$CH_3CH_2CN + OH^- + H_2O \rightarrow CH_3CH_2\overset{\overset{\displaystyle O}{\|}}{C}-O^- + NH_3$$

Some compounds contain more than one carboxyl group. Examples include

$$\begin{array}{ccc}
\begin{array}{c}
COOH \\
| \\
COOH \\
\text{oxalic acid}
\end{array}
& \text{and} &
\begin{array}{c}
CH_2COOH \\
| \\
HO-C-COOH \\
| \\
CH_2COOH \\
\text{citric acid}
\end{array}
\end{array}$$

Carboxylic acids react with alcohols to produce compounds known as esters.

$$CH_3\overset{\overset{\displaystyle O}{\|}}{C}-OH + CH_3CH_2OH \rightarrow \left[\begin{array}{c} OH \\ | \\ CH_3C-OH \\ | \\ OCH_2CH_3 \end{array} \right] \rightarrow$$

$$CH_3\overset{\overset{\displaystyle O}{\|}}{C}-OCH_2CH_3 + H_2O$$
$$\text{ethyl acetate}$$

Esterification reactions are reversible and proceed to equilibrium; they may be forced in either direction by the appropriate choice of conditions. The name of an ester reflects the alcohol and acid from which it is derived, the ending *-ate* being employed with the base of the name of the acid to give the second portion of the name of the ester.

The lower molecular weight esters have pleasant, fruity odors. Esters of high-molecular-weight carboxylic acids and glycerol are animal and vegetable **fats:** glyceryl esters that are liquids at room temperature are commonly called **oils.**

$$\begin{array}{c}
R-\overset{\overset{\displaystyle O}{\|}}{C}-O-CH_2 \\
| \\
R'-\overset{\overset{\displaystyle O}{\|}}{C}-O-CH \\
| \\
R''-\overset{\overset{\displaystyle O}{\|}}{C}-O-CH_2
\end{array}$$

The alkyl groups indicated in the preceding general formula are part of the carboxylic acids from which the compound may be considered to have been derived; they may be alike or different. The carboxylic acids are long chain structures and may be saturated

$$CH_3(CH_2)_{14}COOH$$

palmitic acid

or unsaturated

$$CH_3(CH_2)_7CH\!=\!CH(CH_2)_7COOH$$

oleic acid

Liquid fats, or oils, contain a high percentage of glyceryl esters of unsaturated acids. Hydrogenation of vegetable oils produces solid fats. In commercial practice, the process is run only until a solid of the desired consistency is obtained; not all of the olefinic linkages are saturated.

The alkaline hydrolysis of an ester produces an alcohol and a salt of a carboxylic acid.

$$\underset{\text{RCOR}'}{\overset{O}{\overset{\|}{}}} + OH^- \rightarrow R\!-\!\overset{O}{\overset{\|}{C}}\!-\!O^- + R'OH$$

The salts of long chain carboxylic acids are soaps. These compounds, together with glycerol, are produced by the alkaline hydrolysis of fats, and the process is commonly called **saponification** (soap making).

17.9 Amines and Amides

The **amines** may be considered as derivatives of ammonia with one, two, or three hydrogen atoms replaced by alkyl groups.

$$\underset{\substack{\text{methylamine}\\ \text{a primary amine}}}{\overset{\overset{\displaystyle H}{\overset{\displaystyle |}{}}}{CH_3\!-\!N\!-\!H}} \qquad \underset{\substack{\text{dimethylamine}\\ \text{a secondary amine}}}{\overset{\overset{\displaystyle CH_3}{\overset{\displaystyle |}{}}}{CH_3\!-\!N\!-\!H}} \qquad \underset{\substack{\text{trimethylamine}\\ \text{a tertiary amine}}}{\overset{\overset{\displaystyle CH_3}{\overset{\displaystyle |}{}}}{CH_3\!-\!N\!-\!CH_3}}$$

The amines resemble ammonia in that they are weak bases.

$$CH_3NH_2 + H_2O \rightleftharpoons CH_3NH_3^+ + OH^-$$

$$(CH_3)_2NH + H_2O \rightleftharpoons (CH_3)_2NH_2^+ + OH^-$$

$$(CH_3)_3N + H_2O \rightleftharpoons (CH_3)_3NH^+ + OH^-$$

Ionization constants for some amines are listed in Table 17.5. The amines form ionic salts with acids

$$CH_3NH_2 + HCl \rightarrow CH_3NH_3^+ + Cl^-$$

which may be decomposed by hydroxides

$$CH_3NH_3^+ + OH^- \rightarrow CH_3NH_2 + H_2O$$

TABLE 17.5.
PROPERTIES OF SOME AMINES.

Amine	Formula	Melting Point (°C)	Boiling Point (°C)	Ionization Constant at 25°C
methylamine	CH_3NH_2	-93	-7	5×10^{-4}
dimethylamine	$(CH_3)_2NH$	-96	7	7.4×10^{-4}
trimethylamine	$(CH_3)_3N$	-124	4	7.4×10^{-5}
ethylamine	$CH_3CH_2NH_2$	-81	17	5.6×10^{-4}
propylamine	$CH_3CH_2CH_2NH_2$	-83	49	4.7×10^{-4}
aniline	$C_6H_5NH_2$	-6	184	4.6×10^{-10}

The last reaction is the reverse of the ionization of methylamine in water; it is forced to yield the free amine by employment of an excess of OH^- or by warming.

Amines may be prepared by reacting alkyl halides with ammonia. These reactions are nucleophilic substitutions.

$$NH_3 + CH_3CH_2Br \rightarrow CH_3CH_2NH_3^+ + Br^-$$

Treatment of the amine salt with hydroxide ion yields the free amine. Mixtures of primary, secondary, and tertiary amines are produced by this type of reaction.

Primary amines may be produced by the catalytic hydrogenation of alkyl cyanides.

$$CH_3CH_2C\equiv N + 2H_2 \rightarrow CH_3CH_2CH_2-NH_2$$

Aniline is produced by the reduction of nitrobenzene. Iron and steam, with a trace of hydrochloric acid, serve as the reducing agent.

Some compounds that contain more than one amino group are important. Ethylenediamine (1,2-diaminoethane, $H_2N-CH_2-CH_2-NH_2$) is a useful chelating agent (Section 16.1), and hexamethylenediamine (1,6-diaminohexane, $H_2N(CH_2)_6NH_2$) is used in the manufacture of nylon.

Amides may be produced from ammonia and carboxylic acids. The preparation proceeds through the formation of ammonium salts which eliminate water upon heating.

$$CH_3\overset{\displaystyle O}{\overset{\|}{C}}-O^-NH_4^+ \rightarrow CH_3\overset{\displaystyle O}{\overset{\|}{C}}-NH_2 + H_2O$$

ammonium acetate   acetamide

Amides may also be prepared by the nucleophilic substitution reaction of ammonia on an ester.

$$NH_3 + CH_3\overset{\displaystyle O}{\overset{\|}{C}}-OCH_2CH_3 \rightarrow CH_3\overset{\displaystyle O}{\overset{\|}{C}}-NH_2 + CH_3CH_2OH$$

Primary and secondary amines react with acids in a similar manner to produce substituted amides, compounds in which one or two alkyl radicals replace hydrogen atoms of the $-NH_2$ group.

17.10 Amino Acids and Proteins

Carboxylic acid molecules that contain an amino group, $-NH_2$, on the carbon atom adjacent to the carboxyl carbon (the so-called α carbon atom) are called α-**amino acids.** The simplest such compound is amino-acetic acid, or glycine.

$$\underset{\displaystyle NH_2}{\overset{\displaystyle O}{CH_2\overset{\|}{-}\overset{\displaystyle}{C}-OH}}$$

Amino acids are both acidic and basic

$$H_2N-CH_2\overset{\displaystyle O}{\overset{\|}{C}}-OH + OH^- \rightleftharpoons H_2N-CH_2\overset{\displaystyle O}{\overset{\|}{C}}-O^- + H_2O$$

$$H_2N-CH_2\overset{\displaystyle O}{\overset{\|}{C}}-OH + H_3O^+ \rightleftharpoons {}^+H_3N-CH_2\overset{\displaystyle O}{\overset{\|}{C}}-OH + H_2O$$

Thus internal neutralization, producing a **zwitter ion,** can occur.

$${}^+H_3N-CH_2-\overset{\displaystyle O}{\overset{\|}{C}}-O^-$$

For a given compound, the acid strength and base strength, which depend upon molecular structure, are generally not exactly equal. The **isoelectric point** is the pH at which the internal neutralization of a given amino acid is at a maximum.

The acid hydrolysis of proteins yields amino acids. Many different amino acids have been synthesized, but only about two dozen have been obtained from proteins. The general formula of these compounds is

$$H_2N-CH-\overset{\overset{\displaystyle O}{\|}}{C}-OH$$
$$\underset{R}{|}$$

The radicals, R in the preceding formula, vary considerably in structure. Some of the radicals contain additional amino groups or carboxyl groups; a number include rings (some of them aromatic rings); some incorporate sulfur atoms or hydroxyl groups in their structures; and one contains iodine.

In protein molecules, many amino acid units are linked together in long chains so that the molecular weights of proteins range from approximately 10^4 to about 10^7. When two amino acids combine, the amino group of one molecule joins, with the elimination of water, to the carboxyl group of the second molecule, and a **peptide linkage,** $-\overset{\overset{\displaystyle O}{\|}}{C}-\overset{\overset{\displaystyle H}{|}}{N}-$, is formed.

$$H_2N-\underset{R}{\underset{|}{CH}}-\overset{\overset{\displaystyle O}{\|}}{C}-OH \; + \; H_2N-\underset{R}{\underset{|}{CH}}-\overset{\overset{\displaystyle O}{\|}}{C}-OH \; \rightarrow$$

$$H_2N-\underset{R}{\underset{|}{CH}}-\overset{\overset{\displaystyle O}{\|}}{C}-\overset{\overset{\displaystyle H}{|}}{N}-\underset{R}{\underset{|}{CH}}-\overset{\overset{\displaystyle O}{\|}}{C}-OH \; + \; H_2O$$

This product has a free amino group and a free carboxyl group and can condense with other amino acid molecules to form long chains, or polypeptides. The hydrolysis of polypeptide chains is the reverse of the condensation process and produces amino acids.

The amino acids provide examples of a type of stereoisomerism called **optical isomerism** (Section 16.3). The simplest optical isomers are compounds that contain asymmetric carbon atoms—carbon atoms to which four different types of groups are bonded (Figure 17.7). Such compounds, and carbon atoms, are called asymmetric because they possess no element of symmetry.

Optical isomers have molecular structures that are mirror images (enantiomorphs) and are not superimposable. Thus the structures of Figure 17.7 are mirror reflections of one another, and a study of the figure reveals that the two configurations cannot be superimposed. If groups 1 and 3 of the structures are superimposed, group 4 of one structure coincides with group 2 of the other. No matter how the two structures are oriented, it is impossible to make all four groups of one

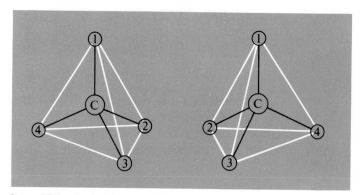

Figure 17.7   Optical isomers of a compound containing an asymmetric carbon atom.

structure coincide with the same four groups of the other structure; two different isomers exist.

The physical properties of optical isomers are identical except for their effects on plane-polarized light. The isomers are said to be optically active because they rotate the plane of plane-polarized light in either a clockwise or a counterclockwise direction. The isomer that rotates the plane to the right (clockwise) is said to be **dextrorotatory** ($+$); the other isomer rotates the plane an equal amount to the left and is said to be **levorotatory** ($-$).

With the exception of glycine (aminoacetic acid), the α-carbon atoms of α-amino acids are asymmetric.

$$
\begin{array}{c}
\overset{\displaystyle H}{}\ \ \overset{\displaystyle O}{} \\
H_2N-C-C-OH \\
R
\end{array}
$$

The two-dimensional representation of optical isomers is difficult; structures of the optical isomers of amino acids are usually diagrammed

$$
\begin{array}{cc}
\overset{\displaystyle O}{} & \overset{\displaystyle O}{} \\
C-OH & C-OH \\
H_2N-C-H & H-C-NH_2 \\
R & R \\
\text{L-amino acid} & \text{D-amino acid}
\end{array}
$$

The diagrams represent structures in which the asymmetric carbon atoms are in the plane of the paper, the —COOH and —R groups are behind the plane of the paper, and the —H and —NH$_2$ groups are in front of the plane of the paper. With such an arrangement of groups, the L- form is that in which the amino group is to the left of the chain, and the D- form is that in which the amino group is to the right. The structures can be related to the diagrams of Figure 17.7; the L-form is the one on the left in the figure if group 1 = —COOH, 2 = —R, 3 = —H, and 4 = —NH$_2$.

All of the amino acids derived from proteins are L-amino acids. Only the L- forms can be utilized in the metabolic processes of the body. The sign of rotation should not be confused with the symbols D- or L- which are used to designate the configuration of the asymmetric carbon atom. Thus the L- isomer of alanine (2-aminopropanoic acid) is dextrorotatory.

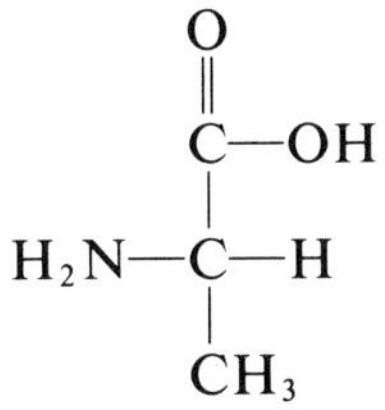

$$
\begin{array}{c}
O \\
\parallel \\
C\text{—OH} \\
| \\
H_2N\text{—}C\text{—H} \\
| \\
CH_3
\end{array}
$$

L-(+)-alanine

17.11 Carbohydrates

Sugars, starches, and cellulose belong to a group of organic compounds called **carbohydrates;** the name derives from the fact that most (but not all) such compounds have the general formula $C_x(H_2O)_y$. Carbohydrates are hydroxy aldehydes, hydroxy ketones, or substances that yield hydroxy carbonyl compounds upon hydrolysis.

The optical isomers of glucose, an important simple sugar, have the formulas

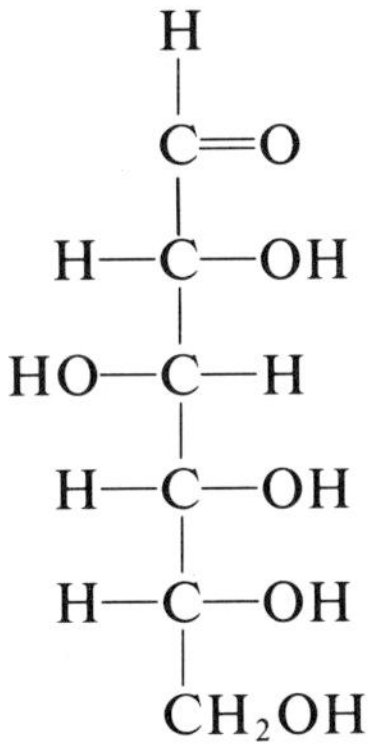

$$
\begin{array}{cc}
\begin{array}{c}
H \\
| \\
C\text{=}O \\
| \\
H\text{—}C\text{—OH} \\
| \\
HO\text{—}C\text{—H} \\
| \\
H\text{—}C\text{—OH} \\
| \\
H\text{—}C\text{—OH} \\
| \\
CH_2OH
\end{array}
&
\begin{array}{c}
H \\
| \\
C\text{=}O \\
| \\
HO\text{—}C\text{—H} \\
| \\
H\text{—}C\text{—OH} \\
| \\
HO\text{—}C\text{—H} \\
| \\
HO\text{—}C\text{—H} \\
| \\
CH_2OH
\end{array}
\\
\text{D-(+)-glucose} & \text{L-(−)-glucose}
\end{array}
$$

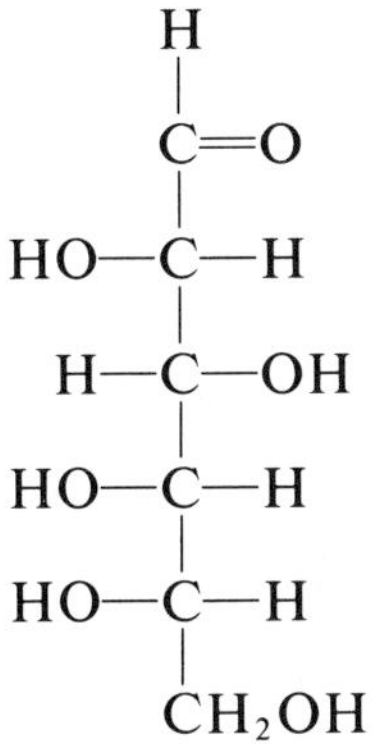

There are four asymmetric carbon atoms in the molecule (the terminal carbon atoms do not hold four different groups and are not asymmetric). Sixteen optical isomers (eight D,L pairs) of this formula exist; only the preceding pair are called glucose.

D-glucose forms a cyclic molecule by an addition reaction involving the carbonyl group and a hydroxyl group.

$$\begin{array}{c} CH_2OH \\ | \\ C \text{------} O \text{---} H \text{-----} \\ H \diagup | \quad\quad H | \\ C \quad H \quad\quad C{=}O \\ | \quad OH \quad\quad H \\ OH \diagdown | \quad\quad | \\ C \text{------} C \\ | \quad\quad | \\ H \quad\quad OH \end{array}$$

Ring formation generates a new asymmetric center, and two ring iso-mers of D-glucose exist which differ in the orientation of the new OH group.

$$\begin{array}{cc} \alpha\text{-D-glucose} & \beta\text{-D-glucose} \end{array}$$

In these diagrams, the carbon atoms of the ring are not shown. The rings are actually puckered, not planar. Notice that in the α form, the OH group of the extreme right-hand carbon atom is on the same side of the ring as the OH group of the adjacent carbon atom; these OH groups may be said to be *cis* to each other. In aqueous solution, α and β forms of D-glucose exist in equilibrium, together with a low concentration of the open-chain form.

Fructose is a hydroxy ketone.

$$\begin{array}{cc} CH_2OH & CH_2OH \\ | & | \\ C{=}O & C{=}O \\ | & | \\ HO{-}C{-}H & H{-}C{-}OH \\ | & | \\ H{-}C{-}OH & HO{-}C{-}H \\ | & | \\ H{-}C{-}OH & NO{-}C{-}H \\ | & | \\ CH_2OH & CH_2OH \\ \text{D-(}-\text{)-fructose} & \text{L-(}+\text{)-fructose} \end{array}$$

There are three asymmetric carbon atoms in this molecule and eight stereoisomers (or four D,L pairs) of this formula are known. Cyclic forms of D-fructose are known with five- or six-membered rings.

Glucose and fructose are known as monosaccharides. Sucrose, cane sugar, is a disaccharide. Acid hydrolysis yields the two simple sugars D-glucose and D-fructose. In the sucrose molecule, a D-glucose unit and a D-fructose unit are joined through two OH groups by the elimination of a molecule of water.

D-glucose unit   D-fructose unit

Cellulose and starch are polysaccharides that yield only D-glucose upon hydrolysis. It is estimated that the number of D-glucose units in the molecular structures of these substances may be as high as several thousand. The D-glucose units of cellulose are linked in long chains in β combination.

The D-glucose units of starch are linked in a different manner; there are occasional cross links between long chains of D-glucose units arranged in α combination.

Starch is an important food material, and cellulose cannot be digested by man—an important distinction brought about by difference in the way that the D-glucose units are linked together.

17.12 Polymers

Starch, cellulose, and proteins are examples of natural **polymers**—molecules of high molecular weight that are formed from simpler molecules, called **monomers.** Important polymers, or **macromolecules,** that do not occur in nature have been synthesized; most of these are linear, or chain-type, structures although some are cross-linked.

Many polymers are formed from compounds that contain carbon-carbon double bonds by a process that is called **addition polymerization.** For example, ethene (ethylene) polymerizes upon heating ($100°$–$400°C$) under high pressure (1000 atm); the product is called polyethylene.

$$
\begin{array}{ccc}
\underset{\underset{H}{|}}{\overset{\overset{H}{|}}{C}}=\underset{\underset{H}{|}}{\overset{\overset{H}{|}}{C} } + \underset{\underset{H}{|}}{\overset{\overset{H}{|}}{C}}=\underset{\underset{H}{|}}{\overset{\overset{H}{|}}{C}} \rightarrow -\underset{\underset{H}{|}}{\overset{\overset{H}{|}}{C}}-\underset{\underset{H}{|}}{\overset{\overset{H}{|}}{C}}-\underset{\underset{H}{|}}{\overset{\overset{H}{|}}{C}}-\underset{\underset{H}{|}}{\overset{\overset{H}{|}}{C}}-
\end{array}
$$

The preceding equation shows the combination of only two molecules of ethane; the actual polymerization process continues, by successive additions of CH_2=CH_2 molecules, until chains of hundreds or thousands of —CH_2—CH_2— units are produced. The product, polyethylene, is a tough, waxy solid.

Important polymers have been made from ethene derivatives. Orlon and acrilan are polymers of acrylonitrile, CH_2=CH—C≡N; the polymers have the structure

$$
-CH_2-\underset{\underset{CN}{|}}{CH}\left(-CH_2-\underset{\underset{CN}{|}}{CH}\right)_n -CH_2-\underset{\underset{CN}{|}}{CH}-
$$

Teflon is a polymer of tetrafluoroethene, CF_2=CF_2. Vinyl chloride, CH_2=$CHCl$, and vinyl acetate, CH_2=CH—O—$\overset{\overset{\displaystyle O}{\|}}{C}$—$CH_3$, are important monomers in the preparation of vinyl plastics. Lucite, or Plexiglas, is a polymer of methyl methacrylate, CH_2=$C(CH_3)COOCH_3$.

Natural rubber is a polymer of the diolefin 2-methyl-1,3-butadiene, or isoprene.

$$
CH_2=\underset{\underset{CH_3}{|}}{C}-CH=CH_2
$$

Such a system of alternating double and single bonds is called a **conjugated system.** Rubber consists of thousands of these units joined in a chain.

$$
-CH_2-\underset{\underset{CH_3}{|}}{C}=CH-CH_2-\left(CH_2-\underset{\underset{CH_3}{|}}{C}=CH-CH_2\right)_n CH_2-\underset{\underset{CH_3}{|}}{C}=CH-CH_2-
$$

Notice that the polymer contains double bonds. Crude rubber is vulcanized by heating with sulfur. It is thought that the sulfur atoms add to some of the double bonds, thereby linking adjacent chains into a complex network. This process adds strength to the final product.

A number of types of synthetic rubber have been made utilizing such monomers as 1,3-butadiene (CH_2=CH—CH=CH_2), 2-chloro-1,3-butadiene (chloroprene, CH_2=$C(Cl)$—CH=CH_2), and 2,3-dimethyl-1, 3-butadiene (CH_2=$C(CH_3)$—$C(CH_3)$=CH_2) alone or in combination. The product formed by the polymerization of two different monomers is called a **copolymer;** the molecular structures and properties of such materials depend upon the proportions of the two monomers employed. Buna S rubber is a copolymer of 1,3-butadiene and styrene (C_6H_5CH=CH_2). A section of the chain of this material has the structure

$$—CH_2—CH=CH—CH_2—CH—CH_2—$$

An addition polymerization is thought to proceed by either a free-radical or a carbonium-ion chain mechanism. The free-radical type may be initiated by small amounts of hydrogen peroxide or organic peroxides, which are readily split into free radicals (indicated by $Z\cdot$ in the equations that follow).

$$Z_2 \rightarrow 2Z\cdot$$

A free radical from an initiator combines with one of the π electrons of a molecule of the monomer to form a new free radical.

$$Z\cdot + CH_2=CH_2 \rightarrow Z—CH_2—CH_2\cdot$$

Chain propagation occurs by the combination of this free radical with another molecule of the monomer

$$Z—CH_2—CH_2\cdot + CH_2=CH_2 \rightarrow Z—CH_2—CH_2—CH_2—CH_2\cdot$$

and the molecule grows by repeated additions. Chain termination is caused by the combination of two free radicals or by other means, such as the elimination of a hydrogen atom.

A carbonium-ion chain polymerization is initiated by a Lewis acid, such as $AlCl_3$ or BF_3. In the equations that follow, the proton is used to indicate the Lewis-acid, or electrophilic, initiator although stronger Lewis acids are more frequently employed. Combination of the initiator with a molecule of the monomer produces a carbonium ion.

$$H^+ + CH_2=CH_2 \rightarrow CH_3—CH_2^+$$

Chain propagation occurs through the combination of the carbonium ion with both π electrons of a molecule of the monomer.

$$CH_3—CH_2^+ + CH_2=CH_2 \rightarrow CH_3—CH_2—CH_2—CH_2^+$$

Chain termination may occur by the elimination of a proton from a long-chain carbonium ion.

$$CH_3—CH_2-(CH_2—CH_2)_n-CH_2—CH_2^+ \rightarrow$$

$$CH_3—CH_2-(CH—CH_2)_n-CH=CH_2 + H^+$$

Condensation polymerization occurs between molecules of monomers by the elimination of a small molecule, usually water. Proteins and polysaccharides are condensation polymers. Nylon, like the proteins, is a polyamide. It is formed by the condensation of a diamine (such as hexamethylenediamine, $H_2N(CH_2)_6NH_2$) and a dicarboxylic acid (such as adipic acid, $HOOC(CH_2)_4COOH$). The polymerization is accompanied by the loss of water, and the chain has the structure

$$---\overset{\overset{H}{|}}{N}—\overset{\overset{O}{\|}}{C}—(CH_2)_4—\overset{\overset{O}{\|}}{C}—\overset{\overset{H}{|}}{N}—(CH_2)_6—\overset{\overset{H}{|}}{N}—\overset{\overset{O}{\|}}{C}---$$

Dacron is a polyester formed by the elimination of water between ethylene glycol ($HOCH_2CH_2OH$) and a dicarboxylic acid (such as terephthalic acid, p-$HOOCC_6H_4COOH$).

$$-\overset{\overset{O}{\|}}{C}—O—CH_2—CH_2—O—\overset{\overset{O}{\|}}{C}-\!\!\!\bigcirc\!\!\!-\overset{\overset{O}{\|}}{C}—O-$$

Bakelite is a cross-linked polymer formed from phenol and formaldehyde by the elimination of water. Notice that the formaldehyde units condense in the *ortho* and *para* positions of phenol.

SOME SUGGESTED READINGS

Allinger, N., and Allinger, J., *Structures of Organic Molecules*, Englewood Cliffs, N. J., Prentice-Hall, 1965 (paper).

Benfey, O. T., *From Vital Force to Structural Formulas*, Boston, Houghton Mifflin, 1964 (paper).

Bonner, W. A., and Castro, A. J., *Essentials of Modern Organic Chemistry*, New York, Reinhold, 1965.

Breslow, R., *Organic Reaction Mechanisms*, New York, Benjamin, 1965 (paper).

Cahn, R. S., *Introduction to Chemical Nomenclature*, 2nd ed., Washington, D.C., Butterworth, 1964 (paper).

Herz, W., *The Shape of Carbon Compounds: An Introduction to Organic Chemistry*, New York, Benjamin, 1963 (paper).

Mislow, K., *Introduction to Stereochemistry*, New York, Benjamin, 1965 (paper).

O'Driscoll, K., *The Nature and Chemistry of High Polymers*, New York, Reinhold, 1964 (paper).

Saunders, W. H., Jr., *Ionic Aliphatic Reactions*, Englewood Cliffs, N. J., Prentice-Hall, 1965 (paper).

Smith, L. O., Jr., and Cristol, S. J., *Organic Chemistry*, New York, Reinhold, 1966.

Stewart, R., *Investigation of Organic Reactions*, Englewood Cliffs, N. J., Prentice-Hall, 1966 (paper).

Vander Werf, C. A., *Acids, Bases and the Chemistry of the Covalent Bond*, New York, Reinhold, 1961 (paper).

PROBLEMS

17.1 Write the structural formulas for the following compounds: (a) 2,2-dimethyl-3-isopropyl-4-ethylhexane, (b) 2,2,4-trimethyl-2-pentene, (c) *o*-chlorophenol, (d) 3-ethyl-2-pentanone, (e) cyclobutane, (f) diethylmethylamine, (g) hexanoic acid.

17.2 Name each of the following compounds:

(a) $(CH_3)_2CHCHO$ (d) CH_3CONH_2

(b) $CH_3COCH_2CH_3$ (e) $CH_3CH_2OCH_2CH_3$

(c) $CH_3COOCH_2CH_3$ (f) $CH_3(CH_3CH_2)NH$

17.3 Write structural formulas for all of the isomers that have the formula C_6H_{12}.

17.4 What is incorrect about each of the following names? (a) 2-isopropylpentane, (b) 1-propyne, (c) 2-methyl-2-butyne, (d) 2-ethylbutane, (e) 3-propanal, (f) 2-propanal, (g) 2-propanone, (h) 3-methyl-2-pentene.

17.5 Write structural formulas for all of the isomers of each of the following: (a) dinitrobenzene, (b) trinitrobenzene, (c) chlorodinitrobenzene.

17.6 Give examples of each of the following types of isomers: (a) chain, (b) position, (c) functional group, (d) geometric, (e) optical.

17.7 What Grignard reagent and what carbonyl compound should be used to prepare each of the following? (a) 2-methyl-2-butanol, (b) 2-methyl-1-butanol, (c) 3-methyl-2-butanol.

17.8 What are the products when the following compounds are oxidized? (a) 2-butyne, (b) 2-methyl-2-butene, (c) toluene, (d) 2-butanol, (e) butanal, (f) methane.

17.9   What are the products when the following compounds are reacted with hydrogen? (a) 3-ethyl-2-hexene, (b) propanal, (c) propanone, (d) nitro-benzene, (e) ethyl cyanide.

17.10 State the formulas of all products formed by the reaction of HBr with each of the following. If more than one compound is formed, tell which is produced in the greatest quantity.

(a) CH_3CH_2OH (d) $CH_3C{\equiv}CH$
(b) CH_3CH_2MgBr (e) $CH_3CH_2COO^-Na^+$
(c) $(CH_3CH_2)_2C{=}CH_2$ (f) $(CH_3CH_2)_2NH$

17.11 State the compound formed when each of the following is treated with aqueous NaOH.

(a) $(CH_3)_2CHCOOH$ (d) $CH_3CH_2CH_2COOCH_2CH_3$
(b) $(CH_3)_2CHBr$ (e) $CH_3CH_2NH_3^+Cl^-$
(c) $CH_3CH_2CH_2CN$

17.12 What is the difference in meaning between the designations D and $(+)$ as applied to amino acids?

17.13 Show how the following may be prepared from ethanol. Any inorganic substance may be employed, but ethanol is the only organic compound to be used. The preparation should consist of a minimum number of steps. (a) propanoic acid, (b) 2-butanone, (c) ethyl acetate, (d) 3-methyl-2-pentanol, (e) 2-butene, (f) 3-methylpentane.

17.14 Show how 3-methyl-2-butanone may be converted into 2-methyl-2-bu-tanol.

17.15 State the steps necessary to convert 2-methyl-2-pentene into 2-methyl-3-pentanol.

17.16 How may 1-butanol be converted into each of the following? (a) 2-bu-tanol, (b) 1,2-dibromobutane, (c) pentanoic acid, (d) 4-octanol.

17.17 When the terms primary, secondary, and tertiary are applied to amines they have different meanings from when they are applied to alcohols. Explain the distinction.

17.18 Compare and contrast the mechanism of a substitution reaction of an alkane with the mechanism of a substitution reaction of an aromatic hydrocarbon.

17.19 Interpret the following in terms of the Lewis theory: (a) an S_N1 reaction of an alkyl halide, (b) an S_N2 reaction of an alcohol, (c) the addition of HBr to an olefin, (d) the addition of HCN to a ketone.

17.20 (a) A 3.00 g sample of tartaric acid is burned in oxygen; 1.79 liters of CO_2 (measured at STP) and 1.08 g of H_2O are collected from the combustion. Tartaric acid contains only carbon, hydrogen, and oxygen. What is the empirical formula of this compound? (b) A mixture of 0.050 g of tar-taric acid and 0.500 g of camphor melts at 153°C. The melting point of pure camphor is 179°C, and the molal freezing point depression constant is 39.7°/m. What is the molecular formula of tartaric acid? (c) A 0.300 g sample of pure tartaric acid requires 25.0 ml of 0.160N NaOH for com-plete neutralization. What is the equivalent weight of the acid? (d) Draw a structural formula for tartaric acid consistent with the data given in this problem.

17.21 Arrange the following in order of strength as Brønsted bases:
$CH_3CH_2OCH_2CH_3$, CH_3CH_2OH, $CH_3CH_2O^-$, CH_3COO^-, OH^-, CH_3COOH.

17.22 Describe, with examples: (a) addition polymers, (b) copolymers, (c) condensation polymers.

17.23 What explanation can you give for the fact that aromatic systems based on C_4H_4 or C_8H_8 rings are not known?

17.24 Why is aniline a much weaker base than methylamine or ammonia?

17.25 Draw structural formulas for all of the mono-, di-, tri-, and tetra-substituted chloro derivatives of propane.

17.26 (a) Draw the resonance structures of $RCOO^-$. (b) Sketch a π-bond picture of this ion.

18

Nuclear Chemistry

Ordinary chemical reactions involve only the extranuclear electrons; in such reactions, the nucleus is important only insofar as it influences the electrons. However, matter does undergo important transformations that involve the nucleus directly. The study of nuclear reactions and radioactivity has enlarged our understanding of the nature of matter and the courses of chemical and biological processes, and many technological applications have been developed as a result of these investigations.

18.1 The Nucleus

The nuclei of atoms are thought to contain protons and neutrons, particles that are collectively called **nucleons** (Sections 2.6 and 2.7). The number of protons in a specific atomic nucleus corresponds to the atomic number (or nuclear charge), Z, and the total number of nucleons is given by the mass number, A. Thus the number of neutrons equals $(A - Z)$. This information is indicated on the chemical symbol of a given nuclide by appending the atomic number as a subscript and the mass number as a superscript. The symbols for the two naturally occurring isotopes of lithium are

$$\text{}^{6}_{3}\text{Li} \quad \text{and} \quad \text{}^{7}_{3}\text{Li}$$

Much is known about the structure of the nucleus, but much more remains to be learned. Determination of the radii of a large number of atomic nuclei show that the radius of a given nucleus, r, is directly related to the cube root of its mass number.

$$r = (1.3 \times 10^{-13}\,\text{cm})A^{1/3}$$

The volume of a sphere is $\frac{4}{3}\pi r^3$, and if we assume a spherical nucleus, it follows that nuclear volume varies directly with mass number. In other words, the mass of a nucleus determines its volume, and nuclear density is, therefore, approximately constant for all atomic nuclei. This density is about 2.44×10^{14} g/cm^3, an amazingly high value; 1 cm^3 of this nuclear matter would weigh over 250 million tons.

The density of a liquid is constant and independent of the size of any drop considered. Since all nuclei have approximately the same density, a fluid-droplet model of the nucleus has been proposed. The nature of the cohesive forces holding the nucleons into a nuclear fluid is far from completely understood. It is clear that cohesive forces of some short-range type exist and that they effectively overcome the forces of repulsion between the charged protons of the nucleus.

It is also clear that the neutron has an important role in binding the nucleus. There is evidence that neutron–proton attractions are stronger than neutron–neutron or proton–proton attractions; the deuteron, $^2_1$H, which consists of one proton and one neutron is a stable (nonradioactive) particle, whereas no particle consisting of two neutrons or two protons has ever been observed. In 1935, Hidekei Yukawa postulated that neutrons and protons were bound by the very rapid exchange of a nuclear particle called a π meson.

In Figure 18.1, the number of neutrons is plotted against the number of protons for the naturally occurring, nonradioactive nuclei. The points, representing stable combinations of protons and neutrons, lie in what may be called a **zone of stability**. Nuclei that have compositions represented by points that lie outside of this zone spontaneously undergo radioactive transformations that tend to bring their compositions into, or closer to, this zone (Section 18.2).

The stable nuclei of the lighter elements contain approximately equal numbers of neutrons and protons, a neutron/proton ratio of 1. The heavier nuclei contain more neutrons than protons. With increasing atomic number, more and more protons are packed into a tiny nucleus, and the electrostatic forces of repulsion increase sharply. A larger and larger excess of neutrons is required to diminish the effect of these repulsion forces, and the neutron/proton ratio increases with increasing atomic number until the ratio is approximately 1.5 at the end of the curve of Figure 18.1. There appears to be an upper limit to the number of protons that can be packed into a nucleus, no matter how many neutrons are present. The largest stable nucleus is $^{209}_{83}$Bi; nuclei that are larger than this exist, but all of them are radioactive.

Most naturally occurring stable nuclides have an even number of protons and an even number of neutrons; only five ($^2_1$H, $^6_3$Li, $^{10}_5$B, $^{14}_7$N, and $^{180}_{73}$Ta) have an odd number of protons and an odd number of neutrons (Table 18.1). For each odd atomic number, there are never

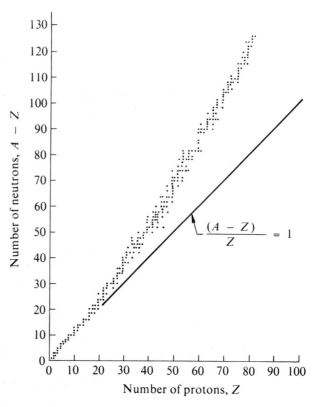

Figure 18.1   Neutron/proton ratio.

more than two stable nuclides, whereas for an even atomic number, as many as ten stable nuclides may occur. The two elements of atomic number less than 83 that have never been proven to be naturally existing ($_{43}$Tc and $_{61}$Pm) have odd atomic numbers. Empirical observations such as these suggest that there is a periodicity in nuclear structure similar to the periodicity of atomic structure, and a nuclear shell model, as yet incompletely developed, has been suggested.

Periodic variations are observed in many nuclear properties. Certain nuclides have relatively high binding energies (indicative of com-

TABLE 18.1.
DISTRIBUTION OF NATURALLY OCCURRING STABLE NUCLIDES.

Protons	Neutrons	Number of Nuclides	
even	even	157	} 209
even	odd	52	
odd	even	50	} 55
odd	odd	5	

paratively great stability; Sections 2.9 and 18.7) compared to nuclides of close atomic number or mass number. Exceptional nuclear stability is also shown by certain nuclides that have a poor ability to capture neutrons (Section 18.5). Comparison of data from these and other studies of nuclear properties indicates that unusual nuclear stability is associated with nuclides having either a number of protons, or a number of neutrons, equal to a magic number: 2, 8, 20, 28, 50, 82, and 126. It is thought that the magic numbers indicate closed nuclear shells in the same way that the atomic numbers of the noble gases: 2, 10, 18, 36, 54, and 86, indicate stable electronic configurations. In general, elements that have an atomic number equal to a magic number have a larger number of stable isotopes than neighboring elements.

18.2 Radioactivity

Unstable nuclei spontaneously undergo certain changes that result in the attainment of more stable nuclear compositions. Some unstable nuclides are naturally occurring; others are man-made. Certain synthetic radioactive nuclides undergo some types of radioactive decay that have not been observed for any naturally occurring unstable nuclide.

Alpha emission consists of the ejection of α particles, which have an atomic number of 2 and a mass number of 4 and may be considered to be $^4_2$He nuclei. Both synthetic and natural nuclides undergo α decay which is common only for nuclides of mass number greater than 209 and atomic number greater than 82. Nuclides such as these have too many protons for stability; points indicating the composition of these nuclides fall outside the plot of Figure 18.1, to the upper right, beyond the zone of stability. The emission of α particles reduces the number of protons by two and the number of neutrons by two and adjusts the composition of the nucleus downward, closer to the stability zone.

An example of α decay is

$$^{210}_{84}\text{Po} \longrightarrow \ ^{206}_{82}\text{Pb} + \ ^4_2\text{He}$$

Notice that the equation indicates the conservation of mass number (superscripts) and atomic number (subscripts). Equations such as these are written to indicate nuclear changes only; the extranuclear electrons are customarily ignored. An α particle is emitted as $^4_2$He nucleus, without electrons, and with a 2+ charge. Subsequent to its emission, however, the particle attracts electrons from other atoms (which become cations), and the α particle becomes a neutral atom of $^4_2$He. The $^{206}_{82}$Pb is left, therefore, with a surplus of two electrons and a 2− charge; these excess electrons are rapidly lost to surrounding cations.

The energy released in this process is readily calculated in the same way that binding energy is calculated (Section 2.9); it is the energy equivalent of the difference in mass between the reactant (parent nucleus) and products (daughter nucleus and α particle). The masses of neutral *atoms*, rather than the masses of *nuclei*, are generally recorded, but this causes no trouble in the calculation. If the mass of the $^{210}_{84}$Po *atom* is used, the mass of 84 electrons is included; for the products, the mass of the $^{206}_{82}$Pb *atom* includes the mass of 82 electrons, and the mass of the $^4_2$He *atom* includes the mass of 2 electrons. Thus the masses of the extra-nuclear electrons cancel when atomic masses are employed for the calculation.

$$(\text{mass } ^{210}_{84}\text{Po}) - (\text{mass } ^{206}_{82}\text{Pb} + \text{mass } ^4_2\text{He})$$

$$209.9829\ u - (205.9745\ u + 4.0026\ u) = 0.0058\ u$$

The energy equivalent of this mass difference may be calculated by means of Einstein's equation (Section 2.9); $1\ u = 931$ mev, and thus

$$0.0058\ u \times 931\ \text{mev}/u = 5.4\ \text{mev}$$

Beta emission is observed for nuclides that have too high a neutron/proton ratio for stability; points representing such nuclides lie to the left of the zone of stability of Figure 18.1. The β particle is an electron, indicated $_{-1}^{0}e$, which may be considered to result from the transformation of a nuclear neutron into a nuclear proton; electrons, as such, do not exist in the nucleus. The net effect of β emission is that the number of neutrons is decreased by 1 and the number of protons is increased by 1. Thus the neutron/proton ratio is decreased; the mass number does not change.

Beta decay is a very common mode of radioactive disintegration and is observed for both natural and synthetic nuclides. Examples include

$$^{186}_{73}\text{Ta} \longrightarrow\ ^{186}_{74}\text{W} +\ _{-1}^{0}e$$

$$^{82}_{35}\text{Br} \longrightarrow\ ^{82}_{36}\text{Kr} +\ _{-1}^{0}e$$

$$^{27}_{12}\text{Mg} \longrightarrow\ ^{27}_{13}\text{Al} +\ _{-1}^{0}e$$

$$^{14}_{6}\text{C} \longrightarrow\ ^{14}_{7}\text{N} +\ _{-1}^{0}e$$

Notice that the sums of the subscripts and superscripts on the right side of the equation equal the subscript and superscript of the parent nucleus on the left.

The last equation represents the mode of decay of the radioactive carbon isotope that is present in small amount in the atmosphere. The energy released by this process may be calculated, using atomic masses, from the relation

$$(\text{mass } ^{14}_{6}\text{C}) - (\text{mass } ^{14}_{7}\text{N})$$

The parent atom, $^{14}_{6}$C, has six orbital electrons; a daughter *ion*, $^{14}_{7}$N$^+$, is produced (with only six orbital electrons) plus the electron ejected as a β particle. Thus there is a total of seven electrons represented on the right side of the equation, and the atomic mass of $^{14}_{7}N$ includes the mass of seven electrons.

$$(\text{mass } ^{14}_{6}C) - (\text{mass } ^{14}_{7}N)$$

$$14.00324\,u - 14.00307\,u = 0.00017\,u = 0.16\text{ mev}$$

Unstable nuclides that have neutron/proton ratios below those required for stability (points below the zone of stability of Figure 18.1) do not occur in nature. Many such artificial nuclides are known, however, and two types of radioactive processes are observed that increase the neutron/proton ratio of this type of nuclide; positron emission and K capture.

Positron emission, or β^{+} emission, consists of the ejection of a positive electron, called a positron and indicated $^{0}_{1}e$, from the nucleus. A positron has the same mass as an electron but an opposite charge; it arises from the conversion of a nuclear proton into a neutron. Positron emission results in a decrease of 1 in the number of protons and an increase of 1 in the number of neutrons; no change in mass number occurs. Hence, positron emission raises the numerical value of the neutron/proton ratio.

Examples of this mode of radioactive decay include

$$^{122}_{53}I \longrightarrow\ ^{122}_{52}Te +\ ^{0}_{1}e$$

$$^{38}_{19}K \longrightarrow\ ^{38}_{18}Ar +\ ^{0}_{1}e$$

$$^{23}_{12}Mg \longrightarrow\ ^{23}_{11}Na +\ ^{0}_{1}e$$

$$^{15}_{8}O \longrightarrow\ ^{15}_{7}N +\ ^{0}_{1}e$$

We can use atomic masses to calculate the energy released by the process described in the last equation if we remember to account for all eight electrons present in the parent atom, $^{15}_{8}O$. The atomic mass of $^{15}_{7}N$ includes the masses of only seven electrons; the positron was ejected *from the nucleus* and does not represent an orbital electron. Thus the mass difference is

$$(\text{mass } ^{15}_{8}O) - (\text{mass } ^{15}_{7}N + \text{mass } ^{0}_{-1}e + \text{mass } ^{0}_{1}e)$$

Since the mass of a positron is identical to that of an electron,

$$(\text{mass } ^{15}_{8}O) - [\text{mass } ^{15}_{7}N + 2(\text{mass } ^{0}_{-1}e)]$$

$$15.00308\,u - [15.00011\,u + 2(0.00055\,u)]$$

$$15.00308\,u - 15.00121\,u = 0.00187\,u = 1.74\text{ mev}$$

For spontaneous positron emission, the atomic mass of the parent must exceed the atomic mass of the daughter by at least $0.00110\,u$, the mass of two electrons.

K capture, another process through which the neutron/proton ratio of an unstable nuclide is increased, occurs when the mass difference between parent and daughter does not exceed $0.00110\ u$. In this process, the nucleus captures an electron from the K shell, and the captured electron converts a nuclear proton into a neutron. The transformation results in a daughter nuclide with 1 less proton and 1 more neutron than the parent; consequently, the atomic number of the daughter is 1 less than that of the parent, and the mass number does not change. Examples are

$$_{-1}^{0}e + {}_{80}^{197}\mathrm{Hg} \xrightarrow{K\ \text{capture}} {}_{79}^{197}\mathrm{Au}$$

$$_{-1}^{0}e + {}_{47}^{106}\mathrm{Ag} \xrightarrow{K\ \text{capture}} {}_{46}^{106}\mathrm{Pd}$$

$$_{-1}^{0}e + {}_{18}^{37}\mathrm{Ar} \xrightarrow{K\ \text{capture}} {}_{17}^{37}\mathrm{Cl}$$

$$_{-1}^{0}e + {}_{4}^{7}\mathrm{Be} \xrightarrow{K\ \text{capture}} {}_{3}^{7}\mathrm{Li}$$

$$_{-1}^{0}e + {}_{26}^{55}\mathrm{Fe} \xrightarrow{K\ \text{capture}} {}_{25}^{55}\mathrm{Mn}$$

The energy involved can be calculated directly from the difference between the atomic masses of the parent and daughter since the daughter has both 1 proton less (converted to a neutron) and 1 electron less (captured from the K shell) than the parent. Thus for the last example,

$$(\text{mass } {}_{26}^{55}\mathrm{Fe}) - (\text{mass } {}_{25}^{55}\mathrm{Mn})$$

$$54.9406\ u - 54.9381\ u = 0.0025\ u = 2.3\ \text{mev}$$

Gamma radiation is electromagnetic radiation of very short wavelength; its emission is caused by energy changes within the nucleus, and its emission alone does not cause changes in the mass number or the atomic number of the nucleus. At times, nuclides are produced in excited states by nuclear reactions (Section 18.5), and such nuclides revert to their ground states by the emission of the excess energy in the form of γ radiation.

$$[{}_{52}^{125}\mathrm{Te}]^* \longrightarrow {}_{52}^{125}\mathrm{Te} + \gamma$$
$$\text{excited state} \qquad \text{ground state}$$

The γ-rays emitted by a specific nucleus have a definite energy value, or set of energy values, because they correspond to transitions between discrete energy levels of the nucleus. Thus an emission spectrum of γ radiation is analogous to the line spectrum that results from transitions of electrons between energy levels in an excited atom.

Gamma radiation frequently accompanies the α, β^-, or β^+ emission of a radioactive decay. The daughter nucleus is often produced in an excited state and emits γ radiation to reach the ground state.

$$_{94}^{240}\mathrm{Pu} \longrightarrow [{}_{92}^{236}\mathrm{U}]^* + {}_{2}^{4}\mathrm{He}$$
$$[{}_{92}^{236}\mathrm{U}]^* \longrightarrow {}_{92}^{236}\mathrm{U} + \gamma$$

In cases such as this, deductions can be made concerning the energy levels of the daughter nucleus. The emission of a 5.16 mev α particle results directly in the production of $^{236}_{92}U$ in the ground state; no γ radiation accompanies such α particles. However, for the process outlined in the set of equations, a 5.12 mev α particle is emitted along with a 0.04 mev γ-ray. It is assumed that the energy of the γ-ray corresponds to the energy difference between the ground state and the first excited state of $^{236}_{92}U$. Alpha particles of other energies are also emitted, and the complete analysis of these energies results in a more detailed picture of the energy levels of the $^{236}_{92}U$ nucleus.

18.3 Rate of Radioactive Decay

Many techniques are employed to study the emissions of radioactive substances. Radiations from these materials affect photographic film in the same way that ordinary light does. In fact, radioactivity was discovered in 1856 by Henri Becquerel when he noticed that a photographic plate that had been placed in a drawer with uranium minerals had become fogged. Photographic techniques for the qualitative and quantitative detection of radiation are employed, but they are not very accurate nor are they suitable for rapid analysis.

The energy of emissions from radioactive sources are absorbed by some materials (e.g., zinc sulfide) and transformed into radiant energy of visible wavelength. The zinc sulfide is said to **fluoresce,** and a little flash of light may be observed from the impact of each particle from the radioactive source. This property has been put to use in an instrument known as a **scintillation counter.** The window of a sensitive photoelectric tube is coated with ZnS, and the flash of light emitted by the ZnS when it is struck by a particle causes a pulse of electric current to pass through the photoelectric tube. These signals are amplified and made to operate various kinds of counting devices.

The **Wilson cloud chamber** enables the path of ionizing radiation to be seen. The chamber contains air saturated with water vapor. By the movement of a piston, the air in the chamber is suddenly expanded and cooled; this causes droplets of water to condense on the ions that are formed by the particles as they move through the vapor, and makes the paths of the particles visible. Photographs of these cloud tracks may be made and studied. Such photographs provide information on the length of the paths, collisions undergone by the particles, the speed of the particles, and the effects of external forces on the behavior of the particles.

The essential features of a **Geiger-Muller counter** are diagrammed in Figure 18.2. The radiation enters the tube through a thin window. As a particle or a γ-ray traverses the tube, which contains argon gas, it knocks electrons off the argon atoms in its path and forms Ar^+ ions. A

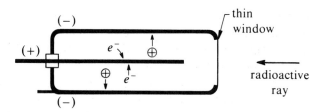

Figure 18.2   *Essential features of a Geiger-Muller counter tube.*

potential of about 1000 to 1200 v is applied between the electrodes of the tube, and the electrons and Ar^+ ions cause a pulse of electric current to flow through the circuit. This pulse is amplified to cause a clicker to sound or an automatic counting device to operate.

The rates of decay of all radioactive substances have been found to be of first order (Section 12.5) and independent of temperature. This lack of temperature dependence implies that the activation energy of any radioactive-decay process is zero. The rate of decay, therefore, depends upon the amount of radioactive material present—a relationship similar to the rate at which money accumultes at compound interest, with the distinction that radioactive decay represents a loss, not an accumulation. We may express this relationship as

$$-\frac{\Delta N}{\Delta t} = kN$$

where N is the number of atoms of radioactive material; t is time; and k is the rate constant; the rate expression is negative because it represents the disappearance of the radioactive substance.

Rearrangement of the rate expression gives

$$-\frac{\Delta N}{N} = k\Delta t$$

which states that the fraction lost $(-\Delta N/N)$ in a given time interval (Δt) is directly proportional to the length of the time interval. Therefore the time required for half of the sample to decay (the **half life**, $t_{1/2}$) is a constant.

The curve of Figure 18.3, showing number of radioactive atoms versus time, is typical of first-order processes. After a single half life period has elapsed, one-half of the original number of atoms remain $(\frac{1}{2}N_0)$. This number is reduced by half (to $\frac{1}{4}N_0$) by the time that another half life has passed. Each radioactive isotope has a characteristic half life, and these vary widely; for example, ^5_3Li has a half life estimated to be 10^{-21} sec, and $^{238}_{92}U$ has a half life of 4.51×10^9 years.

The rate equation may be written in its differential form,

$$-\frac{dN}{dt} = kN$$

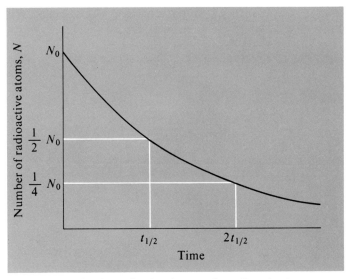

Figure 18.3   Curve showing the rate of a radioactive decay.

and by means of the calculus, this equation may be integrated,

$$-2.303 \log \left(\frac{N}{N_0}\right) = kt$$

where N_0 is the amount present at time zero, and N is the amount present at time t. The last equation may be rearranged to give

$$\log \left(\frac{N_0}{N}\right) = \frac{kt}{2.303}$$

An expression for the half life may be derived by allowing

$$N = \tfrac{1}{2} N_0$$

$$\frac{N_0}{N} = 2$$

Therefore,

$$\log 2 = \frac{k(t_{1/2})}{2.303}$$

$$t_{1/2} = \frac{2.303 \log 2}{k} = \frac{0.693}{k}$$

According to the rate law, a radioactive substance never completely disappears. However, the rate law describes the behavior of a sample containing a large number of atoms. When the number of atoms in the sample declines to a very small value, the rate law is no longer followed exactly. How can a fraction of an atom disintegrate?

Example 18.1   The isotope $_{27}^{60}$Co has a half life of 5.27 years. What amount of a 0.0100 g sample of $_{27}^{60}$Co remains after 1.00 year?

Solution   The rate constant for this disintegration is

$$k = \frac{0.693}{t_{1/2}}$$

$$= \frac{0.693}{5.27 \text{ years}} = 0.132/\text{year}$$

The fraction remaining undecomposed at the end of 1.00 year may be found in the following way.

$$\log\left(\frac{N_0}{N}\right) = \frac{kt}{2.30}$$

$$= \frac{(0.132/\text{year})(1.00 \text{ year})}{2.30} = 0.0573$$

$$\log\left(\frac{N}{N_0}\right) = -0.0573$$

$$\frac{N}{N_0} = 0.876$$

Therefore the amount remaining after 1.00 year is

$$0.876 \times 0.0100 \text{ g} = 0.0088 \text{ g}$$

The radioactive isotope $_6^{14}$C is produced in the atmosphere by the action of cosmic-ray neutrons on $_7^{14}$N.

$$_7^{14}\text{N} + {_0^1}\text{n} \longrightarrow {_6^{14}}\text{C} + {_1^1}\text{H}$$

The $_6^{14}$C is oxidized to CO_2, and this radioactive CO_2 mixes with non-radioactive CO_2. The radiocarbon disappears through radioactive decay, but it is also constantly being made. The steady state is reached when the proportion is 1 atom of $_6^{14}$C to 10^{12} ordinary carbon atoms, which represents 15.3 ± 0.1 disintegrations per minute per gram of carbon.

The CO_2 of the atmosphere is absorbed by plants through the process of photosynthesis, and the ratio of $_6^{14}$C to ordinary carbon in plant materials that are alive and growing is the same ratio as that in the atmosphere. When the plant dies, however, the amount of $_6^{14}$C diminishes through radioactive decay and is not replenished by the assimilation of atmospheric CO_2 by the plant.

The half life of $_6^{14}$C, a β emitter, is 5770 years. The age of a wooden object can be determined by comparing the radiocarbon activity of the object with that of growing trees. This method of **radiocarbon dating** has been applied to many archeological finds and objects of historical interest.   By this means, the Dead Sea scrolls were determined to be 1917 ± 200 years old.

Example 18.2   A sample of carbon from a wooden artifact is found to give 7.00 $^{14}_{6}C$ counts per minute per gram of carbon.   What is the approximate age of the artifact?

Solution   The half life of $^{14}_{6}C$ is 5770 years.   Therefore

$$k = \frac{0.693}{t_{1/2}}$$

$$= \frac{0.693}{5770 \text{ years}} = 1.20 \times 10^{-4}/\text{year}$$

The $^{14}_{6}C$ from wood recently cut down decays at the rate of 15.3 disintegrations per minute per gram of carbon.   Therefore

$$\log\left(\frac{N_0}{N}\right) = \frac{kt}{2.30}$$

$$\log\left(\frac{15.3 \text{ disintegrations/min}}{7.00 \text{ disintegrations/min}}\right) = \frac{(1.20 \times 10^{-4}/\text{year})t}{2.30}$$

$$t = \frac{2.30 \log 2.19}{1.20 \times 10^{-4}/\text{year}} = 6520 \text{ years}$$

The amount of radiation emanating from a source per unit time is termed the **activity** of the source.

$$\text{activity} = -\frac{dN}{dt} = kN$$

Activities are generally expressed in curies; 1 curie (c) is defined as 3.70×10^{10} disintegrations per second, and 1 microcurie (μc) is 3.70×10^{4} disintegrations per second.

Example 18.3   The half life of $^{100}_{43}Tc$, a β emitter, is 16 sec.   How many atoms of $^{100}_{43}Tc$ are present in a sample with an activity of 0.200 μc?   What is the weight of the sample?

Solution   For this radioactive decay, the rate constant, k, is

$$k = \frac{0.693}{t_{1/2}}$$

$$= \frac{0.693}{16 \text{ sec}} = 0.0433/\text{sec}$$

The activity of the sample in terms of disintegrations per second is

$$0.200(3.70 \times 10^4 \text{ disintegrations/sec}) = 7.40 \times 10^3 \text{ disintegrations/sec}$$

This represents the decay of 7.40×10^3 atoms/sec and

$$\text{activity} = kN$$
$$(7.40 \times 10^3 \text{ atoms/sec}) = (4.33 \times 10^{-2}/\text{sec})N$$
$$N = 1.71 \times 10^5 \text{ atoms}$$

The weight of the sample can be derived from the fact that the atomic weight of ^{100}Tc to three significant figures is 100; thus,

$$? \text{ g Tc} = 1.71 \times 10^5 \text{ atoms Tc}\left(\frac{100 \text{ g Tc}}{6.02 \times 10^{23} \text{ atoms Tc}}\right)$$
$$= 2.84 \times 10^{-19} \text{ g Tc}$$

18.4 Radioactive Disintegration Series

The examples of α, β^-, and β^+ emission and of K capture given in Section 18.2 are one-step processes that lead to stable nuclides. Frequently, however, the daughter nucleus produced by a radioactive process is itself radioactive. The repetition of this situation creates a chain, or series, of disintegration processes involving many radioactive nuclides and leading ultimately to the production of a stable nuclide.

Three such **disintegration series,** involving only α and β emission, occur in nature. The $^{238}_{92}\text{U}$ series, which leads finally to the stable nuclide $^{206}_{82}\text{Pb}$, is diagrammed in Figure 18.4. In several places in the series, branching occurs, and the series proceeds by two different routes. The branches, however, always rejoin at a later point, and commonly one branch is preferred over the other (note the percentage figures in Figure 18.4). By any given route, the $^{238}_{92}\text{U}$ series consists of 14 steps—8 involving α decay, and 6 involving β decay.

The radioactive nuclides that occur in nature are those that have very long half lives or those that are constantly being produced by the disintegration of other nuclides. This last type of naturally occurring radioactive nuclide eventually exists in a steady state at which time the amount of the nuclide remains essentially constant because the material is being produced at the same rate that it is decomposing.

The natural disintegration series serve as the basis of a method of geological dating. A sample of rock may be analyzed for its $^{206}_{82}\text{Pb}$ and $^{238}_{92}\text{U}$ content, and the length of time to produce this ratio of lead to uranium may be calculated from the decay constants of the series. Results from studies such as these place the age of some rocks at from 3 to 3.5 billion years; the age of the earth is estimated to be 4.5 billion years.

Decay series, some more elaborate than others, are known for artificial nuclides. Positron emission and K capture are observed in some of these series as well as α and β emission. Following are three examples of simple, two-step, disintegration series of artificial nuclides.

$$^{20}_{8}O \xrightarrow[14 \text{ sec}]{\beta^-} \ ^{20}_{9}F \xrightarrow[11 \text{ sec}]{\beta^-} \ ^{20}_{10}Ne$$

$$^{30}_{16}S \xrightarrow[1.4 \text{ sec}]{\beta^+} \ ^{30}_{15}P \xrightarrow[2.6 \text{ min}]{\beta^+} \ ^{30}_{14}Si$$

$$^{76}_{36}Kr \xrightarrow[10 \text{ hours}]{K \text{ capture}} \ ^{76}_{35}Br \xrightarrow[16.5 \text{ hours}]{\substack{\beta^+ \text{ or} \\ K \text{ capture}}} \ ^{76}_{34}Se$$

18.5 Nuclear Reactions

In 1915, Ernest Rutherford reported that the following transformation occurs when α particles, from $^{214}_{84}Po$, are passed through nitrogen.

$$^{14}_{7}N + ^{4}_{2}He \longrightarrow ^{17}_{8}O + ^{1}_{1}H$$

This was the first artificial transmutation of one element into another to be reported; in the years following, thousands of such nuclear transformations have been studied. It is assumed that the projectile (in this case, an α particle) forms a compound nucleus with the target ($^{14}_{7}N$) and that the compound nucleus very rapidly ejects a subsidiary particle ($^{1}_{1}H$) to form the product nucleus ($^{17}_{8}O$). Other projectiles, such as neutrons, deuterons ($^{2}_{1}H$), protons, and ions of low atomic number, are used in addition to α particles.

Particle-particle reactions are usually classified according to the type of projectile employed and the subsidiary particle ejected. Thus the preceding reaction is called an (α, p) reaction, and the complete trans-

Figure 18.4 Disintegration series of $^{238}_{92}U$. Half lives of isotopes are indicated.

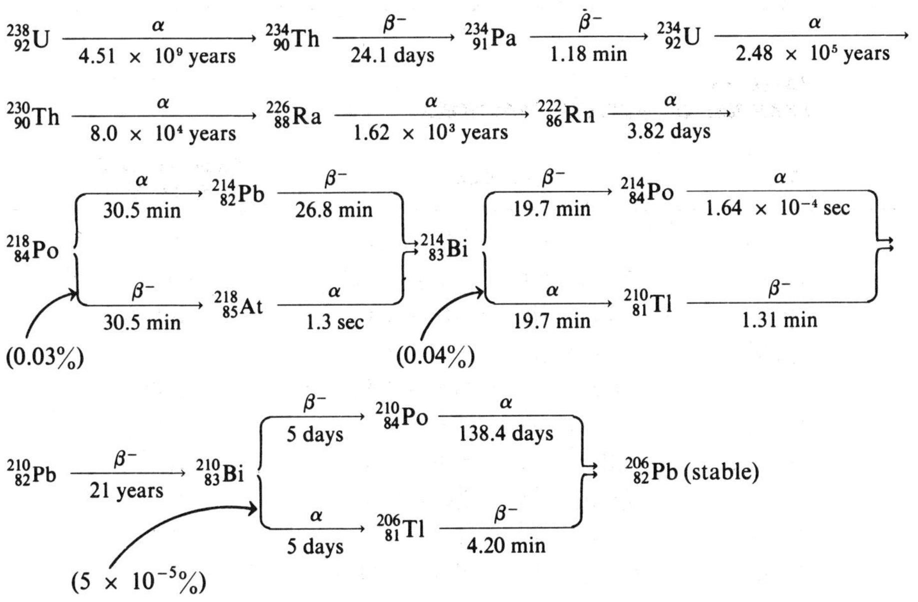

formation is indicated by the notation $^{14}_{7}N(\alpha,p)^{17}_{8}O$. Examples of several of the more common types of nuclear transformations are listed in Table 18.2.

The first artificial, radioactive nuclide produced was made by the (α, n) reaction

$$^{27}_{13}Al + {}^{4}_{2}He \longrightarrow {}^{30}_{15}P + {}^{1}_{0}n$$

The product, $^{30}_{15}P$, decays by positron emission,

$$^{30}_{15}P \longrightarrow {}^{30}_{14}Si + {}^{0}_{1}e$$

Except for the nature of the product, there is no difference between nuclear reactions that produce stable nuclides and those that yield radioactive nuclides.

Projectile particles that bear a positive charge are repelled by target nuclei; this is particularly true of the heavier nuclei which have high charges. Consequently, these positive particles as they are emitted from radioactive sources can bring about only a small number of nuclear transformations. Various particle accelerators are used to give protons, deuterons, α particles, and other cationic projectiles sufficiently high kinetic energies to overcome the electrostatic repulsions of the target nuclei. The **cyclotron,** Figure 18.5, is one such instrument.

The ion source is located between two hollow D-shaped plates (D_1 and D_2), called dees, that are separated by a gap. The dees are enclosed in an evacuated chamber located between the poles of a powerful electromagnet (not shown in the figure). A high-frequency generator keeps the dees oppositely charged. Under the influence of the magnetic and electrical fields, the ions move from the source in a circular path. Each time

TABLE 18.2.
EXAMPLES OF NUCLEAR REACTIONS.

Type	Reaction	Radioactivity of Product Nuclide
(α, n)	$^{75}_{33}As + {}^{4}_{2}He \longrightarrow {}^{78}_{35}Br + {}^{1}_{0}n$	β^{+}
(α, p)	$^{106}_{46}Pd + {}^{4}_{2}He \longrightarrow {}^{109}_{47}Ag + {}^{1}_{1}H$	stable
(p, n)	$^{7}_{3}Li + {}^{1}_{1}H \longrightarrow {}^{7}_{4}Be + {}^{1}_{0}n$	K capture
(p, γ)	$^{14}_{7}N + {}^{1}_{1}H \longrightarrow {}^{15}_{8}O + \gamma$	β^{+}
(p, α)	$^{9}_{4}Be + {}^{1}_{1}H \longrightarrow {}^{6}_{3}Li + {}^{4}_{2}He$	stable
(d, p)	$^{31}_{15}P + {}^{2}_{1}H \longrightarrow {}^{32}_{15}P + {}^{1}_{1}H$	β^{-}
(d, n)	$^{209}_{83}Bi + {}^{2}_{1}H \longrightarrow {}^{210}_{84}Po + {}^{1}_{0}n$	α
(n, γ)	$^{59}_{27}Co + {}^{1}_{0}n \longrightarrow {}^{60}_{27}Co + \gamma$	β^{-}
(n, p)	$^{45}_{21}Sc + {}^{1}_{0}n \longrightarrow {}^{45}_{20}Ca + {}^{1}_{1}H$	β^{-}
(n, α)	$^{27}_{13}Al + {}^{1}_{0}n \longrightarrow {}^{24}_{11}Na + {}^{4}_{2}He$	β^{-}

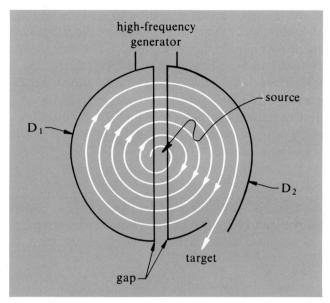

Figure 18.5   Path of a particle in a cyclotron.

they reach the gap between the dees, the polarity of the dees is reversed. Thus the positively charged particles are pushed out of a positive dee and attracted into a negative dee. Each time they traverse the gap, therefore, they are accelerated. Because of this, the particles travel an ever increasing spiral path; eventually they penetrate a window in the instrument and, moving at extremely high speed, impinge on a target.

The **linear accelerator** (Figure 18.6) operates in much the same way except that no magnetic field is employed. The particles are accelerated through a series of tubes enclosed in an evacuated chamber. A positive ion from the source is attracted into tube 1 which is negatively charged. At this time, the odd numbered tubes have negative charges and the even numbered tubes have positive charges. As the particle emerges from tube 1, the charges of the tubes are reversed so that the even numbered tubes are now negatively charged. The particle is repelled out of tube 1 (now positive) and attracted into tube 2 (now negative); as a result, it is accelerated.

Figure 18.6   Schematic representation of a linear accelerator.

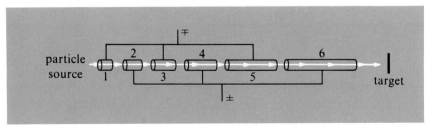

Each time the particle leaves one tube to enter another, the charges of the tubes are reversed. Since the polarity of the tubes is reversed at a constant time interval, and since the speed of the particle increases constantly, each tube must be longer than the preceding one. The accelerated particles leave the last tube at high speed and strike the target.

Neutrons are particularly important projectiles because they bear no charge and therefore are not repelled by the positive charge of the target nuclei. A mixture of beryllium and an α emitter (such as $^{222}_{86}\text{Rn}$) is a convenient neutron source.

$$^{9}_{4}\text{Be} + {}^{4}_{2}\text{He} \longrightarrow {}^{12}_{6}\text{C} + {}^{1}_{0}\text{n}$$

This reaction was used by James Chadwick in his experiments that characterized the neutron (1932). The bombardment of beryllium by accelerated deuterons, from a cyclotron, is a more intense source of neutrons.

$$^{9}_{4}\text{Be} + {}^{2}_{1}\text{H} \longrightarrow {}^{10}_{5}\text{B} + {}^{1}_{0}\text{n}$$

A very important source of neutrons is the nuclear reactor (Section 18.6).

Neutrons from nuclear reactions are known as **fast neutrons;** they cause reactions in which a subsidiary particle is ejected [such as (n, α) and (n, p) reactions]. **Slow neutrons,** or **thermal neutrons,** are produced when the neutrons derived from a nuclear reaction are passed through a moderator (such as carbon, paraffin, hydrogen, deuterium, or oxygen). Through collisions with the nuclei of the moderator, the kinetic energies of the neutrons are decreased to values approximating those of ordinary gas molecules. Bombardments using slow neutrons bring about (n, γ) reactions which are also called neutron-capture reactions since no subsidiary particle is ejected.

$$^{34}_{16}\text{S} + {}^{1}_{0}\text{n} \longrightarrow {}^{35}_{16}\text{S} + \gamma$$

Isotopes of practically every element have been prepared by this type of reaction.

Nuclear reactions have been used to prepare isotopes belonging to elements that do not exist in nature or that exist in extremely minute concentrations. Thus isotopes of technetium and astatine have been prepared by the reactions

$$^{96}_{42}\text{Mo} + {}^{2}_{1}\text{H} \longrightarrow {}^{97}_{43}\text{Tc} + {}^{1}_{0}\text{n}$$

$$^{209}_{83}\text{Bi} + {}^{4}_{2}\text{He} \longrightarrow {}^{211}_{85}\text{At} + 2{}^{1}_{0}\text{n}$$

The elements following uranium in the periodic classification are called the **transuranium elements;** none of these elements is naturally occurring, but many have been made by nuclear reactions. Some of these reactions use targets of artificial nuclides, and in these cases, the final products are therefore the result of syntheses consisting of several steps. Examples of these preparations are

$$^{238}_{92}U + ^{1}_{0}n \longrightarrow ^{239}_{92}U + \gamma$$

$$^{239}_{92}U \longrightarrow ^{239}_{93}Np + ^{0}_{-1}e$$

$$^{239}_{93}Np \longrightarrow ^{239}_{94}Pu + ^{0}_{-1}e$$

$$^{239}_{94}Pu + ^{2}_{1}H \longrightarrow ^{240}_{95}Am + ^{1}_{0}n$$

$$^{239}_{94}Pu + ^{4}_{2}He \longrightarrow ^{242}_{96}Cm + ^{1}_{0}n$$

In addition to the common projectiles, ions of elements of low atomic number are used in some bombardment reactions.

$$^{238}_{92}U + ^{12}_{6}C \longrightarrow ^{244}_{98}Cf + 6^{1}_{0}n$$

$$^{238}_{92}U + ^{14}_{7}N \longrightarrow ^{246}_{99}Es + 6^{1}_{0}n$$

$$^{238}_{92}U + ^{16}_{8}O \longrightarrow ^{250}_{100}Fm + 4^{1}_{0}n$$

$$^{252}_{98}Cf + ^{10}_{5}B \longrightarrow ^{257}_{103}Lw + 5^{1}_{0}n$$

18.6   Nuclear Fission and Fusion

Nuclear fission reactions are more famous, and infamous, than particle-particle or particle-capture transformations. In a **fission** process, a heavy nucleus is split into nuclei of lighter elements and several neutrons. The fission of a given nuclide results in more than one set of products. Two possible reactions for the slow neutron induced fission of $^{235}_{92}U$ are

$$^{235}_{92}U + ^{1}_{0}n \longrightarrow ^{93}_{36}Kr + ^{140}_{56}Ba + 3^{1}_{0}n$$

$$^{235}_{92}U + ^{1}_{0}n \longrightarrow ^{90}_{38}Sr + ^{144}_{54}Xe + 2^{1}_{0}n$$

Heavy nuclei have much larger neutron/proton ratios than nuclei of moderate mass (Figure 18.7). The neutrons released in the fission process lower the neutron/proton ratios of the product nuclei; nevertheless, these nuclei are generally radioactive, and further adjustment of the neutron/proton ratios occurs, usually through β emission. Certain fissions can be induced by protons, deuterons, or α particles, but the most important are those that are brought about by neutrons.

Tremendous amounts of energy are released by fission reactions. In Figure 18.7, mass number is plotted against the binding energy per nucleon (Section 2.9) for the nuclides. Binding energy may be thought of as the energy released by the hypothetical condensation of nucleons into a nucleus and is calculated from the difference in mass between the constituent nucleons and the resultant nucleus.

Inspection of the curve shows that nuclides of intermediate mass have larger values of binding energy per nucleon than the heavier nuclides. Thus the fission of $^{235}_{92}U$ produces more stable, lighter nuclei, and energy

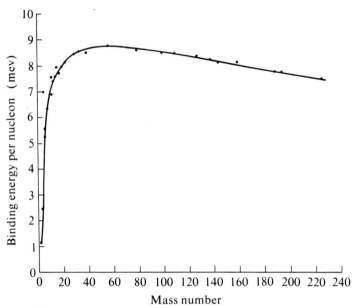

Figure 18.7   *Binding energy per nucleon versus mass number.*

is liberated. The sum of the masses of the products of a fission reaction is less than the sum of the masses of the reactants. A typical fission of a $^{235}_{92}U$ nucleus releases approximately 200 mev.

The fission of each $^{235}_{92}U$ nucleus is induced by a single neutron and produces several neutrons; in the overall process, an average of approximately 2.5 neutrons are produced per fission. If each neutron causes the fission of another $^{235}_{92}U$ nucleus, an explosively rapid chain reaction ensues. Using a reproduction factor of 2 for simplicity, the first fission would cause 2 first-generation fissions. Each of these would cause 2 fissions—a total of 4 second-generation fissions; these would be followed by 8, 16, 32, etc., fissions in succeeding generations. In the nth generation, 2^n fissions would occur. Since each fission is extremely rapid, an explosion results, and if 200 mev is released by each fission, a tremendous amount of energy is liberated.

In a small amount of $^{235}_{92}U$ undergoing fission, many of the neutrons produced are lost from the surface of the mass before they can bring about nuclear reactions. If the size of the fissionable material exceeds a certain **critical mass,** however, the neutrons are captured before they can leave the mass and an explosive chain reaction results. An atomic bomb is detonated by bringing together two pieces of fissionable material, each of subcritical size, together into one piece of supercritical size. The reaction is started by a stray neutron.

A number of nuclei, such as $^{238}_{92}U$, $^{231}_{91}Pa$, $^{237}_{93}Np$, and $^{232}_{90}Th$, undergo fission with fast, but not slow neutrons. Slow neutrons, however, can induce fission in $^{233}_{92}U$, $^{235}_{92}U$ and $^{239}_{94}Pu$. The latter two isotopes are those commonly employed as nuclear fuels. The isotope $^{235}_{92}U$, which comprises only about 0.7% of natural uranium, was employed in the construction of the first atomic bomb. The separation of $^{235}_{92}U$ from the principal uranium isotope, $^{238}_{92}U$, was carried out in many ways, the most successful being the separation of gaseous $^{235}UF_6$ from $^{238}UF_6$ by thermal diffusion through porous barriers (Section 5.11). The isotope $^{239}_{94}Pu$ does not occur in nature but may be prepared from $^{238}_{92}U$ by the series of nuclear reactions given in Section 18.5.

The controlled fission of nuclear fuels in a **nuclear reactor**, or **nuclear pile**, serves as a source of energy and as a source of neutrons for the production of artificial isotopes. In a nuclear reactor rods of the nuclear fuel, comprising at least a critical mass, are inserted into a graphite block. The graphite serves as a moderator for the neutrons produced by the fission, slowing them down and thus increasing the possibility of their capture.

The neutron reproduction factor must be maintained at a value close to 1. If it falls below this value the reaction will eventually stop, and if it increases much above this value, the reaction may become explosively violent. Cadmium rods are used in the pile to capture excess neutrons and prevent a runaway pile.

$$^{113}_{48}Cd + {}^1_0n \longrightarrow {}^{114}_{48}Cd + \gamma$$

The $^{114}_{48}Cd$ isotope is not radioactive.

Nuclear **fusion** is a process in which very light nuclei are fused into a heavier nucleus. The curve of Figure 18.7 shows that such processes should liberate more energy than fission processes. The hydrogen bomb is based on nuclear fusion. Extremely high activation energies are required for fusion reactions, and in actual practice, a fission bomb is used to supply the high temperatures required. The energy of the sun is believed to be derived from the conversion of hydrogen nuclei into helium nuclei by nuclear fusion. Such reactions as the following are postulated.

$$^1_1H + {}^1_1H \longrightarrow {}^2_1H + {}^0_1e$$
$$^2_1H + {}^1_1H \longrightarrow {}^3_2He + \gamma$$
$$^3_2He + {}^3_2He \longrightarrow {}^4_2He + 2{}^1_1H$$

18.7 Uses of Isotopes

A large number of uses have been developed for the isotopes that are the products of the processes run in nuclear reactors. Thickness gauges have been developed in which a radioactive source is placed on one side of the material to be tested (cigarettes, metal plates, etc.) and a counting device on the other. The amount of radiation reaching the counter is a measure of the thickness of the material.

The effectiveness of lubricating oils is measured in an engine constructed from metal into which radioactive isotopes have been incorporated. After the engine has been run for a fixed time period, the oil is withdrawn and tested for the presence of radioactive particles accumulated through engine wear.

When a single pipeline is used to transfer more than one petroleum derivative, a small amount of a radioactive isotope is placed in the last portion of one substance to signal its end and the start of another. The radiation may be used to activate an automatic valve system so that the liquids are diverted into different tanks.

The use of radiocarbon in determining the age of materials of plant origin has been mentioned. Photosynthesis has been studied by tracing the absorption of CO_2 containing $^{14}_{6}C$ by plants. In this way much has been learned about the conversion of CO_2 into sugars, starches, and cellulose.

Radioactive isotopes have found many uses in medical research, therapy, and diagnosis. The radiations from $^{60}_{27}Co$, a β and γ emitter, are used in cancer therapy. The isotope $^{131}_{53}I$ is used in the diagnosis and treatment of thyroid disorders since this gland concentrates ingested iodine.

Radioactive tracers have found wide use in chemical studies. The following structure of the thiosulfate ion

$$\left[\begin{array}{c} S \\ | \\ O-S-O \\ | \\ O \end{array} \right]^{2-}$$

is indicated by studies using $^{35}_{16}S$. The tiosulfate ion is prepared by heating a sulfite with the radioactive sulfur.

$$^{35}S(s) + SO_3^{2-}(aq) \longrightarrow [^{35}SSO_3]^{2-}(aq)$$

Upon the acidification of this thiosulfate solution, the radioactive sulfur is quantitatively precipitated; none is found in the resulting SO_2 gas.

$$[^{35}SSO_3]^{2-}(aq) + 2H^+(aq) \longrightarrow {}^{35}S(s) + SO_2(g) + H_2O$$

In addition, upon the decomposition of silver thiosulfate derived from this ion, all of the radioactive sulfur ends in the silver sulfide.

$$Ag_2[^{35}SSO_3](s) + H_2O \xrightarrow{\text{heat}} Ag_2{}^{35}S(s) + SO_4^{2-}(aq) + 2H^+(aq)$$

These results indicate that the two sulfur atoms of the thiosulfate ion are not equivalent and that the proposed structure is likely.

Radioactive isotopes have been used to study reaction rates and mechanisms as well as the action of catalysts. By using radioactive tracers, it becomes possible to follow the progress of tagged molecules and atoms through a chemical reaction. Determinations of very small vapor pressures and very low solubilities may be conveniently made by using tagged materials.

SOME SUGGESTED READINGS

Adler, I., *Inside the Nucleus*, New York, New American Library, 1963 (paper).

Bethe, H. A., and Morrison, P., *Elementary Nuclear Theory*, New York, Wiley, 1966 (paper).

Choppin, G. R., *Nuclei and Radioactivity*, New York, Benjamin, 1964 (paper).

Cook, C. S., *Structure of Atomic Nuclei*, Princeton, N. J., Van Nostrand, 1964 (paper).

Cunninghamme, J. G., *Introduction to the Atomic Nucleus*, New York, Elsevier, 1964 (paper).

Elton, L. R. B., *Introductory Nuclear Theory*, Philadelphia, Saunders, 1966.

Harvey, B. G., *Nuclear Chemistry*, Englewood Cliffs, N. J., Prentice-Hall, 1965 (paper).

Katz, J., and Rabinowich, E., *The Chemistry of Uranium*, New York, Dover, 1961 (paper).

Lane, A. M., *Nuclear Theory*, New York, Benjamin, 1963 (paper).

Overman, R. T., *Basic Concepts of Nuclear Chemistry*, New York, Reinhold, 1963 (paper).

Seaborg, G. T., *Man-Made Transuranium Elements*, Englewood Cliffs, N. J., Prentice-Hall, 1963 (paper).

PROBLEMS

18.1 (a) The radius of a nucleus may be approximated by the formula: $r = (1.3 \times 10^{-13} \text{ cm}) A^{1/3}$. Find the radius of the ^4_2He nucleus. (b) In Problem 5.13, the diameter of the helium atom was calculated to be 2.65 Å by means of the van der Waals constant b. What percentage of the total volume of the helium atom is occupied by the nucleus?

18.2 Write equations for the following examples of radioactive decay. (a) Alpha emission by $^{225}_{89}\text{Ac}$, (b) Beta emission by $^{32}_{15}\text{P}$, (c) Positron emission by $^{61}_{29}\text{Cu}$, and (d) K-capture by $^{41}_{20}\text{Ca}$.

18.3 The daughter of the radioactive decay of $^{37}_{18}\text{Ar}$ is $^{37}_{17}\text{Cl}$. Is it energetically possible for $^{37}_{18}\text{Ar}$ (mass, 36.96678 u) to decay to $^{37}_{17}\text{Cl}$ (mass, 36.96590 u) by positron emission, or must the process occur by K capture?

18.4 What is the minimum disintegration energy (in mev) that must accompany positron emission?

18.5 The disintegration energy of the decay of $^{51}_{24}\text{Cr}$ by K capture is 0.75 mev. The daughter nuclide, $^{51}_{23}\text{V}$, has a mass of 50.9440 u. What is the mass of $^{51}_{24}\text{Cr}$?

18.6 The disintegration energy of the decay of $^{30}_{15}\text{P}$ by positron emission is 4.30 mev. The daughter nuclide, $^{30}_{14}\text{Si}$, has a mass of 29.97376 u. What is the mass of $^{30}_{15}\text{P}$?

18.7 The nuclide $^{192}_{78}Pt$ decays to $^{188}_{76}Os$ by alpha emission. The mass of $^{192}_{78}Pt$ is 191.9614 u, and the mass of $^{188}_{76}Os$ is 187.9560 u. Calculate the energy effect accompanying this decay.

18.8 The nuclide $^{18}_{9}F$ decays by positron emission. The rate is such that 10.0% of the original quantity remains after 369 minutes. (a) What is the rate constant for this radioactive disintegration? (b) What is the half-life of $^{18}_{9}F$?

18.9 The nuclide $^{7}_{4}Be$ has a half-life of 53 days. How much of a 0.0100 g sample remains at the end of 60 days?

18.10 The nuclide $^{223}_{87}Fr$ has a half-life of 22 minutes. How long will it take for 75% of the original sample to disappear?

18.11 The carbon from the heartwood of a giant sequoia tree gives 10.8 $^{14}_{6}C$ counts per minute per gram of carbon whereas the wood from the outer portion of the tree gives 15.3 $^{14}_{6}C$ counts per minute per gram of carbon. How old is the tree?

18.12 The half-life of $^{43}_{21}Sc$ is 3.9 hours. (a) How many atoms of $^{43}_{21}Sc$ are in a sample that has an activity of 2.00 curies? (b) What is the weight of the sample? (c) What is the activity of the sample after 48 hours?

18.13 A sample of a radioactive nuclide gives 2000 counts/minute, and 30 minutes later gives 1900 counts/minute. What is the half-life of the nuclide?

18.14 One of the naturally occurring decay series is that of the nuclide $^{232}_{90}Th$. The particles successively emitted in one route are: α, β, β, α, α, α, β, α, β, α. Determine, in order, the daughter members of the chain.

18.15 Starting with $^{210}_{86}Rn$, the successive steps of an artificial decay chain are: α, K capture, β^{+}. What are the daughter members of the chain?

18.16 Write equations for the following induced nuclear reactions:

    (a) $^{82}_{35}Br\,(n,\gamma)$ (e) $^{130}_{52}Te(d,2n)$

    (b) $^{10}_{5}B(n,\alpha)$ (f) $^{43}_{20}Ca(\alpha,p)$

    (c) $^{35}_{17}Cl(n,p)$ (g) $^{237}_{93}Np(\alpha,n)$

    (d) $^{7}_{3}Li(p,n)$ (h) $^{238}_{92}U(^{22}_{10}Ne,4n)$

18.17 Calculate the energy released by the fusion process:

$$^{3}_{2}He + {}^{3}_{2}He \longrightarrow {}^{4}_{2}He + 2^{1}_{1}H$$

The masses of the pertinent atoms are: $^{3}_{2}He$, 3.01603 u; $^{4}_{2}He$, 4.00260 u; $^{1}_{1}H$, 1.007825.

Appendix A

Values of Some Constants and Conversion Factors

Avogadro's number (N)	6.02252×10^{23}/mole
Electronic charge, unit charge (e)	1.60210×10^{-19} coulomb
	4.80298×10^{-10} cm$^{3/2}$ g$^{1/2}$/sec (or esu)
Electron rest mass (m)	9.1091×10^{-28} g
	5.48597×10^{-4} u
Proton rest mass	1.67252×10^{-24} g
	1.00727663 u
Neutron rest mass	1.67482×10^{-24} g
	1.0086654 u
Unified atomic mass unit (u)	1.66037×10^{-24} g
	931.437 mev
Electron volt (ev)	2.3061×10^{4} cal/mole
Defined calorie (cal)	4.1840 joules
Planck's constant (h)	6.6256×10^{-27} erg sec
Speed of light (c)	2.997925×10^{10} cm/sec
Faraday (F)	9.64870×10^{4} coulombs/mole
Gas constant (R)	8.2058×10^{-2} liter atm/°K mole
	8.3143 joule/°K mole
	1.9872 cal/°K mole
Molar volume, ideal gas at STP	22.4136 liters

Appendix B

Solubility Products at 25° C

Bromides

$PbBr_2$	4.6×10^{-6}
Hg_2Br_2	1.3×10^{-22}
$AgBr$	5.0×10^{-13}

Carbonates

$BaCO_3$	1.6×10^{-9}
$CdCO_3$	5.2×10^{-12}
$CaCO_3$	4.7×10^{-9}
$CuCO_3$	2.5×10^{-10}
$FeCO_3$	2.1×10^{-11}
$PbCO_3$	1.5×10^{-15}
$MgCO_3$	1×10^{-15}
$MnCO_3$	8.8×10^{-11}
Hg_2CO_3	9.0×10^{-17}
$NiCO_3$	1.4×10^{-7}
Ag_2CO_3	8.2×10^{-12}
$SrCO_3$	7×10^{-10}
$ZnCO_3$	2×10^{-10}

Chlorides

$PbCl_2$	1.6×10^{-5}
Hg_2Cl_2	1.1×10^{-18}
$AgCl$	1.7×10^{-10}

Chromates

$BaCrO_4$	8.5×10^{-11}
$PbCrO_4$	2×10^{-16}
Hg_2CrO_4	2×10^{-9}
Ag_2CrO_4	1.9×10^{-12}
$SrCrO_4$	3.6×10^{-5}

Fluorides

BaF_2	2.4×10^{-5}
CaF_2	3.9×10^{-11}
PbF_2	4×10^{-8}
MgF_2	8×10^{-8}
SrF_2	7.9×10^{-10}

Hydroxides

$Al(OH)_3$	5×10^{-33}
$Ba(OH)_2$	5.0×10^{-3}
$Cd(OH)_2$	2.0×10^{-14}
$Ca(OH)_2$	1.3×10^{-6}
$Cr(OH)_3$	6.7×10^{-31}
$Co(OH)_2$	2.5×10^{-16}
$Co(OH)_3$	2.5×10^{-43}
$Cu(OH)_2$	1.6×10^{-19}
$Fe(OH)_2$	1.8×10^{-15}
$Fe(OH)_3$	6×10^{-38}
$Pb(OH)_2$	4.2×10^{-15}
$Mg(OH)_2$	8.9×10^{-12}
$Mn(OH)_2$	2×10^{-13}
$Hg(OH)_2$ (HgO)	3×10^{-26}
$Ni(OH)_2$	1.6×10^{-16}
$AgOH$ (Ag$_2$O)	2.0×10^{-8}
$Sr(OH)_2$	3.2×10^{-4}
$Sn(OH)_2$	3×10^{-27}
$Zn(OH)_2$	4.5×10^{-17}

Iodides

PbI_2	8.3×10^{-9}
Hg_2I_2	4.5×10^{-29}
AgI	8.5×10^{-17}

Oxalates

BaC_2O_4	1.5×10^{-8}
CaC_2O_4	1.3×10^{-9}
PbC_2O_4	8.3×10^{-12}
MgC_2O_4	8.6×10^{-5}
$Ag_2C_2O_4$	1.1×10^{-11}
SrC_2O_4	5.6×10^{-8}

Phosphates

$Ba_3(PO_4)_2$	6×10^{-39}
$Ca_3(PO_4)_2$	1.3×10^{-32}
$Pb_3(PO_4)_2$	1×10^{-54}
Ag_3PO_4	1.8×10^{-18}
$Sr_3(PO_4)_2$	1×10^{-31}

Sulfates

$BaSO_4$	1.5×10^{-9}
$CaSO_4$	2.4×10^{-5}
$PbSO_4$	1.3×10^{-8}
Ag_2SO_4	1.2×10^{-5}
$SrSO_4$	7.6×10^{-7}

Sulfides

Bi_2S_3	1.6×10^{-72}
CdS	1.0×10^{-28}
CoS	5×10^{-22}
CuS	8×10^{-37}
FeS	4×10^{-19}
PbS	7×10^{-29}
MnS	7×10^{-16}
HgS	1.6×10^{-54}
NiS	3×10^{-21}
Ag_2S	5.5×10^{-51}
SnS	1×10^{-26}
ZnS	2.5×10^{-22}

Miscellaneous

$NaHCO_3$	1.2×10^{-3}
$KClO_4$	8.9×10^{-3}
$K_2[PtCl_6]$	1.4×10^{-6}
$AgC_2H_3O_2$	2.3×10^{-3}
$AgCN$	1.6×10^{-14}
$AgCNS$	1.0×10^{-12}

Appendix C   Logarithms

	0	1	2	3	4	5	6	7	8	9
10	0000	0043	0086	0128	0170	0212	0253	0294	0334	0374
11	0414	0453	0492	0531	0569	0607	0645	0682	0719	0755
12	0792	0828	0864	0899	0934	0969	1004	1038	1072	1106
13	1139	1173	1206	1239	1271	1303	1335	1367	1399	1430
14	1461	1492	1523	1553	1584	1614	1644	1673	1703	1732
15	1761	1790	1818	1847	1875	1903	1931	1959	1987	2014
16	2041	2068	2095	2122	2148	2175	2201	2227	2253	2279
17	2304	2330	2355	2380	2405	2430	2455	2480	2504	2529
18	2553	2577	2601	2625	2648	2672	2695	2718	2742	2765
19	2788	2810	2833	2856	2878	2900	2923	2945	2967	2989
20	3010	3032	3054	3075	3096	3118	3139	3160	3181	3201
21	3222	3243	3263	3284	3304	3324	3345	3365	3385	3404
22	3424	3444	3464	3483	3502	3522	3541	3560	3579	3598
23	3617	3636	3655	3674	3692	3711	3729	3747	3766	3784
24	3802	3820	3838	3856	3874	3892	3909	3927	3945	3962
25	3979	3997	4014	4031	4048	4065	4082	4099	4116	4133
26	4150	4166	4183	4200	4216	4232	4249	4265	4281	4298
27	4314	4330	4346	4362	4378	4393	4409	4425	4440	4456
28	4472	4487	4502	4518	4533	4548	4564	4579	4594	4609
29	4624	4639	4654	4669	4683	4698	4713	4728	4742	4757
30	4771	4786	4800	4814	4829	4843	4857	4871	4886	4900
31	4914	4928	4942	4955	4969	4983	4997	5011	5024	5038
32	5051	5065	5079	5092	5105	5119	5132	5145	5159	5172
33	5185	5198	5211	5224	5237	5250	5263	5276	5289	5302
34	5315	5328	5340	5353	5366	5378	5391	5403	5416	5428
35	5441	5453	5465	5478	5490	5502	5514	5527	5539	5551
36	5563	5575	5587	5599	5611	5623	5635	5647	5658	5670
37	5682	5694	5705	5717	5729	5740	5752	5763	5775	5786
38	5798	5809	5821	5832	5843	5855	5866	5877	5888	5899
39	5911	5922	5933	5944	5955	5966	5977	5988	5999	6010
40	6021	6031	6042	6053	6064	6075	6085	6096	6107	6117
41	6128	6138	6149	6160	6170	6180	6191	6201	6212	6222
42	6232	6243	6253	6263	6274	6284	6294	6304	6314	6325
43	6335	6345	6355	6365	6375	6385	6395	6405	6415	6425
44	6435	6444	6454	6464	6474	6484	6493	6503	6513	6522
45	6532	6542	6551	6561	6571	6580	6590	6599	6609	6618
46	6628	6637	6646	6656	6665	6675	6684	6693	6702	6712
47	6721	6730	6739	6749	6758	6767	6776	6785	6794	6803
48	6812	6821	6830	6839	6848	6857	6866	6875	6884	6893
49	6902	6911	6920	6928	6937	6946	6955	6964	6972	6981
50	6990	6998	7007	7016	7024	7033	7042	7050	7059	7067
51	7076	7084	7093	7101	7110	7118	7126	7135	7143	7152
52	7160	7168	7177	7185	7193	7202	7210	7218	7226	7235
53	7243	7251	7259	7267	7275	7284	7292	7300	7308	7316
54	7324	7332	7340	7348	7356	7364	7372	7380	7388	7396

	0	1	2	3	4	5	6	7	8	9
55	7404	7412	7419	7427	7435	7443	7451	7459	7466	7474
56	7482	7490	7497	7505	7513	7520	7528	7536	7543	7551
57	7559	7566	7574	7582	7589	7597	7604	7612	7619	7627
58	7634	7642	7649	7657	7664	7672	7679	7686	7694	7701
59	7709	7716	7723	7731	7738	7745	7752	7760	7767	7774
60	7782	7789	7796	7803	7810	7818	7825	7832	7839	7846
61	7853	7860	7868	7875	7882	7889	7896	7903	7910	7917
62	7924	7931	7938	7945	7952	7959	7966	7973	7980	7987
63	7993	8000	8007	8014	8021	8028	8035	8041	8048	8055
64	8062	8069	8075	8082	8089	8096	8102	8109	8116	8122
65	8129	8136	8142	8149	8156	8162	8169	8176	8182	8189
66	8195	8202	8209	8215	8222	8228	8235	8241	8248	8254
67	8261	8267	8274	8280	8287	8293	8299	8306	8312	8319
68	8325	8331	8338	8344	8351	8357	8363	8370	8376	8382
69	8388	8395	8401	8407	8414	8420	8426	8432	8439	8445
70	8451	8457	8463	8470	8476	8482	8488	8494	8500	8506
71	8513	8519	8525	8531	8537	8543	8549	8555	8561	8567
72	8573	8579	8585	8591	8597	8603	8609	8615	8621	8627
73	8633	8639	8645	8651	8657	8663	8669	8675	8681	8686
74	8692	8698	8704	8710	8716	8722	8727	8733	8739	8745
75	8751	8756	8762	8768	8774	8779	8785	8791	8797	8802
76	8808	8814	8820	8825	8831	8837	8842	8848	8854	8859
77	8865	8871	8876	8882	8887	8893	8899	8904	8910	8915
78	8921	8927	8932	8938	8943	8949	8954	8960	8965	8971
79	8976	8982	8987	8993	8998	9004	9009	9015	9020	9025
80	9031	9036	9042	9047	9053	9058	9063	9069	9074	9079
81	9085	9090	9096	9101	9106	9112	9117	9122	9128	9133
82	9138	9143	9149	9154	9159	9165	9170	9175	9180	9186
83	9191	9196	9201	9206	9212	9217	9222	9227	9232	9238
84	9243	9248	9253	9258	9263	9269	9274	9279	9284	9289
85	9294	9299	9304	9309	9315	9320	9325	9330	9335	9340
86	9345	9350	9355	9360	9365	9370	9375	9380	9385	9390
87	9395	9400	9405	9410	9415	9420	9425	9430	9435	9440
88	9445	9450	9455	9460	9465	9469	9474	9479	9484	9489
89	9494	9499	9504	9509	9513	9518	9523	9528	9533	9538
90	9542	9547	9552	9557	9562	9566	9571	9576	9581	9586
91	9590	9595	9600	9605	9609	9614	9619	9624	9628	9633
92	9638	9643	9647	9652	9657	9661	9666	9671	9675	9680
93	9685	9689	9694	9699	9703	9708	9713	9717	9722	9727
94	9731	9736	9741	9745	9750	9754	9759	9763	9768	9773
95	9777	9782	9786	9791	9795	9800	9805	9809	9814	9818
96	9823	9827	9832	9836	9841	9845	9850	9854	9859	9863
97	9868	9872	9877	9881	9886	9890	9894	9899	9903	9908
98	9912	9917	9921	9926	9930	9934	9939	9943	9948	9952
99	9956	9961	9965	9969	9974	9978	9983	9987	9991	9996

Appendix D

Instability Constants at 25° C

AlF_6^{3-}	1.4×10^{-20}	$HgBr_4^{2-}$	2.3×10^{-22}
$Al(OH)_4^-$	1.3×10^{-34}	$HgCl_4^{2-}$	1.1×10^{-16}
$Al(OH)^{2+}$	7.1×10^{-10}	$Hg(CN)_4^{2-}$	4×10^{-42}
$Cd(NH_3)_4^{2-}$	7.5×10^{-8}	HgI_4^{2-}	5.3×10^{-31}
$Cd(CN)_4^{2-}$	1.4×10^{-19}	$Ni(NH_3)_4^{2+}$	1×10^{-8}
$Cr(OH)^{2+}$	5×10^{-11}	$Ni(NH_3)_6^{2+}$	1.8×10^{-9}
$Co(NH_3)_6^{2+}$	1.3×10^{-5}	$Ag(NH_3)_2^+$	6.0×10^{-8}
$Co(NH_3)_6^{3+}$	2.2×10^{-34}	$Ag(CN)_2^-$	1.8×10^{-19}
$Cu(NH_3)_2^+$	1.4×10^{-11}	$Ag(S_2O_3)_2^{3-}$	5×10^{-14}
$Cu(NH_3)_4^{2+}$	4.7×10^{-15}	$Ag(S_2O_3)_3^{5-}$	9.9×10^{-15}
$Cu(CN)_2^-$	1×10^{-16}	$Zn(NH_3)_4^{2+}$	3.4×10^{-10}
$Cu(OH)^+$	1×10^{-8}	$Zn(CN)_4^{2-}$	1.2×10^{-18}
$Fe(CN)_6^{4-}$	1×10^{-35}	$Zn(OH)_4^{2-}$	3.6×10^{-16}
$Fe(CN)_6^{3-}$	1×10^{-42}	$Zn(OH)^+$	4.1×10^{-5}
$Pb(OH)^+$	1.5×10^{-8}		

Answers

to Selected Numerical Problems

Chapter 2

2.1 19.9% ^{10}B, 80.1% ^{11}B; **2.11 (a)** 1.73, 2.83, 3.87, 4.90, 5.92, **(b)** 2.83; **2.17 (a)** 3.33 Å, **(b)** 2.19×10^8 cm/sec; **2.18 (a)** 2.12 Å for $n = 2$, 4.77 Å for $n = 3$, **(b)** $n = 1$, -2.17×10^{-11} erg; $n = 2$, -5.43×10^{-12} erg; $n = 3$, -2.42×10^{-12} erg; **(c)** 2.91×10^{15}/sec, 1.03×10^3 Å, 2.46×10^{15}/sec, 1.22×10^3 Å, 4.54×10^{14}/sec, 6.61×10^3 Å.

Chapter 3

3.8 43.3%

Chapter 4

4.1 1.00×10^{22} atoms; **4.3 (a)** 37.5%, **(b)** 68.5%; **4.5** $P_6N_7Cl_9$; **4.7** 1220 lb; **4.9** 12.4 g; **4.11** 228 g; **4.12** 22.8%; **4.15** 45.0; **4.16** -35.1 kcal/mole; **4.17** -31.1 kcal; **4.20** -103.5 kcal; **4.24** 20.0%

Chapter 5

5.1 3.95×10^{13} atoms; **5.3** 460 mm; **5.6** 20 mm; **5.9** 43.9 g/mole; **5.12 (a)** 24.6 atm, **(b)** 21.4 atm; **5.14 (a)** 4.61×10^{-4} cm/sec, **(b)** 5.39×10^4 cm/sec; **5.17 (a)** 0.105, **(b)** 9.91% C_2H_6; **5.19** $H_2/D_2 = 1.41$, $HCl/DCl = 1.01$, $NH_3/ND_3 = 1.08$; **5.21** 0.738 g; **5.24 (a)** 1.44 moles, **(b)** 44%, **(c)** 0.611, **(d)** 0.39 atm N_2O_4, 0.61 atm NO_2; **5.26** 2.82 g

Chapter 6

6.2 3.87 kcal/mole; **6.6 (a)** 4.618 Å, **(b)** 0.856 g/cm^3; **6.9 (a)** 1, **(b)** 2, **(c)** 4, **(d)** body-centered; **6.12 (a)** 4, **(b)** 58.42, **(c)** 0.06%

Chapter 7

7.5 (a) 49.0, **(b)** 17.0, **(c)** 45.0, **(d)** 49.0

Chapter 8

8.3 4.10 ml; **8.5 (a)** 0.641M, **(b)** 0.654m; **8.7 (a)** 0.033M, **(b)** 6.0N, **(c)** 0.015M; **8.8** 24.0%; **8.10** 84.0; **8.12 (a)** 210 mm, **(b)** 0.852; **8.15** 87.4; **8.18** 1.1°C; **8.21** 2.55

Chapter 9

9.1 0.107 amp; **9.4** 0.126; **9.6 (a)** 18.1 g, **(b)** 16.7 liters; **9.7** 205 g; **9.10** 0.221M; **9.12 (f)** $+2.12$ v; **9.17** -1.46 v; **9.18** -0.828 v, $+1.229$ v; **9.20 (a)** $+1.32$ v, **(b)** -61.0 kcal

Chapter 10

10.5 (a) 20.7%, (b) 0.743 g

Chapter 11

11.1 (a) -59.68 kcal/mole, (b) -58.79 kcal/mole; **11.3** 47.1%; **11.5** (a) $+6.41$ kcal/mole, (b) $+5.78$ kcal/mole, (c) $+20.1$ cal/°K mole, (d) 0; **11.8** $+0.222$ v; **11.10** -90.2 kcal/mole; **11.12** -9.8381 kcal

Chapter 12

12.2 (a) 1/8, (b) 1/27, (c) 2, (d) 4; **12.6** (a) 0.80 mole N_2O_4, 0.40 mole NO_2, (b) 1.20 mole, (c) 0.667 atm for N_2O_4, 0.333 atm for NO_2, (d) 0.167 atm; **12.8** (a) 0.50 atm, (b) 1.22 atm for N_2O_4, 0.78 atm for NO_2; **12.12** 7.1×10^{-8} atm; **12.13** 2.9×10^{-9} mole/liter; **12.16** (a) 3×10^{25}, (b) -34.7 kcal; **12.19** (a) $+0.883$ v, (b) -40.8 kcal

Chapter 14

14.2 (a) $[H^+] = [ClO^-] = 5.7 \times 10^{-5}M, [HClO] = 0.10M$, (b) 5.7×10^{-4} or 5.7×10^{-2}%; **14.4** $[HC_7H_5O_2] = 0.20M, [C_7H_5O_2^-] = 0.10M, [H^+] = 1.2 \times 10^{-4}M, [Na^+] = 0.30M, [Cl^-] = 0.20M, [OH^-] = 8.3 \times 10^{-11}M$; **14.8** (a) 9.3, (b) $5.0 \times 10^{-10}M$; **14.10** 8.9×10^{-9}; **14.12** (a) 4.7, (b) 7.6×10^{-2}%; **14.15** 0.75 moles; **14.16** 8.8×10^{-12}; **14.19** 8.3×10^{-9}; **14.22** 1.5×10^{-6} moles; **14.25** (a) $SrSO_4$, (b) $[Sr^{2+}] = 6.3 \times 10^{-3}M$, (c) 6.3%; **14.28** $5.8 \times 10^{-2}M$; **14.29** (a) $8.5 \times 10^{-3}M$, (b) $8.5 \times 10^{-3}M$, (c) $5.6 \times 10^{-8}M$, (d) $2.0 \times 10^{-18}M$, (e) $0.29M$; **14.34** $8.5 \times 10^{-7}M$; **14.37** (a) none, (b) $0.070M$, (c) 0.10 g S; **14.38** $0.083M$; **14.40** 0.49 moles/liter; **14.43** $0.18M$; **14.46** 4.6×10^{-3} moles; **14.47** $0.03M$; **14.50** 1.6×10^{-5}; **14.52** (a) 17.8, (b) $[Fe^{2+}] = 0.189M, [Cd^{2+}] = 0.011M$

Chapter 15

15.2 2.4 cm; **15.12** 1.7×10^{-12}

Chapter 16

16.13 (a) 0, 2, 1, 1, 2, 3, 2, 1, (b) 0, 2, 3, 5, 4, 3, 2, 1

Chapter 17

17.20 (a) $C_2H_3O_3$, (b) $C_4H_6O_6$, (c) 75, (d) COOHCHOHCHOHCOOH

Chapter 18

18.1 (a) 2.07×10^{-5} Å, (b) 3.8×10^{-13}%; **18.5** 50.9448 u; **18.8** (a) 6.24×10^{-3}/min, (b) 111 min.; **18.11** 2930 years; **18.13** 6.8 hours; **18.17** 12.9 mev

Index

PERIODIC CLASSIFICATION OF TH

IA								
1 **H** 1.00797	IIA							
3 **Li** 6.939	4 **Be** 9.0122							
11 **Na** 22.9898	12 **Mg** 24.312	IIIB	IVB	VB	VIB	VIIB		VIIIB
' 19 **K** 39.102	20 **Ca** 40.08	21 **Sc** 44.956	22 **Ti** 47.90	23 **V** 50.942	24 **Cr** 51.996	25 **Mn** 54.9380	26 **Fe** 55.847	27 **Co** 58.9332
37 **Rb** 85.47	38 **Sr** 87.62	39 **Y** 88.905	40 **Zr** 91.22	41 **Nb** 92.906	42 **Mo** 95.94	43 **Tc** (97)	44 **Ru** 101.07	45 **Rh** 102.905
55 **Cs** 132.905	56 **Ba** 137.34	57 * **La** 138.91	72 **Hf** 178.49	73 **Ta** 180.948	74 **W** 183.85	75 **Re** 186.2	76 **Os** 190.2	77 **Ir** 192.2
87 **Fr** (223)	88 **Ra** (226)	89 ** **Ac** (227)						

	58 **Ce** 140.12	59 **Pr** 140.907	60 **Nd** 144.24	61 **Pm** (145)	62 **Sm** 150.35
*					
**	90 **Th** 232.038	91 **Pa** (231)	92 **U** 238.03	93 **Np** (237)	94 **Pu** (244)

aAtomic weights based on $^{12}_{6}C$. Mass numbers of isotopes with longest half lives